STEPS IN
THE SCIENTIFIC TRADITION

STEPS IN
THE SCIENTIFIC TRADITION:

Readings in the History of Science

EDITED BY

Richard S. Westfall
and
Victor E. Thoren

DEPARTMENT OF THE HISTORY
AND PHILOSOPHY OF SCIENCE

INDIANA UNIVERSITY

JOHN WILEY AND SONS, INC.

NEW YORK   LONDON   SYDNEY

Preface

Within the past two decades, the discipline of the history of science has undergone a considerable development. Dedication to the task of cataloguing scientists and chronicling discoveries has abated. Historians of science now tend to concern themselves more with the background of discoveries than with the discoveries themselves—more with the questions posed than with the answers provided. It seems likely that there has been a corresponding shift of emphasis in the teaching of undergraduate courses in the subject. At least there has been in the course that we offer, and the present set of readings has grown out of the set of paperbacks that we have used.

The importance of source books in courses on the history of science is borne out by the several volumes already in print. In a course expressive of the current state of the discipline, source readings are absolutely vital. No amount of exposition, written or oral, can convey the insights into the conceptual framework employed by a scientist that the student can derive from direct reading of the sources themselves. Existing sets of readings, however, do not fulfill the needs of such a course. Some have been compiled and arranged and provided with sufficient editorial comment to appear virtually as histories of science, in which the crucial passages are supplied in the original words of the scientists in question. Most attempt to announce every important discovery and include every important name. Virtually all are collections of short selections (known derogatorily as "snippets") intended to put the reader into direct touch with the great moments in the history of science. For our purpose, such short passages do not suffice. Ideally, of course, reading should not be in selections at all, but in whole works and groups of works. Practically, students cannot be required to buy the number of books (even in paperback, were they available) implicit in such an enterprise. Nor can libraries reasonably be ordered to stock the number of copies needed to accommodate all the students in even a class of normal size. Moreover, the very nature of an introductory course, which aims at extensive coverage rather than at intensive understanding, demands a certain amount of editing to bring the reading assigned into relation with the time available. Since entire works cannot generally be used, selections must serve, but the selections must be sufficiently extensive to convey a considerable

v

portion of the conceptual content of the entire work. Simply to tear out the paragraph in which the triumphant conclusion of the scientist is stated, without providing the argument that led to it, is to serve the student different fare than what we intend. Hence we have been guided in our selection less by the importance of the passage itself in the history of science than by the extent to which its content illustrates the questions being considered and the concepts being used. Inevitably, we have chosen readings expressing the major developments in the history of science; the readings would have no internal rationale had we done otherwise. But our set of readings deliberately eschews all aspirations to completeness or self-sufficiency. It is conceived explicitly as a supplement to an introductory course, or possibly to one of the published histories of science. Our goal is to lead the student, not to detailed knowledge of the chronology of scientists and discoveries, but toward an understanding of the expanding investigation of nature, which is the substance of the history of science, and of the changing patterns of thought that the investigation has employed.

In compiling a selection of readings intended to serve an introductory course in the history of science, we had to face squarely the question of balance. Nearly all historians of science agree that the first half of the 16th century is the dividing line for the primary periodization of their subject; about then the framework of ancient and medieval science began to disintegrate and the foundations of modern science began to be laid. Not all introductory courses are divided at that point, however. Because of the rapid expansion of scientific enterprise after the 16th century, many introductory courses include at least some aspects of the scientific revolution in the first semester. We have attempted to conform to the greater quantity of material to be covered in dealing with modern science by allotting only about one third of our space to ancient and medieval science. We have selected the passages to present the basic patterns of scientific thought before the age of modern science. The selections from the 17th century express the new conception of nature in the scientific revolution and provide a contrast with those from ancient and medieval science. Their extent is such that, with the selections from the earlier period, they comprise roughly one half of the book. The other half of the book is devoted to the major developments that modern science has witnessed during the last two and a half centuries.

We can scarcely dispute the fact that the choice of themes to be presented in this text is highly arbitrary. Clearly, there are many other important themes equally deserving of representation among the significant steps in the development of science. Our choices would have been more difficult if language were no problem; hopefully, our readers will appreciate the necessity of the bias involved in the fact that two thirds of the selections originally written in a modern language were written in English. Aside from such considerations, we have made our decisions primarily with an eye toward provoking class discussion. This desideratum militates against inclusion of highly technical material, for even if it were comprehensible to the majority of a given class, such material is rarely open-ended enough either to encourage or to require group treatment. The decision to include a particular theme or author, of course, is the easy part of the editorial work. Selection of the actual passages is more involved, and it is in this task that the editor steps most dangerously between the author and the reader. Even if he manages to present a balanced and objective set of passages from an author's writings, he will frequently, by the very fact of his abbreviation, endow the ideas with a clarity and simplicity that may well have been lacking in the author himself. We cannot claim to have eliminated such problems, but we have tried to make our interference conspicuous. Where we have merely omitted paragraph-long amplifications or digressions that appeared to be either unnecessary or undesirable, we have indicated the break in the normal manner. Where the break is so serious that a whole new context is involved, we have entered a line of spaced asterisks to warn the reader of the discontinuity. In many cases, there are book and chapter designations that will provide an indication of the extent of the gap.

We have left the interpretation of the material to the individual lecturer. Obviously we have influenced the situation in choosing the passages, but beyond that we have tried to remain neutral. The introductions are intended primarily to provide the context of the work—to describe its place in the author's life and the intellectual milieu in which it was conceived. Insofar as we have commented on the actual content of the work, it has been with the idea of raising questions for the student rather than answering them.

The student interested in further reading will find that most of the works can be found in his college library, if not in the cited form, then in some other edition or translation. A few are even available in recent paperback reprints. Our indebtedness to the past efforts of various translators will be obvious; in some cases we have altered their renderings slightly in order to modernize archaic spellings, usages, or punctuations. In addition, we should like to express our thanks to John Wiley & Sons, Inc., for their interest in making these readings available.

RICHARD S. WESTFALL

VICTOR E. THOREN

CONTENTS

STEPS IN
THE SCIENTIFIC TRADITION

1

ARISTOTLE

If there is any personality in the history of science who needs no introduction, it must surely be Aristotle. Student of Plato, tutor to Alexander, a bold originator of new ideas, and a transcendent systematizer of existing ones, he influenced his own era and dominated succeeding ones in a manner unparalleled in intellectual history. Within a lifetime of 62 years (384–322 B.C.), he not only absorbed, extended, and reformulated the results of virtually all preceding thought, but launched unprecedented investigations into such diverse disciplines as formal logic and political science as well. It is scarcely surprising that he was also able to reverse the whole trend of contemporary philosophy.

As a veteran of 20 years' association with Plato's Academy, Aristotle was not only thoroughly conversant with, but sincerely respectful of, the doctrines and views of its founder. Yet he was by no means simply an uncritical disciple; he took his own stand on several issues, most of them bearing directly on natural philosophy. The most important of his departures concerned Plato's celebrated doctrine of Ideas. Although agreeing to the significance and reality of universals, Aristotle reversed their relationship to particulars. His insistence that universals were to be apprehended through consideration of particulars rather than *vice versa* entailed fundamental changes in the methodological pursuit and epistemological status of empirical knowledge. He also disagreed strongly with the prevailing view of the extent to which natural philosophy should be prosecuted. Refusing to acquiesce in the Socratically inspired concentration on practical (moral) philosophy, Aristotle argued instead for the restoration of natural philosophy to a place of prominence in the total intellectual scheme.

Aristotle was not one simply to advocate a course of action. Nor did he have the concept of leaving even a part of the task to others. Searching through the chaotic mass of cosmological speculation bequeathed by his pre-Socratic predecessors, he formulated questions by which to define branches of inquiry, selected material from which to extract

1

answers, and organized the results into a coherent model of the physical world. So detailed were his efforts that his researches extended to several treatises. The perils involved in attempting to convey the content of those works in a few extracts will be obvious. The justification of those chosen rests on their relevance to Aristotle's own summary of his work (*Meteorologica*, I, 1) as involving discussions of "the first causes of nature and all natural motion; . . . the ordered movements of the stars in the heavens; the number, kinds, and mutual transformations of the four elements; and growth and decay in general." In more familiar terms, the following passages illustrate Aristotle's conceptions of what things in nature require explanation, what counts as an explanation of them, and how to proceed toward such explanations.

1

The Physics

BOOK II

Chapter 2

Now that we have determined the different senses in which "nature" may be understood (as signifying either "material" or "form"), we have next to consider how the mathematician differs from the physicist or natural philosopher; for natural bodies have surfaces and occupy spaces, have lengths and present points, all which are subjects of mathematical study. And then there is the connected question whether astronomy is a separate science from physics or only a special branch of it; for if the student of Nature is concerned to know what the sun and moon are, it were strange if he could avoid inquiry into their essential properties; especially as we find that writers on Nature have, as a fact, discoursed on the shape of the moon and sun and raised the question whether the earth, or the cosmos, is spherical or otherwise.

Physicists, astronomers, and mathematicians, then, all have to deal with lines, figures and the rest. But the mathematician is not concerned with these concepts *qua* boundaries of natural bodies, nor with their properties as manifested in such bodies. Therefore he abstracts them from physical conditions; for they are capable of being considered in the mind in separation from the motions of the bodies to which they pertain, and such abstraction does not affect the validity of the reasoning or lead to any false conclusions.

Now the exponents of the philosophy of "Ideas" also make abstractions, but in doing so they fall unawares into error; for they abstract physical entities, which are not really susceptible to the process as mathematical entities are. And this would become obvious if one should undertake to define, respectively, the mathematical and the "ideal" en-

Reprinted by permission of the publishers and The Loeb Classical Library from Aristotle, *The Physics,* P. H. Wicksteed and F. M. Cornford, trs., Cambridge, Mass.: Harvard University Press, 1929 and 1934.

tities, together with their properties; for the concepts "odd," "even," "straight," "curved," will be found to be independent of movement; and so too with "number," "line," and "figure." But of "flesh" and "bone" and "man" this is no longer true, for these are in the same case as a "turned-up nose," not in the same case as "curved." The point is further illustrated by those sciences which are rather physical than mathematical, though combining both disciplines, such as optics, harmonics, and astronomy; for the relations between them and geometry are, so to speak, reciprocal; since the geometer deals with physical lines, but not *qua* physical, whereas optics deals with mathematical lines, but *qua* physical not *qua* mathematical.

Since "nature" is used ambiguously, either for the form or for the matter, Nature, as we have seen, can be regarded from two points of view; and therefore our speculations about it may be likened to an inquiry as to what "snubnosed-ness" is; that is to say, it can neither be isolated from the material subject in which it exists, nor is it constituted by it.

At this point, in fact, we may again raise two questions. Which of the two aspects of Nature is it that claims the attention of the physicist? Or is his subject the *compositum* that combines the two? In that case— if he is concerned with the *compositum*—he must also inquire into its two factors; and then we must ask further whether this inquiry is the same for both factors or different for each.

In reading the ancients one might well suppose that the physicist's only concern was with the material; for Empedocles and Democritus have remarkably little to say about kinds of things and what is the constituent essence of them. But if art imitates Nature, and if in the arts and crafts it pertains to the same branch of knowledge both to study its own distinctive aspect of things and likewise (up to a point) the material in which the same is manifested (as the physician, for instance, must study health and also bile and phlegm, the state of which constitutes health; and the builder must know what the house is to be like and also that it is built of bricks and timber; and so in all other cases), it seems to follow that physics must take cognizance both of the formal and of the material aspect of Nature.

And further the same inquiry must embrace both the purpose or end and the means to that end. And the "nature" is the goal for the sake of which the rest exist; for if any systematic and continuous movement is directed to a goal, this goal is an end in the sense of the purpose to which the movement is a means. (A confusion on this point betrayed the poet into the unintentionally comic phrase in reference to a man's death: "He has reached his end, for the sake of which he was born."

For the "goal" does not mean any kind of termination, but only the best.) For in the arts, too, it is in view of the end that the materials are either made or suitably prepared, and we make use of all the things that we have at our command as though they existed for our sake; for we too are, in some sort, a goal ourselves. For the expression "that for the sake of which" a thing exists or is done has two senses (as we have explained in our treatise On Philosophy). Accordingly, the arts which control the material and possess the necessary knowledge are two: the art which uses the product and the art of the master-craftsman who directs the manufacture. Hence the art of the user also may in a sense be called the master-art; the difference is that this art is concerned with knowing the form, the other, which is supreme as controlling the manufacture, with knowing the material. Thus, the helmsman knows what are the distinctive characteristics of the helm as such—that is to say, its form—and gives his orders accordingly; while what the other knows is out of what wood and by what manipulations the helm is produced. In the crafts, then, it is we that prepare the material for the sake of the function it is to fulfil, but in natural products Nature herself has provided the material. In both cases, however, the preparation of the material is commanded by the end to which it is directed.

And again, the conception of "material" is relative, for it is different material that is suited to receive the several forms.

How far then, is the physicist concerned with the form and identifying essence of things and how far with their material? With the form primarily and essentially, as the physician is with health; with the material up to a certain point, as the physician is with sinew and the smith with bronze. For his main concern is with the goal, which is formal; but he deals only with such forms as are conceptually, but not factually, detachable from the material in which they occur. In Nature man generates man; but the process presupposes and takes place in natural material already organized by the solar heat and so forth. But how we are to take the sejunct and what it is, is a question for First Philosophy to determine.

Chapter 3

We have next to consider in how many senses "because" may answer the question "why." For we aim at understanding, and since we never reckon that we understand a thing till we can give an account of its "how and why," it is clear that we must look into the "how and why" of things coming into existence and passing out of it, or more generally into the essential constituents of physical change, in order to trace back any object of our study to the principles so ascertained.

Well then, (1) the existence of *material* for the generating process to start from (whether specifically or generically considered) is one of the essential factors we are looking for. Such is the bronze for the statute, or the silver for the phial. (Material cause.) Then, naturally, (2) the thing in question cannot be there unless the material has actually received the *form* or characteristics of the type, conformity to which brings it within the definition of the thing we say it is, whether specifically or generically. Thus the interval between two notes is not an octave unless the notes are in the ratio of 2 to 1; nor do they stand at a musical interval at all unless they conform to one or other of the recognized ratios. (Formal cause.) Then again (3), there must be something to initiate the process of the change or its cessation when the process is completed, such as the act of a voluntary agent (of the smith, for instance), or the father who begets a child; or more generally the prime, conscious or unconscious, *agent* that produces the effect and starts the material on its way to the product, changing it from what it was to what it is to be. (Efficient cause.) And lastly, (4) there is the *end* or purpose, for the sake of which the process is initiated, as when a man takes exercise for the sake of his health. "Why does he take exercise?" we ask. And the answer "Because he thinks it good for his health" satisfies us. (Final cause.) Then there are all the intermediary agents, which are set in motion by the prime agent and make for the goal, as means to the end. Such are the reduction of superfluous flesh and purgation, or drugs and surgical instruments, as means to health. For both actions and tools may be means, or "*media,*" through which the efficient cause reaches the end aimed at.

This is a rough classification of the causal determinants of things; but it often happens that, when we specify them, we find a number of them coalescing as joint factors in the production of a single effect, and that not merely incidentally; for it is *qua* statue that the statue depends for its existence alike on the bronze and on the statuary. The two, however, do not stand on the same footing, for one is required as the material and the other as initiating the change.

Also, it can be said of certain things indifferently that either of them is the cause or the effect of the other. Thus we may say that a man is in fine condition "because" he has been in training, or that he has been in training "because" of the good condition he expected as the result. But one is the cause as aim (final) and the other as initiating the process (efficient).

Again, the same cause is often alleged for precisely opposite effects. For if its presence causes one thing, we lay the opposite to its account if it is absent. Thus, if the pilot's presence would have brought the ship safe to harbour, we say that he caused its wreck by his absence.

But in all cases the essential and causal determinants we have enumerated fall into four main classes. For letters are the causes of syllables, and the material is the cause of manufactured articles, and fire and the like are causes of physical bodies, and the parts are causes of the whole, and the premises are causes of the conclusion, in the sense of that out of which these respectively are made; but of these things some are causes in the sense of the *substratum* (*e.g.* the parts stand in this relation to the whole), others in the sense of the *essence*—the whole or the synthesis or the form. And again, the fertilizing sperm, or the physician, or briefly the voluntary or involuntary *agent* sets going or arrests the transformation or movement. And finally, there is the goal or *end* in view, which animates all the other determinant factors as the best they can attain to; for the attainment of that "for the sake of which" anything exists or is done is its final and best possible achievement (though of course "best" in this connexion means no more than "taken to be the best").

These are the main classes of determinant factors and causes.

*   *   *   *

BOOK III

Chapter 1

Since Nature is the principle of movement and change, and it is Nature that we are studying, we must understand what "movement" is; for, if we do not know this, neither do we understand what Nature is. When we have defined the meaning of movement or progress from this to that, we must attempt in the same way a discussion of the associated conceptions to which it leads. Now, movement is clearly one of the things we think of as "continuous," and it is in connexion with continuity that we first encounter the concept of the "unlimited." And this is why in definitions of continuity this concept of the "illimitable" frequently occurs, as when we say that the continuous is that which is susceptible of division without limit. Further, movement (it is said) cannot occur except in relation to place, void, and time. Evidently, then, for these reasons and because these four things—movement, place, void, and time—are universal conditions common to all natural phenomena, we must consider each of them on the threshold of our inquiry; for the treatment of peculiar properties must come after that of properties common to all natural things.

We must begin, then, as already said, with movement in general or progress from this to that. Now, some potentialities never exist apart, but always reveal themselves as actualized; others, while they are something actually, are capable of becoming something else than they are, that is to say, have potentialities not realized at the moment; and these potentialities may concern their substantive being (what they are) or their quantity or their qualities; and so on with the other categories of existence. And under the category of "relation" may be relations between the "more" and the "less," or between that which is active and that which is acted on, and generally between that which "moves" (or changes) something as the agent and that which is moved (or changed) by it as the patient. For that which has the power of producing a change can only act in reference to a thing capable of being changed; and that which is capable of being changed can only suffer change under the action of that which has the power to change it.

Now, motion and change cannot exist in themselves apart from what moves and changes. For, wherever anything changes, it always changes either from one thing to another, or from one magnitude to another, or from one quality to another, or from one place to another; but there is nothing that embraces all these kinds of change in common, and is itself neither substantive nor quantitative nor qualitative nor pertaining to any of the other categories, but existing in detachment; so neither can movement or change exist independently of these, for there is nothing independent of them.

Again, in each of these four cases, there are two poles between which the change moves; in substantive existence, for example, form and shortage from form; in quality, white and black; in quantity, the perfectly normal and an achievement short of perfection; and so, too, in the case of vection, up and down, or the action of levity and gravity. So there are as many kinds of change as there are categories of existence.

Reverting, therefore, to the universal distinction already established between "being-at-the-goal" in actuality and being in potentiality "such-as-is-capable-of-attaining-the-goal," we can now define motion or change as the progress of the realizing of a potentiality, *qua* potentiality, *e.g.* the actual progress of qualitative modification in any modifiable thing *qua* modifiable; the actual growing or shrinking (for we have no single word to include them both) of anything capable of expanding or contracting; the process of coming into existence or passing out of it of that which is capable of so coming and passing; the actual moving of the physical body capable of changing its place. That this is what we really mean by motion or change may be shown thus: building material is actualizing the potentialities in virtue of which we call it "building material" when it is in the act of being built into a structure, and this act is the process or "movement" of "building"; and so too with other processes—learning, healing, rolling, jumping, maturing, aging.

And since in certain cases the same thing may have both an actuality and a potentiality (not indeed at the same time or not in the same respect, but potentially hot, for instance, and actually cold), it follows that many things act on, and are acted on by, each other; for anything will be at once capable of acting and of being acted upon. And so it happens that every physical body which causes motion must be capable of being moved; for whenever it causes motion it is itself under the action of some other body which is keeping it in motion. But the inference that has sometimes been drawn, that there is *no* cause of a thing being in motion, which cause is not itself in motion, is false. The truth in this matter will be explained later on; suffice it now to say that there *is* a cause of things being in motion, which cause is itself immovable; but motion is the functioning of a movable thing, all the time that it is bringing its potentiality into act, not *qua* itself, but *qua* movable.

To illustrate what I mean by "*qua*" this or that. The bronze is potentially the statue, but neither to be the statue nor to move or change in any respect is the self-realizing of the bronze *qua* bronze; for it is not the same thing to be bronze and to be potentially movable or changeable. Were it the same thing, absolutely and by definition, then indeed moving would be its self-realization; but it is not the same. (It is clear in the case of opposites: the potentiality of health and the potentiality of disease are different things—otherwise being diseased and being healthy would be identical—but whatever it is, humour or blood, that is subject to the healthy or unhealthy condition is one and the same thing in both cases.) And since it is not the same (any more than colour and visibility, for instance, are the same), it is clear that motion must be the realization of the specific potentiality in question and of the subject only *qua* seat of this specific potentiality.

Clearly, then, this is the nature of movement, and a thing is moving just as long as it is actually functioning in this particular way, and neither before nor after. For anything capable of this special kind of functioning may be exercising it at one time, but not at another; for instance, the building materials are functioning *as materials for building* only so long as they are in process of being built with; for as soon as the edifice itself is actually raised, the functioning of what were materials for a house is merged in the functioning of the house itself; but as long as they are being built with, they are functioning as materials for a house. The act of building, then, is the energizing or bringing into actuality of the potentiality of the materials *qua* materials; and the passage of the materials of a house into the texture of the house itself, so long as it is in progress, is their "movement" *qua* materials of building. And this is the theory of all the other "movements" equally.

On Coming-To-Be and Passing-Away

BOOK II

Chapter 1

We have now dealt with the way in which mixture, contact and action-and-passion are attributable to things which undergo natural change; we have, moreover, explained how unqualified coming-to-be and passing-away exist, and with what they are concerned and owing to what cause they occur. Similarly, we have dealt with "alteration" and explained how it differs from coming-to-be and passing-away. It remains to consider the so-called elements of bodies.

Coming-to-be and passing-away occur in all naturally constituted substances, if we presuppose the existence of perceptible bodies. Some people assert that the matter underlying these bodies is one; for example, they suppose it to be Air or Fire, or an intermediate between these two, but still a single separate body. Others hold that there are more than one material, some thinking that they are Fire and Earth, others adding Air as a third, others (like Empedocles) adding Water as a fourth; and it is, they say, from the association and separation or alteration of these that coming-to-be and passing-away of things comes about.

Let us, then, be agreed that the primary materials from the changes of which, either by association or by separation or by some other kind of change, coming-to-be and passing-away occur, are rightly described as "sources" and "elements." But (a) those who postulate that there is a single matter, besides the bodies which we have mentioned, and that this is corporeal and separable, are mistaken; for it is impossible that this body can exist without "perceptible contrariety," for this "infinite," which some say must be the source of reality, must be either light or heavy, or hot or cold. And (b) what is written in the *Timaeus* is not accurately defined; for Plato has not clearly stated whether his "omni-recipient" has any existence apart from the elements, nor does he make

Reprinted by permission of the publishers and The Loeb Classical Library from Aristotle, *On Coming-to-be and Passing-away*, E. S. Forster, tr., Cambridge, Mass.: Harvard University Press, 1955.

any use of it, after saying that it is a *substratum* prior to the so-called elements, just as gold is the *substratum* of objects made of gold. (Yet put in this way the statement is not a happy one. Things of which there is coming-to-be and passing-away cannot be called after that out of which they have come-to-be, though it is possible for things which are altered to keep the name of that of which they are alterations. However, what he actually says is that by far the truest account is to say that each of the objects is "gold.") However, he carries the analysis of the elements, though they are solids, back to "planes," and it is impossible for the "Nurse," that is the primary matter, to consist of planes. Our theory is that there is matter of which the perceptible bodies consist, but that it is not separable but always accompanied by contrariety, and it is from this that the so-called elements come into being; but a more accurate account of these things has been given elsewhere. However, since the primary bodies are also derived in this way from matter, we must explain about these also, reckoning as a source and as primary the matter which is inseparable from, but underlies, the contrarieties; for "the hot" is not matter for "the cold," nor "the cold" for "the hot," but the *substratum* is matter for them both. Therefore, firstly, the potentially perceptible body, secondly, the contrarieties (for example, heat and cold), and thirdly, Fire and Water and the like are "sources." For the bodies in this third class change into one another and are not as Empedocles and others describe them (otherwise alteration could not have taken place), whereas the contrarieties do not change. Nevertheless, even so the question must be decided what kinds of contrariety and how many of them there are which are sources of body; for all other philosophers assume and make use of them without stating why they are these and why they are of a particular number.

Chapter 2

Since, therefore, we are seeking the sources of perceptible bodies, and this means tangible, and tangible is that of which the perception is touch, it is clear that not all the contrarieties constitute "forms" and "sources" of body, but only those connected with touch; for it is in the matter of contrariety that they differ, that is, tangible contrariety. There-fore neither whiteness and blackness, nor sweetness and bitterness, nor any of the other perceptible contrarieties constitute an element. Yet sight is prior to touch, so that its subject is also prior; but it is a quality of tangible body not in virtue of its tangibility but because of something else, even though it happens to be naturally prior.

Of the tangible differences and contrarieties themselves we must dis-tinguish which are primary. The following are contrarieties according to touch: hot and cold, dry and moist, heavy and light, hard and soft, viscous and brittle, rough and smooth, coarse and fine. Of these heavy and light are not active nor yet passive; for they do not get their names because they act on something else or are acted upon by something else; elements, on the other hand, must be mutually active and passive, for they mix and change into one another. But hot and cold, and dry and moist are terms of which the first pair get their names because they are active, the second pair because they are passive; for "hot" is that which associates things of the same kind (for to "dissociate," which, they say, is an action of Fire, is to associate things of the same class, since the result is to destroy things which are foreign), but cold is that which brings together and associates alike both things which are of the same kind and things which are not of the same class. Moist is that which, though easily adaptable to form, cannot be confined within limits of its own, while dry is that which is easily confined within its own limits but is not easily adaptable in form. From the moist and the dry are derived the fine and the coarse, the viscous and the brittle, the hard and the soft and the other contrasted pairs. For since "capacity for filling up something" is characteristic of the moist, because it is not confined within bounds but is adaptable in form and follows the shape of that which comes into contact with it, and that which is "fine" is "capable of filling up something" (for it consists of small particles, and that which consists of small particles is capable of filling up something, for the whole is in contact with the whole, and that which is fine consists of the smallest possible particles), it is clear that the fine is derived from the moist and the coarse derived from the dry. Again, the viscous is derived from the moist (for that which is viscous is moisture which has undergone a certain treatment, as in the case of oil), and the brittle is derived from the dry; for the completely dry is brittle, so that it has become solid through lack of moisture. Further, the soft is derived from the moist (for the soft is that which gives way and sinks into itself but does not change its position, as does the moist; hence, too, the moist is not soft, but the soft is derived from the moist). The hard, on the other hand, is derived from the dry; for that which has solidified is hard, and the solid is dry. Now "dry" and "moist" are used in several senses; for both moist and damp are opposed to dry, and, again, solid as well as dry is opposed to moist. But all these qualities are derived from the dry and the moist which we mentioned originally. For the dry is opposed to the damp, and the damp is that which has foreign moisture on its surface, soaked being that which is damp to its innermost depth, while dry is that which is deprived of foreign moisture. Therefore, clearly the damp will be derived from the moist, and the dry, which is opposed to it, will be derived from the primary dry. So likewise, on the other hand, with the moist and the solidified; for moist is that which contains its own moisture in its depth, while soaked is that which contains foreign moisture there, and solidified is that which has lost its foreign moisture; so that of these the latter derives from the dry, the former from the moist. It is clear, then, that all the other differences are reduced to the first four, and these cannot be further reduced to a lesser number; for the hot is not that which is essentially moist or essentially dry, nor is the moist essentially hot or essentially cold, nor do the cold and the dry fall in the category of one another nor in that of the hot and moist; hence these must necessarily be four of these elementary qualities.

Chapter 3

Now since the elementary qualities are four in number and of these four six couples can be formed, but contraries are not of a nature which permits of their being coupled—for the same thing cannot be hot and cold, or again, moist and dry—it is clear that the pairs of elementary qualities will be four in number, hot and dry, hot and moist, and, again, cold and moist, and cold and dry. And, according to theory, they have attached themselves to the apparently simple bodies, Fire, Air, Water and Earth; for Fire is hot and dry, Air is hot and moist (Air, for example, is vapour), Water is cold and moist, and Earth is cold and dry. Thus the variations are reasonably distributed among the primary bodies, and the number of these is according to theory. For all those who make out that the simple bodies are elements make them either one or two or three or four. Therefore (a) those who hold that there is only *one* and then generate everything else by condensation and rarefaction, as a result make the sources two in number, the rare and the dense or the hot and the cold; for these are the creative forces, and "the one" underlies them as matter. But (b) those who hold that there are *two* from the beginning—as Parmenides held that there were Fire and Earth—make the intermediates, Air and Water, mixtures of these; and (c) the same thing is done also by those who hold that there are *three,* as Plato does in the "Divisions," for he makes "the middle" a mixture. Those who hold that there are two and those who postulate *three* say practically the same things, except that the former divide the middle into two, while the latter treat it as one. But (d) some declare that there are four from the start, for instance Empedocles, though he also reduces these to two, for he too opposes all the others to Fire.

Fire, however, and Air and each of the other bodies which we have mentioned are not simple but mixed, while the simple forms of them are similar to them but not the same as they are; for example, that which is like fire is "fiery," not fire, and that which is like air is "air-like," and similarly with the rest. But fire is an excess of heat, just as ice is an excess of cold; for freezing and boiling are excesses, the former of cold, the latter of heat. If, therefore, ice is a freezing of moist and cold, so fire will be a boiling of dry and hot; and that is why nothing comes to be from ice or from fire.

The simple bodies, then, being four in number, make up two pairs belonging to two regions; for Fire and Air form the body which is carried along towards the "limit," while Earth and Water form the body which is carried along towards the centre; and Fire and Earth are extremes and very pure, while Water and Air are intermediates and more mixed. Further, the members of each pair are contrary to the members of the other pair, Water being the contrary of Fire, and Earth of Air, for they are made up of different qualities. However, since they are four, each is described simply as possessing a single quality, Earth a dry rather than a cold quality, Water a cold rather than a moist, Air a moist rather than a hot, and Fire a hot rather than a dry.

Chapter 4

Since it has been determined in a former discussion that the coming-to-be of simple bodies is out of one another, and at the same time, too, it is evident from sense-perception that they *do* come-to-be (for otherwise there would have been no alteration—for alteration is concerned with the qualities of tangible things), we must state (*a*) what is the manner of their reciprocal change, and (*b*) whether any one of them can come-to-be out of any other one of them, or some can do so and others cannot. Now it is manifest that all of them are of such a nature as to change into one another; for coming-to-be is a process into contraries and out of contraries, and all the elements are characterized by contrarieties one to another, because their distinguishing qualities are contrary. In some of them both qualities are contrary, for example, in Fire and Water (for the former is dry and hot, the latter is moist and cold), in others only one, for example, in Air and Water (for the former is moist and hot, the latter is moist and cold). Hence, it is clear, if we take a general view, that every one of them naturally comes-to-be out of every one of them and, if we take them separately, it is not difficult now to see how this happens; for all will be the product of all, but there will be a difference owing to the greater and less speed and the greater and less difficulty of the process. For the change will be quick in those things which have qualities which correspond with one another, but slow when these do not exist, because it is easier for one thing to change than for many; for example, Air will result from Fire by the change of one quality; for Fire, as we said, is hot and dry, while Air is hot and moist, so that Air will result if the dry is overpowered by the moist. Again, Water will result from Air, if the hot is overpowered by the cold; for Air, as we said, is hot and moist, while Water is cold and moist, so that Water will result if the hot undergoes a change. In the same way, too, Earth will result from Water, and Fire from Earth; for both members of each pair have qualities which correspond to one another, since Water is moist and cold, and Earth is cold and dry, and so, when the moist is overpowered, Earth will result. Again, since Fire is dry and hot, and Earth is cold and dry, if the cold were to pass away, Fire will result from Earth.

It is clear, therefore, that the coming-to-be of simple bodies will be cyclical; and this manner of change will be very easy, because the corresponding qualities are already present in the elements which are next to one another. The change, however, from Fire to Water and from Air to Earth, and again from Water and Earth to Air and Fire *can* take place, but is more difficult, because the change involves more stages. For if Fire is to be produced from Water, both the cold and the moist must be made to pass-away; and, again, if Air is to be produced from Earth, both the cold and the dry must be made to pass-away. In like manner, too, if Water and Earth are to be produced from Fire and Air, there must be a change of both qualities. This method of coming-to-be is, therefore, a lengthier process; but if one quality of each element were to be made to pass away, the change will be easier but not reciprocal; but from Fire and Water will come Earth and (alternatively) Air, and from Air and Earth, Fire and (alternatively) Water; for when the cold of the Water and the dryness of the Fire have passed-away, there will be Air (for the heat of the Fire and the moisture of the Water are left), but, when the heat of the Fire and the moisture of the Water have passed-away, there will be Earth, because the dryness of the Fire and the cold of the Water are left. In the same manner also Fire and Water will result from Air and Earth; for when the heat of the Air and the dryness of the Earth pass-away, there will be Water (for the moisture of the Air and the cold of the Earth are left), but when the moisture of the Air and the cold of the Earth have passed-away, there will be Fire, because the heat of the Air and the dryness of the Earth, which are, as we saw, the constituents of Fire, are left. Now the manner in which Fire comes-to-be is confirmed by our sense-perception; for flame is the most evident form of Fire, and flame is burning smoke, and smoke is composed of Air and Earth.

No change, however, into any of the bodies can take place from the passing-away of one of the elements in each of them taken in their consecutive order, because either the same or the contrary qualities are left in the pair, and a body cannot come-to-be out of identical or contrary qualities; for example, it would not result if the dryness of Fire and the moisture of the Air were to pass-away (for the heat is left in both), but, if the heat passes-away from both, the contraries, dryness and moisture, are left. So likewise with the others too; for in all the consecutive elements there exists one identical and one contrary quality. It is, therefore, at the same time clear that some elements come-to-be by being transformed from one into one by the passing-away of one quality, but others come-to-be by being transformed from two into one by the passing-away of more than one quality. We have now stated that all the elements come-to-be from any one of them, and how their change into one another takes place.

On The Heavens

The question of the nature of this Whole, whether it is of infinite magnitude or its total bulk is limited, must be left until later. We have now to speak of its formally distinct parts, and we may start from this, that all natural bodies and magnitudes are capable of moving of themselves in space; for nature we have defined as the principle of motion in them. Now all motion in space (locomotion) is either straight or circular or a compound of the two, for these are the only simple motions, the reason being that the straight and circular lines are the only simple magnitudes. By "circular motion" I mean motion around the centre, by "straight," motion up and down. "Up" means away from the centre, "down" towards the centre. It follows that all simple locomotion is either away from the centre or towards the centre or around the centre. This appears to follow consistently on what was said at the beginning: body was completed by the number three, and so now is its motion.

Of bodies some are simple, and some are compounds of the simple. By "simple" I mean all bodies which contain a principle of natural motion, like fire and earth and their kinds, and the other bodies of the same order. Hence motions also must be similarly divisible, some simple and others compound in one way or another; simple bodies will have simple motions and composite bodies composite motions, though the movement may be according to the prevailing element in the compound.

If we take these premises, (a) that there is such a thing as simple motion, (b) that circular motion is simple, (c) that simple motion is the motion of a simple body (for if a composite body moves with a simple motion, it is only by virtue of a simple body prevailing and imparting its direction to the whole), then it follows that there exists a simple body naturally so constituted as to move in a circle in virtue of its own

Reprinted by permission of the publishers and The Loeb Classical Library from Aristotle, *On the Heavens*, W. K. C. Guthrie, tr., Cambridge, Mass.: Harvard University Press, 1939.

nature. By force it can be brought to move with the motion of another, different body, but not naturally, if it is true that each of the simple bodies has one natural motion only. Moreover, granted that (a) unnatural motion is the contrary of natural, (b) a thing can have only one contrary, then circular motion, seeing it is one of the simple motions, must, if it is not the motion natural to the moved body, be contrary to its nature. Suppose now that the body which is moving in a circle be fire or some other of the four elements, then its natural motion must be contrary to the circular. But a thing can have only one contrary, and the contrary of upward is downward, and *vice versa*. Suppose on the other hand that this body which is moving in a circle contrary to its own nature is something other than the elements, there must be some other motion which is natural to it. But that is impossible: for if the motion were upward, the body would be fire or air, if downward, water or earth.

Furthermore, circular motion must be primary. That which is complete is prior in nature to the incomplete, and the circle is a complete figure, whereas no straight line can be so. An infinite straight line cannot, for to be complete it would have to have an end or completion, nor yet a finite, for all finite lines have something beyond them: any one of them is capable of being extended. Now if (a) a motion which is prior to another is the motion of a body prior in nature, (b) circular motion is prior to rectilinear, (c) rectilinear motion is the motion of the simple bodies (as *e.g.* fire moves in a straight line upwards and earthy bodies move downwards towards the centre), then circular motion also must of necessity be the motion of some simple body. (We have already made the reservation that the motion of composite bodies is determined by whatever simple body predominates in the mixture.) From all these premises therefore it clearly follows that there exists some physical substance besides the four in our sublunary world, and moreover that it is more divine than, and prior to, all these. The same can also be proved on the further assumption that all motion is either natural or unnatural, and that motion which is unnatural to one body is natural to another, as the motions up and down are natural or unnatural to fire and earth respectively; from these it follows that circular motion too, since it is unnatural to these elements, is natural to some other. Moreover, if circular motion is natural to anything, it will clearly be one of the simple and primary bodies of such a nature as to move naturally in a circle, as fire moves upward and earth downward. If on the other hand it be maintained that the revolutionary motion of the body which is carried round in a circle is unnatural, it is strange, in fact quite absurd, that being unnatural it should yet be the only continuous and eternal motion, seeing that in the rest of nature what is unnatural is the quickest to fall into decay. And so, if fire be the body carried round, as some say, this motion will be no less unnatural to it than motion downwards; for we see the natural motion of fire to be in a straight line away from the centre.

Thus the reasoning from all our premises goes to make us believe that there is some other body separate from those around us here, and of a higher nature in proportion as it is removed from the sublunary world.

Chapter 3

After what has been said, whether laid down as hypothesis or demonstrated in the course of the argument, it becomes clear that not every body has either lightness or weight. However, we must first lay down what we mean by heavy and light, at present only so far as it is necessary for the purpose in hand, but later with more precision, when we come to investigate the real nature of the two. Let "the heavy" then be that whose nature it is to move towards the centre, "the light" that whose nature it is to move away from the centre, "heaviest" that which sinks below all other bodies whose motion is downwards, and "lightest" that which rises to the top of the bodies whose motion is upwards. Thus every body which moves downwards or upwards must have either lightness or weight or both. (A body cannot of course be both heavy and light in relation to the same thing, but the elements are so in relation to each other, e.g. air is light in comparison with water, but water in comparison with earth.) Now the body whose motion is circular cannot have either weight or lightness, for neither naturally nor unnaturally can it ever move towards or away from the centre. (a) Naturally it cannot have rectilinear motion, because it was laid down that each simple body has only one natural motion, and therefore it would itself be one of the bodies whose natural motion is rectilinear. (b) But suppose it moves in a straight line contrary to its nature, then if the motion is downwards, upward motion will be its natural one, and vice versa; for it was one of our hypotheses that of two contrary motions, if one is unnatural the other is natural. Taking into account then the fact that a whole and its part move naturally in the same direction (as do e.g. all earth together and a small clod), we have established (a) that it has neither lightness nor weight, since otherwise it would have been able to move naturally either towards the centre or away from the centre, (b) that it cannot move locally by being violently forced either up or down, for it is impossible for it to move, either naturally or unnaturally, with any other motion but its own, either itself as a whole or any of its parts, seeing that the same argument applies to whole and part.

With equal reason we may regard it as ungenerated and indestructible, and susceptible neither to growth nor alteration. (a) Everything that is generated comes into being out of an opposite and a substrate, and is destroyed only if it has a substrate, and through the agency of an opposite, and passes into its opposite, as has been explained in our first discussions. (b) Opposites have opposite motions. (c) There cannot be an opposite to the body under discussion, because there cannot be an opposite motion to the circular. It looks then as if nature had providently abstracted from the class of opposites that which was to be ungenerated and indestructible, because generation and destruction take place among opposites. Moreover anything which is subject to growth [or diminution] grows [or diminishes] in consequence of substance of the same kind being added to it and dissolving into its matter; but this body has no such matter. And if it is subject neither to growth nor to destruction, the same train of thought leads us to suppose that it is not subject to alteration either. Alteration is movement in respect of quality, and the temporary or permanent states of quality, health and disease for example, do not come into being without changes of affection. But all physical bodies which possess changing affections may be seen to be subject also to growth and diminution. Such are, for example, the bodies of animals and plants and their parts, and also those of the elements. If then the body whose natural motion is circular cannot be subject to growth or diminution, it is a reasonable supposition that it is not subject to alteration either.

From what has been said it is clear why, if our hypotheses are to be trusted, the primary body of all is eternal, suffers neither growth nor diminution, but is ageless, unalterable and impassive. I think too that the argument bears out experience and is borne out by it. All men have a conception of gods, and all assign the highest place to the divine, both barbarians and Hellenes, as many as believe in gods, supposing, obviously, that immortal is closely linked with immortal. It could not, they think, be otherwise. If then—and it is true—there is something divine, what we have said about the primary bodily substance is well said. The truth of it is also clear from the evidence of the senses, enough at least to warrant the assent of human faith; for throughout all past time, according to the records handed down from generation to generation, we find no trace of change either in the whole of the outermost heaven or in any one of its proper parts. It seems too that the name of this first body has been passed down to the present time by the ancients, who thought of it in the same way as we do, for we cannot help believing that the same ideas recur to men not once nor twice but over and over again. Thus they, believing that the primary body was something different from earth and fire and air and water, gave the name *aither* to the uppermost region, choosing its title from the fact that it "runs always" and eternally. (Anaxagoras badly misapplies the word when he uses *aither* for fire.)

It is also clear from what has been said why the number of the simple bodies, as we call them, cannot be more than we have mentioned. A simple body must have a simple motion, and we hold that these are the only simple motions, circular and rectilinear, the latter of two sorts, away from the centre and towards the centre.

Chapter 4

The shape of the heaven must be spherical. That is most suitable to its substance, and is the primary shape in nature. But let us discuss the question of what is the primary shape, both in plane surfaces and in solids. Every plane figure is bounded either by straight lines or by a circumference; the rectilinear is bounded by several lines, the circular by one only. Thus since in every genus the one is by nature prior to the many, and the simple to the composite, the circle must be the primary plane figure. Also, if the term "perfect" is applied, according to our previous definition, to that outside which no part of itself can be found, and addition to a straight line is always possible, to a circle never, the circumference of the circle must be a perfect line: granted therefore that the perfect is prior to the imperfect, this argument too demonstrates the priority of the circle to other figures. By the same reasoning the sphere is the primary solid, for it alone is bounded by a single surface, rectilinear solids by several. The place of the sphere among solids is the same as that of the circle among plane figures. Even those who divide bodies up into surfaces and generate them out of surfaces seem to agree with this, for the sphere is the one solid which they do not divide, holding that it has only one surface, not a plurality; for their division into surfaces does not mean division in the manner of one cutting a whole into its parts, but division into elements specifically different.

It is clear, then, that the sphere is the first solid figure, and it would also be most natural to give it that place if one ranked figures according to number, the circle corresponding to one and the triangle to two, on account of its two right angles—for if one gives unity to the triangle, the circle will cease to be a figure. But the primary figure belongs to the primary body, and the primary body is that which is at the farthest circumference, hence it, the body which revolves in a circle, must be spherical in shape.

The same must be true of the body which is contiguous to it, for what is contiguous to the spherical is spherical, and also of those bodies which lie nearer the centre, for bodies which are surrounded by the spherical and touch it at all points must themselves be spherical, and the lower bodies are in contact with the sphere above. It is, then, spherical through and through, seeing that everything in it is in continuous contact with the spheres.

Again, since it is an observed fact, and assumed in these arguments, that the whole revolves in a circle, and it has been shown that beyond the outermost circumference there is neither void nor place, this provides another reason why the heaven must be spherical. For if it is bounded by straight lines, that will involve the existence of place, body, and void. A rectilinear body revolving in a circle will never occupy the same space, but owing to the change in position of the corners there will at one time be no body where there was body before, and there will be body again where now there is none. It would be the same if it were of some other shape whose radii were unequal, that of a lentil or an egg for example. All will involve the existence of place and void outside the revolution, because the whole does not occupy the same space throughout.

Again, the revolution of the heaven is the measure of all motions, because it alone is continuous and unvarying and eternal, the measure in every class of things is the smallest member, and the shortest motion is the quickest, therefore the motion of the heaven must clearly be the quickest of all motions. But the shortest path of those which return upon their starting-point is represented by the circumference of a circle and the quickest motion is that along the shortest path. If therefore the heaven (a) revolves in a circle and (b) moves faster than anything else, it must be spherical.

One might also be brought to this belief by consideration of the bodies situated around the centre; for if water is found around the earth, air around water, and fire around air, the upper bodies will follow the same arrangement, seeing that, although not co-terminous, they are contiguous with the others. But the surface of water is spherical, and what is co-terminous with the spherical or lies around it must be of the same shape itself. So by this argument too the spherical shape of the heaven is clear.

As for the sphericity of the surface of water, that is demonstrable from the premise that it always runs together into the hollowest place, and "hollowest" means "nearest to the centre." Let AB and AC be straight lines drawn from the centre, and joined by BC (Figure 1). Then the line AD, drawn as far as the base, is shorter than the original lines from the centre, and the place occupied by D is a hollow. Hence the water will flow round it until it has filled it up. The line AE, on the other hand, is equal to the radii, and thus it is at the extremities of the radii that the water must lie: there it will be at rest. But the line which is at

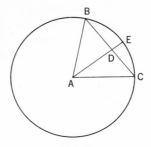

FIGURE 1

the extremities of the radii is the circumference of a circle. Therefore the surface of water, represented by BEC, is spherical.

Our arguments have clearly shown that the universe is spherical, and so accurately turned that nothing made by man, nor anything visible to us on the earth, can be compared to it. For of the elements of which it is composed, none is capable of taking such a smooth and accurate finish as the nature of the body which encompasses the rest; for the more distant elements must become ever finer in texture in proportion as water is finer than earth.

*   *   *   *

Chapter 11

The shape of each star is spherical, at least according to the most reasonable supposition. For it has been demonstrated that they do not naturally move themselves; but Nature makes nothing which is purposeless or doomed to frustration; she must therefore have provided immobile objects with the sort of shape which is least adapted to motion. Now the least adapted to motion is the sphere, for it possesses no instrument to serve for that purpose. Clearly therefore the stars will consist of masses spherical in shape.

Again, one and all are alike, and the moon can be shown by the evidence of sight to be spherical. Were it any other shape, it would not appear crescent-shaped or gibbous during the greater part of its waxing and waning, and only at one moment semicircular. Or the proof can be taken from astronomy, which demonstrates that the sun in eclipse would not be crescent-shaped. If, then, one of the heavenly bodies is spherical, the others will clearly be spherical also.

*   *   *   *

Chapter 13

It remains to speak of the earth, where it is, whether it should be classed among things at rest or things in motion, and of its shape.

Concerning its position there is some divergence of opinion. Most of those who hold that the whole Universe is finite say that it lies at the centre, but this is contradicted by the Italian school called Pythagoreans. These affirm that the centre is occupied by fire, and that the earth is one of the stars, and creates night and day as it travels in a circle about the centre. In addition they invent another earth, lying opposite our own, which they call by the name of "counter-earth," not seeking accounts and explanations in conformity with the appearances, but trying by violence to bring the appearances into line with accounts and opinions of their own. There are many others too who might agree that it is wrong to assign the central position to the earth, men who see proof not in the appearances but rather in abstract theory. These reason that the most honourable body ought to occupy the most honourable place, that fire is more honourable than earth, that a limit is a more honourable place than what lies between limits, and that the centre and outer boundary are the limits. Arguing from these premises, they say it must be not the earth, but rather fire, that is situated at the centre of the sphere.

The Pythagoreans make a further point. Because the most important part of the Universe—which is the centre—ought more than any to be guarded, they call the fire which occupies this place the Watch-tower of Zeus, as if it were the centre in an unambiguous sense, being at the same time the geometrical centre and the natural centre of the thing itself. But we should rather suppose the same to be true of the whole world as is true of animals, namely that the centre of the animal and the centre of its body are not the same thing. For this reason there is no need for them to be alarmed about the Universe, nor to call in a guard for its mathematical centre; they ought rather to consider what sort of thing the true centre is, and what is its natural place. For it is that centre which should be held in honour as a starting-point; the local centre would seem to be rather an end than a starting-point, for that which is defined is the local centre, that which defines it is the boundary: but that which encompasses and sets bounds is of more worth than that which is bounded, for the one is matter, the other the substance of the structure.

This then is the opinion of some about the position of the earth, and on the question of its rest or motion there are conformable views. Here again all do not think alike. Those who deny that it lies at the centre suppose that it moves in a circle about the centre, and not the earth alone, but also the counter-earth, as we have already explained. Some even think it possible that there are a number of such bodies carried round the centre, invisible to us owing to the interposition of the earth. This serves them too as a reason why eclipses of the moon are more frequent than those of the sun, namely that it is blocked by each of these moving bodies, not only by the earth. Since the earth's surface is not in any case the centre, but distant the whole hemisphere from the centre, they do not feel any difficulty in supposing that the phenomena are the same although we do not occupy the centre as they would be if the earth were in the middle. For even on the current view there is nothing to show that we are distant from the centre by half the earth's diameter. Some again say that although the earth lies at the centre, it "winds," i.e. is in motion, "round the axis which stretches right through," as is written in the *Timaeus*.

There is just as much disagreement about the shape of the earth. Some think it spherical, others flat and shaped like a drum. These latter adduce as evidence the fact that the sun at its setting and rising shows a straight instead of a curved line where it is cut off from view by the horizon, whereas were the earth spherical, the line of section would necessarily be curved. They fail to take into consideration either the distance of the sun from the earth, or the size of the earth's circumference, and the appearance of straightness which it naturally presents when seen on the surface of an apparently small circle a great distance away. This phenomenon therefore gives them no cogent ground for disbelieving in the spherical shape of the earth's mass. But they add to their argument by saying that its immobility necessarily involves the other shape.

It is certainly true that the theories which have been held about the motion or rest of the earth are manifold. Indeed, everyone must be impressed by the difficulty of the question. His must surely be a careless mind who does not wonder how it is that a small particle of the earth, if raised to a height and then set free, should refuse to remain where it was but begin to travel, and travel the quicker the bigger it is, whereas if one held the whole earth in the air and let it go, it would not move. But in fact, for all its weight, it is at rest. Consider too that if one removed the earth from the path of one of its particles before it had fallen, it would travel downwards so long as there was nothing to oppose it.

This question, then, has become, as one might expect, a subject of general inquiry. But one may well wonder that the answers suggested are not recognized as being more incomprehensible than the question which they set out to solve. It has led some to assert that the earth extends downwards indefinitely, saying with Xenophanes of Colophon that it is "infinite in its roots," to save themselves the trouble of looking for a reason. This called forth the censure of Empedocles, in the words:

If verily the depths of the earth were infinite and the ample ether, a saying which has run foolishly off the tongues of many and dropped from their mouths, men who have perceived but little of the whole.

Others say that it rests on water. This is the most ancient explanation which has come down to us, and is attributed to Thales of Miletus. It supposes that the earth is at rest because it can float like wood and similar substances, whose nature it is to rest upon water, though none of them could rest on air. But (i) this is to forget that the same thing may be said of the water supporting the earth as was said of the earth itself. It is not the nature of water, any more than of earth, to remain suspended: it rests upon something. (ii) Just as air is lighter than water, so water is lighter than earth. How then can the lighter substance lie underneath that which is naturally heavier? (iii) If it is the nature of the earth as a whole to float on water, the same should be true of every piece of it: but this is plainly contrary to fact, for a piece taken at random sinks to the bottom, and the larger it is the quicker it sinks. Thus we may say of these theorists that they pursued the difficulty up to a point, but not as far as they might have. This is a habit which we all share, of relating an inquiry not to the subject-matter itself, but to our opponent in argument. A man will even pursue a question in his own mind no farther than the point at which he finds nothing to say against his own arguments. Therefore to be a good investigator a man must be alive to the objections inherent in the genus of his subject, an awareness which is the result of having studied all its differentiae.

Anaximenes, Anaxagoras and Democritus name the flatness of the earth as the cause of its remaining at rest. It does not cleave the air beneath it, but settles on it like a lid, as flat bodies to all appearances do: owing to their resistance, they are not easily moved even by the wind. The earth, they say, owing to its flatness behaves in the same way in relation to the air immediately underneath it, which, not having sufficient room to change its place, is compressed and stays still owing to the air beneath, like the water in *klepsydrae*. For this power of the air to bear a great weight when it is shut up and its motion stopped, they bring forward plenty of evidence. Now in the first place, if the earth is not flat, it cannot be owing to its flat shape that it is at rest. But in fact their arguments do not make its flatness the cause of its immobility, but rather its size. It is for lack of room that the air stays as it does, because it has no way out and on account of its mass; and the quantity of it is due to the greatness of the earth confining a large amount. These conditions will be provided, even though the earth is spherical, if it is of the requisite size: it will still be at rest according to their argument.

But we need not argue over details. Our quarrel with the men who talk like that about motion does not concern particular parts, but an undivided whole. I mean that we must decide from the very beginning whether bodies have a natural motion or not, or whether, not having a natural motion, they have an enforced one. And since our decisions on these points have already been made, so far as our available means allowed, we must use them as data. If, we said, they have no natural motion, they will have no enforced motion either; and if there is neither natural nor enforced motion, nothing will ever move at all. We have already determined what would necessarily happen in these circumstances; in addition to the foregoing, things could not even be at rest, for rest is either natural or enforced in the same way as motion. But if they have any motion at all by nature, then they cannot have either enforced motion only or enforced rest only; so that if the earth's rest is due to constraint, it must have been under the action of the vortex that it travelled into the middle. (This is the name which all agree in giving to the cause, reasoning from what happens in liquids and in the air, where larger and heavier things always move towards the middle of a vortex.) Therefore all who hold that the world had a beginning, say that the earth travelled to the middle. They then seek the reason of its remaining there, and some claim, as we have said, that its flatness and size are the cause; others agree with Empedocles that it is the excessive swiftness of the motion of the heaven as it swings around in a circle which prevents motion on the part of the earth. They compare it to the water in a cup, which in fact, when the cup is swung round in a circle, is prevented from falling by the same cause, although it often finds itself underneath the bronze and it is its nature to move downwards. Yet if neither the vortex nor its own flatness hindered its falling, but the air had been withdrawn from below, where would it go? It moved to the centre by constraint, and it rests there by constraint; but it must have some natural motion. Is this then upwards or downwards or where? There must be a motion, and if it is as likely to be upwards as downwards, and the air above it does not prevent it from moving upwards, no more would the air beneath it prevent it from moving downwards: for the same causes must produce the same effects on the same objects.

Against Empedocles there is another objection that might be made. When the elements had been separated off by Strife, what was the cause of the earth's immobility? He cannot assert that even at that time the vortex was the cause.

It was irrational too not to take into account the question: if formerly the parts of the earth were brought together by the vortex, what is the reason why at the present time everything that has weight moves towards the earth? Surely the vortex does not come close to us. Again, why does fire move upwards? Not I imagine on account of the vortex. But if it has a natural motion somewhere, we must presume that earth has too. Nor, again, are heavy and light defined by the vortex: rather, heavy and light things existed first, and then the motion caused them to go either to the centre or the surface. Light and heavy, then, were there before the vortex arose, but by what were they distinguished, and how or where was it their nature to move? In an infinite space there can be no *up* or *down*, yet it is these that distinguish heavy and light.

These are the causes which engage the attention of the majority of thinkers. But there are some who name its "indifference" as the cause of its remaining at rest, *e.g.* among the early philosophers Anaximander. These urge that that which is situated at the centre and is equally related to the extremes has no impulse to move in one direction—either upwards or downwards or sideways—rather than in another; and since it is impossible for it to accomplish movement in opposite directions at once, it necessarily remains at rest. This argument is ingenious, but not true: for according to it, whatever is placed at the centre must remain there, even fire; the property is not peculiar to earth. But besides that, it is superfluous: for the earth may be seen not only to rest at the centre, but also to travel towards the centre. (For where any part of it moves, we must assume the whole moves too.) And whither it is natural for it to go, there it is natural for it to remain. Therefore the reason is not its impartial relation to the extremes: that could be shared by any other element, but motion towards the centre is peculiar to earth.

It was irrational too to ask the question why the earth remains at the centre, but not why fire remains at the extremity. If the extremity is the natural place for fire, there must plainly be some natural place for earth also. If on the other hand the place where the earth rests is not its natural place, but the cause of its remaining there is the constraint of its "indifference" (on the analogy of the hair which, stretched strongly but evenly at every point, will not break, or the man who is violently, but equally, hungry and thirsty, and stands at an equal distance from food and drink, and who therefore must remain where he is), then they ought to have inquired into the presence of fire at the extremes.

It was also strange to inquire about the resting of these elements but not their motion, that is, the reason why, if nothing interferes, the one moves upward and the other downward.

Finally, what they say is not even true. Thus much happens acciden-

tally to be true, that everything must remain at the centre which has no
reason to move in one or another particular direction; but so far as their
argument goes, a body need not remain there but can move—not, however, as a whole, but scattering in different directions. For the same reasoning may be applied to fire. Fire when placed at the centre is under
as much necessity to remain there as earth, for it will be related in the
same way to any one of the points on the extremity; but in fact it will
leave the centre, and move as we observe it to do, if nothing prevents it,
towards the extremity; only, it will not move as a whole in the direction
of a single point (this is the only consequence necessitated by the argument from indifference), but each part towards the corresponding part
of the extremity. I mean, for example, a quarter of it will seek a quarter
of the outer boundary, since no body is an indivisible point. And just as
in the process of condensation a body can contract from a larger place
into a smaller, so by rarefaction it can exchange a smaller place for a
larger: this then is a form of motion from the centre which the earth
too could perform, so far as the argument from indifference goes, were
it not that the centre is its natural place.

We may assume that this completes the tale of theories about the
shape, the place, and the rest or motion of the earth.

Chapter 14

For ourselves, let us first state whether it is in motion or at rest. Some,
as we have said, make it one of the stars, whereas others put it at the
centre but describe it as winding and moving about the pole as its axis.
But the impossibility of these explanations is clear if we start from this,
that if the earth moves, whether at the centre or at a distance from it,
its movement must be enforced: it is not the motion of the earth itself,
for otherwise each of its parts would have the same motion, but as it is
their motion is invariably in a straight line towards the centre. The motion therefore, being enforced and unnatural, could not be eternal; but
the order of the world is eternal.

Secondly, all the bodies which move with the circular movement are
observed to lag behind and to move with more than one motion, with
the exception of the primary sphere: the earth therefore must have a
similar double motion, whether it move around the centre or as situated
at it. But if this were so, there would have to be passings and turnings
of the fixed stars. Yet these are not observed to take place: the same stars
always rise and set at the same places on the earth.

Thirdly, the natural motion of the earth as a whole, like that of its
parts, is towards the centre of the Universe: that is the reason why it is
now lying at the centre. It might be asked, since the centre of both is

the same point, in which capacity the natural motion of heavy bodies, or parts of the earth, is directed towards it; whether as centre of the Universe or of the earth. But it must be towards the centre of the Universe that they move, seeing that light bodies like fire, whose motion is contrary to that of the heavy, move to the extremity of the region which surrounds the centre. It so happens that the earth and the Universe have the same centre, for the heavy bodies do move also towards the centre of the earth, yet only incidentally, because it has its centre at the centre of the Universe. As evidence that they move also towards the centre of the earth, we see that weights moving towards the earth do not move in parallel lines but always at the same angles to it: therefore they are moving towards the same centre, namely that of the earth. It is now clear that the earth must be at the centre and immobile. To our previous reasons we may add that heavy objects, if thrown forcibly upwards in a straight line, come back to their starting-place, even if the force hurls them to an unlimited distance.

From these considerations it is clear that the earth does not move, neither does it lie anywhere but at the centre. In addition the reason for its immobility is clear from our discussions. If it is inherent in the nature of earth to move from all sides to the centre (as observation shows), and of fire to move away from the centre towards the extremity, it is impossible for any portion of earth to move from the centre except under constraint; for one body has one motion and a simple body a simple motion, not two opposite motions, and motion from the centre is the opposite of motion towards it. If then any particular portion is incapable of moving from the centre, it is clear that the earth itself as a whole is still more incapable, since it is natural for the whole to be in the place towards which the part has a natural motion. If then it cannot move except by the agency of a stronger force, it must remain at the centre. This belief finds further support in the assertions of mathematicians about astronomy: that is, the observed phenomena—the shifting of the figures by which the arrangemet of the stars is defined—are consistent with the hypothesis that the earth lies at the centre. This may conclude our account of the situation and the rest or motion of the earth.

Its shape must be spherical. For every one of its parts has weight until it reaches the centre, and thus when a smaller part is pressed on by a larger, it cannot surge round it, but each is packed close to, and combines with, the other until they reach the centre. To grasp what is meant we must imagine the earth as in the process of generation in the manner which some of the natural philosophers describe (except that they make external compulsion responsible for the downward movement: let us rather substitute the true statement that this takes place because it is the nature of whatever has weight to move towards the centre). In these systems, when the mixture existed in a state of potentiality, the particles in process of separation were moving from every side alike towards the centre. Whether or not the portions were evenly distributed at the extremities, from which they converged towards the centre, the same result will be produced. It is plain, first, that if particles are moving from all sides alike towards one point, the centre, the resulting mass must be similar on all sides; for if an equal quantity is added all round, the extremity must be at a constant distance from the centre. Such a shape is a sphere. But it will make no difference to the argument even if the portions of the earth did not travel uniformly from all sides towards the centre. A greater mass must always drive on a smaller mass in front of it, if the inclination of both is to go as far as the centre, and the impulsion of the less heavy by the heavier persists to that point.

A difficulty which might be raised finds its solution in the same considerations. If, the earth being at the centre and spherical in shape, a weight many times its own were added to one hemisphere, the centre of the Universe would no longer coincide with that of the earth. Either, therefore, it would not remain at the centre, or, if it did, it might even as it is be at rest although not occupying the centre, *i.e.* though in a situation where it is natural for it to be in motion. That then is the difficulty. But it is not hard to understand, if we make a little further effort and define the manner in which we suppose any magnitude, possessed of weight, to travel towards the centre. Not, clearly, to the extent of only touching the centre with its edge: the larger portion must prevail until it possesses the centre with its own centre, for its impulse extends to that point. It makes no difference whether we posit this of any chance portion or clod, or of the earth as a whole, for the fact as explained does not depend on smallness or greatness, but applies to everything which has an impulse towards the centre. Therefore whether the earth moved as a whole or in parts, it must have continued in motion until it occupied the centre evenly all round, the smaller portions being equalized by the greater under the forward pressure of their common impulse.

If then the earth has come into being, this must have been the manner of its generation, and it must have grown in the form of a sphere: if on the other hand it is ungenerated and everlasting, it must be the same as it would have been had it developed as the result of a process. Besides this argument for the spherical shape of the earth, there is also the point that all heavy bodies fall at similar angles, not parallel to each other; this naturally means that their fall is towards a body whose nature is spherical. Either then it *is* spherical, or at least it is natural for it to be so, and we must describe each thing by that which is its natural goal or its permanent state, not by any enforced or unnatural characteristics.

Further proof is obtained from the evidence of the senses. (i) If the earth were not spherical, eclipses of the moon would not exhibit segments of the shape which they do. As it is, in its monthly phases the moon takes on all varieties of shape—straight-edged, gibbous and concave—but in eclipses the boundary is always convex. Thus if the eclipses are due to the interposition of the earth, the shape must be caused by its circumference, and the earth must be spherical. (ii) Observation of the stars also shows not only that the earth is spherical but that it is of no great size, since a small change of position on our part southward or northward visibly alters the circle of the horizon, so that the stars above our heads change their position considerably, and we do not see the same stars as we move to the North or South. Certain stars are seen in Egypt and the neighbourhood of Cyprus, which are invisible in more northerly lands, and stars which are continuously visible in the northern countries are observed to set in the others. This proves both that the earth is spherical and that its periphery is not large, for otherwise such a small change of position could not have had such an immediate effect. For this reason those who imagine that the region around the Pillars of Heracles joins on to the regions of India, and that in this way the ocean is one, are not, it would seem, suggesting anything utterly incredible. They produce also in support of their contention the fact that elephants are a species found at the extremities of both lands, arguing that this phenomenon at the extremes is due to communication between the two. Mathematicians who try to calculate the circumference put it at 400,000 stades.

From these arguments we must conclude not only that the earth's mass is spherical but also that it is not large in comparison with the size of the other stars.

2

ARISTOTLE

As the descendant of a long line of physicians, Aristotle was endowed with his special concern for living things by virtue of his birth. Reared in the family medical tradition, he was probably imbued in his youth with the habits of observation that were later to prompt his empirical approach to natural philosophy. Consistent with his status as son of the Macedonian court physician, of course, Aristotle was also exposed to the best formal education available, culminating in entrance to Plato's Academy at the age of seventeen. Somewhere along the line he found that his comprehensive intellect was more happily applied to the general problems of philosophy than to the specific ones of medicine. Aristotle ultimately remained at the Academy for 20 years, and occupied himself in the philosophical mode of the day by dealing with issues of essence and ethics; he set out his conclusions in the form of dialogues, which have long since been lost. Only when he left the Academy (upon finding himself passed over in the election of a successor to Plato) did his biological heritage assert itself. The next five years proved to be the most important of his life. Free of outside influence and conflicting activities, he gave full rein to his predilection for natural history. Working on the coast of Asia Minor, he conducted detailed observations on marine life and formulated the theories that eventually constituted the foundation not only of his system of biology, but of his outlook on natural philosophy in general. Returning first to Macedonia (as court tutor) and then to Athens (as founder of the Lyceum), Aristotle devoted the remaining twenty years of his life to the task of articulating the system that was to be synonymous with "knowledge" for generations to come.

Aristotle's biological researches are contained in four major works constituting an integral part of his system of natural philosophy: *History of Animals, Generation of Animals, Progression of Animals,* and *Parts of Animals.* The essence of natural philosophy, or physics, for Aristotle was the explanation of change or motion in nature; and the changes in which he was most interested were those occurring in the organic world. Nothing is more indicative of Aristotle's fundamentally biological orientation, than that his basic mode of explanation should have been teleological, as expressed by final causes. And nothing is more indicative of the relationship of the *Physics* to his biological works than that his elaboration and defense of the doctrine of final causes should have been presented in the *Physics*. In the following selections, his discussion has been taken out of its theoretical context and presented with passages in which Aristotle's use of teleological explanation is conspicuous. These passages illustrate clearly that Aristotle's efforts were labors of love. Naturally, he attained to varying degrees of success, but even his discussions of such internal organs as the brain contain numerous observation statements, while his masterful summary of birds manifests an unsurpassed zeal in the collection and organization of data.

2

The Physics

BOOK II

Chapter 8

We must now consider why Nature is to be ranked among causes that are final, that is to say purposeful; and further we must consider what is meant by "necessity" when we are speaking of Nature. For thinkers are for ever referring things to necessity as a cause, and explaining that, since hot and cold and so forth are what they are, this or that exists or comes into being "of necessity"; for even if one or another of them alleges some other cause, such as "Sympathy and Antipathy" or "Mind," he straight away drops it again, after a mere acknowledgement.

So here the question rises whether we have any reason to regard Nature as making for any goal at all, or as seeking any one thing as preferable to any other. Why not say, it is asked, that Nature acts as Zeus drops the rain, not to make the corn grow, but of necessity (for the rising vapour must needs be condensed into water by the cold, and must then descend, and incidentally, when this happens, the corn grows), just as, when a man loses his corn on the threshing-floor, it did not rain on purpose to destroy the crop, but the result was merely incidental to the raining? So why should it not be the same with natural organs like the teeth? Why should it not be a coincidence that the front teeth come up with an edge, suited to dividing the food, and the back ones flat and good for grinding it, without there being any design in the matter? And so with all other organs that seem to embody a purpose. In cases where a coincidence brought about such a combination as might have been arranged on purpose, the creatures, it is urged, having been suitably formed by the operation of chance, survived; otherwise they perished, and still perish, as Empedocles says of his "man-faced oxen."

Reprinted by permission of the publishers and The Loeb Classical Library from Aristotle, *The Physics*, P. H. Wicksteed and F. M. Cornford, trs., Cambridge, Mass.: Harvard University Press, 1929 and 1934.

Such and suchlike are the arguments which may be urged in raising this problem; but it is impossible that this should really be the way of it. For all these phenomena and all natural things are either constant or normal, and this is contrary to the very meaning of luck or chance. No one assigns it to chance or to a remarkable coincidence if there is abundant rain in the winter, though he would if there were in the dog-days; and the other way about, if there were parching heat. Accordingly, if the only choice is to assign these occurrences either to coincidence or to purpose, and if in these cases chance coincidence is out of the question, then it must be purpose. But, as our opponents themselves would admit, these occurrences are all natural. There is purpose, then, in what is, and in what happens, in Nature.

Further, in any operation of human art, where there is an end to be achieved, the earlier and successive stages of the operation are performed for the purpose of realizing that end. Now, when a thing is produced by Nature, the earlier stages in every case lead up to the final development in the same way as in the operation of art, and *vice versa*, provided that no impediment balks the process. The operation is directed by a purpose; we may, therefore, infer that the natural process was guided by a purpose to the end that is realized. Thus, if a house were a natural product, the process would pass through the same stages that it in fact passes through when it is produced by art; and if natural products could also be produced by art, they would move along the same line that the natural process actually takes. We may therefore say that the earlier stages are for the purpose of leading to the later. Indeed, as a general proposition, the arts either, on the basis of Nature, carry things further than Nature can, or they imitate Nature. If, then, artificial processes are purposeful, so are natural processes too; for the relation of antecedent to consequent is identical in art and in Nature.

This principle comes out most clearly when we consider the other animals. For their doings are not the outcome of art (design) or of previous research or deliberation; so that some raise the question whether the works of spiders and ants and so on should be attributed to intelligence or to some similar faculty. And then, descending step by step, we find that plants too produce organs subservient to their perfect development—leaves, for instance, to shelter the fruit. Hence, if it is by nature and also for a purpose that the swallow makes her nest and the spider his web, and that plants make leaves for the sake of the fruit and strike down (and not up) with their roots in order to get their nourishment, it is clear that causality of the kind we have described is at work in things that come about or exist in the course of Nature.

Also, since the term "nature" is applied both to material and to form, and since it is the latter that constitutes the goal, and all else is for the sake of that goal, it follows that the form is the final cause.

Now there are failures even in the arts (for writers make mistakes in writing and physicians administer the wrong dose); so that analogous failures in Nature may evidently be anticipated as possible. Thus, if in art there are cases in which the correct procedure serves a purpose, and attempts that fail are aimed at a purpose but miss it, we may take it to be the same in Nature, and monstrosities will be like failures of purpose in Nature. So if, in the primal combinations, such "ox-creatures" as could not reach an equilibrium and goal, should appear, it would be by the miscarriage of some principle, as monstrous births are actually produced now by abortive developments of sperm. Besides, the sperm must precede the formation of the animal, and Empedocles' "primal all-generative" is no other than such sperm.

In plants, too, though they are less elaborately articulated, there are manifest indications of purpose. Are we to suppose, then, that as there were "ox-creatures man-faced" so also there were "vine-growths olive-bearing"? Incongruous as such a thing seems, it ought to follow if we accept the principle in the case of animals. Moreover, it ought still to be a matter of chance what comes up when you sow this seed or that.

In general, the theory does away with the whole order of Nature, and indeed with Nature's self. For natural things are exactly those which do move continuously, in virtue of a principle inherent in themselves, towards a determined goal; and the final development which results from any one such principle is not identical for any two species, nor yet is it any random result; but in each there is always a tendency towards an identical result, if nothing interferes with the process. A desirable result and the means to it may also be produced by chance, as for instance we say it was "by luck" that the stranger came and ransomed the prisoner before he left, where the ransoming is done as if the man had come for that purpose, though in fact he did not. In this case the desirable result is incidental; for, as we have explained, chance is an incidental cause. But when the desirable result is effected invariably or normally, it is not an incidental or chance occurrence; and in the course of Nature the result always is achieved either invariably or normally, if nothing hinders. It is absurd to suppose that there is no purpose because in Nature we can never detect the moving power in the act of deliberation. Art, in fact, does not deliberate either, and if the shipbuilding art were incorporate in the timber, it would proceed by nature in the same way in which it now proceeds by art. If purpose, then, is inherent in art, so is it in Nature also. The best illustration is the case of a man being his own physician, for Nature is like that—agent and patient at once.

That Nature is a cause, then, and a goal-directed cause, is above dispute.

De Partibus Animalium
(On the Parts of Animals)

BOOK I

Chapter 1

Every systematic science, the humblest and the noblest alike, seems to admit of two distinct kinds of proficiency; one of which may be properly called scientific knowledge of the subject, while the other is a kind of educational acquaintance with it. For an educated man should be able to form a fair off-hand judgement as to the goodness or badness of the method used by a professor in his exposition. To be educated is in fact to be able to do this; and even the man of universal education we deem to be such in virtue of his having this ability. It will, however, of course, be understood that we only ascribe universal education to one who in his own individual person is thus critical in all or nearly all branches of knowledge, and not to one who has a like ability merely in some special subject. For it is possible for a man to have this competence in some one branch of knowledge without having it in all.

It is plain then that, as in other sciences, so in that which inquires into nature, there must be certain canons, by reference to which a hearer shall be able to criticize the method of a professed exposition, quite independently of the question whether the statements made be true or false. Ought we, for instance (to give an illustration of what I mean), to begin by discussing each separate species—man, lion, ox, and the like— taking each kind in hand independently of the rest, or ought we rather to deal first with the attributes which they have in common in virtue of some common element of their nature, and proceed from this as a basis for the consideration of them separately? For genera that are quite distinct yet oftentimes present many identical phenomena, sleep, for instance, respiration, growth, decay, death, and other similar affections and conditions, which may be passed over for the present, as we are

The Works of Aristotle Translated into English, Volume 5, Part 1, translated from the Greek by William Ogle, Oxford: Clarendon Press, 1911.

not yet prepared to treat of them with clearness and precision. Now it is plain that if we deal with each species independently of the rest, we shall frequently be obliged to repeat the same statements over and over again; for horse and dog and man present, each and all, every one of the phenomena just enumerated. A discussion therefore of the attributes of each such species separately would necessarily involve frequent repetitions as to characters, themselves identical but recurring in animals specifically distinct. (Very possibly also there may be other characters which, though they present specific differences, yet come under one and the same category. For instance, flying, swimming, walking, creeping, are plainly specifically distinct, but yet are all forms of animal progression.) We must, then, have some clear understanding as to the manner in which our investigation is to be conducted; whether, I mean, we are first to deal with the common or generic characters, and afterwards to take into consideration special peculiarities; or whether we are to start straight off with the ultimate species. For as yet no definite rule has been laid down in this matter. So also there is a like uncertainty as to another point now to be mentioned. Ought the writer who deals with the works of nature to follow the plan adopted by the mathematicians in their astronomical demonstrations, and after considering the phenomena presented by animals, and their several parts, proceed subsequently to treat of the causes and the reason why; or ought he to follow some other method? And when these questions are answered, there yet remains another. The causes concerned in the generation of the works of nature are, as we see, more than one. There is the final cause and there is the motor cause. Now we must decide which of these two causes comes first, which second. Plainly, however, that cause is the first which we call the final one. For this is the Reason, and the Reason forms the starting-point, alike in the works of art and in works of nature. For consider how the physician or how the builder sets about his work. He starts by forming for himself a definite picture, in the one case perceptible to mind, in the other to sense, of his end—the physician of health, the builder of a house—and this he holds forward as the reason and explanation of each subsequent step that he takes, and of his acting in this or that way as the case may be. Now in the works of nature the good end and the final cause is still more dominant than in works of art such as these, nor is necessity a factor with the same significance in them all; though almost all writers, while they try to refer their origin to this cause, do so without distinguishing the various senses in which the term necessity is used. For there is absolute necessity, manifested in eternal phenomena; and there is hypothetical necessity, manifested in everything that is generated by nature as in everything that is produced by art, be it a house or what it may. For if a house or other such final object is to be realized, it is necessary that such and such material shall exist; and it is necessary that first this and then that shall be produced, and first this and then that set in motion, and so on in continuous succession, until the end and final result is reached, for the sake of which each prior thing is produced and exists. As with these productions of art, so also is it with the productions of nature. The mode of necessity, however, and the mode of ratiocination are different in natural science from what they are in the theoretical sciences; of which we have spoken elsewhere. For in the latter the starting-point is that which is; in the former that which is to be. For it is that which is yet to be—health, let us say, or a man—that, owing to its being of such and such characters, necessitates the pre-existence or previous production of this and that antecedent; and not this or that antecedent which, because it exists or has been generated, makes it necessary that health or a man is in, or shall come into, existence. Nor is it possible to trace back the series of necessary antecedents to a starting-point, of which you can say that, existing itself from eternity, it has determined their existence as its consequent. These however, again, are matters that have been dealt with in another treatise. There too it was stated in what cases absolute and hypothetical necessity exist; in what cases also the proposition expressing hypothetical necessity is simply convertible, and what cause it is that determines this convertibility.

Another matter which must not be passed over without consideration is, whether the proper subject of our exposition is that with which the ancient writers concerned themselves, namely, what is the process of formation of each animal; or whether it is not rather, what are the characters of a given creature when formed. For there is no small difference between these two views. The best course appears to be that we should follow the method already mentioned, and begin with the phenomena presented by each group of animals, and, when this is done, proceed afterwards to state the causes of those phenomena, and to deal with their evolution. For elsewhere, as for instance in house building, this is the true sequence. The plan of the house, or the house, has this and that form; and because it has this and that form, therefore is its construction carried out in this or that manner. For the process of evolution is for the sake of the thing finally evolved, and not this for the sake of the process. Empedocles, then, was in error when he said that many of the characters presented by animals were merely the results of incidental occurrences during their development; for instance, that the backbone was divided as it is into vertebrae, because it happened to be broken owing to the contorted position of the foetus in the womb. In so saying he overlooked the fact that propagation implies a creative seed endowed with certain formative properties. Secondly, he neglected another fact, namely, that the parent animal pre-exists, not only in idea, but actually in time. For man is generated from man; and thus it is the possession of certain characters by the parent that determines the development of like characters in the child. The same statement holds good also for the operations of art, and even for those which are apparently spontaneous. For the same result as is produced by art may occur spontaneously. Spontaneity, for instance, may bring about the restoration of health. The products of art, however, require the pre-existence of an efficient cause homogeneous with themselves, such as the statuary's art, which must necessarily precede the statue; for this cannot possibly be produced spontaneously. Art indeed consists in the conception of the result to be produced before its realization in the material. As with spontaneity, so with chance; for this also produces the same result as art, and by the same process.

The fittest mode, then, of treatment is to say, a man has such and such parts, because the conception of a man includes their presence, and because they are necessary conditions of his existence, or, if we cannot quite say this, which would be best of all, then the next thing to it, namely, that it is either quite impossible for him to exist without them, or, at any rate, that it is better for him that they should be there; and their existence involves the existence of other antecedents. Thus we should say, because man is an animal with such and such characters, therefore is the process of his development necessarily such as it is; and therefore is it accomplished in such and such an order, this part being formed first, that next, and so on in succession; and after a like fashion should we explain the evolution of all other works of nature.

Now that with which the ancient writers, who first philosophized about Nature, busied themselves, was the material principle and the material cause. They inquired what this is, and what its character; how the universe is generated out of it, and by what motor influence, whether, for instance, by antagonism or friendship, whether by intelligence or spontaneous action, the substratum of matter being assumed to have certain inseparable properties; fire, for instance, to have a hot nature, earth a cold one; the former to be light, the latter heavy. For even the genesis of the universe is thus explained by them. After a like fashion do they deal also with the development of plants and of animals. They say, for instance, that the water contained in the body causes by its currents the formation of the stomach and the other receptacles of food or of excretion; and that the breath by its passage breaks open the outlets of the nostrils; air and water being the materials of which bodies are made; for all represent nature as composed of such or similar substances.

But if men and animals and their several parts are natural phenomena, then the natural philosopher must take into consideration not merely the ultimate substances of which they are made, but also flesh, bone, blood, and all the other homogeneous parts; not only these, but also the heterogeneous parts, such as face, hand, foot; and must examine how each of these comes to be what it is, and in virtue of what force. For to say what are the ultimate substances out of which an animal is formed, to state, for instance, that it is made of fire or earth, is no more sufficient than would be a similar account in the case of a couch or the like. For we should not be content with saying that the couch was made of bronze or wood or whatever it might be, but should try to describe its design or mode of composition in preference to the material; or, if we did deal with the material, it would at any rate be with the concretion of material and form. For a couch is such and such a form embodied in this or that matter, or such and such a matter with this or that form; so that its shape and structure must be included in our description. For the formal nature is of greater importance than the material nature.

Does, then, configuration and colour constitute the essence of the various animals and of their several parts? For if so, what Democritus says will be strictly correct. For such appears to have been his notion. At any rate he says that it is evident to every one what form it is that makes the man, seeing that he is recognizable by his shape and colour. And yet a dead body has exactly the same configuration as a living one; but for all that is not a man. So also no hand of bronze or wood or constituted in any but the appropriate way can possibly be a hand in more than name. For like a physician in a painting, or like a flute in a sculpture, in spite of its name it will be unable to do the office which that name implies. Precisely in the same way no part of a dead body, such I mean as its eye or its hand, is really an eye or a hand. To say, then, that shape and colour constitute the animal is an inadequate statement, and is much the same as if a woodcarver were to insist that the hand he had cut out was really a hand. Yet the physiologists, when they give an account of the development and causes of the animal form, speak very much like such a craftsman. What, however, I would ask, are the forces by which the hand or the body was fashioned into its shape? The woodcarver will perhaps say, by the axe or the auger; the physiologist, by air and by earth. Of these two answers the artificer's is the better, but it is nevertheless insufficient. For it is not enough for him to say that by the stroke of his tool this part was formed into a concavity, that into a flat surface; but he must state the reasons why he struck his blow in such a way as to effect this, and what his final object was; namely, that the piece of wood should develop eventually into this or that shape. It is plain, then, that the teaching of the old physiologists is inadequate, and that the true method is to state what the definitive characters are that distinguish the animal as a whole; to explain what it is both in substance and in form, and to deal after the same fashion with its several organs; in fact, to proceed in exactly the same way as we should do, were we giving a complete description of a couch.

If now this something that constitutes the form of the living being be the soul, or part of the soul, or something that without the soul cannot exist; as would seem to be the case, seeing at any rate that when the soul departs, what is left is no longer a living animal, and that none of the parts remain what they were before, excepting in mere configuration, like the animals that in the fable are turned into stone; if, I say, this be so, then it will come within the province of the natural philosopher to inform himself concerning the soul, and to treat of it, either in its entirety, or, at any rate, of that part of it which constitutes the essential character of an animal; and it will be his duty to say what this soul or this part of a soul is; and to discuss the attributes that attach to this essential character, especially as nature is spoken of in two senses, and the nature of a thing is either its matter or its essence; nature as essence including both the motor cause and the final cause. Now it is in the latter of these two senses that either the whole soul or some part of it constitutes the nature of an animal; and inasmuch as it is the presence of the soul that enables matter to constitute the animal nature, much more than it is the presence of matter which so enables the soul, the inquirer into nature is bound on every ground to treat of the soul rather than of the matter. For though the wood of which they are made constitutes the couch and the tripod, it only does so because it is capable of receiving such and such a form.

What has been said suggests the question, whether it is the whole soul or only some part of it, the consideration of which comes within the province of natural science. Now if it be of the whole soul that this should treat, then there is no place for any other philosophy beside it. For as it belongs in all cases to one and the same science to deal with correlated subjects—one and the same science, for instance, deals with sensation and with the objects of sense—and as therefore the intelligent soul and the objects of intellect, being correlated, must belong to one and the same science, it follows that natural science will have to include the whole universe in its province. But perhaps it is not the whole soul, nor all its parts collectively, that constitutes the source of motion; but there may be one part, identical with that in plants, which is the source of growth, another, namely the sensory part, which is the source of change of quality, while still another, and this not the intellectual part, is the source of locomotion. I say not the intellectual part; for other animals than man have the power of locomotion, but in none but him is there intellect. Thus then it is plain that it is not of the whole soul that we have to treat. For it is not the whole soul that constitutes the animal nature, but only some part or parts of it. Moreover, it is impossible that any abstraction can form a subject of natural science, seeing that everything that Nature makes is means to an end. For just as human creations are the products of art, so living objects are manifestly the products of an analogous cause or principle, not external but internal, derived like the hot and the cold from the environing universe. And that the heaven, if it had an origin, was evolved and is maintained by such a cause, there is therefore even more reason to believe, than that mortal animals so originated. For order and definiteness are much more plainly manifest in the celestial bodies than in our own frame; while change and chance are characteristic of the perishable things of earth. Yet there are some who, while they allow that every animal exists and was generated by nature, nevertheless hold that the heaven was constructed to be what it is by chance and spontaneity; the heaven, in which not the faintest sign of haphazard or of disorder is discernible! Again, whenever there is plainly some final end, to which a motion tends should nothing stand in the way, we always say that such final end is the aim or purpose of the motion; and from this it is evident that there must be a something or other really existing, corresponding to what we call by the name of Nature. For a given germ does not give rise to any chance living being, nor spring from any chance one; but each germ springs from a definite parent and gives rise to a definite progeny. And thus it is the germ that is the ruling influence and fabricator of the offspring. For these it is by nature, the offspring being at any rate that which in nature will spring from it. At the same time the offspring is anterior to the germ; for germ and perfected progeny are related as the developmental process and the result. Anterior, however, to both germ and product is the organism from which the germ was derived. For every germ implies two organisms, the parent and the progeny. For germ or seed is both the seed of the organism from which it came, of the horse, for instance, from which it was derived, and the seed of the organism that will eventually arise from it, of the mule, for example, which is developed from the seed of the horse. The same seed then is the seed both of the horse and of the mule, though in different ways as here set forth. Moreover, the seed is potentially that which will spring from it, and the relation of potentiality to actuality we know. . . .

It is plain then that there are two modes of causation [necessity and the final end], and that both of these must, so far as possible, be taken into account in explaining the works of nature, or that at any rate an attempt must be made to include them both; and that those who fail in this tell us in reality nothing about nature. For primary cause constitutes the nature of an animal much more than does its matter. There are indeed passages in which even Empedocles hits upon this, and following the guidance of fact, finds himself constrained to speak of the ratio as constituting the essence and real nature of things. Such, for instance, is the case when he explains what is a bone. For he does not merely describe its material, and say it is this one element, or those two or three elements, or a compound of all the elements, but states the ratio of their combination. As with a bone, so manifestly is it with the flesh and all other similar parts.

The reason why our predecessors failed in hitting upon this method of treatment was, that they were not in possession of the notion of essence, nor of any definition of substance. The first who came near it was Democritus, and he was far from adopting it as a necessary method in natural science, but was merely brought to it, in spite of himself, by constraint of facts. In the time of Socrates a nearer approach was made to the method. But at this period men gave up inquiring into the works of nature, and philosophers diverted their attention to political science and to the virtues which benefit mankind.

Of the method itself the following is an example. In dealing with respiration we must show that it takes place for such or such a final object; and we must also show that this and that part of the process is necessitated by this and that other stage of it. By necessity we shall sometimes mean hypothetical necessity, the necessity, that is, that the requisite antecedents shall be there, if the final end is to be reached; and sometimes absolute necessity, such necessity as that which connects substances and their inherent properties and characters. For the alternate discharge and re-entrance of heat and the inflow of air are necessary if we are to live. Here we have at once a necessity in the former of the two senses. But the alternation of heat and refrigeration produces of necessity an alternate admission and discharge of the outer air, and this is a necessity of the second kind.

In the foregoing we have an example of the method which we must adopt, and also an example of the kind of phenomena, the causes of which we have to investigate.

Chapter 2

Some writers propose to reach the definitions of the ultimate forms of animal life by bipartite division. But this method is often difficult, and often impracticable.

Sometimes the final differentia of the subdivision is sufficient by itself, and the antecedent differentiae are mere surplusage. Thus in the series Footed, Two-footed, Cleft-footed, the last term is all-expressive by itself, and to append the higher terms is only an idle iteration.

Again it is not permissible to break up a natural group, Birds for instance, by putting its members under different bifurcations, as is done in the published dichotomies, where some birds are ranked with animals of the water, and others placed in a different class. The group Birds and the group Fishes happen to be named, while other natural groups have no popular names; for instance, the groups that we may call Sanguineous and Bloodless are not known popularly by any designations. If such natural groups are not to be broken up, the method of Dichotomy cannot be employed, for it necessarily involves such breaking up and dislocation. The group of the Many-footed, for instance, would, under this method, have to be dismembered, and some of its kinds distributed among land animals, others among water animals.

Chapter 3

Again, privative terms inevitably form one branch of dichotomous division, as we see in the proposed dichotomies. But privative terms in their character of privatives admit of no subdivision. For there can be no specific forms of a negation, of Featherless for instance or of Footless, as there are of Feathered and of Footed. Yet a generic differentia must be subdivisible; for otherwise what is there that makes it generic rather than specific? There are to be found generic, that is specifically subdivisible, differentiae; Feathered for instance and Footed. For feathers are divisible into Barbed and Unbarbed, and feet into Manycleft, and Twocleft, like those of animals with bifid hoofs, and Uncleft or Undivided, like those of animals with solid hoofs. Now even with differentiae capable of this specific subdivision it is difficult enough so to make the classification, as that each animal shall be comprehended in some one subdivision and in not more than one; but far more difficult, nay impossible, is it to do this, if we start with a dichotomy into two contradictories. (Suppose for instance we start with the two contradictories, Feathered and Unfeathered; we shall find that the ant, the glow-worm, and some other animals fall under both divisions.) For each differentia must be presented by some species. There must be some species, therefore, under the privative heading. Now specifically distinct animals cannot present in their essence a common undifferentiated element, but any apparently common element must really be differentiated. (Bird and Man for instance are both Two-footed, but their two-footedness is diverse and differentiated. So any two sanguineous groups must have some difference in their blood, if their blood is part of their essence.) From this it follows that a privative term, being insusceptible of differentiation, cannot be a generic differentia; for, if it were, there would be a common undifferentiated element in two different groups.

Again, if the species are ultimate indivisible groups, that is, are groups with indivisible differentiae, and if no differentia be common to several groups, the number of differentiae must be equal to the number of species. If a differentia though not divisible could yet be common to several groups, then it is plain that in virtue of that common differentia specifically distinct animals would fall into the same division. It is necessary then, if the differentiae, under which are ranged all the ultimate and indivisible groups, are specific characters, that none of them shall be common; for otherwise, as already said, specifically distinct animals will come into one and the same division. But this would violate one of the requisite conditions, which are as follows. No ultimate group must be included in more than a single division; different groups must not be included in the same division; and every group must be found in some division. It is plain then that we cannot get at the ultimate specific forms of the animal, or any other, kingdom by bifurcate division. If we could, the number of ultimate differentiae would equal the number of ultimate animal forms. For assume an order of beings whose prime differentiae are White and Black. Each of these branches will bifurcate, and their branches again, and so on till we reach the ultimate differentiae, whose number will be four or some other power of two, and will also be the number of the ultimate species comprehended in the order.

(A species is constituted by the combination of differentia and matter. For no part of an animal is purely material or purely immaterial; nor can a body, independently of its condition, constitute an animal or any of its parts, as has repeatedly been observed.)

Further, the differentiae must be elements of the essence, and not merely essential attributes. Thus if Figure is the term to be divided, it must not be divided into figures whose angles are equal to two right angles, and figures whose angles are together greater than two right angles. For it is only an attribute of a triangle and not part of its essence that its angles are equal to two right angles.

Again, the bifurcations must be opposites, like White and Black, Straight and Bent; and if we characterize one branch by either term, we must characterize the other by its opposite, and not, for example, characterize one branch by a colour, the other by a mode of progression, swimming for instance.

Furthermore, living beings cannot be divided by the functions common to body and soul, by Flying, for instance, and Walking, as we see them divided in the dichotomies already referred to. For some groups, Ants for instance, fall under both divisions, some ants flying while others do not. Similarly as regards the division into Wild and Tame; for it also would involve the disruption of a species into different groups. For in almost all species in which some members are tame, there are other members that are wild. Such, for example, is the case with Men, Horses, Oxen, Dogs in India, Pigs, Goats, Sheep; groups which, if double, ought to have what they have not, namely, different appellations; and which, if single, prove that Wildness and Tameness do not amount to specific differences. And whatever single element we take as a basis of division the same difficulty will occur.

The method then that we must adopt is to attempt to recognize the natural groups, following the indications afforded by the instincts of mankind, which led them for instance to form the class of Birds and the class of Fishes, each of which groups combines a multitude of differentiae, and is not defined by a single one as in dichotomy. The method of dichotomy is either impossible (for it would put a single group under different divisions or contrary groups under the same division), or it only furnishes a single ultimate differentia for each species, which either alone or with its series of antecedents has to constitute the ultimate species.

If, again, a new differential character be introduced at any stage into the division, the necessary result is that the continuity of the division becomes merely a unity and continuity of agglomeration, like the unity and continuity of a series of sentences coupled together by conjunctive particles. For instance, suppose we have the bifurcation Feathered and Featherless, and then divide Feathered into Wild and Tame, or into White and Black. Tame and White are not a differentiation of Feathered, but are the commencement of an independent bifurcation, and are foreign to the series at the end of which they are introduced.

As we said then, we must define at the outset by a multiplicity of differentiae. If we do so, private terms will be available, which are unavailable to the dichotomist.

The impossibility of reaching the definition of any of the ultimate forms by dichotomy of the larger group, as some propose, is manifest also from the following considerations. It is impossible that a single differentia, either by itself or with its antecedents, shall express the whole essence of a species. (In saying a single differentia by itself I mean such an isolated differentia as Cleft-footed; in saying a single differentia with antecedent I mean, to give an instance, Many-cleft-footed preceded by Cleft-footed. The very continuity of a series of successive differentiae in a division is intended to show that it is their combination that expresses the character of the resulting unit, or ultimate group. But one is misled by the usages of language into imagining that it is merely the final term of the series, Many-cleft-footed for instance, that constitutes the whole differentia, and that the antecedent terms, Footed, Cleft-footed, are superfluous. Now it is evident that such a series cannot consist of many terms. For if one divides and subdivides, one soon reaches the final differential term, but for all that will not have got to the ultimate division, that is, to the species.) No single differentia, I repeat, either by itself or with its antecedents, can possibly express the essence of a species. Suppose, for example, Man to be the animal to be defined; the single differentia will be Cleft-footed, either by itself or with its antecedents, Footed and Two-footed. Now if man was nothing more than a Cleft-footed animal, this single differentia would duly represent his essence. But seeing that this is not the case, more differentiae than this one will necessarily be required to define him; and these cannot come under one division; for each single branch of a dichotomy ends in a single differentia, and cannot possibly include several differentiae belonging to one and the same animal.

It is impossible then to reach any of the ultimate animal forms by dichotomous division.

Chapter 4

It deserves inquiry why a single name denoting a higher group was not invented by mankind, as an appellation to comprehend the two groups of Water animals and Winged animals. For even these have certain attributes in common. However, the present nomenclature is just. Groups that only differ in degree, and in the more or less of an identical element that they possess, are aggregated under a single class; groups whose attributes are not identical but analogous are separated. For instance, bird differs from bird by gradation, or by excess and defect; some birds have long feathers, others short ones, but all are feathered. Bird and Fish are more remote and only agree in having analogous organs; for what in the bird is feather, in the fish is scale. Such analogies can scarcely, however, serve universally as indications for the formation of groups, for almost all animals present analogies in their corresponding parts.

The individuals comprised within a species, such as Socrates and

Coriscus, are the real existences; but inasmuch as these individuals possess one common specific form, it will suffice to state the universal attributes of the species, that is, the attributes common to all its individuals, once for all, as otherwise there will be endless reiteration, as has already been pointed out.

But as regards the larger groups—such as Birds—which comprehend many species, there may be a question. For on the one hand it may be urged that as the ultimate species represent the real existences, it will be well, if practicable, to examine these ultimate species separately, just as we examine the species Man separately; to examine, that is, not the whole class Birds collectively, but the Ostrich, the Crane, and the other indivisible groups or species belonging to the class.

On the other hand, however, this course would involve repeated mention of the same attribute, as the same attribute is common to many species, and so far would be somewhat irrational and tedious. Perhaps, then, it will be best to treat generically the universal attributes of the groups that have a common nature and contain closely allied subordinate forms, whether they are groups recognized by a true instinct of mankind, such as Birds and Fishes, or groups not popularly known by a common appellation, but withal composed of closely allied subordinate groups; and only to deal individually with the attributes of a single species, when such species—man, for instance, and any other such, if such there be—stands apart from others, and does not constitute with them a larger natural group.

It is generally similarity in the shape of particular organs, or of the whole body, that has determined the formation of the larger groups. It is in virtue of such a similarity that Birds, Fishes, Cephalopoda, and Testacea have been made to form each a separate class. For within the limits of each such class, the parts do not differ in that they have no nearer resemblance than that of analogy—such as exists between the bone of man and the spine of fish—but differ merely in respect of such corporeal conditions as largeness smallness, softness hardness, smoothness roughness, and other similar oppositions, or, in one word, in respect of degree.

We have now touched upon the canons for criticizing the method of natural science, and have considered what is the most systematic and easy course of investigation; we have also dealt with division, and the mode of conducting it so as best to attain the ends of science, and have shown why dichotomy is either impracticable or inefficacious for its professed purposes.

Having laid this foundation, let us pass on to our next topic.

Chapter 5

Of things constituted by nature some are ungenerated, imperishable, and eternal, while others are subject to generation and decay. The former are excellent beyond compare and divine, but less accessible to knowledge. The evidence that might throw light on them, and on the problems which we long to solve respecting them, is furnished but scantily by sensation; whereas respecting perishable plants and animals we have abundant information, living as we do in their midst, and ample data may be collected concerning all their various kinds, if only we are willing to take sufficient pains. Both departments, however, have their special charm. The scanty conceptions to which we can attain of celestial things give us, from their excellence, more pleasure than all our knowledge of the world in which we live; just as a half glimpse of persons that we love is more delightful than a leisurely view of other things, whatever their number and dimensions. On the other hand, in certitude and in completeness our knowledge of terrestrial things has the advantage. Moreover, their greater nearness and affinity to us balances somewhat the loftier interest of the heavenly things that are the objects of the higher philosophy. Having already treated of the celestial world, as far as our conjectures could reach, we proceed to treat of animals, without omitting, to the best of our ability, any member of the kingdom, however ignoble. For if some have no graces to charm the sense, yet even these, by disclosing to intellectual perception the artistic spirit that designed them, give immense pleasure to all who can trace links of causation, and are inclined to philosophy. Indeed, it would be strange if mimic representations of them were attractive, because they disclose the mimetic skill of the painter or sculptor, and the original realities themselves were not more interesting, to all at any rate who have eyes to discern the reasons that determined their formation. We therefore must not recoil with childish aversion from the examination of the humbler animals. Every realm of nature is marvellous: and as Heraclitus, when the strangers who came to visit him found him warming himself at the furnace in the kitchen and hesitated to go in, is reported to have bidden them not to be afraid to enter, as even in that kitchen divinities were present, so we should venture on the study of every kind of animal without distaste; for each and all will reveal to us something natural and something beautiful. Absence of haphazard and conduciveness of everything to an end are to be found in Nature's works in the highest degree, and the resultant end of her generations and combinations is a form of the beautiful.

If any person thinks the examination of the rest of the animal kingdom an unworthy task, he must hold in like disesteem the study of man. For no one can look at the primordia of the human frame—blood, flesh, bones, vessels, and the like—without much repugnance. Moreover, when any one of the parts or structures, be it which it may, is under discussion, it must not be supposed that it is its material composition to which attention is being directed or which is the object of the discussion, but the relation of such part to the total form. Similarly, the true object of architecture is not bricks, mortar, or timber, but the house; and so the principal object of natural philosophy is not the material elements, but their composition, and the totality of the form, independently of which they have no existence.

The course of exposition must be first to state the attributes common to whole groups of animals, and then to attempt to give their explanation. Many groups, as already noticed, present common attributes, that is to say, in some cases absolutely identical affections, and absolutely identical organs,—feet, feathers, scales, and the like; while in other groups the affections and organs are only so far identical as that they are analogous. For instance, some groups have lungs, others have no lung, but an organ analogous to a lung in its place; some have blood, others have no blood, but a fluid analogous to blood, and with the same office. To treat of the common attributes in connexion with each individual group would involve, as already suggested, useless iteration. For many groups have common attributes. So much for this topic.

As every instrument and every bodily member subserves some partial end, that is to say, some special action, so the whole body must be destined to minister to some plenary sphere of action. Thus the saw is made for sawing, for sawing is a function, and not sawing for the saw. Similarly, the body too must somehow or other be made for the soul, and each part of it for some subordinate function, to which it is adapted.

*   *   *   *

BOOK II

Chapter 7

From the marrow we pass on in natural sequence to the brain. For there are many who think that the brain itself consists of marrow, and that it forms the commencement of that substance, because they see that the spinal marrow is continuous with it. In reality the two may be said to be utterly opposite to each other in character. For of all the parts of the body there is none so cold as the brain; whereas the marrow is of a hot nature, as is plainly shown by its fat and unctuous character. Indeed this is the very reason why the brain and spinal marrow are continuous with each other. For, wherever the action of any part is in excess, nature so contrives as to set by it another part with an excess of contrary action, so that the excesses of the two may counterbalance each other. Now that the marrow is hot is clearly shown by many indications. The coldness of the brain is also manifest enough. For in the first place it is cold even to the touch; and, secondly, of all the fluid parts of the body it is the driest and the one that has the least blood; for in fact it has no blood at all in its proper substance. This brain is not residual matter, nor yet is it one of the parts which are anatomically continuous with each other; but it has a character peculiar to itself, as might indeed be expected. That it has no continuity with the organs of sense is plain from simple inspection, and is still more clearly shown by the fact, that, when it is touched, no sensation is produced; in which respect it resembles the blood of animals and their excrement. The purpose of its presence in animals is no less than the preservation of the whole body. For some writers assert that the soul is fire or some such force. This, however, is but a rough and inaccurate assertion; and it would perhaps be better to say that the soul is incorporate in some substance of a fiery character. The reason for this being so is that of all substances there is none so suitable for ministering to the operations of the soul as that which is possessed of heat. For nutrition and the imparting of motion are offices of the soul, and it is by heat that these are most readily effected. To say then that the soul is fire is much the same thing as to confound the auger or the saw with the carpenter or his craft, simply because the work is wrought by the two in conjunction. So far then this much is plain, that all animals must necessarily have a certain amount of heat. But as all influences require to be counterbalanced, so that they may be reduced to moderation and brought to the mean (for in the mean, and not in either extreme, lies the true and rational position), nature has contrived the brain as a counterpoise to the region of the heart with its contained heat, and has given it to animals to moderate the latter, combining in it the properties of earth and water. For this reason it is, that every sanguine-ous animal has a brain; whereas no bloodless creature has such an organ, unless indeed it be, as the Poulp, by analogy. For where there is no blood, there in consequence there is but little heat. The brain, then, tempers the heat and seething of the heart. In order, however, that it may not itself be absolutely without heat, but may have a moderate amount, branches run from both blood-vessels, that is to say from the great vessel and from what is called the aorta, and end in the membrane which surrounds the brain; while at the same time, in order to prevent any injury from the heat, these encompassing vessels, instead of being few and large, are numerous and small, and their blood scanty and clear, instead of being abundant and thick. We can now understand why defluxions have their origin in the head, and occur whenever the parts about the brain have more than a due proportion of coldness. For when the nutriment steams upwards through the blood-vessels, its refuse portion is chilled by the influence of this region, and forms defluxions of phlegm and serum. We must suppose, to compare small things with great, that the like happens here as occurs in the production of showers. For when vapour steams up from the earth and is carried by the heat into the upper regions, so soon as it reaches the cold air that is above the earth, it condenses again into water owing to the refrigeration, and falls back to the earth as rain. These, however, are matters which may be suitably considered in the Principles of Diseases, so far as natural philosophy has anything to say to them.

It is the brain again—or, in animals that have no brain, the part analogous to it—which is the cause of sleep. For either by chilling the blood that streams upwards after food, or by some other similar influences, it produces heaviness in the region in which it lies (which is the reason why drowsy persons hang the head), and causes the heat to escape downwards in company with the blood. It is the accumulation of this in excess in the lower region that produces complete sleep, taking away the power of standing upright from those animals to whom that posture is natural, and from the rest the power of holding up the head. These, however, are matters which have been separately considered in the treatises on Sensation and on Sleep.

That the brain is a compound of earth and water is shown by what occurs when it is boiled. For, when so treated, it turns hard and solid, inasmuch as the water is evaporated by the heat, and leaves the earthy part behind. Just the same occurs when pulse and other fruits are boiled. For these also are hardened by the process, because the water which enters into their composition is driven off and leaves the earth, which is their main constituent, behind.

Of all animals, man has the largest brain in proportion to his size; and it is larger in men than in women. This is because the region of the heart and of the lung is hotter and richer in blood in man than in any other animal; and in men than in women. This again explains why man, alone of animals, stands erect. For the heat, overcoming any opposite inclination, makes growth take its own line of direction, which is from the centre of the body upwards. It is then as a counterpoise to his excessive heat that in man's brain there is this superabundant fluidity and coldness; and it is again owing to this superabundance that the cranial bone, which some call the Bregma, is the last to become solidified; so

long does evaporation continue to occur through it under the influence
of heat. Man is the only sanguineous animal in which this takes place.
Man, again, has more sutures in his skull than any other animal, and the
male more than the female. The explanation is again to be found in the
greater size of the brain, which demands free ventilation, proportionate
to its bulk. For if the brain be either too fluid or too solid, it will not
perform its office, but in the one case will freeze the blood, and in the
other will not cool it at all; and thus will cause disease, madness, and
death. For the cardiac heat and the centre of life is most delicate in its
sympathies, and is immediately sensitive to the slightest change or affection of the blood on the outer surface of the brain.

*   *   *   *

BOOK III

Chapter 2

We have now to treat of horns; for these also, when present, are appendages of the head. They exist in none but viviparous animals;
though in some ovipara certain parts are metaphorically spoken of as
horns, in virtue of a certain resemblance. To none of such parts, however, does the proper office of a horn belong; for they are never used, as
are the horns of vivipara, for purposes which require strength, whether
it be in self-protection or in offensive strife. So also no polydactylous
animal is furnished with horns. For horns are defensive weapons, and
these polydactylous animals possess other means of security. For to some
of them nature has given claws, to others teeth suited for combat, and
to the rest some other adequate defensive appliance. There are horns,
however, in most of the cloven-hoofed animals, and in some of those
that have a solid hoof, serving them as an offensive weapon, and in some
cases also as a defensive one. There are horns also in all animals that
have not been provided by nature with some other means of security;
such means, for instance, as speed, which has been given to horses; or
great size, as in camels; for excessive bulk, such as has been given to
these animals, and in a still greater measure to elephants, is sufficient in
itself to protect an animal from being destroyed by others. Other animals again are protected by the possession of tusks; and among these are
the swine, though they have a cloven hoof.

All animals again, whose horns are but useless appendages, have been
provided by nature with some additional means of security. Thus deer
are endowed with speed; for the large size and great branching of their
horns makes these a source of detriment rather than of profit to their

possessors. Similarly endowed are the Bubalus and gazelle; for though these animals will stand up against some enemies and defend themselves with their horns, yet they run away from such as are fierce and pugnacious. The Bonasus again, whose horns curve inwards towards each other, is provided with a means of protection in the discharge of its excrement; and of this it avails itself when frightened. There are some other animals besides the Bonasus that have a similar mode of defence. In no case, however, does nature ever give more than one adequate means of protection to one and the same animal.

Most of the animals that have horns are cloven-hoofed; but the Indian ass, as they call it, is also reported to be horned, though its hoof is solid.

Again as the body, so far as regards its organs of motion, consists of two distinct parts, the right and the left, so also and for like reasons the horns of animals are, in the great majority of cases, two in number. Still there are some that have but a single horn; the Oryx, for instance, and the so-called Indian ass; in the former of which the hoof is cloven, while in the latter it is solid. In such animals the horn is set in the centre of the head; for as the middle belongs equally to both extremes, this arrangement is the one that comes nearest to each side having its own horn.

Again, it would appear consistent with reason that the single horn should go with the solid rather than with the cloven hoof. For hoof, whether solid or cloven, is of the same nature as horn; so that the two naturally undergo division simultaneously and in the same animals. Again, since the division of the cloven hoof depends on deficiency of material, it is but rationally consistent, that nature, when she gave an animal an excess of material for the hoofs, which thus became solid, should have taken away something from the upper parts and so made the animal to have but one horn.

Rightly too did she act when she chose the head whereon to set the horns; and Æsop's Momus is beside the mark, when he finds fault with the bull for not having its horns upon its shoulders. For from this position, says he, they would have delivered their blow with the greatest force, whereas on the head they occupy the weakest part of the whole body. Momus was but dull-sighted in making this hostile criticism. For had the horns been set on the shoulders, or had they been set on any other part than they are, the encumbrance of their weight would have been increased, not only without any compensating gain whatsoever, but with the disadvantage of impeding many bodily operations. For the point whence the blows could be delivered with the greatest force was not the only matter to be considered, but the point also whence they could be delivered with the widest range. But as the bull has no hands and cannot possibly have its horns on its feet or on its knees, where they would prevent flexion, there remains no other site for them but the head; and this therefore they necessarily occupy. In this position, moreover, they are much less in the way of the movements of the body than they would be elsewhere.

Deer are the only animals in which the horns are solid throughout, and are also the only animals that cast them. This casting is not simply advantageous to the deer from the increased lightness which it produces, but, seeing how heavy the horns are, is a matter of actual necessity.

In all other animals the horns are hollow for a certain distance, and the end alone is solid, this being the part of use in a blow. At the same time, to prevent even the hollow part from being weak, the horn, though it grows out of the skin, has a solid piece from the bones fitted into its cavity. For this arrangement is not only that which makes the horns of the greatest service in fighting, but that which causes them to be as little of an impediment as possible in the other actions of life.

Such then are the reasons for which horns exist; and such the reasons why they are present in some animals, absent from others.

Let us now consider the character of the material nature whose necessary results have been made available by rational nature for a final cause.

In the first place, then, the larger the bulk of animals, the greater is the proportion of corporeal and earthy matter which they contain. Thus no very small animal is known to have horns, the smallest horned animal that we are acquainted with being the gazelle. But in all our speculations concerning nature, what we have to consider is the general rule; for that is natural which applies either universally or generally. And thus when we say that the largest animals have most earthy matter, we say so because such is the general rule. Now this earthy matter is used in the animal body to form bone. But in the larger animals there is an excess of it, and this excess is turned by nature to useful account, being converted into weapons of defence. Part of it necessarily flows to the upper portion of the body, and this is allotted by her in some cases to the formation of tusks and teeth, in others to the formation of horns. Thus it is that no animal that has horns has also front teeth in both jaws, those in the upper jaw being deficient. For nature by subtracting from the teeth adds to the horns; the nutriment which in most animals goes to the former being here spent on the augmentation of the latter. Does, it is true, have no horns and yet are equally deficient with the males as regards the teeth. The reason, however, for this is that they, as much as the males, are naturally horn-bearing animals; but they have been stripped of their horns, because these would not only be useless to them but actually baneful; whereas the greater strength of the males causes these organs, though equally useless, to be less of an impediment. In other animals, where this material is not secreted from the body in the shape of horns, it is used to increase the size of the teeth; in some cases of all the teeth, in others merely of the tusks, which thus become so long as to resemble horns projecting from the jaws.

So much, then, of the parts which appertain to the head.

*   *   *   *

BOOK IV

Chapter 12

The differences of birds compared one with another are differences of magnitude, and of the greater or smaller development of parts. Thus some have long legs, others short legs; some have a broad tongue, others a narrow tongue; and so on with the other parts. There are few of their parts that differ save in size, taking birds by themselves. But when birds are compared with other animals the parts present differences of form also. For in some animals these are hairy, in others scaly, and in others have scale-like plates, while birds are feathered.

Birds, then, are feathered, and this is a character common to them all and peculiar to them. Their feathers, too, are split and distinct in kind from the undivided feathers of insects; for the bird's feather is barbed, these are not; the bird's feather has a shaft, these have none.

A second strange peculiarity which distinguishes birds from all other animals is their beak. For as in elephants the nostril serves in place of hands, and as in some insects the tongue serves in place of mouth, so in birds there is a beak, which, being bony, serves in place of teeth and lips. Their organs of sense have already been considered.

All birds have a neck extending from the body; and the purpose of this neck is the same as in such other animals as have one. This neck in some birds is long, in others short; its length, as a general rule, being pretty nearly determined by that of the legs. For long-legged birds have a long neck, short-legged birds a short one, to which rule, however, the web-footed birds form an exception. For to a bird perched up on long legs a short neck would be of no use whatsoever in collecting food from the ground; and equally useless would be a long neck, if the legs were short. Such birds, again, as are carnivorous would find length in this part interfere greatly with their habits of life. For a long neck is weak, and it is on their superior strength that carnivorous birds depend for their subsistence. No bird, therefore, that has talons ever has an elongated neck. In web-footed birds, however, and in those other birds belonging to the same class, whose toes though actually separate have flat marginal lobes, the neck is elongated, so as to be suitable for collecting food from the water; while the legs are short, so as to serve in swimming.

The beaks of birds, as their feet, vary with their modes of life. For in some the beak is straight, in others crooked; straight, in those who use it merely for eating; crooked, in those that live on raw flesh. For a crooked beak is an advantage in fighting; and these birds must, of course, get their food from the bodies of other animals, and in most cases by violence. In such birds, again, as live in marshes and are herbivorous the beak is broad and flat, this form being best suited for digging and cropping, and for pulling up plants. In some of these marsh birds, however, the beak is elongated, as too is the neck, the reason for this being that the bird gets its food from some depth below the surface. For most birds of this kind, and most of those whose feet are webbed, either in their entirety or each part separately, live by preying on some of the smaller animals that are to be found in water, and use these parts for their capture, the neck acting as a fishing-rod, and the beak representing the line and hook.

The upper and under sides of the body, that is of what in quadrupeds is called the trunk, present in birds one unbroken surface, and they have no arms or forelegs attached to it, but in their stead wings, which are a distinctive peculiarity of these animals; and, as these wings are substitutes for arms, their terminal segments lie on the back in the place of a shoulder-blade.

The legs are two in number, as in man; not however, as in man, bent outwards, but bent backwards like the (hind) legs of a quadruped. The wings are bent like the forelegs of a quadruped, having their convexity turned outwards. That the feet should be two in number is a matter of necessity. For a bird is essentially a sanguineous animal, and at the same time essentially a winged animal; and no sanguineous animal has more than four points for motion. In birds, then, as in those other sanguineous animals that live and move upon the ground, the limbs attached to the trunk are four in number. But, while in all the rest these four limbs consist of a pair of arms and a pair of legs, or of four legs as in quadrupeds, in birds the arms or forelegs are replaced by a pair of wings, and this is their distinctive character. For it is of the essence of a bird that it shall be able to fly; and it is by the extension of wings that this is made possible. Of all arrangements, then, the only possible, and so the necessary, one is that birds shall have two feet; for this with the wings will give them four points for motion. The breast in all birds is sharp-edged, and fleshy. The sharp edge is to minister to flight, for broad surfaces move with considerable difficulty, owing to the large quantity of air which they have to displace; while the fleshy character acts as a protection, for the breast, owing to its form, would be weak, were it not amply covered.

Below the breast lies the belly, extending, as in quadrupeds and in man, to the vent and to the place where the legs are jointed to the trunk.

Such, then, are the parts which lie between the wings and the legs. Birds like all other animals, whether produced viviparously or from eggs, have an umbilicus during their development, but, when the bird has attained to fuller growth, no signs of this remain visible. The cause of this is plainly to be seen during the process of development; for in birds the umbilical cord unites with the intestine, and is not a portion of the vascular system, as is the case in viviparous animals.

Some birds, again, are well adapted for flight, their wings being large and strong. Such, for instance, are those that have talons and live on flesh. For their mode of life renders the power of flight a necessity, and it is on this account that their feathers are so abundant and their wings so large. Besides these, however, there are also other genera of birds that can fly well; all those, namely, that depend on speed for security, or that are of migratory habits. On the other hand, some kinds of birds have heavy bodies and are not constructed for flight. These are birds that are frugivorous and live on the ground, or that are able to swim and get their living in watery places. In those that have talons the body, without the wings, is small; for the nutriment is consumed in the production of these wings, and of the weapons and defensive appliances; whereas in birds that are not made for flight the contrary obtains, and the body is bulky and so of heavy weight. In some of these heavy-bodied birds the legs are furnished with what are called spurs, which replace the wings as a means of defence. Spurs and talons never co-exist in the same bird. For nature never makes anything superfluous; and if a bird can fly, and has talons, it has no use for spurs; for these are weapons for fighting on the ground, and on this account are an appanage of certain heavy-bodied birds. These latter, again, would find the possession of talons not only useless but actually injurious; for the claws would stick into the ground and interfere with progression. This is the reason why all birds with talons walk so badly, and why they never settle upon rocks. For the character of their claws is ill-suited for either action.

All this is the necessary consequence of the process of development. For the earthy matter in the body issuing from it is converted into parts that are useful as weapons. That which flows upwards gives hardness or size to the beak; and, should any flow downwards, it either forms spurs upon the legs or gives size and strength to the claws upon the feet. But it does not at one and the same time produce both these results, one in the legs, the other in the claws; for such a dispersion of this residual matter would destroy all its efficiency. In other birds this earthy residue furnishes the legs with the material for their elongation; or sometimes, in place of this, fills up the interspaces between the toes. Thus it is simply a matter of necessity, that such birds as swim shall either be actually web-footed, or shall have a kind of broad blade-like margin running along the whole length of each distinct toe. The forms, then, of these feet are simply the necessary results of the causes that have been mentioned. Yet at the same time they are intended for the animal's advantage. For they are in harmony with the mode of life of these birds, who, living on the water, where their wings are useless, require that their feet shall be such as to serve in swimming. For these feet are so developed as to resemble the oars of a boat, or the fins of a fish; and the destruction of the foot-web has the same effect as the destruction of the fins; that is to say, it puts an end to all power of swimming.

In some birds the legs are very long, the cause of this being that they inhabit marshes. I say the cause, because nature makes the organs for the functions, and not the function for the organs. It is, then, because these birds are not meant for swimming that their feet are without webs, and it is because they live on ground that gives way under the foot that their legs and toes are elongated, and that these latter in most of them have an extra number of joints. Again, though all birds have the same material composition, they are not all made for flight; and in these, therefore, the nutriment that should go to their tail-feathers is spent on the legs and used to increase their size. This is the reason why these birds when they fly make use of their legs as a tail, stretching them out behind, and so rendering them serviceable, whereas in any other position they would be simply an impediment.

In other birds, where the legs are short, these are held close against the belly during flight. In some cases this is merely to keep the feet out of the way, but in birds that have talons the position has a further purpose, being the one best suited for rapine. Birds that have a long and a thick neck keep it stretched out during flight; but those whose neck though long is slender fly with it coiled up. For in this position it is protected, and less likely to get broken, should the bird fly against any obstacle.

In all birds there is an ischium, but so placed and of such length that it would scarcely be taken for an ischium, but rather for a second thigh-bone; for it extends as far as to the middle of the belly. The reason for this is that the bird is a biped, and yet is unable to stand erect. For if its ischium extended but a short way from the fundament, and then immediately came the leg, as is the case in man and in quadrupeds, the bird would be unable to stand up at all. For while man stands erect, and while quadrupeds have their heavy bodies propped up in front by the forelegs, birds can neither stand erect owing to their dwarf-like shape, nor have anterior legs to prop them up, these legs being replaced by wings. As a remedy for this Nature has given them a long ischium, and brought it to the centre of the body, fixing it firmly; and she has placed the legs under this central point, that the weight on either side may be equally balanced, and standing or progression rendered possible. Such then is the reason why a bird, though it is a biped, does not stand erect. Why its legs are destitute of flesh has also already been stated; for the reasons are the same as in the case of quadrupeds.

In all birds alike, whether web-footed or not, the number of toes in each foot is four. For the Libyan ostrich may be disregarded for the present, and its cloven hoof and other discrepancies of structure as compared with the tribe of birds will be considered further on. Of these four toes three are in front, while the fourth points backwards, serving, as a heel, to give steadiness. In the long-legged birds this fourth toe is much shorter than the others, as is the case with the Crex, but the number of their toes is not increased. The arrangement of the toes is such as has been described in all birds with the exception of the wryneck. Here only two of the toes are in front, the other two behind; and the reason for this is that the body of the wryneck is not inclined forward so much as that of other birds. All birds have testicles; but they are inside the body. The reason for this will be given in the treatise on the Generation of Animals.

3

PTOLEMY

Less is known about Claudius Ptolemy than about any other historical figure of equal eminence. Except for conflicting reports on his place of birth, all that has come down is an Arabic tradition that he enjoyed a life span of 78 years. When and where he passed those years is known only indirectly, through his citations of astronomical observations made at or near Alexandria during the period 127 to 151 A.D. But the obscurity of Ptolemy's life circumstances is more than compensated for by the prominence of his lifework. Few could wish for a more splendid memorial than the accomplishments of Ptolemy. Not only was his astronomical work sufficient to the establishment of several reputations, but he also made fundamental contributions in optics. In addition, he composed outstanding syntheses of every branch of ancient mathematical science: astronomy, astrology, cosmology, optics, harmonics, and geography.

The first two selections are taken from the *Almagest*. Formally titled the *Mathematical Composition*, it treats all of the quantitative aspects of ancient astronomy in 13 books. The first two contain the background mathematics and the doctrine of the sphere, which constitute the foundation for all of the succeeding material. Book 3 deals with the motion of the sun—the simplest problem in all of planetary theory. Since the subject had already been exhausted by Hipparchus 300 years earlier, it required virtually no new development by Ptolemy. As usual, the major portion of his discussion is devoted to justifying and tabulating the various parameters of the model. Only the finished products—the solar theory and relevant tables—are presented here: the goal is to acquaint the student with the geometry of the basic model and to enable him to compute the sun's position at any arbitrary time. Recourse to the sample calculation should remove any difficulties that might arise.

Following the solar theory, Ptolemy presents the lunar theory (Book 4, with important modifications in Book 5), and shows how to coordinate the two for the prediction of eclipses (Book 6). He then lists his star catalogue (Books 7 and 8) to complete the exposition of the science of astronomy insofar as it had been satisfactorily developed down to his day.

In the last five books, Ptolemy undertakes the problem of planetary motion. By his own testimony, all previous attempts had ended in failure. Perhaps he exaggerates. Perhaps he was not the first to provide a reasonable account of planetary positions all around the orbit. But if he was not, his work so far excelled the existing accounts that nothing has been heard of them since. This work constitutes the subject of our second extract. Taken from the beginning of Book 9, it shows Ptolemy first laying down the practical and theoretical guidelines of his researches, and then giving a qualitative description of his results—of the generalized model of planetary theory which reigned supreme through 1400 years.

3

The Almagest

BOOK III

Chapter 1. On the Year's Magnitude

Now that we have methodically gone through, in all that has been put together up until now, those things which have first to be completely grasped mathematically concerning the heavens and the earth, and also concerning the obliquity of the sun's path through the middle of the zodiac [along the ecliptic] and its particular incidents in the right sphere and the oblique sphere for each latitude, we consider it proper after all this to treat of the sun and moon and to take account of the incidents concerning their movements, since without a prior understanding of them none of the appearances having to do with the stars can be discovered. And we find the treatise on the sun's movement advanced first, for again, without this, matters concerning the moon could not be grasped in detail. . . .

And as regards the scrutiny of the movements of the sun and the other planets in their particularities, which is best furnished ready to hand and all set out by the orderly construction of tables, we believe it is the necessary purpose and aim of the mathematician to show forth all the appearances of the heavens as products of regular and circular motions. And it is incumbent upon him to construct such tables as, proper and consequent upon this purpose, separate out the particular regular motions from the anomaly which seems to result from the hypotheses of circles, and show forth their apparent movements as a combination and union of all together. In order, then, that we may get this sort of thing in more serviceable form for the demonstration under consideration, we shall set out the regular movements of the sun in their particularities in this way.

Great Books of the Western World, Volume 16, translated from the Greek by R. Catesby Taliaferro, Chicago: Encyclopedia Britannica, 1952, pp. 77-91, 102-104, 270-273, and 291-293. Reprinted by permission of the Encyclopedia Britannica.

For since a return has been proved to be 365 days 14'48", if we divide these into the 360° of one circle, we shall have the sun's mean daily movement along the ecliptic as approximately $0°59^i8^{ii}17^{iii}13^{iv}12^v31^{vi}$; for it will suffice to carry out the fractions to this power of sixtieths. And again, taking 1/24 of the daily movement along the ecliptic, we shall have for the hourly movement approximately $0°2^i27^{ii}50^{iii}43^{iv}3^v1^{vi}$. Likewise multiplying the daily movement by the 30 days of a month, we shall have the mean monthly movement of $29°34^i8^{ii}36^{iii}36^{iv}15^v30^{vi}$; and multiplying by the 365 days of an Egyptian year we shall have the mean yearly movement of $359°45^i24^{ii}45^{iii}21^{iv}8^v35^{vi}$. Again multiplying the mean yearly movement by 18 years, because of the symmetry which will appear in

Chapter 2

[Abbreviated]ᵃ Table of the Sun's Regular Movement

Distance from the apogee 265°15'; mean epoch 330°45'

18-Year periods	deg.	i	ii	iii	iv	v	vi	Egyptian months	deg.	i	ii	iii	iv	v	vi
18	355	37	25	36	20	34	30								
36	351	14	51	12	41	9	0	30	29	34	8	36	36	15	30
54	346	52	16	49	1	43	30	60	59	8	17	13	12	31	0
72	342	29	42	25	22	18	0	90	88	42	25	49	48	46	30
90	338	7	8	1	42	52	30	..	..	..	..	..	..	..	..
108	333	44	33	38	3	27	0	..	..	..	..	..	..	..	..
..	..	..	..	..	..	..	..	360	354	49	43	19	15	6	0
..	..	..	..	..	..	..	..								
774	171	49	21	2	44	43	30								
792	167	26	46	39	5	18	0	Days							
810	163	4	12	15	25	52	30	1	0	59	8	17	13	12	31
								2	1	58	16	34	26	25	2
								3	2	57	24	51	39	37	33
Single years								..	..	..	..	..	..	..	..
1	359	45	24	45	21	8	35	..	..	..	..	..	..	..	..
2	359	30	49	30	42	17	10	30	29	34	8	36	36	15	30
3	359	16	14	16	3	25	45								
..	..	..	..	..	..	..	..	Hours							
..	..	..	..	..	..	..	..	1	0	2	27	50	43	3	1
18	355	37	25	36	20	34	30	2	0	4	55	41	26	6	2
								3	0	7	23	32	9	9	3
								..	..	..	..	..	..	..	..
								..	..	..	..	..	..	..	..
								24	0	59	8	17	13	12	31

ᵃ Ptolemy provides a complete tabulation of these five tables between the limits listed. Omitted values can be obtained simply by adding or multiplying given ones.

the construction of the tables, and subtracting the whole circles, we shall have the surplus for the 18-year period, that is $355°37^{i}25^{ii}36^{iii}20^{iv}34^{v}30^{vi}$.

We have accordingly drawn up three tables of the regular movement of the sun. . . . The numbers designating the time are set out in the first columns, and in the next columns the degrees, minutes, etc., are put beside them according to the proper combinations of each. And the tables are on page 70.

Chapter 3. On the Hypotheses Concerning Regular and Circular Movement

Since the next thing is to explain the apparent irregularity of the sun, it is first necessary to assume in general that the motions of the planets in the direction contrary to the movement of the heavens are all regular and circular by nature, like the movement of the universe in the other direction. That is, the straight lines, conceived as revolving the stars or their circles, cut off in equal times on absolutely all circumferences equal angles at the centres of each; and their apparent irregularities result from the positions and arrangements of the circles on their spheres through which they produce these movements, but no departure from their unchangeableness has really occurred in their nature in regard to the supposed disorder of their appearances.

But the cause of this irregular appearance can be accounted for by as many as two primary simple hypotheses. For if their movement is considered with respect to a circle in the plane of the ecliptic concentric with the cosmos so that our eye is the centre, then it is necessary to suppose that they make their regular movements either along circles not concentric with the cosmos, or along concentric circles; not with these simply, but with other circles borne upon them called epicycles. For according to either hypothesis it will appear possible for the planets seemingly to pass, in equal periods of time, through unequal arcs of the ecliptic circle which is concentric with the cosmos.

For if, in the case of the hypothesis of eccentricity, we conceive the eccentric circle $ABCD$ on which the star moves regularly, with E as centre and with diameter AED, and the point F on it as your eye so that the point A becomes the apogee and the point D the perigee; and if, cutting off equal arcs AB and DC, we join BE, BF, CE, and CF, then it will be evident that the star moving through each of the arcs AB and CD in an equal period of time will seem to have passed through unequal arcs on the circle described around F as a centre (Figure 1). For since

$$\text{angle } BEA = \text{angle } CED,$$

therefore angle BFA is less than either of them, and angle CFD greater.

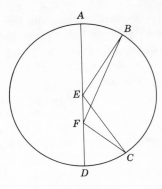

FIGURE 1

And if in the hypothesis of the epicycle we conceive the circle *ABCD* concentric with the ecliptic with centre *E* and diameter *AEC,* and the epicycle *FGHK* borne on it on which the star moves, with its centre at *A,* then it will be immediately evident also that as the epicycle passes regularly along the circle *ABCD,* from *A* to *B* for example, and the star along the epicycle, the star will appear indifferently to be at *A* the centre of the epicycle when it is at *F* or *H;* but when it is at other points, it will not. But having come to *G,* for instance, it will seem to have produced a movement greater than the regular movement by the arc *AG;* and having come to *K,* likewise less by the arc *AK* (Figure 2).

Then with the hypothesis of eccentricity it is always the case that the least movement belongs to the apogee and the greatest movement to the perigee, since angle *AFB* is always less than angle *DFC.* But both cases can come about with the hypothesis of the epicycle. For when the epi-

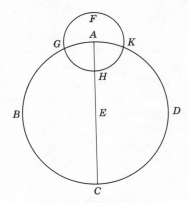

FIGURE 2

cycle moves contrary to the heavens, for example from *A* to *B*, if the star so moves on the epicycle that it goes from the apogee again contrary to the heavens (that is, from *F* in the direction of *G*), there will result at the apogee the greatest advance, because the epicycle and the star are moving the same way. But if the movement of the star on the epicycle is in the direction of that of the heavens, that is, from *F* towards *K*, conversely the least advance will be effected at the apogee because the star is then moving contrary to the movement of the epicycle.

With these things established, it must next be understood that, in the case of those planets which effect two anomalies, it is possible to combine both of these hypotheses, as we shall show in the chapters concerning them. But, in the case of those planets subject to only one anomaly, one of the hypotheses will suffice. And it must be understood that all the appearances can be cared for interchangeably according to either hypothesis, when the same ratios are involved in each. In other words, the hypotheses are interchangeable when, in the case of the hypothesis of the epicycle, the ratio of the epicycle's radius to the radius of the circle carrying it [deferent] is the same as, in the case of the hypothesis of eccentricity, the ratio of the line between the centres (that is, between the eye and the centre of the eccentric circle), to the eccentric circle's radius; with the added conditions that the star move on the epicycle from the apogee in the direction of the movement of the heavens with the same angular velocity as the epicycle moves on the circle concentric with the eye in the direction opposite to that of the heavens, and that the star move regularly on the eccentric circle with the same angular velocity also and in the direction opposite to the movement of the heavens. . . .

And next it will be clearly seen that, even in the other particular movements, in the case of both hypotheses, for equal times, all the same things will occur with respect to the regular and apparent movements and the differences between them—that is, the anomalistic difference (Figure 3).

For let there be the circle *ABC* with centre *D*, concentric with the ecliptic; and the eccentric *EFG* with center *H*, equal to the concentric circle *ABC*; and the diameter *EAHD* common to both, through the centres *D* and *H* and the apogee *E*. And with arc *AB* taken at random length on the concentric circle, let the epicycle *KF* with centre *B* and radius *DH* be described, and let *KBD* be joined.

I say that the star will be borne by either movement to *F*, the intersection of the eccentric circle and the epicycle, in the same amount of time. That is, the three arcs, *EF* on the eccentric, *AB* on the concentric,

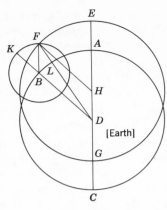

FIGURE 3

and *KF* on the epicycle are similar to each other; and the difference between the regular and irregular movements, and the apparent passage
of the star, will be similar and the same under either hypothesis.

For let *FH*, *BF*, and *DF* be joined. Since the opposite sides of the
quadrilateral *BDHF* are equal to each other, *FH* to *BD*, and *BF* to *DH*,
the quadrilateral *BDFH* is a parallelogram. Therefore the three angles
EHF, *ADB*, and *FBK* are equal. And so, since they are angles at the
centres, the arcs subtended by them—*EF* on the eccentric, *AB* on the
concentric, and *KF* on the epicycle—are similar to one another. Therefore by either motion, the star will be brought to the same point *F* in an
equal period of time, and will appear to have passed from the apogee
along the same arc of the ecliptic, *AL*. And accordingly the anomalistic
difference will be the same according to either hypothesis, since we have
already proved that the difference contained by angle *DFH* on the hypothesis of eccentricity is of the same kind as that contained by angle
BDF on the hypothesis of the epicycle, and since these angles are here
also alternate and equal, with *FH* proved parallel to *BD*.

And it is clear that for all distances these same results will follow,
HDFB being always a parallelogram and the eccentric circle being described by the movement of the star on the epicycle whenever the relations under either hypothesis are both similar and equal.

*   *   *   *

Chapters 4 and 5 constitute the heart of the discussion, but are somewhat
technical. Their function is to provide the numerical basis of the theory; that
is, to demonstrate the means by which the qualitative model can be converted
into a quantitative theory that accounts for the actual motion of the sun.

Ptolemy follows Hipparchus in finding parameters (derived from differences in the observed lengths of the four astronomical seasons) of $\frac{1}{24}$ and $65°30'$; $\frac{1}{24}$ determines the size of the maximum departures from uniform circular motion, and $65°30'$ determines the longitudes of those maximum departures. On the epicycle model, the one number gives the ratio between the radii of epicycle and deferent, while the other provides the longitude of apogee, or the position of the center of the epicycle at the time the sun reaches the outermost point on the epicycle. From these data, the angle (BDF) between the sun's mean (DB) and true (DF) longitudes can be determined trigonometrically for any position in the epicycle. For convenience, however, Ptolemy computes the corrections at regular intervals and tabulates them as Chapter 6.

Chapter 6

Table of the Sun's Anomaly

1. 2. Common Numbers (Degrees of Regular Movement)		3. Additive— Subtractive Differences		1. 2. Common Numbers (Degrees of Regular Movement)		3. Additive— Subtractive Differences	
6°	354°	0°	14′	120°	240°	2°	6′
12°	348°	0°	28′	123°	237°	2°	2′
18°	342°	0°	42′	126°	234°	1°	58′
24°	336°	0°	56′	129°	231°	1°	54′
30°	330°	1°	9′	132°	228°	1°	49′
36°	324°	1°	21′	135°	225°	1°	44′
42°	318°	1°	32′	138°	222°	1°	39′
48°	312°	1°	43′	141°	219°	1°	33′
54°	306°	1°	53′	144°	216°	1°	27′
60°	300°	2°	1′	147°	213°	1°	21′
66°	294°	2°	8′	150°	210°	1°	14′
72°	288°	2°	14′	153°	207°	1°	7′
78°	282°	2°	18′	156°	204°	1°	0′
84°	276°	2°	21′	159°	201°	0°	53′
90°	270°	2°	23′	162°	198°	0°	46′
93°	267°	2°	23′	165°	195°	0°	39′
96°	264°	2°	23′	168°	192°	0°	32′
99°	261°	2°	22′	171°	189°	0°	24′
102°	258°	2°	21′	174°	186°	0°	16′
105°	255°	2°	20′	177°	183°	0°	8′
108°	252°	2°	18′	180°	180°	0°	0′
111°	249°	2°	16′				
114°	246°	2°	13′				
117°	243°	2°	10′				

Chapter 8. On Calculating the Sun

Whenever we wish to know the course of the sun for any desired time, taking the total time from the epoch to the proposed date with reference to the hour in Alexandria and taking it to the tables of mean movement, we add the degrees corresponding to the particular numbers to the 265°15′ of the distance found above; and striking the complete circles out of the result, we subtract the rest from the 5°30′ within the Twins backwards in the order of the signs [i.e., add 65°30′]. And wherever the number falls, there we find the mean course of the sun. Next we take the same number (that is, the number of degrees from the apogee to the mean course) to the Table of Anomaly. And, if the number falls in the first column (that is, if it is not greater than 180°), then we subtract the corresponding degrees in the third column from the position of the mean course; but, if it falls in the second column (that is, if it is greater than 180°), then we add it to the mean course. And thus we find the true and apparent sun.

SAMPLE CALCULATION

Suppose Ptolemy wishes to know the sun's position at 5:20 P.M. on the 13th day of the 3rd Egyptian month of the 20th year of the reign of Hadrian (*Almagest*: V,13). The steps are as follows.

I.   Find the time interval.

The major problem is to convert the date of observation from its designation in the Roman calendar to its equivalent in the Egyptian (astronomical) calendar. That having already been done, it is necessary only to know that from the epoch (Ptolemy arbitrarily chose the first year of Nabonassar, 747 B.C., as his reference) to the first year of Hadrian is 863 Egyptian years. It follows then, that the additional elapsed time is 19 years, 2 months, 12 days, and 5⅓ hours.

II. Find the progress of the sun during 882 years, 72 days, and 5⅓ hours.

810 years	163°	4′	Accuracy to VI's is point-
72 years	342	30	less: We can round to
60 days	59	8	minutes.
12 days	11	50	
5⅓ hours		13	

936° 45′ or 216°45′

III. Knowing the position of the sun at the epoch, and its net advance to the date in question, compute (*a*) its mean position, (*b*) the correction for the epicycle, and (*c*) its true position (Figure 4).

(a) At the epoch, the center of the epicycle was at 330°45′. It has moved 216°45′, so the new mean longitude is 187°30′.

(b) At the epoch, the sun was 265°15′ past apogee. It has likewise moved

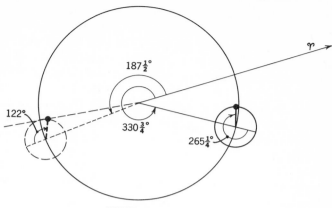

FIGURE 4

216°45′, so the new mean anomaly is 122°. The appropriate correction from the Table of Anomaly is about 2°3′.

(c) The diagram shows the sun to be *behind* the center of the epicycle, so the correction must be subtracted, leaving a true longitude of 185°27′.

*   *   *   *

BOOK IX

Chapter 1. Concerning the Order of the Spheres of the Sun and Moon and Five Planets

Now, certainly whatever one could say in general about the fixed stars, to the extent that the appearances up until now fall under our apprehension, would be pretty much like this. But since this Composition still lacks a treatment of the five planets, we shall give an exposition of them, going as far as possible with what they have in common to avoid repetition, and then adding on the plan of each one in particular.

First, then, concerning the order of their spheres, all of which have their positions about the poles of the ecliptic, we see the foremost mathematicians agree that all these spheres are nearer the earth than the sphere of the fixed stars, and farther from the earth than that of the moon; that the three—of which Saturn's is the largest, Jupiter's next earthward, and Mars' below that—are all farther from the earth than the others and that of the sun. On the other hand, the spheres of Venus and Mercury are placed by the earlier mathematicians below the sun's, but by some of the later ones above the sun's because of their never having seen the sun eclipsed by them. But this judgment seems to us unsure since these planets could be below the sun and never yet have been in any of the planes through the sun and our eye but in another, and therefore not have appeared in a line with it; just as in the case of the moon's conjunctive passages there are for the most part no eclipses.

Since there is no other way of getting at this because of the absence of any sensible parallax in these stars, from which appearance alone linear distances are gotten, the order of the earlier mathematicians seems the more trustworthy, using the sun as a natural dividing line between those planets which can be any angular distance from the sun and those which cannot but which always move near it. Besides, it does not place them far enough at their perigees to produce a sensible parallax.

Chapter 2. On the Aim of the Planetary Hypotheses

So much, then, for the orders of the spheres. Now, since our problem is to demonstrate, in the case of the five planets as in the case of the sun and moon, all their apparent irregularities as produced by means of regular and circular motions (for these are proper to the nature of divine things which are strangers to disparities and disorders) the successful accomplishment of this aim as truly belonging to mathematical theory in philosophy is to be considered a great thing, very difficult and as yet unattained in a reasonable way by anyone. For, since, in the case of the researches about the periodic movements of each planet, whatever slight error the eye makes in systematic observations produces a sensible difference more quickly when the examination has been over a shorter interval than when over a greater one, the time for which we have observations of the planets recorded (being short for grasping such a considerable lay-out), furnishes an unsure prediction over long periods. In the case of research about the anomalies, the fact that there are two anomalies appearing for each of the planets, and that they are unequal in magnitude and in the times of their returns, works a good deal of confusion. For one of the anomalies is seen to have relation to the sun, and the other to the parts of the zodiac, but both are mixed together so it is very hard to determine what belongs to each; and most of the old observations were thrown together carelessly and grossly. The more continuous of them contain stations and apparitions, and the apprehension of these properties is not certain. The stations cannot indicate the exact time, since the planet's local motion remains impercepitble for many days before and after its station; and the apparitions not only make the places immediately disappear along with the stars as they are seen for the first or last time, but also can be utterly misleading as to the times because of the differences in the atmosphere and in the eye of the observer. In general, the observations made with reference to some fixed star at a rather great angular distance, unless because of these things one attends to them wisely and clear-sightedly, furnish a magnitude from their measurements hard to calculate and subject to guesswork. And this is so, not only because the lines between the observed stars make different angles with the ecliptic and by no means right angles—whence in the variety of the zodiac's inclinations a great uncertainty is apt to follow in the determination of the longitudinal and latitudinal positions—but also because the same angular distances appear to the eye greater near the horizon and smaller near the culminations, and so they can be measured as sometimes greater and sometimes smaller than the real angular distance.

And so I consider Hipparchus to have been most zealous after the truth, both because of all these things and especially because of his having left us more examples of accurate observations than he ever got from his predecessors. He sought out the hypotheses of the sun and moon, and demonstrated as far as possible and by every available means that they were accomplished through uniform circular movements, but he did not attempt to give the principle of the hypotheses of the five planets, as far as we can tell from those memoirs of his which have come down to us, but only arranged the observations in a more useful way and showed the appearances to be inconsistent with the hypotheses of the mathematicians of that time. For not only did he think it necessary as it seemed to declare that, because of the double anomaly of each planet, the regressions of each are unequal and of such and such a magnitude, while the other mathematicians gave their geometrical demonstrations on one and the same anomaly and regression, but he also thought that these movements could not be effected either by eccentric circles, or by circles concentric with the ecliptic but bearing epicycles, or even by both together, although the zodiacal anomaly was of one magnitude and the anomaly with respect to the sun of another. For these are the means used by nearly all those who have wished to demonstrate uniform circular movement by the so-called perpetual table, but in a false and inconsequential way, some getting nowhere at all, some following the problem to a limited extent. But Hipparchus reasoned that no one who has progressed through the whole of mathematics to such a point of accuracy and zeal for truth would be content to stop at this like the rest; but that anyone who was to persuade himself and those in touch with him would have to demonstrate the magnitude and periods of each of the anomalies by clear and consistent appearances; and, putting both together, he would have to find out the position and order of the circles by which these anomalies are produced and the mode of their movement and finally show about all the appearances to be consistent with the peculiar property of this hypothesis of the circles. I think this is difficult, and it seemed so to him. We have said all this not through ostentation, but in order that, if we are forced by the problem itself either (1) to use something contrary to the general argument, as when, for example, for ease we make our demonstrations of the circles described by the movement in the planetary spheres as if they were simple and in the same plane with the ecliptic; or if we are forced (2) to presuppose something without immediate foundation in the appearances, an apprehension gotten from continuous trial and adjustment; or (3) to suppose not everywhere the same mode of movement or inclination of the circles—in order that, I say, we may then reasonably agree that (1) using something of the sort that no appreciable difference is to result from it will not falsify the subject in hand; (2) that things supposed without proof, once they are conceived in such a way as to be consistent with appearances, cannot be found without some plan and knowledge even if the way of getting hold of them is hard to explain (after all, generally speaking, the cause of first principles is either nothing or hard to interpret in its nature) ; and (3) that, since the appearances relative to the stars are also found to be dissimilar, one should not reasonably think it strange or absurd to vary the mode of the hypotheses of the circles, especially when, along with saving the regular circular movement absolutely everywhere, each of the appearances is demonstrated in its more lawful and general character.

And so we have used for the demonstrations of each planet only those observations which cannot be disputed, that is those taken at contact or great proximity with the stars or even with the moon, and above all those taken with the astrolabe where the eye is lined up with the diametrically opposite sights in the circles, sees on every side equal angular distances by means of similar arcs, and can accurately apprehend the passages relative to the middle of each star in longitude and latitude by moving to and fro to the observed stars the astrolabe's ecliptic circle and the diametrically opposite sights in the circles through its poles.

*   *   *   *

Chapter 5. Preliminaries of the Hypotheses of the Five Planets

Now, the relation of the anomalies to the longitudinal passage of the five planets follows the exposition of these mean movements, and we have attempted a general outline of it in the following way.

For, as we said, the very simple movements together sufficient for the problem in hand are two: one effected by circles eccentric to the ecliptic, and the other by circles concentric with the ecliptic but bearing epicycles. And likewise also the apparent anomalies for each star considered singly are two: one observed with respect to the parts of the zodiac and the other with respect to the configurations of the sun. In the case of this latter anomaly, we find, from different configurations observed in contiguity and in the same parts of the zodiac, that, for the five planets, the time from the greatest movement to the mean movement is always longer than from the mean to the least. And such a property (σύμπτωμα) cannot follow from the hypothesis of eccentricity, but its contrary follows, because the greatest passage is always effected at the perigee, and in both hypotheses the arc from the perigee to the point of mean passage is less than that from this point to the apogee. But it can occur in the hypothesis of epicycles when the greatest passage is not effected at the perigee as in the case of the moon, but at the apogee—that is, when the star, starting from the apogee, moves not westward as the moon, but eastward in the opposite direction. And so we suppose this anomaly to be produced by epicycles.

But in the case of the anomaly observed with respect to the parts of the zodiac, we find, by means of the arcs of the zodiac taken at the same phases or configurations, that, on the contrary, the time from the least movement to the mean is always greater than the time from the mean movement to the greatest. But this property can follow from either hypothesis, and at the beginning of the composition of the sun [III, 3] we showed how they were alike in this. But since it is more proper to the eccentric hypothesis, we suppose this anomaly is effected according to it, and also because the other anomaly is peculiar to the epicyclic hypothesis.

But immediately on applying the particular positions observed to the courses constructed from the combination of both hypotheses and continually examining them together, we find things cannot proceed so simply: (1) The planes in which we describe the eccentric circles are not immobile, so that the straight line through both their centres and the ecliptic's centre, along which the apogees and perigees are sighted, always remains at the same angular distances from the tropic and equinoctial points. (2) The epicycles do not have their centres borne on the eccentric circles whose centres are those with respect to which the epicycles' centres revolve in a regular eastward motion and cut off equal angles in equal times. But (1) the eccentrics' apogees make a slight regular shift eastward from the tropic points around the ecliptic's centre and nearly as much for each planet as the sphere of the fixed stars is found to make—that is, one degree in a hundred years, as far as one can detect from present data. And (2) the epicycles' centres are borne on circles equal to the eccentrics effecting the anomaly, but described about other centres. And these other centres, in the case of all except Mercury, bisect the straight lines between the centres of the eccentrics effecting the anomaly and the centre of the ecliptic. But in the case of Mercury alone, this other centre is the same distance from the centre revolving it [centre of equant] as this centre revolving it is in turn from the centre effecting the anomaly on the side of the apogee, and as this last centre effecting the anomaly is in turn from the centre placed at the eye. For, in the case of that star alone as also with the moon, we find the eccentric circle revolved by the aforesaid centre, contrariwise to the epicycle, back westward one revolution in a year's time, since it appears to be twice perigee in one revolution, just as the moon is also twice so in one month's time.

Chapter 6. On the Mode and Difference of These Hypotheses

The mode of the hypotheses just derived would be more easy to understand in this way (Figure 5):

In the case of the hypothesis of all the planets except Mercury, first let there be conceived the eccentric circle *ABC* about the centre *D*, and the diameter *ADC* through *D* and the centre of the ecliptic. And on this diameter let *E* be made the centre of the ecliptic, the point *A* the apogee, and *C* the perigee. And let *DE* be bisected at *F*; and with *F* as centre and *DA* as radius, let circle *GHK* be drawn, equal of course to circle *ABC*. And with *H* as centre let the epicycle *LM* be drawn, and let the straight line *LHMD* be joined.

Then first we suppose the plane of the eccentric circles to be inclined to that of the ecliptic, and again the plane of the epicycle to that of the eccentric, because of the latitudinal passage of the stars to be demonstrated by us hereafter. But to make things easy as far as the longitudinal passages are concerned, we suppose that they are all conceived in the one

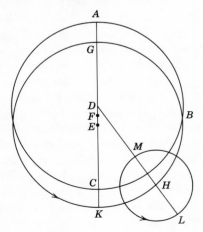

FIGURE 5

plane of the ecliptic, since there will be no appreciable difference in longitude resulting from such inclinations as will be found for each of the stars.

Then we say that the whole plane revolves eastward in the direction of the signs about centre E, moving the apogees and perigees one degree in a hundred years; that the epicycle's diameter LHM in turn is revolved regularly by centre D eastward in the direction of the signs at the rate of the star's longitudinal return; and that at the same time it revolves the points of the epicycle L and M, its centre H always borne on the eccentric GHK, and the star itself. And the star in turn moves on the epicycle LM, regularly with respect to the diameter always pointing to centre D, and makes its returns at the rate of the mean cycle of the anomaly with respect to the sun, moving eastward in the order of the signs at the apogee L.

4

PTOLEMY

In terms of gross human impact, Ptolemy's "four books on prognostication by means of astronomy" (*Tetrabiblos*) was probably his most effective work; for in spite of various attempts to suppress astrology, it constituted a fundamental article of belief and a major source of guidance at all levels of society from Hellenistic times to the end of the 17th century. The concept of divination in general and astrology in particular entered the Greek world from Mesopotamia, where it had long been utilized to direct affairs of state. The highly individualistic Greeks quickly adapted it for use at the personal level. Already by the 4th century B.C. the casting of horoscopes must have attained a certain vogue, for both Eudoxus and Theophrastus are reputed to have inveighed against the practice; but general acceptance of astrology seems to have been a concomitant of the rise and spread of Stoic philosophy in and after the 3rd century B.C.

Although astrology, like technical astronomy, was developed in a serious way for some 400 years before Ptolemy's time, the *Tetrabiblos*, like the *Almagest*, is the oldest surviving systematic account of the discipline. Extinguishing any predecessors that might have existed, and discouraging any successors that might have been contemplated, it dominated its intellectual province to the same extent that other treatises by Ptolemy (or Aristotle or Galen, as the case may have been) dominated theirs. Its success is readily understood, for the *Tetrabiblos* presents all the material—from first principles to last details—of an extremely complex subject in an orderly and comprehensible fashion. Book I deals with the fundamental assumptions of the system. In it are set forth the specific properties of the various planets, and the influence arising from the presence of each in the various constellations or the alignment of several in certain special configurations. Book II presents the gross generalities that affect or pertain to large numbers of people sharing common circumstances. Finally, Books III and IV elaborate the process to illustrate the derivation of knowledge concerning the fate of the individual.

Samples of Ptolemy's approach to each of the three tasks mentioned above are included in the following selection. What is particularly interesting, however, is his introductory defense of the foundations of the discipline. Rarely has a serious academic work been accompanied by so candid an appraisal of its status. Ptolemy, by the very fact of his labors, is bound to contend that astrology deserves serious consideration as an element in the spectrum of man's intellectual activity. What is the basis of his argument? Does he succeed in applying it consistently? What is the difference, for him, between an astronomical generalization and an astrological one—between an erroneous prediction from the one, and an erroneous prediction from the other?

4

Tetrabiblos or Four Books on the Influence of the Stars

BOOK I

Chapter 1

The studies preliminary to astronomical prognostication, O Syrus! are two: the one, first alike in order and in power, leads to the knowledge of the figurations of the Sun, the Moon, and the stars; and of their relative aspects to each other, and to the earth: the other takes into consideration the changes which their aspects create, by means of their natural properties, in objects under their influence.

The first mentioned study has been already explained in the Almagest to the utmost practicable extent; for it is complete in itself, and of essential utility even without being blended with the second; to which this treatise will be devoted, and which is not equally self-complete. The present work shall, however, be regulated by that due regard for truth which philosophy demands: and since the material quality of the objects acted upon renders them weak and variable, and difficult to be accurately apprehended, no positive or infallible rules (as were given in detailing the first doctrine, which is always governed by the same immutable laws) can be here set forth: while, on the other hand, a due observation of most of those general events, which evidently trace their causes to the Ambient, shall not be omitted.

It is, however, a common practice with the vulgar to slander everything which is difficult of attainment, and surely they who condemn the first of these two studies must be considered totally blind, whatever arguments may be produced in support of those who impugn the second. There are also persons who imagine that whatever they themselves have not been able to acquire, must be utterly beyond the reach of all understanding; while others again will consider as useless any science of which

Translated from the Greek by J. M. Ashmand, London, c. 1820.

(although they may have been often instructed in it) they have failed to preserve the recollection, owing to its difficulty of retention. In reference to these opinions, therefore, an endeavour shall be made to investigate the extent to which prognostication by astronomy is practicable, as well as serviceable, previously to detailing the particulars of the doctrine.

Chapter 2. Knowledge May Be Acquired by Astronomy to a Certain Extent

That a certain power, derived from the æthereal nature, is diffused over and pervades the whole atmosphere of the earth, is clearly evident to all men. Fire and air, the first of the sublunary elements, are encompassed and altered by the motions of the æther. These elements in their turn encompass all inferior matter, and vary it as they themselves are varied; acting on earth and water, on plants and animals.

The Sun, always acting in connection with the Ambient, contributes to the regulation of all earthly things: not only by the revolution of the seasons does he bring to perfection the embryo of animals, the buds of plants, the spring of waters, and the alteration of bodies, but by his daily progress also he operates other changes in light, heat, moisture, dryness and cold; dependent upon his situation with regard to the zenith.

The Moon, being of all the heavenly bodies the nearest to the Earth, also dispenses much influence; and things animate and inanimate sympathize and vary with her. By the changes of her illumination, rivers swell and are reduced; the tides of the sea are ruled by her risings and settings; and plants and animals are expanded or collapsed, if not entirely at least partially, as she waxes or wanes.

The stars likewise (as well the fixed stars as the planets), in performing their revolutions, produce many impressions on the Ambient. They cause heats, winds, and storms, to the influence of which earthly things are conformably subjected.

And, further, the mutual configurations of all these heavenly bodies, by commingling the influence with which each is separately invested, produce a multiplicity of changes. The power of the Sun however predominates, because it is more generally distributed; the others either co-operate with his power or diminish its effect: the Moon more frequently and more plainly performs this at her conjunction, at her first and last quarter, and at her opposition: the stars act also to a similar purpose, but at longer intervals and more obscurely than the Moon; and their operation principally depends upon the mode of their visibility, their occultation and their declination.

From these premises it follows not only that all bodies, which may be already compounded, are subjected to the motion of the stars, but also that the impregnation and growth of the seeds from which all bodies proceed, are framed and moulded by the quality existing in the Ambient at the time of such impregnation and growth. And it is upon this principle that the more observant husbandmen and shepherds are accustomed, by drawing their inferences from the particular breezes which may happen at seed-time and at the impregnation of their cattle, to form predictions as to the quality of the expected produce. In short, however unlearned in the philosophy of nature, these men can foretell, solely by their previous observation, all the more general and usual effects which result from the plainer and more visible configurations of the Sun, Moon, and stars. It is daily seen that even most illiterate persons, with no other aid than their own experienced observation, are capable of predicting events which may be consequent on the more extended influence of the Sun and the more simple order of the Ambient, and which may not be open to variation by any complex configurations of the Moon and stars towards the Sun. There are, moreover, among the brute creation, animals who evidently form prognostication, and use this wonderful instinct at the changes of the several seasons of the year, spring, summer, autumn, and winter; and, also, at the changes of the wind.

In producing the changes of the seasons, the Sun itself is chiefly the operating and visible cause. There are, however, other events which, although they are not indicated in so simple a manner, but dependent on a slight complication of causes in the Ambient, are also foreknown by persons who have applied their observation to that end. Of this kind, are tempests and gales of wind, produced by certain aspects of the Moon, or the fixed stars, towards the Sun, according to their several courses, and the approach of which is usually foreseen by mariners. At the same time, prognostication made by persons of this class must be frequently fallacious, owing to their deficiency in science and their consequent inability to give necessary consideration to the time and place, or to the revolutions of the planets; all which circumstances, when exactly defined and understood, certainly tend towards accurate foreknowledge.

When, therefore, a thorough knowledge of the motions of the stars, and of the Sun and Moon, shall have been acquired, and when the situation of the place, the time, and all the configurations actually existing at that place and time, shall also be duly known; and such knowledge be yet further improved by an acquaintance with the natures of the heavenly bodies—not of what they are composed, but of the effective influences they possess; as, for instance, that heat is the property of the Sun, and moisture of the Moon, and that other peculiar properties respectively appertain to the rest of them;—when all these qualifications for prescience may be possessed by any individual, there seems no obstacle to deprive him of the insight, offered at once by nature and his own judgment, into the effects arising out of the quality of all the various influences compounded together. So that he will thus be competent to predict the peculiar constitution of the atmosphere in every season, as, for instance, with regard to its greater heat or moisture, or other similar qualities; all which may be foreseen by the visible position or configuration of the stars and the Moon towards the Sun.

Since it is thus clearly practicable, by an accurate knowledge of the points above enumerated, to make predictions concerning the proper quality of the seasons, there also seems no impediment to the formation of similar prognostication concerning the destiny and disposition of every human being. For by the constitution of the Ambient, even at the time of any individual's primary conformation, the general quality of that individual's temperament may be perceived; and the corporeal shape and mental capacity with which the person will be endowed at birth may be pronounced; as well as the favourable and unfavourable events indicated by the state of the Ambient, and liable to attend the individual at certain future periods; since, for instance, an event dependent on one disposition of the Ambient will be advantageous to a particular temperament, and that resulting from another unfavourable and injurious. From these circumstances, and others of similar import, the possibility of prescience is certainly evident.

There are, however, some plausible assailants of this doctrine, whose attacks although greatly misapplied seem yet worthy of the following observations.

In the first place, the science demands the greatest study and a constant attention to a multitude of different points; and as all persons who are but imperfectly practised in it must necessarily commit frequent mistakes, it has been supposed that even such events as have been truly predicted have taken place by chance only, and not from any operative cause in nature. But it should be remembered that these mistakes arise, not from any deficiency or want of power in the science itself, but from the incompetency of unqualified persons who pretend to exercise it. And, besides this, the majority of the persons who set themselves up as professors of this science, avail themselves of its name and credit for the sake of passing off some other mode of divination; by that means defrauding the ignorant, and pretending to foretell many things which from their nature cannot possibly be foreknown; and consequently affording opportunities to more intelligent people to impugn the value even of such predictions as can rationally be made. The reproach, however, thus brought upon the science is wholly unmerited; for it would be equally just to condemn all other branches of philosophy, because each numbers among its professors some mischievous pretenders.

Secondly, it is not attempted to be denied that any individual, although he may have attained to the greatest possible accuracy in the science, must still be liable to frequent error, arising out of the very nature of his undertaking, and from the weakness of his limited capacity in comparison with the magnitude of his object. For the whole theory of the quality of matter is supported by inference rather than by positive and scientific proof; and this is caused principally by the concretion of its temperament out of a multitude of dissimilar ingredients. And, although the former configurations of the planets have been observed to produce certain consequences (which have been adapted to configurations now taking place), and are, after long periods, and in a greater or less degree, resembled by subsequent configurations, yet these subsequent configurations never become exactly similar to those which have preceded them. For an entire return of all the heavenly bodies to the exact situation in which they have once stood with regard to the earth will never take place, or at least not in any period determinable by human calculation, whatever vain attempts may be made to acquire such unattainable knowledge. The examples referred to for guidance being therefore not exactly similar to the existing cases to which they are now applied, it must naturally follow that predictions are sometimes not borne out by the events. Hence arises the sole difficulty in the consideration of events produced by the Ambient. For no other concurrent cause has been hitherto combined with the motion of the heavenly bodies; although the doctrine of nativities, particularly that part of it relating to peculiar individual temperament, demands also the consideration of other concomitant causes, which are neither trifling nor unimportant, but essentially potent in affecting the individual properties of the creatures born. Thus the variety in seed has the chief influence in supplying the peculiar quality of each species; for, under the same disposition of the Ambient and of the horizon, each various kind of seed prevails in determining the distinct formation of its own proper species; thus man is born, or the horse is foaled; and by the same law are brought forth all the other various creatures and productions of the earth. It is also to be remembered, that considerable variations are caused in all creatures by the respective places where they may be brought forth: for although, under the same disposition of the Ambient, the germs of the future creatures may be of one species, whether human or of the horse, the difference in situation, of the places in which they are generated, produces a dissimilarity in the body and spirit of one from the body and spirit of another: and in addition to this it must be considered that different modes of nurture, and the variety of ranks, manners, and customs, contribute to render the course of life of one individual greatly different from that of another; consequently, unless every one of these varieties be duly blended with the causes arising in the Ambient, the prejudgment of any event will doubtless be very incomplete. For, although the greatest multiplicity of power exists in the Ambient, and although all other things act as concurrent causes in union with it, and can never claim it as a concurrent cause in subservience to them, there will still, nevertheless, be a great deficiency in predictions attempted to be made by means of the heavenly motions alone, without regard to the other concurrent causes just now adverted to.

Under these circumstances, it would seem judicious neither to deny altogether the practicability of prescience, because prognostications thus imperfectly derived are sometimes liable to be fallacious; nor, on the other hand, to admit that all events, whatever, are open to previous inquiry; as if such inquiry could in all cases be securely conducted without having recourse to mere inference, and as if it were not limited by the narrow extent of mere human abilities. The art of navigation, for instance, is not rejected, although it is in many points incomplete; therefore the bare fact that predictions are frequently imperfect cannot authorise the rejection of the art of prescience: the magnitude of its scope, and the faint resemblance that it bears to a divine attribute, should rather demand grateful commendations, and receive the utmost regard and attention. And, since no weakness is imputed to a physician, because he inquires into the individual habit of his patient, as well as into the nature of the disease, no imputation can justly attach to the professor of prognostication, because he combines the consideration of species, nurture, education and country, with that of the motion of the heavens: for as the physician acts but reasonably, in thus considering the proper constitution of the sick person as well as his disease; so, in forming predictions, it must surely be justifiably allowable to comprehend in that consideration every other thing connected with the subject in addition to the motion of the heavens, and to collect and compare with that motion all other co-operating circumstances arising elsewhere.

*   *   *   *

Chapter 4. The Influences of the Planetary Orbs

The Sun is found to produce heat and moderate dryness. His magnitude, and the changes which he so evidently makes in the seasons, render his power more plainly perceptible than that of the other heavenly bodies; since his approach to the zenith of any part of the earth creates a greater degree of heat in that part and proportionately disposes its inhabitants after his own nature.

The Moon principally generates moisture; her proximity to the earth renders her highly capable of exciting damp vapours, and of thus operating sensibly upon animal bodies by relaxation and putrefaction. She has, however, also a moderate share in the production of heat, in consequence of the illumination she receives from the Sun.

Saturn produces cold and dryness, for he is most remote both from the Sun's heat and from the earth's vapours. But he is more effective in the production of cold than of dryness. And he and the rest of the planets derive their energy from the positions which they hold with regard to the Sun and Moon; and they are all seen to alter the constitution of the Ambient in various ways.

Mars chiefly causes dryness, and is also strongly heating, by means of his own fiery nature, which is indicated by his colour, and in consequence of his vicinity to the Sun; the sphere of which is immediately below him.

Jupiter revolves in an intermediate sphere between the extreme cold of Saturn and the burning heat of Mars, and has consequently a temperate influence: he therefore at once promotes both warmth and moisture. But, owing to the spheres of Mars and the Sun, which lie beneath him, his warmth is predominant: and hence he produces fertilizing breezes.

To Venus also the same temperate quality belongs, although it exists conversely; since the heat she produces by her vicinity to the Sun is not so great as the moisture which she generates by the magnitude of her light, and by appropriating to herself the moist vapours of the earth, in the same manner that the Moon does.

Mercury sometimes produces dryness, and at other times moisture, and each with equal vigour. His faculty of absorbing moisture and creating dryness proceeds from his situation with regard to the Sun, from which he is at no time far distant in longitude; and, on the other hand, he produces moisture, because he borders upon the Moon's sphere, which is nearest to the earth; and, being thus excited by the velocity of his motion with the Sun, he consequently operates rapid changes tending to produce alternately either quality.

Chapter 5. Benefics and Malefics

Of the four temperaments or qualities above mentioned, two are nutritive and prolific, viz. heat and moisture; by these all matter coalesces and is nourished: the other two are noxious and destructive, viz. dryness and cold; by these all matter is decayed and dissipated.

Therefore, two of the planets, on account of their temperate quality, and because heat and moisture are predominant in them, are considered by the ancients as benefic, or causers of good: these are Jupiter and Venus. And the Moon also is so considered for the same reasons.

But Saturn and Mars are esteemed of a contrary nature, and malefic, or causers of evil: the first from his excess of cold, the other from his excess of dryness.

The Sun and Mercury are deemed of common influence, and productive either of good or evil in unison with whatever planets they may be connected with.

Chapter 6. Masculine and Feminine

There are two primary sexes, male and female; and the female sex partakes chiefly of moisture. The Moon and Venus are therefore said to be feminine, since their qualities are principally moist.

The Sun, Saturn, Jupiter, and Mars are called masculine. Mercury is common to both genders, because at certain times he produces dryness, and at others moisture, and performs each in an equal ratio.

The stars, however, are also said to be masculine and feminine, by their positions with regard to the Sun. While they are matutine and preceding the Sun, they are masculine; when vespertine and following the Sun, they become feminine.

And they are further regulated in this respect by their positions with regard to the horizon. From the ascendants to the mid-heaven, or from the angle of the west to the lower heaven, they are considered to be masculine, being then oriental: and in the other two quadrants, feminine, being then occidental.

*   *   *   *

BOOK II

Chapter 1. General Division of the Subject

The great and leading points, requiring to be attended to as a necessary means of introduction to the consideration of particular predictions, having been succinctly defined, the further parts of the subject, comprehending everything which may tend to facilitate prediction, and render it complete, shall now be duly proceeded in; and, at the same time, care shall be taken to confine the whole doctrine within the limits of natural reason.

The foreknowledge to be acquired by means of Astrology is to be regarded in two great and principal divisions. The first, which may be properly called General, or Universal, concerns entire nations, countries, or cities; and the second, denominated Particular, or Genethliacal, relates to men individually.

In considering these respective divisions, it seems proper to give priority to that which has the more general application and influence: because, in the first place, general events are produced by causes greater and more compulsatory than the causes of particular events; secondly, because natures of more extended potency must invariably control those which are more limited in action; and, thirdly, because particular events, or individual affections, are comprehended in those of general influence. It is therefore especially necessary, in desiring to investigate particular events, to treat first of those which are general.

Again, general events are subdivided according to their operation upon entire countries, and upon certain cities or districts: one subdivision being regarded as affecting entire countries, and the other certain cities or districts only. They are also separately considered according to the causes by which they are produced; war, pestilence, famine, earthquakes, inundations, and other similar visitations being dependent on such greater and more important causes, as arise only after considerable periods; while slighter causes, arising more frequently, have reference only to the revolution of the seasons; their greater or less variation in cold and heat; the severity or mildness of the weather; the occasional abundance or scarcity of provisions; and other like occurrences.

Hence the consideration of those events which concern whole countries, and are dependent on the greater causes (since it has a more extended scope than the other, which attaches only to certain cities, or districts, and is subject to slighter causes) takes precedence. And, for its due investigation, two essential points are to be attended to: the first is, the appropriate familiarity of the zodiacal signs and the fixed stars with the several regions which may be concerned; and the second comprises the indications occasionally arising in those parts of the heavens where such familiarity is found: for instance, the eclipses of the Sun and Moon, and such transits as may be made by the planets, when matutine, and in their respective stations.

The nature of the sympathy between these things must, however, be explained first; and a brief description will therefore be given of the chief peculiarities observable in whole nations; in regard to their manners and customs, as well as to their bodily formation and temperament; considered agreeably to their familiarity with those stars and signs whence the natural cause of their peculiarities duly proceeds.

Chapter 2. *Peculiarities Observable Throughout Every Entire Climate*

The peculiarities of all nations are distinguished according to entire parallels and entire angles, and by their situation with regard to the Sun and the Ecliptic.

The climate which we inhabit is situated in one of the Northern Quadrants: but other nations, which lie under more southern parallels, that is to say, in the space between the equinoctial line and the summer tropic, have the Sun in their zenith, and are continually scorched by it. They are consequently black in complexion, and have thick and curled hair. They are, moreover, ugly in person, of contracted stature, hot in disposition, and fierce in manners, in consequence of the incessant heats to which they are exposed; and they are called by the common name of Æthiopians. But the human race does not alone afford evidence of the violent heat in these regions; it is shown also by all other animals and by the state of the surrounding atmosphere.

The natives of those countries which lie under the more remote northern parallels (that is to say, under the Arctic circle and beyond it) have their zenith far distant from the zodiac and the Sun's heat. Their constitutions, therefore, abound in cold, and are also highly imbued with moisture, which is in itself a most nutritive quality, and, in these latitudes, is not exhausted by heat: hence they are fair in complexion, with straight hair, of large bodies and full stature. They are cold in disposition, and wild in manners, owing to the constant cold. The state of the surrounding atmosphere and of animals and plants, corresponds with that of men; who (as natives of these countries) are designated by the general name of Scythians.

The nations situated between the summer tropic and the Arctic circle, having the meridian Sun neither in their zenith nor yet far remote from it, enjoy a well-tempered atmosphere. This favourable temperature, however, still undergoes variation, and changes alternatively from heat to cold; but the variation is never vast nor violent. The people who enjoy this kindly atmosphere are consequently of proportionate stature and complexion, and of good natural disposition: they live not in a state of dispersion, but dwell together in societies, and are civilised in their habits. Among the nations comprehended in this division, those verging towards the south are more industrious and ingenious than the others, and more adapted to the sciences: and these qualifications are engendered in them by the vicinity of the zodiac to their zenith, and by the familiarity thus subsisting between them and the planets moving in the zodiac, which familiarly gives activity and an intellectual impulse to their minds. Again, the natives of those countries which lie towards the east excel in courage, acting boldly and openly under all circumstances; for in all their characteristics they are principally conformed to the Sun's nature, which is oriental, diurnal, masculine and dexter—(and it is plainly apparent that the dexter parts of all animals are much stronger than others)—hence results the greater courage of the inhabitants of the East. And as the Moon, on her first appearance after conjunction, is always seen in the west, the western parts are therefore lunar, and consequently feminine and sinister, whence it follows that the inhabitants of the west are milder, more effeminate and reserved.

Thus, in all countries, certain respective peculiarities exist in regard to manners, customs and laws; and in each it is found that some portion of the inhabitants differ partially and individually from the usual habits and condition of their race. These variations arise similarly to the variations perceptible in the condition of the atmosphere; as in all countries, the general state of whose atmosphere may be either hot or cold, or temperate, certain districts are found to possess a particular temperature of their own, and to be more or less hot, or cold, by being more or less elevated than the general face of the country. So, likewise certain people become navigators owing to their proximity to the sea while others are equestrian, because their country is a plain; and others again, become domiciliated by the fertility of their soil.

And thus, in each particular climate, certain peculiar qualities are to be found, arising from the natural familiarity which it holds with the stars and the twelve signs. And although these qualities do not pervade it, in such a manner as to be necessarily exhibited by every individual native, yet they are so far generally distributed as to be of much utility in investigating particular events; and it is highly important to take at least a brief notice of them.

Chapter 3. The Familiarity of the Regions of the Earth with the Triplicities and the Planets

It has been already stated that there are four triplicities distinguishable in the zodiac. The first, composed of Aries, Leo, and Sagittarius, is the north-west triplicity; and Jupiter has chief dominion over it on behalf of its northern proportion; but Mars also rules with him in reference to the west. The second, consisting of Taurus, Virgo, and Capricorn, is the south-east; and in this triplicity Venus bears chief rule, in consequence of the southern proportion; but Saturn also governs with her in consideration of the east. The third, composed of Gemini, Libra, and Aquarius, is north-east; and Saturn is here the principal lord, in consequence of the eastern proportion; Jupiter, however, governs with him in reference to the north. The fourth triplicity is constituted of Cancer, Scorpio, and Pisces, and is south-west; it owns Mars as its principal ruler, in consideration of its western proportion; and, on behalf of the south, it is also governed by Venus.

The four triplicities being thus established, the whole inhabited earth is accordingly divided into four parts, agreeing with the number of the triplicities. It is divided latitudinally by the line of the Mediterranean Sea, from the Straits of Hercules to the Issican Gulf, continued onwards through the mountainous ridge extending towards the east; and by this latitudinal division its southern and northern parts are defined. Its longitudinal division is made by the line of the Arabian Gulf, the Ægean Sea, Pontus, and the lake Mæotis; and by this line are separated its eastern and western parts.

Of the four quadrants of the earth, thus agreeing in number with the four triplicities, one is situated in the north-west of the entire earth, and contains Celto-galatia; or, as it is commonly called, Europe. Opposed to this quadrant lies that of the south-east, towards Eastern Æthiopia; it is called the southern part of Asia Magna. Another quadrant of the entire earth is in the north-east, about Scythia, and is called the northern part of Asia Magna. To this is opposed the quadrant of the south-west, which lies about Western Æthiopia, and is known by the general name of Libya.

Each of these quadrants contains certain parts, which, in comparison with its other parts, lie more contiguous to the middle of the earth; and these parts, in respect of the quadrant to which they belong, have a situation opposite to the rest of that quadrant, in the same manner as that quadrant itself is situated in regard to the rest of the earth. For instance, in the quadrant of Europe, which is situated on the north-west of the whole earth, those parts of it which lie towards the middle of the earth, and near the angles of the other quadrants, are manifestly situated in the south-east of that quadrant. The like rule obtains in regard to the other quadrants. And hence it is evident that each quadrant is in familiarity with two oppositely-placed triplicities, its whole extent being adapted to the one triplicity which governs it as an entire quadrant; but its particular parts, situated about the middle of the earth, and lying, as regards the rest of the quadrant, in a direction contrary to that assigned to the whole quadrant altogether, being adapted to the other triplicity which rules the particular quadrant lying opposite to it. The planets exercising dominion in both these triplicities also hold familiarity with these particular parts; but, with the other more remote parts of any quadrant, only those planets hold familiarity which rule in the single triplicity to which the whole quadrant is allotted. With the said particular parts about the middle of the earth, Mercury also, as well as the other planets in dominion, bears familiarity, in consideration of his meditative condition and common nature.

Under this arrangement, it follows that the north-western parts of the first quadrant, or that of Europe, are in familiarity with the north-west triplicity, composed of Aries, Leo, and Sagittarius; and they are accordingly governed by the lords of that triplicity, Jupiter and Mars, vespertine. These parts, as distinguished by their appropriation to entire nations, are Britain, Galatia, Germany, Barsania, Italy, Apulia, Sicily, Gaul, Tuscany, Celtica, and Spain. And, since the triplicity itself and the planets connected with it in dominion are adapted to command, the natives of these countries are consequently impatient of restraint, lovers of freedom, warlike, industrious, imperious, cleanly, and high-minded. But, owing to the vespertine configuration of Jupiter and Mars, as well as the masculine condition of the anterior parts of the triplicity, and the feminine condition of its latter parts, the said nations regard women with scorn and indifference. They are, however, still careful of the community, brave and faithful, affectionate in their families, and perform good and kind actions.

Among the countries before named, Britain, Galatia, Germany, and Barsania have a greater share of familiarity with Aries and Mars; and their inhabitants are accordingly wilder, bolder, and more ferocious. Italy, Apulia, Sicily, and Gaul are in familiarity with Leo and the Sun; and the natives of these countries are more imperious, yet kind and benevolent, and careful of the commonwealth. Tuscany, Celtica, and Spain, are connected with Sagittarius and Jupiter; and their inhabitants are lovers of freedom, simplicity, and elegance.

The south-eastern parts of this quadrant, which are situated towards the middle of the earth, viz. Thrace, Macedonia, Illyria, Hellas, Achaia, and Crete, as well as the Cyclad Isles and the shores of Asia Minor and of Cyprus, assume, in addition, a connection with the south-east triplicity, which is composed of Taurus, Virgo, and Capricorn, and ruled by Venus and Saturn; and, in consequence of the vicinity of these regions to the middle of the earth, Mercury likewise has a proportionate dominion over them. Hence their inhabitants, being subjected to the rulers of both triplicities, enjoy a favourable temperament of mind and of body. From Mars they imbibe their fitness for command, their courage, and impatience of restraint; from Jupiter their love of freedom, their self-rule, their skill in guiding public affairs, and in legislation: through the influence of Venus they are also lovers of the arts and sciences, as well as of music and poetry, of public shows, and all the refinements of life; and from Mercury they deduce their hospitality, their fondness for society and communion, their love of equity and of literature, and their power of eloquence. They are also in the highest degree conversant with sacred mysteries, owing to the vespertine figuration of Venus.

It is further to be observed of these last-named countries, that the inhabitants of the Cyclad Isles, and of the shores of Asia Minor and of Cyprus, are more particularly under the influence of Taurus and Venus, and are therefore voluptuous, fond of elegance, and over-studious in their attention to the body. The people of Hellas, Achaia, and Crete, have a stronger familiarity with Virgo and Mercury, and are therefore learned and scientific, preferring the cultivation of the mind to the care of the body. The people of Macedonia, Thrace, and Illyria, are chiefly influenced by Capricorn and Saturn; whence they are greedy of wealth, inferior in civilization, and have no ordinances of civil polity. . . .

The remaining quadrant is the vast tract known by the general name of Libya. Its several parts, distinguished by the particular names of Numidia, Carthage, Africa. Phazania, Nasamonitis, Garamantica, Mauritania, Getulia, and Metagonitis, are situated in the south-west of the entire earth, and have due familiarity with the south-west triplicity, composed of Cancer, Scorpio, and Pisces; their rulers therefore are Mars and Venus, in vespertine position. From this figuration of the planets it results that the dwellers in these regions are doubly governed by a man and a woman, who are both children of the same mother; the man rules the males, and the woman the females. They are extremely hot in constitution, and desirous of women; their marriages are usually made by violence, and in many districts the local princes first enjoy the brides of their subjects: in some places, however, the women are common to all. The influence of Venus causes the whole people to delight in personal ornaments, and in being arrayed in female attire: nevertheless, that of Mars renders them courageous, crafty, addicted to magic, and fearless of dangers.

Again, however, of the above-named countries, Numidia, Carthage, and Africa, are more particularly in familiarity with Cancer and the Moon: their inhabitants, consequently, live in community, attend to mercantile pursuits, and enjoy abundantly all the blessings of nature. The natives of Metagonitis, Mauritania, and Getulia, are influenced by Scorpio and Mars, and are consequently ferocious and pugnacious in the highest degree; eaters of human flesh, utterly indifferent to danger, and so regardless and prodigal of blood, as to slay each other without hesitation on the slightest cause. The people in Phazania, Nasamonitis, and Garamantica, are connected with Pisces and Jupiter, and are accordingly frank and simple in manners, fond of employment, well disposed, fond of the decencies of life, and for the most part, free and unrestrained in their actions: they worship Jupiter by the name of Ammon.

The other parts of this quadrant, which lies near the middle of the entire earth, are Cyrenaica, Marmarica, Ægypt, Thebais, Oasis, Troglo-dytica, Arabia, Azania, and Middle Æthiopia. These countries, being situated in the north-east of their quadrant, have due familiarity with the north-east triplicity (consisting of Gemini, Libra, and Aquarius), and are governed by Saturn and Jupiter, and also by Mercury. Their inhabi-tants, therefore, participate in the influence of all the five planets in vespertine figuration, and consequently cherish due love and reverence for the gods, and dedicate themselves to their service. They are addicted to sepulchral ceremonies; and, owing to the said vespertine position, they bury their dead in the earth, and remove them from the public eye. They use various laws and customs, and worship divers gods. In a state of subjection, they are submissive, cowardly, abject, and most patient; but when they command, they are brave, generous, and high-minded. Polygamy is frequent among them, and practised by the women as well as the men: they are most licentious in sexual intercourse, and allow incestuous commerce between brothers and sisters. Both men and women are extraordinarily prolific, and correspond in this respect with the fecundity of their soil. Many of the men are, however, effeminate and debased in mind; in consequence of the figuration of the malefics, together with the vespertine position of Venus; and some of them mutilate their persons. . . .

BOOK III

Chapter 1

In the preceding pages, such events as effect the world generally have been discussed in priority; because they are operated by certain principal and paramount causes, which are, at the same time, predominant over particular and minor events applicable only to the separate properties and natural peculiarities of individuals. The foreknowledge of these particular events is called Genethlialogy, or the science of Nativities.

It must be remembered that the causation, by which all effects, whether general or particular, are produced and foreknown, is essentially one and the same; for the motions of the planets, and of the Sun and Moon, present the operative causation of events which happen to any individual, as well as of those which happen generally; and the fore-knowledge of both may be obtained by the several creatures and sub-stances, subjected to the influence of the heavenly bodies, and by due attention to the changes produced in those natures, by the configurations displayed in the Ambient by the planetary motion.

Still, however, the causes of general events are greater and more complete than those of particular events; and, although it has been now stated, that one single identical power supplies both the causation and the foreknowledge of general as well as particular events, yet there does not belong to the two sorts of events a similar origin or beginning, at which observation of the celestial configurations must be made, for prognostication. In regard to general events, the dates of origin and commencement are many and various; for all general events cannot be traced to one origin, neither is their origin always considered by means of the matter subjected to their operation, for it may be also established by circumstances occurring in the Ambient and presenting the causation. It may, in fact, almost be said that they all originate in eminent eclipses of the Luminaries, and in remarkable transits made by the stars, at various times.

Particular events, however, which concern men individually, may be traced to one origin, single as well as manifold. Their origin is single, in respect to the primary composition of the nascent man; but it is also manifold, in respect to other circumstances subsequently indicated by dispositions in the Ambient, correlative to the primary origin. In all particular events, the origin, or birth, of the subjected matter itself, must, of course, be the primary origin; and, in succession thereto, the various beginnings of other subsequent circumstances are to be assumed. Hence, therefore, at the origin of the subjected matter, all the properties and peculiarities of its contemperament must be observed; and then the subsequent events, which will happen at certain periods, sooner or later, are to be considered by means of the division of time, or the scale of the ensuing years.

*   *   *   *

Chapter 4. Distribution of the Doctrine of Nativities

After due attention to the preceding instructions, the doctrine of genethliacal prognostication should be separately and distinctly considered, for the sake of order and perspicuity, in its first, second and successive divisions or heads of inquiry. It will thus be found to present a mode of investigation, at once practicable, competent and agreeable to nature.

One division is applicable only to certain circumstances established previously to the birth; as, for instance, to those which concern the parents; another to circumstances, which may be established both before and after the birth; as those respecting brothers and sisters; another to circumstances actually occurring at the very time of birth, and immediately consequent thereupon: and this head of inquiry embraces various points, and is by no means simple: and the last division relates to events liable to take place after the birth, at various periods, earlier or later; and it involves a still more diversified theory.

Thus, the questions to be solved, in regard to the actual circumstances of the birth itself, are, whether the production will be male or female; twins, or even more; whether it will be monstrous; and whether it will be reared.

The questions of the periods subsequent to the birth relate first to the duration of life (which is distinct from the question of rearing), then to the shape and figure of the body, to the bodily affections, and to injuries or defects in the members. After these, further inquiry is instituted as to the quality of the mind, and the mental affections; then, as to fortune, in regard to rank and honours as well as wealth. In succession to these, the character of the employment or profession is sought out; then, the questions relative to marriage and offspring, and to consentaneous friendship, are to be considered; then, that concerning travel; and, lastly, that concerning the kind of death which awaits the native. The question of death, although depending, in fact, upon the same influence as the question of the duration of life, seems yet to find its proper situation in being placed last in the series.

On each of the foregoing points of inquiry, the doctrine and precepts to be followed shall be thoroughly and succinctly detailed; but all idle conceits, promulgated by many persons without any foundation capable of sustaining the test of reason, shall be utterly avoided, in deference to the only true agency, which is derived from primal Nature herself. It is only upon clearly effective influences that this treatise is established: and all matters, which are open to an authorized mode of inquiry by means of the theory of the stars, and their positions and aspects with regard to appropriate places, shall be fully discussed here; but the divination by lots and numbers, unregulated by any systematic causation, must remain unnoticed.

The brief remarks, immediately following, are applicable to all cases generally, and are now at once stated, to avoid the repetition of them, under each particular division or head of inquiry.

Firstly, notice must be taken of that place in the zodiac which corresponds, according to the scheme of the nativity with the particular division of inquiry; for example, the place of the mid-heaven is adapted to questions comprised under the head of employment or profession; and the Sun's place to those relative to the concerns of the father.

Secondly, after the proper place has thus been duly ascertained, the planets holding right of dominion there, by any of the five prerogatives hereinbefore mentioned, are to be observed; and, if any one planet be found to be lord by all these prerogatives, that planet must be admitted as the ruler of the event liable to happen under that particular head of inquiry. If, however, two or three planets hold dominion, that one among them, which may have most claims to the place in question, must be selected as the ruler.

Thirdly, the natures of the ruling planet and of the signs, in which itself and the place which it thus controls may severally be situated, are to be considered as indicating the quality of the event.

Fourthly, the proportionate vigour and strength, or weakness, with which the dominion is exercised, as exhibited either by the actual cosmical position of the ruling planet, or by its position in the scheme of the nativity, will point out to what extent and with what force the event will operate. And a planet is found to be cosmically powerful when in one of its own places, or when oriental, or swift in course; and it is strong in the scheme of the nativity, when transiting an angle or succedent house; especially those of the ascendant, or of the mid-heaven. But it is cosmically weaker, when not in one of its own places; or when occidental, or retarded in its course; and in respect to the scheme of the nativity, it is weak when cadent from the angles.

Lastly, the general time, about which the event will take place, is to be inferred from the ruling planet's matutine or vespertine position, in regard to the Sun and the ascendant, and from the circumstances of its being situated in an angle, or a succedent house. As, if it be matutine, or in an angle, its influence operates earlier and more promptly; but, if vespertine or in a succedent house, later and more tardily. And, in reference to this point, the quadrant which precedes the Sun, and that which precedes the ascendant, together with the quadrants opposite to these, are oriental and matutine; and the other quadrants, following the former, are occidental and vespertine.

*   *   *   *

Chapter 7. Male or Female

After the indications which regard brothers and sisters have been investigated by the foregoing rules, consonant with nature and reason the actual native, or the person to whom the scheme of nativity is specially appropriated, demands attention; and the first and most obvious inquiry is whether the said native will be male or female.

The consideration of this question rests not on a single basis, nor can it be pursued in one sole direction only: it depends, on the contrary, upon the several situations of the two luminaries and the ascendant, and upon such planets as possess any prerogatives in the places of those situations; and all these circumstances should be specially observed at the time of conception, and, in a general manner also, at that of birth.

Observation of the said three places, and of the mode in which the planets ruling them may be constituted, is wholly indispensable: it must be seen whether all, or most of them, may be constituted masculinely or femininely; and prediction must, of course, be regulated in conformity with their disposition, so observed; as tending to produce a male or female birth.

The masculine or feminine nature of the stars is to be distinguished in the manner already pointed out in the commencement of this treatise. For instance, by the nature of the signs in which they are situated, by their relative position to each other, and also by their position towards the earth; as when in the east, they are masculinely disposed, and, when in the west, femininely. Their relative position to the Sun also affords guidance in distinguishing them; since, if they should be matutine, they are considered to signify the male gender; and if vespertine, the female. Thus, from the sex chiefly prevalent, as observed by these rules, that of the native may be rationally inferred.

Chapter 8. Twins

With respect to the probability of the birth of twins, or a greater number at once, the same places must be observed, as those mentioned in the preceding chapter; that is to say, the places of both luminaries and the ascendant.

When two, or all three, of the said places may be situated in bicorporeal signs, births of this kind will occur, in consequence of the combination which then arises; especially, provided all the planets, which control those places, should also be similarly circumstanced: or although only some of them be posited in bicorporeal signs, while the rest may be placed by two or more together. Because even more than twins will be born, in a case wherein all the ruling places may be in bicorporeal signs, most of the planets being, at the same time, posited in the same way, and configurated with them. The number of children, however, to be produced at the birth, is to be inferred from the planet which exercises the right of determining the number: and the sex or sexes are to be predicted by means of the planets in configuration with the Sun, Moon, and ascendant.

And, should the position of the heavens be arranged so that the angle of the mid-heaven, and not that of the ascendant, may be connected with the luminaries, there will, in that case, be produced, almost always, twins; and sometimes even more.

To speak, however, more particularly, three males will be born, as in the nativity of the Anactores, when Saturn, Jupiter, and Mars may be configurated with the places before appointed, in bicorporeal signs; and three females, as in the nativity of the Graces, when Venus and the Moon, with Mercury femininely constituted, may be configurated in like manner. When Saturn, Jupiter, and Venus may be configurated, two males and one female will be born; as in the nativity of the Dioscuri; and, when Venus, the Moon, and Mars may be so configurated, two females and one male; as in the nativity of Ceres, Core, and Liber.

In cases of this kind, however, it most usually happens that the conception has not been complete, and that the children are born with some remarkable imperfections or deformities. And, in some instances, owing to a certain concurrence of events, these numerous productions are quite extraordinary and amazing.

5

LUCRETIUS

The authority on the life of Lucretius is the Christian theologian and scholar Jerome, whose four lines written five centuries later constitute the poet's biography. Lucretius' life fell during the climactic period of Roman history when the tensions born of successful conquest plunged the state into civil conflicts that signalled the demise of the republic. Born apparently in 94 B.C., he lived about forty years and died in 55 B.C. Jerome, who was motivated perhaps by a theological animus, adds that Lucretius was made insane by a love potion, wrote during his lucid periods (a considerable concession on Jerome's part), and died by his own hand. In the history of science, Lucretius occupies a unique position for having successfully subdued the intractable matter of natural philosophy to the aesthetic demands of poetry. To recognition as a significant scientist he has no claim; his philosophy was not his own creation but the borrowed work of others. As a poet, on the other hand, Lucretius belongs to the small handful of distinguished poets that Rome produced, and his one surviving work, *On the Nature of Things* (*De Rerum Natura*), remains the immortal exposition of ancient atomism.

Practical Roman that he was, Lucretius looked upon natural philosophy, not as an end in itself, but as a means to an end. That end was ethical. Lucretius was convinced that religion is the principal obstacle to the good life. By proclaiming the existence of gods, who intervene from outside to shape and dominate human affairs, and the immortality of the soul, which renders a man subject to eternal torment, religion undermines the native dignity of man by filling him with terror. Lucretius set out to liberate men from the fears that torture them. He would prove that the soul is mortal, the gods (such as they are) indifferent to men, and the fears, therefore, without ground. Obviously, natural philosophy had a critical role to play in the fulfillment of such a program.

The particular philosophy to which Lucretius turned was atomism, originally a product of Greek speculation in the 5th century B.C., and more recently expounded by Epicurus. Atomism cannot be called a

107

typical philosophy of the ancient world and, following Lucretius, it disappeared from view for well over a thousand years until it was revived in the 17th century to exert a powerful influence on the modern conception of nature. One reason that it did not have more adherents in antiquity undoubtedly lay in its very acceptability for a program such as Lucretius'. Atomism must not be seen solely in a religious (or antireligious) context, however. It was a product of Greek metaphysical speculation addressed to the nature of ultimate reality, and it contended that the nature of things is radically different from the phenomena by which we know them. In contrast, Aristotle's philosophy expressed a conception of reality far more in harmony with the typical patterns of ancient thought. Much of the interest of atomism stems from its challenge to those patterns. In expressing a view of reality much closer to that of modern science, moreover, it helps by its very contrast to illuminate the fundamental assumptions of the ancient idea of nature.

5

On the Nature of Things

BOOK I

. . . When the life of man lay foul to see and grovelling upon the earth, crushed by the weight of religion, which showed her face from the realms of heaven, lowering upon mortals with dreadful mien, 'twas a man of Greece who dared first to raise his mortal eyes to meet her, and first to stand forth to meet her: him neither the stories of the gods nor thunderbolts checked, nor the sky with its revengeful roar, but all the more spurred the eager daring of his mind to yearn to be the first to burst through the close-set bolts upon the doors of nature. And so it was that the lively force of his mind won its way, and he passed on far beyond the fiery walls of the world, and in mind and spirit traversed the boundless whole; whence in victory he brings us tidings what can come to be and what cannot, yea and in what way each thing has its power limited, and its deepset boundary-stone. And so religion in revenge is cast beneath men's feet and trampled, and victory raises us to heaven.

Herein I have one fear, lest perchance you think that you are starting on the principles of some unholy reasoning, and setting foot upon the path of sin. Nay, but on the other hand, again and again our foe, religion, has given birth to deeds sinful and unholy. Even as at Aulis the chosen chieftains of the Danai, the first of all the host, foully stained with the blood of Iphianassa the altar of the Virgin of the Cross-Roads. For as soon as the band braided about her virgin locks streamed from her either cheek in equal lengths, as soon as she saw her sorrowing sire stand at the altar's side, and near him the attendants hiding their knives, and her countrymen shedding tears at the sight of her, tongue-tied with terror, sinking on her knees she fell to earth. Nor could it avail the luckless maid at such a time that she first had given the name of father to the king. For seized by men's hands, all trembling was she led to the altars, not that, when the ancient rite of sacrifice was fulfilled, she might be

---

Translated from the Latin by Cyril Bailey, Oxford: Clarendon Press, 1910.

escorted by the clear cry of "Hymen", but in the very moment of marriage, a pure victim she might foully fall, sorrowing beneath a father's
slaughtering stroke, that a happy and hallowed starting might be granted
to the fleet. Such evil deeds could religion prompt.

You yourself sometime vanquished by the fearsome threats of the
seer's sayings, will seek to desert from us. Nay indeed, how many a dream
may they even now conjure up before you, which might avail to overthrow your schemes of life, and confound in fear all your fortunes. And
justly so: for if men could see that there is a fixed limit to their sorrows,
then with some reason they might have the strength to stand against the
scruples of religion, and the threats of seers. As it is there is no means,
no power to withstand, since everlasting is the punishment they must
fear in death. For they know not what is the nature of the soul, whether
it is born or else finds its way into them at their birth, and again whether
it is torn apart by death and perishes with us, or goes to see the shades of
Orcus and his waste pools, or by the gods' will implants itself in other
breasts, as our own Ennius sang, who first bore down from pleasant
Helicon the wreath of deathless leaves, to win bright fame among the
tribes of Italian peoples. And yet despite this, Ennius sets forth in the
discourse of his immortal verse that there is besides a realm of Acheron,
where neither our souls nor bodies endure, but as it were images pale
in wondrous wise; and thence he tells that the form of Homer, ever
green and fresh, rose to him, and began to shed salt tears, and in converse to reveal the nature of things. Therefore we must both give good
account of the things on high, in what way the courses of sun and moon
come to be, and by what force all things are governed on earth, and also
before all else we must see by keen reasoning, whence comes the soul
and the nature of the mind, and what thing it is that meets us and
affrights our minds in waking life, when we are touched with disease, or
again when buried in sleep, so that we seem to see and hear hard by us
those who have met death, and whose bones are held in the embrace of
earth.

Nor does it pass unnoticed of my mind that it is a hard task in Latin
verses to set clearly in the light the dark discoveries of the Greeks, above
all when many things must be treated in new words, because of the pov-
erty of our tongue and the newness of the themes; yet your merit and
the pleasure of your sweet friendship, for which I hope, urge me to bear
the burden of any toil, and lead me on to watch through the calm nights,
searching by what words, yea and in what measures, I may avail to
spread before your mind a bright light, whereby you may see to the heart
of hidden things.

This terror then, this darkness of the mind, must needs be scattered not by the rays of the sun and the gleaming shafts of day, but by the outer view and the inner law of nature; whose first rule shall take its start for us from this, that nothing is ever begotten of nothing by divine will. Fear forsooth so constrains all mortal men, because they behold many things come to pass on earth and in the sky, the cause of whose working they can by no means see, and think that a divine power brings them about. Therefore, when we have seen that nothing can be created out of nothing, then more rightly after that shall we discern that for which we search, both whence each thing can be created, and in what way all things come to be without the aid of gods.

For if things came to being from nothing, every kind might be born from all things, nought would need a seed. First men might arise from the sea, and from the land the race of scaly creatures, and birds burst forth from the sky; cattle and other herds, and all the tribe of wild beasts, with no fixed law of birth, would haunt tilth and desert. Nor would the same fruits stay constant to the trees, but all would change: all trees might avail to bear all fruits. Why, were there not bodies to bring each thing to birth, how could things have a fixed unchanging mother? But as it is, since all things are produced from fixed seeds, each thing is born and comes forth into the coasts of light, out of that which has in it the substance and first-bodies of each; and 'tis for this cause that all things cannot be begotten of all, because in fixed things there dwells a power set apart. Or again, why do we see the roses in spring, and the corn in summer's heat, and the vines bursting out when autumn summons them, if it be not that when, in their own time, the fixed seeds of things have flowed together, then is disclosed each thing that comes to birth, while the season is at hand, and the lively earth in safety brings forth the fragile things into the coasts of light? But if they sprang from nothing, suddenly would they arise at uncertain intervals and in hostile times of year, since indeed there would be no first-beginnings which might be kept apart from creative union at an ill-starred season. Nay more, there would be no need for lapse of time for the increase of things upon the meeting of the seed, if they could grow from nothing. For little children would grow suddenly to youths, and at once trees would come forth, leaping from the earth. But of this it is well seen that nothing comes to pass, since all things grow slowly, as is natural, from a fixed seed, and as they grow preserve their kind: so that you can know that each thing grows great, and is fostered out of its own substance. There is this too, that without fixed rain-showers in the year the earth could not put forth its gladdening produce, nor again held apart from food could the nature of living things renew its kind or preserve its life; so that rather you may think that many bodies are common to many things, as we see letters are to words, than that without first-beginnings anything can come to being. Once more, why could not nature produce men so large that on their feet they might wade through the waters of ocean or rend asunder mighty mountains with their hands, or live to overpass many generations of living men, if it be not because fixed substance has been appointed for the begetting of things, from which it is ordained what can arise? Therefore, we must confess that nothing can be brought to being out of nothing, inasmuch as it needs a seed for things, from which each may be produced and brought forth into the gentle breezes of the air. Lastly, inasmuch as we see that tilled grounds are better than the untilled, and when worked by hands yield better produce, we must know that there are in the earth first-beginnings of things, which we call forth to birth by turning the teeming sods with the ploughshare and drilling the soil of the earth. But if there were none such, you would see all things without toil of ours of their own will come to be far better.

Then follows this, that nature breaks up each thing again into its own first-bodies, nor does she destroy ought into nothing. For if anything were mortal in all its parts, each thing would on a sudden be snatched from our eyes, and pass away. For there would be no need of any force, such as might cause disunion in its parts and unloose its fastenings. But as it is, because all things are put together of everlasting seeds, until some force has met them to batter things asunder with its blow, or to make its way inward through the empty voids and break things up, nature suffers not the destruction of anything to be seen. Moreover, if time utterly destroys whatsoever through age it takes from sight, and devours all its substance, how is it that Venus brings back the race of living things after their kind into the light of life, or when she has, how does earth, the quaint artificer, nurse and increase them, furnishing food for them after their kind? how is it that its native springs and the rivers from without, coming from afar, keep the sea full? how is it that the sky feeds the stars? For infinite time and the days that are gone by must needs have devoured all things that are of mortal body. But if in all that while, in the ages that are gone by, those things have existed, of which this sum of things consists and is replenished, assuredly they are blessed with an immortal nature; all things cannot then be turned to nought. And again, the same force and cause would destroy all things alike, unless an eternal substance held them together, part with part interwoven closely or loosely by its fastenings. For in truth a touch would be cause enough of death, seeing that none of these things would be of everlasting body, whose texture any kind of force would be bound to break asunder. But as it is, because the fastenings of the first-elements are variously put together, and their substance is everlasting, things endure with body unharmed, until there meets them a force proved strong enough to overcome the texture of each. No single thing then passes back to nothing, but all by dissolution pass back into the first-bodies of matter. Lastly, the rains pass away, when the sky, our father, has cast them headlong into the lap of earth, our mother; but the bright crops spring up, and the branches grow green upon the trees, the trees too grow and are laden with fruit; by them next our race and the race of beasts is nourished, through them we see glad towns alive with children, and leafy woods on every side ring with the young birds' cry; through them the cattle wearied with fatness lay their limbs to rest over the glad pastures, and the white milky stream trickles from their swollen udders; through them a new brood with tottering legs sports wanton among the soft grass, their baby hearts thrilling with the pure milk. Not utterly then perish all things that are seen, since nature renews one thing from out another, nor suffers anything to be begotten, unless she be requited by another's death.

Come now, since I have taught you that things cannot be created of nought nor likewise when begotten be called back to nothing, lest by any chance you should begin nevertheless to distrust my words, because the first-beginnings of things cannot be descried with the eyes, let me tell you besides of other bodies, which you must needs confess yourself are among things and yet cannot be seen. First of all the might of the awakened wind lashes the ocean and o'erwhelms vast ships and scatters the clouds, and anon scouring the plains with tearing hurricane it strews them with great trees, and harries the mountain-tops with blasts that rend the woods: with such fierce whistling the wind rages and ravens with angry roar. There are therefore, we may be sure, unseen bodies of wind, which sweep sea and land, yea, and the clouds of heaven, and tear and harry them with sudden hurricane; they stream on and spread havoc in no other way than when the soft nature of water is borne on in a flood o'erflowing in a moment, swollen by a great rush of water dashing down from the high mountains after bounteous rains and hurling together broken branches from the woods, and whole trees too; nor can the strong bridges bear up against the sudden force of the advancing flood. In such wise, turbid with much rain, the river rushes with might and main against the piles: roaring aloud it spreads ruin, and rolls and dashes beneath its waves huge rocks and all that bars its flood. Thus then the blasts of wind too must needs be borne on; and when like some strong stream they have swooped towards any side, they push things and dash them on with constant assault; sometimes in eddying whirl they seize them up and bear them away in swiftly swirling hurricane. Wherefore again and again there are unseen bodies of wind, inasmuch as in their deeds and ways they are found to rival mighty streams, whose body all may see. Then again we smell the manifold scents of things, and yet we do not ever descry them coming to the nostrils, nor do we behold warm heat, nor can we grasp cold with the eyes, nor is it ours to descry voices; yet all these things must needs consist of bodily nature, inasmuch as they can make impact on our senses. For, if it be not body, nothing can touch and be touched. Once more, garments hung up upon the shore, where the waves break, grow damp, and again spread in the sun they dry. Yet never has it been seen in what way the moisture of the water has sunk into them, nor again in what way it has fled before the heat. Therefore the moisture is dispersed into tiny particles, which the eyes can in no way see. Nay more, as the sun's year rolls round again and again, the ring on the finger becomes thin beneath by wearing, the fall of dripping water hollows the stone, the bent iron ploughshare secretly grows smaller in the fields, and we see the paved stone streets worn away by the feet of the multitude; again, by the city-gates the brazen statues reveal that their right hands are wearing thin through the touch of those who greet them ever and again as they pass upon their way. All these things then we see grow less, as they are rubbed away: yet what particles leave them at each moment, the envious nature of our sight has shut us out from seeing. Lastly, whatever time and nature adds little by little to things, impelling them to grow in due proportion, the straining sight of the eye can never behold, nor again wherever things grow old through time and decay. Nor where rocks overhang the sea, devoured by the thin salt spray, could you see what they lose at each moment. 'Tis then by bodies unseen that nature works her will.

And yet all things are not held close pressed on every side by the nature of body; for there is void in things. To have learnt this will be of profit to you in dealing with many things; it will save you from wandering in doubt and always questioning about the sum of things, and distrusting my words. There is then a void, mere space untouchable and empty. For if there were not, by no means could things move; for that which is the office of body, to offend and hinder, would at every moment be present to all things; nothing, therefore, could advance, since nothing could give the example of yielding place. But as it is, through seas and lands and the high tracts of heaven, we descry many things by many means moving in diverse ways before our eyes, which, if there were not void, would not so much be robbed and baulked of restless motion, but rather could in no way have been born at all, since matter would on every side be in close-packed stillness. Again, however solid things may be thought to be, yet from this you can discern that they are of rare body. In rocky caverns the liquid moisture of water trickles through, and all weeps with copious dripping: food spreads itself this way and that into the body of every living thing: trees grow and thrust forth their fruit in due season, because the food is dispersed into every part of them from the lowest roots through the stems and all the branches. Noises creep through walls and fly through the shut places in the house, stiffening cold works its way to the bones: but were there no empty spaces, along which each of these bodies might pass, you would not see this come to pass by any means. Again, its size is no whit bigger? For if there is as much body in a bale of wool as in lead, it is natural it should weigh as much, since 'tis the office of body to press all things downwards, but on the other hand the nature of void remains without weight. So because it is just as big, yet seems lighter, it tells us, we may be sure, that it has more void; but on the other hand the heavier thing avows that there is more body in its and that it contains far less empty space within. Therefore, we may be sure, that which we are seeking with keen reasoning, does exist mingled in things—that which we call void.

Herein lest that which some vainly imagine should avail to lead you astray from the truth, I am constrained to forestall it. They say that the waters give place to the scaly creatures as they press forward and open up a liquid path, because the fishes leave places behind, to which the waters may flow together as they yield: and that even so other things too can move among themselves and change place, albeit the whole is solid. In very truth this is all believed on false reasoning. For whither, I ask, will the scaly creatures be able to move forward, unless the waters have left an empty space? again, whither will the waters be able to give place, when the fishes cannot go forward? either then we must deny motion to every body, or we must say that void is mixed with things, from which each thing can receive the first start of movement. Lastly, if two broad bodies leap asunder quickly from a meeting, surely it must needs be that air seizes upon all the void, which comes to be between the bodies. Still, however rapid the rush with which it streams together as its currents hasten round, yet in one instant the whole empty space cannot be filled: for it must needs be that it fills each place as it comes, and then at last all the room is taken up. But if by chance any one thinks that when bodies have leapt apart, then this comes to be because the air condenses, he goes astray; for in that case that becomes empty which was not so before, and again that is filled which was empty before, nor can air condense in such a way, nor, if indeed it could, could it, I trow, without void draw into itself and gather into one all its parts.

*   *   *   *

Come now, learn what remains, and listen to clearer words. Nor do I fail to see in mind how dark are the ways; but a great hope has smitten my heart with the sharp spur of fame, and at once has struck into my breast the sweet love of the muses, whereby now inspired with strong mind I traverse the distant haunts of the Pierides, never trodden before by the foot of man. 'Tis my joy to approach those untasted springs and drink my fill, 'tis my joy to pluck new flowers and gather a glorious coronal for my head from spots whence before the muses have never wreathed the forehead of any man. First because I teach about great things, and hasten to free the mind from the close bondage of religion, then because on a dark theme I trace verses so full of light, touching all with the muses' charm. For that too is seen to be not without good reason; but even as healers, when they essay to give loathsome wormwood to children, first touch the rim all round the cup with the sweet golden moisture of honey, so that the unwitting age of children may be beguiled as far as the lips, and meanwhile may drink the bitter draught of wormwood, and though charmed may not be harmed, but rather by such means may be restored and come to health; so now, since this philosophy full often seems too bitter to those who have not tasted it, and the multitude shrinks back away from it, I have desired to set forth to you my reasoning in the sweet-tongued song of the muses, and as though to touch it with the pleasant honey of poetry, if perchance I might avail by such means to keep your mind set upon my verses, while you come to see the whole nature of things, what is its shape and figure.

But since I have taught that the most solid bodies of matter fly about for ever unvanquished through the ages, come now, let us unfold, whether there be a certain limit to their full sum or not; and likewise the void that we have discovered, or room or space, in which all things are carried on, let us see clearly whether it is all altogether bounded or spreads out limitless and immeasurably deep.

The whole universe then is bounded in no direction of its ways; for then it would be bound to have an extreme point. Now it is seen that nothing can have an extreme point, unless there be something beyond to bound it, so that there is seen to be a spot further than which the nature of our sense cannot follow it. As it is, since we must admit that there is nothing outside the whole sum, it has not an extreme point, it lacks therefore bound and limit. Nor does it matter in which quarter of it you take your stand; so true is it that, whatever place every man takes up, he leaves the whole boundless just as much on every side. Moreover, suppose now that all space were created finite, if one were to run on to the end, to its furthest coasts, and throw a flying dart, would you have it that that dart, hurled with might and main, goes on whither it is sped and flies afar, or do you think that something can check and bar its way? For one or the other you must needs admit and choose. Yet both shut

off your escape and constrain you to grant that the universe spreads out
free from limit. For whether there is something to check it and bring it
about that it arrives not whither it was sped, nor plants itself in the goal,
or whether it fares forward, it set not forth from the end. In this way I
will press on, and wherever you shall set the furthest coasts, I shall ask
what then becomes of the dart. It will come to pass that nowhere can a
bound be set and room for flight ever prolongs the chance of flight.
Lastly, before our eyes one thing is seen to bound another; air is as a
wall between the hills, and mountains between tracts of air, land bounds
the sea, and again sea bounds all lands; yet the universe in truth there
is nothing to limit outside.

Moreover, if all the space in the whole universe were shut in on all
sides, and were created with borders determined, and had been bounded,
then the store of matter would have flowed together with solid weight
from all sides to the bottom, nor could anything be carried on beneath
the canopy of the sky, nor would there be sky at all, nor the light of the
sun, since in truth all matter would lie idle piled together by sinking
down from limitless time. But as it is, no rest, we may be sure, has been
granted to the bodies of the first-beginnings, because there is no bottom
at all, whither they may, as it were, flow together, and make their resting-
place. All things are for ever carried on in ceaseless movement from all
sides, and bodies of matter are even stirred up and supplied from beneath out of limitless space. The nature of room then and the space of
the deep is such that neither could the bright thunderbolts course
through it in their career, gliding on through the everlasting tract of
time, nor bring it about that there remain a whit less to traverse as they
travel; so far on every side spreads out huge room for things, free from
limit in all directions everywhere.

Nay more, nature ordains that the sum of things may not have power
to set a limit to itself, since she constrains body to be bounded by void,
and all that is void to be bounded by body, so that thus she makes the
universe infinite by their interchange, or else at least one of the two, if
the other of them bound it not, yet spreads out immeasurable with nature unmixed. But space I have taught above spreads out without limit.
If then the sum of matter were bounded, neither sea nor earth nor the
gleaming quarters of heaven nor the race of mortal men, nor the hallowed bodies of the gods could exist for the short space of an hour. For
driven apart from its unions the store of matter would be carried all
dissolved through the great void, or rather in truth it could never have
grown together and given birth to anything, since scattered abroad it
could not have been brought to meet. For in very truth, not by design
did the first-beginnings of things place themselves each in their order

with foreseeing mind, nor indeed did they make compact what movements each should start, but because many of them shifting in many ways throughout the world are harried and buffeted by blows from limitless time, by trying movements and unions of every kind, at last they fall into such dispositions as those, whereby our world of things is created and holds together. And it too, preserved from harm through many a mighty cycle of years, when once it has been cast into the movements suited to its being, brings it about that the rivers replenish the greedy sea with the bounteous waters of their streams, and the earth, fostered by the sun's heat, renews its increase, and the race of living things flourishes, sent up from her womb, and the gliding fires of heaven are alive; all this they would in no wise do, unless store of matter might rise up from limitless space, out of which they are used to renew all their losses in due season. For even as the nature of living things, robbed of food, loses its flesh and pines away, so all things must needs be dissolved, when once matter has ceased to come for their supply, turned aside in any way from its due course. Nor can blows from without on all sides keep together the whole of each world which has come together in union. For they can smite on it once and again, and keep a part in place, until others come, and the sum be supplied. Yet sometimes they are constrained to rebound and at once afford space and time for flight to the first-beginnings of things, so that they can pass away freed from union. Therefore, again and again, it must be that many things rise up, yea, and in order that even the blows too may not fail, there must needs be limitless mass of matter on all sides.

Herein shrink far from believing, Memmius, what some say: that all things press towards the centre of a sum, and that 'tis for this cause that the nature of the world stands fast without any blows from outside, and that top and bottom cannot part asunder in any direction, because all things are pressing upon the centre (if indeed you can believe that anything can stand upon itself) : and that all heavy things which are beneath the earth press upwards, and rest placed upside down upon the earth, like the images of things which we see, as it is, through water. And in the same way they maintain that living things walk head downwards, and cannot fall off the earth into the spaces of heaven beneath them any more than our bodies can of their free will fly up into the quarters of heaven: that when they see the sun, we are descrying the stars of night, and that they share with us turn by turn the seasons of the sky, and pass nights equal to our days. But empty error has commended these false ideas to fools, because they embrace and hold a theory with twisted reasoning. For there can be no centre, since the universe is created infinite. Nor, if indeed there were a centre, could anything at all rest there any more for that, rather than be driven away for some far different reason: for all room and space, which we call void, must through centre or not-centre give place alike to heavy bodies, wherever their motions tend. Nor is there any place, to which when bodies have come, they can lose the force of their weight and stand still in the void; nor must aught that is void support anything, but rather hasten to give place, as its own nature desires. It cannot be then that things can be held together in union in such a way, constrained by a yearning for the centre.

Moreover, since they do not pretend that all bodies press towards the centre, but only those of earth and liquid, the moisture of the sea and mighty waters from the mountains, and those things which are, as it were, enclosed in an earthy frame; but on the other hand, they teach that the thin breezes of air and hot fires at the same time are carried away from the centre, and that for this cause all the sky around is twinkling with stars, and the flame of the sun is fed through the blue tracts of heaven, because all the heat fleeing from the centre gathers itself together there; nor again can the topmost branches grow leafy upon trees, unless from the earth little by little each has food supplied by nature, their thoughts are not at harmony with themselves. There must then be an infinite store of matter, lest after the winged way of flames the walls of the world suddenly fly apart, dissolved through the great void, and lest all else follow them in like manner, or the thundering quarters of the sky fall down from above, and the earth in hot haste withdraw itself from beneath our feet, and amid all the mingled ruin of things on earth and of the sky, whereby the frames of bodies are loosed, it pass away through the deep void, so that in an instant of time not a wrack be left behind, except emptied space and unseen first-beginnings. For on whatever side you maintain that the bodies fail first, this side will be the gate of death for things, by this path will all the throng of matter cast itself abroad.

These things you will learn thus, led on with little trouble; for one thing after another shall grow clear, nor will blind night snatch away your path from you, but that you shall see all the utmost truths of nature: so shall things kindle a light for others.

BOOK II

Sweet it is, when on the great sea the winds are buffeting the waters, to gaze from the land on another's great struggles; not because it is pleasure or joy that any one should be distressed, but because it is sweet to perceive from what misfortune you yourself are free. Sweet is it too, to behold great contests of war in full array over the plains, when you have no part in the danger. But nothing is more gladdening than to dwell in the calm high places, firmly embattled on the heights by the teaching of the wise, whence you can look down on others, and see them wandering hither and thither, going astray as they seek the way of life, in strife matching their wits or rival claims of birth, struggling night and day by surpassing effort to rise up to the height of power and gain possession of the world. Ah! miserable minds of men, blind hearts! in what darkness of life, in what great dangers ye spend this little span of years! to think that ye should not see that nature cries aloud for nothing else but that pain may be kept far sundered from the body, and that, withdrawn from care and fear, she may enjoy in mind the sense of pleasure! And so we see that for the body's nature but few things at all are needful, even such as can take away pain. Yes, though pleasantly enough from time to time they can prepare for us in many ways a lap of luxury, yet nature herself feels no loss, if there are not golden images of youths about the halls, grasping fiery torches in their right hands, that light may be supplied to banquets at night, if the house does not glow with silver or gleam with gold, nor do fretted and gilded ceilings re-echo to the lute. And yet, for all this, men lie in friendly groups on the soft grass near some stream of water under the branches of a tall tree, and at no great cost delightfully refresh their bodies, above all when the weather smiles on them, and the season of the year bestrews the green grass with flowers. Nor do fiery fevers more quickly quit the body, if you toss on broidered pictures and blushing purple, than if you must lie on the poor man's plaid. Wherefore since in our body riches are of no profit, nor high birth nor the glories of kingship, for the rest, we must believe that they avail nothing for the mind as well; unless perchance, when you see your legions swarming over the spaces of the Campus, and provoking a mimic war, strengthened with hosts in reserve and forces of cavalry, when you draw them up equipped with arms, all alike eager for the fray, when you see the army wandering far and wide in busy haste, then alarmed by all this the scruples of religion fly in panic from your mind, or that the dread of death leaves your heart empty and free from care. But if we see that these thoughts are mere mirth and mockery, and in very truth the fears of men and the cares that dog them fear not the clash of arms nor the weapons of war, but pass boldly among kings and lords of the world, nor dread the glitter that comes from gold nor the bright sheen of the purple robe, can you doubt that all such power belongs to reason alone, above all when the whole of life is but a struggle in darkness? For even as children tremble and fear everything in blinding darkness, so we sometimes dread in the light things that are no whit more to be feared than what children shudder at in the dark, and imagine will come to pass. This terror then, this darkness of the mind, must needs be scattered not by the rays of the sun and the gleaming shafts of day, but by the outer view and the inner law of nature.

Come now, I will unfold by what movement the creative bodies of matter beget diverse things, and break up those that are begotten, by what force they are constrained to do this, and what velocity is appointed them for moving through the mighty void: do you remember to give your mind to my words. For in very truth matter does not cleave close-packed to itself, since we see each thing grow less, and we perceive all things flow away, as it were, in the long lapse of time, as age withdraws them from our sight: and yet the universe is seen to remain undiminished, inasmuch as all bodies that depart from anything, lessen that from which they pass away, and bless with increase that to which they have come; they constrain the former to grow old and the latter again to flourish, and yet they abide not with it. Thus the sum of things is ever being replenished, and mortals live one and all by give and take. Some races wax and others wane, and in a short space the tribes of living things are changed, and like runners hand on the torch of life.

If you think that the first-beginnings of things can stay still, and by staying still beget new movements in things, you stray very far away from true reasoning. For since they wander through the void, it must needs be that all the first-beginnings of things move on either by their own weight or sometimes by the blow of another. For when quickly, again and again, they have met and clashed together, it comes to pass that they leap asunder at once this way and that; for indeed it is not strange, since they are most hard with solid heavy bodies, and nothing bars them from behind. And the more you perceive all the bodies of matter tossing about, bring it to mind that there is no lowest point in the whole universe, nor have the first-bodies any place where they may come to rest, since I have shown in many words, and it has been proved by true reasoning, that space spreads out without bound or limit, immeasureable towards every quarter everywhere. And since that is certain, no rest, we may be sure, is allowed to the first-bodies moving through the deep void, but rather plied with unceasing, diverse motion, some when they have dashed together leap back at great space apart, others too are thrust but a short way from the blow. And all those which are driven together in more close-packed union and leap back but a little space apart, entangled by their own close-locking shapes, these make the strong roots of rock and the brute bulk of iron and all other things of their kind. Of the rest which wander through the great void, a few leap far apart, and recoil afar with great spaces between; these supply for us thin air and the bright light of the sun. Many, moreover, wander on through the great void, which have been cast back from the unions of things, nor have they anywhere else availed to be taken into them and link their movements. And of this truth, as I am telling it, a likeness and image is ever passing presently before our eyes. For look closely, whenever rays are let in and pour the sun's light through the dark places in houses: for you will see many tiny bodies mingle in many ways all through the empty space right in the light of the rays, and as though in some everlasting strife wage war and battle, struggling troop against troop, nor ever crying a halt, harried with constant meetings and part-ings; so that you may guess from this what it means that the first-beginnings of things are for ever tossing in the great void. So far as may be, a little thing can give a picture of great things and afford traces of a concept. And for this reason it is the more right for you to give heed to these bodies, which you see jostling in the sun's rays, because such jostlings hint that there are movements of matter too beneath them, secret and unseen. For you will see many particles there stirred by un-seen blows change their course and turn back, driven backwards on their path, now this way, now that, in every direction everywhere. You may know that this shifting movement comes to them all from the first-beginnings. For first the first-beginnings of things move of themselves; then those bodies which are formed of a tiny union, and are, as it were, nearest to the powers of the first-beginnings, are smitten and stirred by their unseen blows, and they in their turn, rouse up bodies a little larger. And so the movement passes upwards from the first-beginnings, and little by little comes forth to our senses, so that those bodies move too, which we can descry in the sun's light; yet it is not clearly seen by what blows they do it.

Next, what speed of movement is given to the first-bodies of matter, you may learn, Memmius, in a few words from this. First, when dawn strews the land with new light, and the diverse birds flitting through the distant woods across the soft air fill the place with their clear cries, we see that it is plain and evident for all to behold how suddenly the sun is wont at such a time to rise and clothe all things, bathing them in his light. And yet that heat which the sun sends out, and that calm light of his, is not passing through empty space; therefore, it is constrained to go more slowly, while it dashes asunder, as it were, the waves of air. Nor again do the several particles of heat move on one by one, but entangled one with another, and joined in a mass; therefore they are at once dragged back each by the other, and impeded from without, so that they are constrained to go more slowly. But the first-beginnings, which are of solid singleness, when they pass through the empty void, and nothing checks them without, and they themselves, single wholes with all their parts, are borne, as they press on, towards the one spot which they first began to seek, must needs, we may be sure, surpass in speed of motion, and be carried far more quickly than the light of the sun, and rush through many times the distance of space in the same time in which the flashing light of the sun crowds the sky. . . .

Yet a certain sect, against all this, ignorant that the bodies of matter fly on of their own accord, unvanquished through the ages, believe that nature cannot without the power of the gods, in ways so nicely tempered to the needs of men, change the seasons of the year, and create the crops, and all else besides, which divine pleasure wins men to approach, while she herself, the leader of life, leads on and entices them by the arts of Venus to renew their races, that the tribe of mankind may not perish. But when they suppose that the gods have appointed all things for the sake of men, they are seen in all things to fall exceeding far away from true reason. For however little I know what the first-beginnings of things are, yet this I would dare to affirm from the very workings of heaven, and to prove from many other things as well, that the nature of the world is by no means made by divine grace for us: so great are the flaws with which it stands beset. And this, Memmius, I will make clear to you hereafter. Now I will set forth what yet remains about the movements.

Now is the place, I trow, herein to prove this also to you, that no bodily thing can of its own force be carried upwards or move upwards; lest the bodies of flames give you the lie herein. For upwards indeed the smiling crops and trees are brought to birth, and take their increase, upwards too they grow, albeit all things of weight, as far as in them lies, are borne downwards. Nor when fires leap up to the roofs of houses, and with swift flame lick up beams and rafters, must we think that they do this of their own will, shot up without a driving force. Even as when blood shot out from our body spirts out leaping up on high, and scatters gore. Do you not see too with what force the moisture of water spews up beams and rafters? For the more we have pushed them straight down deep in the water, and with might and main have pressed them, striving with pain many together, the more eagerly does it spew them up and send them back, so that they rise more than half out of the water and leap up. And yet we do not doubt, I trow, but that all these things, as far as in them lies, are borne downwards through the empty void. Just so, therefore, flames too must be able when squeezed out to press on upwards through the breezes of air, albeit their weights are fighting, as far as in them lies, to drag them downwards. And again, the nightly torches of the sky which fly on high, do you not see that they trail long tracts of flames behind towards whatever side nature has given them to travel? do you not descry stars and constellations falling to earth? The sun too from the height of heaven scatters its heat on every side, and sows the fields with his light; 'tis towards the earth then that the sun's heat also tends. And you descry, too, thunderbolts flying crosswise through the rain; now from this side, now from that the fires burst from the clouds and rush together; the force of flame everywhere falls towards the earth.

Herein I would fain that you should learn this too, that when first-bodies are being carried downwards straight through the void by their own weight, at times quite undetermined and at undetermined spots they push a little from their path: yet only just so much as you could call a change of trend. But if they were not used to swerve, all things would fall downwards through the deep void like drops of rain, nor could collision come to be, nor a blow brought to pass for the first-beginnings: so nature would never have brought aught to being.

But if perchance any one believes that heavier bodies, because they are carried more quickly straight through the void, can fall from above on the lighter, and so bring about the blows which can give creative motions, he wanders far away from true reason. For all things that fall through the water and thin air, these things must needs quicken their fall in proportion to their weights, just because the body of water and the thin nature of air cannot check each thing equally, but give place more quickly when overcome by heavier bodies. But, on the other hand, the empty void cannot on any side, at any time, support anything, but rather, as its own nature desires, it continues to give place; wherefore all things must needs be borne on through the calm void, moving at equal rate with unequal weights. The heavier will not then ever be able to fall on the lighter from above, nor of themselves bring about the blows, which make diverse the movements, by which nature carries things on. Wherefore, again and again, it must needs be that the first-bodies swerve a little; yet not more than the very least, lest we seem to be imagining a sideways movement, and the truth refute it. For this we see plain and evident, that bodies, as far as in them lies, cannot travel sideways, since they fall headlong from above, as far as you can descry. But that nothing at all swerves from the straight direction of its path, what sense is there which can descry?

Once again, if every motion is always linked on, and the new always arises from the old in order determined, nor by swerving do the first-beginnings make a certain start of movement to break through the decrees of fate, so that cause may not follow cause from infinite time; whence comes this free will for living things all over the earth, whence, I ask, is it wrested from fate, this will whereby we move forward, where pleasure leads each one of us, and swerve likewise in our motions neither at determined times nor in a determined direction of place, but just where our mind has carried us? For without doubt it is his own will which gives to each one a start for this movement, and from the will the motions pass flooding through the limbs. Do you not see too how, when the barriers are flung open, yet for an instant of time the eager might of the horses cannot burst out so suddenly as their mind itself desires? For the whole store of matter throughout the whole body must be roused to movement, that then aroused through every limb it may strain and follow the eager longing of the mind; so that you see a start of movement is brought to pass from the heart, and comes forth first of all from the will of the mind, and then afterwards is spread through all the body and limbs. Nor is it the same as when we move forward impelled by a blow from the strong might and strong constraint of another. For then it is clear to see that all the matter of the body moves and is hurried on against our will, until the will has reined it back throughout the limbs. Do you not then now see that, albeit a force outside pushes many men and constrains them often to go forward against their will and to be hurried away headlong, yet there is something in our breast, which can fight against it and withstand it? And at its bidding too the store of matter is constrained now and then to turn throughout the limbs and members, and, when pushed forward, is reined back and comes to rest again. Wherefore in the seeds too you must needs allow likewise that there is another cause of motion besides blows and weights, whence comes this power born in us, since we see that nothing can come to pass from nothing. For weight prevents all things coming to pass by blows, as by some force without. But that the very mind feels not some necessity within in doing all things, and is not constrained like a conquered thing to bear and suffer, this is brought about by the tiny swerve of the first-beginnings in no determined direction of place and at no determined time.

Nor was the store of matter ever more closely packed nor again set at larger distances apart. For neither does anything come to increase it nor pass away from it. Wherefore the bodies of the first-beginnings in the ages past moved with the same motion as now, and hereafter will be borne on for ever in the same way; such things as have been wont to come to being will be brought to birth under the same law, will exist and grow and be strong and lusty, inasmuch as is granted to each by the ordinances of nature. Nor can any force change the sum of things; for neither is there anything outside, into which any kind of matter may escape from the universe, nor whence new forces can arise and burst into the universe and change the whole nature of things and alter its motions.

Herein we need not wonder why it is that, when all the first-beginnings of things are in motion, yet the whole seems to stand wholly at rest, except when anything starts moving with its entire body. For all the nature of the first-bodies lies far away from our senses, below their purview; wherefore, since you cannot reach to look upon them, they must needs steal away their motions from you too; above all, since such things as we can look upon, yet often hide their motions, when withdrawn from us on some distant spot. For often the fleecy flocks cropping the glad pasture on a hill creep on whither each is called and tempted by the grass bejewelled with fresh dew, and the lambs fed full gambol and butt playfully; yet all this seems blurred to us from afar, and to lie like a white mass on a green hill. Moreover, when mighty legions fill the spaces of the plains with their chargings, awaking a mimic warfare, a sheen rises there to heaven and all the earth around gleams with bronze, and beneath a noise is roused by the mighty mass of men as they march, and the hills smitten by their shouts turn back the cries to the stars of the firmament, and the cavalry wheel round and suddenly shake the middle of the plains with their forceful onset, as they scour across them. And yet there is a certain spot on the high hills, whence all seems to be at rest and to lie like a glimmering mass upon the plains.

Now come, next in order learn of what kind are the beginnings of all things and how far differing in form, and how they are made diverse with many kinds of shapes, not that but a few are endowed with a like form, but that they are not all alike the same one with another. Nor need we wonder; for since there is so great a store of them, that neither have they any limit, as I have shown, nor any sum, it must needs be, we may be sure, that they are not all of equal bulk nor possessed of the same shape. Moreover, the race of men, and the dumb shoals of scaly creatures which swim the seas, and the glad herds and wild beasts, and the diverse birds, which throng the gladdening watering-places all around the riverbanks and springs and pools, and those which flit about and people the distant forests; of these go and take any single one you will from among its kind, yet you will find that they are different in shape one from another. Nor in any other way could the offspring know its mother, or the mother her offspring; yet we see that they can, and that they are clearly not less known to one another than men. For often before the sculptured shrines of the gods a calf has fallen, slaughtered hard by the altars smoking with incense, breathing out from its breast the hot tide of blood. But the mother bereft wanders over the green glades and seeks on the ground for the footprints marked by those cloven hoofs, scanning every spot with her eyes, if only she might anywhere catch sight of her lost young, and stopping fills the leafy grove with her lament: again and again she comes back to the stall, stabbed to the heart with yearning for her lost calf, nor can the tender willows and the grass refreshed with dew and the loved streams, gliding level with their banks, bring gladness to her mind and turn aside the sudden pang of care, nor yet can the shapes of other calves among the glad pastures turn her mind to new thoughts or ease it of its care: so eagerly does she seek in vain for something she knows as her own. Moreover, the tender kids with their trembling cries know their horned dams and the butting lambs the flocks of bleating sheep: so surely, as their nature needs, do they run back always each to its own udder of milk. Lastly, take any kind of corn, you will not find that every grain is like its fellows, each in its several kind, but that there runs through all some difference between their forms. And in like manner we see the race of shells painting the lap of earth, where with its gentle waves the sea beats on the thirsty sand of the winding shore. Wherefore again and again in the same way it must needs be, since the first-beginnings of things are made by nature and not fashioned by hand to the fixed form of one pattern, that some of them fly about with shapes unlike one another.

It is very easy by reasoning of the mind for us to read the riddle why the fire of lightning is far more piercing than is our fire rising from pine-torches on earth. For you might say that the heavenly fire of lightning is made more subtle and of smaller shapes, and so passes through holes which our fire rising from logs and born of the pine-torch cannot pass. Again light passes through horn-lanterns, but the rain is spewed back. Why? unless it be that those bodies of light are smaller than those of which the quickening liquid of water is made. And we see wine flow through the strainer as swiftly as you will; but, on the other hand, the sluggish olive-oil hangs back, because, we may be sure, it is composed of particles either larger or more hooked and entangled one with the other, and so it comes about that the first-beginnings cannot so quickly be drawn apart, each single one from the rest, and so ooze through the single holes of each thing.

There is this too that the liquids of honey and milk give a pleasant sensation of the tongue, when rolled in the mouth; but on the other hand, the loathsome nature of wormwood and biting centaury set the mouth awry by their noisome taste; so that you may easily know that those things which can touch the senses pleasantly are made of smooth and round bodies, but that on the other hand all things which seem to be bitter and harsh, these are held bound together with particles more hooked, and for this cause are wont to tear a way into our senses, and at their entering in to break through the body.

Lastly, all things good or bad to the senses in their touch fight thus with one another, because they are built up of bodies of different shape; lest by chance you may think that the harsh shuddering sound of the squeaking saw is made of particles as smooth as are the melodies of music which players awake, shaping the notes as their fingers move nimbly over the strings; nor again, must you think that first-beginnings of like shape pierce into men's nostrils, when noisome carcasses are roasting, and when the stage is freshly sprinkled with Cilician saffron, and the altar hard by is breathing the scent of Arabian incense; nor must you suppose that the pleasant colours of things, which can feed our eyes, are made of seeds like those which prick the pupil and constrain us to tears, or look dreadful and loathly in their hideous aspect. For every shape, which ever charms the senses, has not been brought to being without some smoothness in the first-beginnings; but, on the other hand, every shape which is harsh and offensive has not been formed without some roughness of substance. Other particles there are, moreover, which cannot rightly be thought to be smooth nor altogether hooked with bent points, but rather with tiny angles standing out a little, insomuch that they can tickle the senses rather than hurt them; and of this kind is less of wine and the taste of endive. Or again, that hot fires and cold front have particles fanged in different ways to prick the senses of the body, is proved to us by the touch of each. For touch, yea touch, by the holy powers of the gods, is the sense of the body, either when something from without finds its way in, or when a thing which is born in the body hurts us, or gives pleasure as it passes out, or else when the seeds after collision jostle within the body itself and, roused one by another, disturb our sense: as if by chance you should with your hand strike any part of your own body and so make trial. Therefore the first-beginnings must needs have forms far different, which can produce such diverse feelings.

Or, again, things which seem to us hard and compact, these, it must needs be, are made of particles more hooked one to another, and are held together close-fastened at their roots, as it were by branching particles. First of all in this class diamond stones stand in the forefront of the fight, well used to despise all blows, and stubborn flints and the strength of hard iron, and brass sockets, which scream aloud as they struggle against the bolts. Those things indeed must be made of particles more round and smooth, which are liquid with a fluid body: for indeed a handful of poppy-seed moves easily just as a draught of water; for the several round particles are not checked one by the other, and when struck, it will roll downhill just like water. Lastly, all things which you perceive flying asunder, like smoke, clouds and flames, it must needs be that even if they are not made entirely of smooth and round particles, yet they are not hampered by particles closely linked, so that they can prick the body, and pass into rocks, and yet not cling one to another: so that you can easily learn that, whatever we see borne asunder by the tearing winds and meeting our senses as poison, are of elements not closely linked but pointed. But because you see that some things which are fluid, are also bitter, as is the brine of the sea, count it no wonder. For because it is fluid, it is of smooth and round particles, and many rugged bodies mingled in it give birth to pain; and yet it must needs be that they are not hooked and held together: you must know that they are nevertheless spherical, though rugged, so that they can roll on together and hurt the senses. And that you may the more think that rough are mingled with smooth first-beginnings, from which is made the bitter body of the sea-god, there is a way of sundering them and seeing how, apart from the rest, the fresh water, when it trickles many a time through the earth, flows into a trench and loses its harshness; for it leaves behind up above the first-beginnings of its sickly saltness, since the rough particles can more readily stick in the earth.

6

ROGER BACON

Although he was born English, to a wealthy and possibly noble family in about 1214, Roger Bacon early became "Latin" through education in the language, thought, and religion of the universal intellectual community in which he was to pass his life. He began his academic career at Oxford. Sometime after advancing through the arts curriculum to Master, he moved on to Paris, where he lectured in the Arts Faculty during the early 1240's. The succeeding years, although as obscure as the rest of his life, are known to have been crucial ones, for it was then that he developed his enthusiasm for experimental science. His purported Doctor of Theology degree (for which there is tradition, but no evidence) would have been conferred about that time, too, but it is clear that any and all subjects that had previously occupied Bacon's attention were quickly subordinated to his new interests. Returning to England, he entered into studies of optics, astronomy, alchemy, and the like, with such fervor that he soon expended all of his personal resources. In about 1250 he took vows in the Franciscan Order.

Bacon's relations with his Order will probably forever remain an enigma. Twice during the last half of his life he was exiled to Paris for periods exceeding ten years each. The frightful tales of his incarceration now appear to have been somewhat exaggerated. Likewise, the assumption that he was persecuted because of his scientific (that is, astrological and alchemical) interests is now regarded as untenable. Yet Bacon's treatment at the hands of the Franciscans certainly does not exhibit them in the role of patrons of science. Regulations of the Order forced him to work secretly on his program of research in experimental science, with the result that he did not even produce an "abstract" of it until 1268. Steadfastly denied support or encouragement in his efforts, even after they had been made public, Bacon died 25 years later without producing anything to displace the abstract as his "major work."

The *Opus Majus* represented Bacon's chance to exert some influence on 13th-century education in general and theology in particular. Originat-

131

ing as the desperate plea of an exiled and obscure friar for a Cardinal's support, it was inflated to prominence with the Cardinal's elevation to the Papacy as Clement IV. Promised a hearing, Bacon poured his soul into the composition of the work, only to have the wheel of fortune turn full circle. The opportunity that had come out of nowhere evaporated into nothing with the death of "his" Pope. His plea for the promotion of study in mathematics, languages, and the experimental sciences, rationalized primarily in terms of the light that they might shed on theological matters, came to naught.

6

Opus Majus

PART FOUR OF THIS PLEA

IN WHICH IS SHOWN THE POWER OF MATHEMATICS IN THE SCIENCES
AND IN THE AFFAIRS AND OCCUPATIONS OF THIS WORLD

FIRST DISTINCTION

Chapter I

After making it clear that many famous roots of knowledge depend on the mastery of the languages through which there is an entrance into knowledge on the part of the Latins, I now wish to consider the foundations of this same knowledge as regards the great sciences, in which there is a special power in respect to the other sciences and the affairs of this world. There are four great sciences, without which the other sciences cannot be known nor a knowledge of things secured. If these are known any one can make glorious progress in the power of knowledge without difficulty and labor, not only in human sciences, but in that which is divine. The virtue of each of these sciences will be touched upon not only on account of knowledge itself, but in respect to the other matters aforesaid. Of these sciences the gate and key is mathematics, which the saints discovered at the beginning of the world, as I shall show, and which has always been used by all the saints and sages more than all other sciences. Neglect of this branch now for thirty or forty years has destroyed the whole system of study of the Latins. Since he who is ignorant of this cannot know the other sciences nor the affairs of this world, as I shall prove. And what is worse men ignorant of this do not perceive their own ignorance, and therefore do not seek a remedy. And on the contrary the knowledge of this science prepares the mind and elevates it to a certain knowledge of all things, so that if one learns the roots of knowledge placed about it and rightly applies them to the

Bacon, Roger. *Opus Majus.* A Translation by Robert Belle Burke, Two Vols., [1928]. New York: Russell & Russell, 1962.

knowledge of the other sciences and matters, he will then be able to know all that follows without error and doubt, easily and effectually. For without these neither what precedes nor what follows can be known; whence they perfect what precedes and regulate it, even as the end perfects those things pertaining to it, and they arrange and open the way to what follows. This I now intend to intimate through authority and reason; and in the first place I intend to do so in the human sciences and in the matters of this world, and then in divine knowledge, and lastly according as they are related to the Church and the other three purposes.

Chapter II

In Which It Is Proved by Authority That Every Science Requires Mathematics

As regards authority I so proceed. Boetius says in the second prologue to his Arithmetic, "If an inquirer lacks the four parts of mathematics, he has very little ability to discover truth." And again, "Without this theory no one can have a correct insight into truth." And he says also, "I warn the man who spurns these paths of knowledge that he cannot philosophize correctly." And again, "It is clear that whosoever passes these by, has lost the knowledge of all learning." He confirms this by the opinion of all men of weight saying, "Among all the men of influence in the past, who have flourished under the leadership of Pythagoras with a finer mental grasp, it is an evident fact that no one reaches the summit of perfection in philosophical studies, unless he examines the noble quality of such wisdom with the help of the so-called quadrivium." And in particular Ptolemy and Boetius himself are illustrations of this fact. For since there are three essential parts of philosophy, as Aristotle says in the sixth book of the Metaphysics, mathematical, natural, and divine, the mathematical is of no small importance in grasping the knowledge of the other two parts, as Ptolemy teaches in the first chapter of the Almagest, which statement he also explains further in that place. And since the divine part is twofold, as is clear from the first book of the Metaphysics, namely, the first philosophy, which shows that God exists, whose exalted properties it investigates, and civil science, which determines divine worship, and explains many matters concerning God as far as man can receive them. Ptolemy likewise asserts and declares that mathematics is potent in regard to both of these branches. Hence Boetius asserts at the end of his Arithmetic that the mathematical means are discovered in civil polity. For he says that an arithmetic mean is comparable to a state that is ruled by a few, for this reason, that in its lesser terms is the greater proportion; but he states that there is a harmonic mean in an aristocratic state for the reason that in the greater terms the greater proportionality is found. The geometrical mean is comparable to a democratic state equalized in some manner; for whether in their lesser or greater terms, they are composed of an equal proportion of all. For there is among all a certain parity of mean preserving a law of equality in their relations. Aristotle and his expositors teach in the morals in many places that a state cannot be ruled without these means. Concerning these means an exposition will be given with an application to divine truths. Since all the essential parts of philosophy, which are more than forty sciences distinct in their turn, may be reduced to these three, it suffices now that the value of mathematics has been established by the authorities mentioned.

Now the accidental parts of philosophy are grammar and logic. Alpharabius makes it clear in his book on the sciences that grammar and logic cannot be known without mathematics. For although grammar furnishes children with the facts relating to speech and its properties in prose, meter, and rhythm, nevertheless it does so in a puerile way by means of statement and not through causes or reasons. For it is the function of another science to give the reasons for these things, namely, of that science, which must consider fully the nature of tones, and this alone is music, of which there are numerous varieties and parts. For one deals with prose, a second with meter, a third with rhythm, and a fourth with music in singing. And besides these it has more parts. The part dealing with prose teaches the reasons for all elevations of the voice in prose, as regards differences of accents and as regards colons, commas, periods, and the like. The metrical part teaches all the reasons and causes for feet and meters. The part on rhythm teaches about every modulation and sweet relation in rhythms, because all those are certain kinds of singing, although not so treated as in ordinary singing. For it is called "accent" since it is, as it were, song [accantus] from accino, accinis. Hence these subjects pertain to music as Cassiodorus teaches in music, and Censorinus in his book on Accent, and so too in those on other topics. Authorities on music bear witness to this fact as well as do their books on that science. And Alpharabius agrees with them in his book on the Division of the Sciences. Therefore grammar depends causatively on music.

In the same way logic. . . .

Chapter III
In Which It Is Proved by Reason That Every Science Requires Mathematics

What has been shown as regards mathematics as a whole through authority, can now be shown likewise by reason. And I make this statement in the first place, because other sciences use mathematical examples, but examples are given to make clear the subjects treated by the sciences; wherefore ignorance of the examples involves an ignorance of the subjects for the understanding of which the examples are adduced. For since change in natural objects is not found without some augmentation and diminution nor do these latter take place without change; Aristotle was not able to make clear without complications the difference between augmentation and change by any natural example, because augmentation and diminution go together always with change in some way; wherefore he gave the mathematical example of the rectangle which augmented by a gnomon increases in magnitude and is not altered in shape. This example cannot be understood before the twenty-second proposition of the sixth book of the Elements. For in that proposition of the sixth book it is proved that a smaller rectangle is similar in every particular to a larger one and therefore a smaller one is not altered in shape, although it becomes larger by the addition of the gnomon.

Secondly, because comprehension of mathematical truths is innate, as it were, in us. For a small boy, as Tullius states in the first book of the Tusculan Disputations, when questioned by Socrates on geometrical truths, replied as though he had learned geometry. And this experiment has been tried in many cases, and does not hold in other sciences, as will appear more clearly from what follows. Wherefore since this knowledge is almost innate, and as it were precedes discovery and learning, or at least is less in need of them than other sciences, it will be first among sciences and will precede others disposing us toward them; since what is innate or almost so disposes toward what is acquired.

Thirdly, because this science of all the parts of philosophy was the earliest discovered. For this was first discovered at the beginning of the human race. Since it was discovered before the flood and then later by the sons of Adam, and by Noah and his sons, as is clear from the prologue to the Construction of the Astrolabe according to Ptolemy, and from Albumazar in the larger introduction to astronomy, and from the first book of the Antiquities, and this is true as regards all its parts, geometry, arithmetic, music, astronomy. But this would not have been the case except for the fact that this science is earlier than the others and naturally precedes them. Hence it is clear that it should be studied first, that through it we may advance to all the later sciences.

Fourthly, because the natural road for us is from what is easy to that which is more difficult. But this science is the easiest. This is clearly proved by the fact that mathematics is not beyond the intellectual grasp of any one. For the people at large and those wholly illiterate know how to draw figures and compute and sing, all of which are mathematical operations. But we must begin first with what is common to the laity and to the educated; and it is not only hurtful to the clergy, but disgraceful and abominable that they are ignorant of what the laity knows well and profitably. Fifthly, we see that the clergy, even the most ignorant, are able to grasp mathematical truths, although they are unable to attain to the other sciences. Besides a man by listening once or twice can learn more about this science with certainty and reality without error, than he can by listening ten times about the other parts of philosophy, as is clear to one making the experiment. Sixthly, since the natural road for us is to begin with things which befit the state and nature of childhood, because children begin with facts that are better known by us and that must be acquired first. But of this nature is mathematics, since children are first taught to sing, and in the same way they can learn the method of making figures and of counting, and it would be far easier and more necessary for them to know about numbers before singing, because in the relations of numbers in music the whole theory of numbers is set forth by example, just as the authors on music teach, both in ecclesiastical music and in philosophy. But the theory of numbers depends on figures, since numbers relating to lines, surfaces, solids, squares, cubes, pentagons, hexagons, and other figures, are known from lines, figures, and angles. For it has been found that children learn mathematical truths better and more quickly, as is clear in singing, and we also know by experience that children learn and acquire mathematical truths better than the other parts of philosophy. For Aristotle says in the sixth book of the Ethics that youths are able to grasp mathematical truths quickly, not so matters pertaining to nature, metaphysics, and morals. Wherefore the mind must be trained first through the former rather than through these latter sciences. Seventhly, where the same things are not known to us and to nature, there the natural road for us is from the things better known to us to those better known to nature, or known more simply; and more easily do we grasp what is better known to ourselves, and with great difficulty we arrive at a knowledge of those things which are better known to nature. And the things known to nature are erroneously and imperfectly known by us, because our intellect bears the same relation to what is so clear to nature, as the eye of the bat to the light of the sun, as Aristotle maintains in the second book of the Metaphysics; such, for example, are especially God and the angels, and future life and heavenly things, and creatures nobler than others, because the nobler they are the less known are they to us. And these are called things known to nature and known simply. Therefore, on the contrary, where the same things are known both to us and to nature, we make much progress in regard to what is known to nature and in regard to all that is there included, and we are able to attain a perfect knowledge of them. But in mathematics only, as Averroës says in the first book of the Physics and in the seventh of the Metaphysics and in his commentary on the third book of the Heavens and the World, are the same things known to us and to nature or simply. Therefore as in mathematics we touch upon what is known fully to us, so also do we touch upon what is known to nature and known simply. Therefore we are able to reach directly an intimate knowledge of that science. Since, therefore, we have not this ability in other sciences, clearly mathematics is better known. Therefore the acquisition of this subject is the beginning of our knowledge.

Likewise, eighthly, because every doubt gives place to certainty and every error is cleared away by unshaken truth. But in mathematics we are able to arrive at the full truth without error, and at a certainty of all points involved without doubt; since in this subject demonstration by means of a proper and necessary cause can be given. Demonstration causes the truth to be known. And likewise in this subject it is possible to have for all things an example that may be perceived by the senses, and a test perceptible to the senses in drawing figures and in counting, so that all may be clear to the sense. For this reason there can be no doubt in this science. But in other sciences, the assistance of mathematics being excluded, there are so many doubts, so many opinions, so many errors on the part of man, that these sciences cannot be unfolded, as is clear since demonstration by means of a proper and necessary cause does not exist in them from their own nature because in natural phenomena, owing to the genesis and destruction of their proper causes as well as of the effects, there is no such thing as necessity. In metaphysics there can be no demonstration except through effect, since spiritual facts are discovered through corporeal effects and the creator through the creature, as is clear in that science. In morals there cannot be demonstrations from proper causes, as Aristotle teaches. And likewise neither in matters pertaining to logic nor in grammar, as is clear, can there be very convincing demonstrations because of the weak nature of the material concerning which those sciences treat. And therefore in mathematics alone are there demonstrations of the most convincing kind through a necessary cause. And therefore here alone can a man arrive at the truth from the nature of this science. Likewise in the other sciences there are doubts and opinions and contradictions on our part, so that we scarcely agree on the most trifling question or in a single sophism; for in these sciences there are from their nature no processes of drawing figures and of reckonings, by which all things must be proved true. And therefore in mathematics alone is there certainty without doubt.

Wherefore it is evident that if in other sciences we should arrive at certainty without doubt and truth without error, it behooves us to place the foundations of knowledge in mathematics, in so far as disposed through it we are able to reach certainty in other sciences and truth by the exclusion of error. This reasoning can be made clearer by comparison, and the principle is stated in the ninth book of Euclid. The same holds true here as in the relation of the knowledge of the conclusion to the knowledge of the premises, so that if there is error and doubt in these, the truth cannot be arrived at through these premises in regard to the conclusion, nor can there be certainty, because doubt is not verified by doubt, nor is truth proved by falsehood, although it is possible for us to reason from false premises, our reasoning in that case drawing an inference and not furnishing a proof; the same is true with respect to sciences as a whole; those in which there are strong and numerous doubts and opinions and errors, I say at least on our part, should have doubts of this kind and false statements cleared away by some science definitely known to us, and in which we have neither doubts nor errors. For since the conclusions and principles belonging to them are parts of the sciences as a whole, just as part is related to part, as conclusion to premises, so is science related to science, so that a science which is full of doubts and besprinkled with opinions and obscurities, cannot be rendered certain, nor made clear, nor verified except by some other science known and verified, certain and plain to us, as in the case of a conclusion reached through premises. But mathematics alone, as was shown above, remains fixed and verified for us with the utmost certainty and verification. Therefore by means of this science all other sciences must be known and verified. . . .

SECOND DISTINCTION

IN WHICH IT IS SHOWN THAT THE MATTERS OF THIS WORLD REQUIRE MATHEMATICS

Chapter I

In the First Chapter It Is Shown in General That Celestial and Terrestrial Things Require Mathematics

What has just been shown in regard to the sciences can be made clear in regard to things. For the things of this world cannot be made known without a knowledge of mathematics. For this is an assured fact in regard to celestial things, since two important sciences of mathematics treat of them, namely theoretical astrology and practical astrology. The first considers the quantities of all that is included in celestial things, and all things which are reduced to quantity discontinuous as well as continuous. For it gives us definite information as to the number of the heavens and of the stars, whose size can be comprehended by means of instruments, and the shapes of all and their magnitudes and distances from the earth and thicknesses and number, and greatness and smallness, the rising and setting of the signs of the stars, and the motion of the heavens and the stars, and the numbers and varieties of the eclipses. It likewise treats of the size and shape of the habitable earth and of all great divisions which are called climes, and it shows the difference in horizons and days and nights in the different climes. These matters, therefore, are determined by this branch of the subject as well as many things connected with them. Practical astrology enables us to know every hour the positions of the planets and stars, and their aspects and actions, and all the changes that take place in the heavenly bodies; and it treats of those things that happen in the air, such as comets and rainbows and the other changing phenomena there, in order that we may know their positions, altitudes, magnitudes, forms, and many things that must be considered in them. All this information is secured by means of instruments suitable for these purposes, and by tables and by canons, that is, rules invented for the verification of these matters, to the end that a way may be prepared for the judgments that can be formed in accordance with the power of philosophy, not only in the things of nature, but in those which take their tendency from nature and freely follow celestial direction; and not only for judgments in regard to present, past, and future, but for wonderful works, so that all things prosperous in this world may be advanced, and things adverse may be repressed, in a useful and glorious way. Nor are these matters doubtful. For the patriarchs and prophets from the beginning of the world had full information respecting these matters as well as all others. Aristotle restored the knowledge of the ancients and brought it to light. All those informed in great subjects agree in this, and experience teaches it. But concerning these matters an exposition will be given in the proper place.

It is plain, therefore, that celestial things are known by means of mathematics, and that a way is prepared by it to things that are lower. That, moreover, these terrestrial things cannot be learned without mathematics, is clear from the fact that we know things only through causes, if knowledge is to be properly acquired, as Aristotle says. But celestial things are the causes of terrestrial. Therefore these terrestrial things will not be known without a knowledge of the celestial, and the latter cannot be known without mathematics. Therefore a knowledge of these terrestrial things must depend on the same science. In the second place, we can see from their properties that no one of these lower or higher things can be known without the power of mathematics. For everything in nature is brought into being by an efficient cause and the material on which it works, for these two are concurrent at first. For the active cause by its own force moves and alters the matter, so that it becomes a thing. But the efficacy of the efficient cause and of the material cannot be known without the great power of mathematics even as the effects produced cannot be known without it. There are then these three, the efficient cause, the matter, and the effect. In celestial things there is a reciprocal influence of forces, as of light and other agents, and a change takes place in them without, however, any tendency toward their destruction. And so it can be shown that nothing within the range of things can be known without the power of geometry. We learn from this line of reasoning that in like manner the other parts of mathematics are necessary; and they are so for the same reason that holds in the case of geometry; and without doubt they are far more necessary, because they are nobler. If, therefore, the proposition be demonstrated in the case of geometry, it is not necessary in this plea that mention be made of the other parts.

In the first place, I shall demonstrate a proposition in geometry in respect to the efficient cause. For every efficient cause acts by its own force which it produces on the matter subject to it, as the light of the sun produces its own force in the air, and this force is light diffused through the whole world from the solar light. This force is called likeness, image, species, and by many other names, and it is produced by substance as well as accident and by spiritual substance as well as corporeal. Substance is more productive of it than accident, and spiritual substance than corporeal. This species causes every action in this world; for it acts on sense, on intellect, and all the matter in the world for the production of things, because one and the same thing is done by a natural agent on whatsoever it acts, because it has no freedom of choice; and therefore it performs the same act on whatever it meets. But if it acts on the sense and the intellect, it becomes a species, as all know. Accordingly, on the other hand, if it acts on matter it also becomes a species. In those beings that have reason and intellect, although they do many things with deliberation and freedom of will, yet this action, namely, a production of species, is natural in them, just as it is in other things. Hence the substance of the soul multiplies its own force in the body and outside of the body, and any body outside of itself produces its own force, and the angels move the world by means of this kind. But God produces forces out of nothing, which he multiplies in things; created agents do not do so, but in another way about which we need not concern ourselves at the present time. Forces of this kind belonging to agents produce every action in this world. But there are two things now to be noted respecting these forces; one is the multiplication itself of the species and of force from the place of its production; and the other is the varied action in this world due to the production and destruction of things. The second cannot be known without the first. Therefore it is necessary that the multiplication itself be first described.

Chapter II

In Which the Canons of the Multiplication of the Forces of Agents as Respects Lines and Angles Are Explained

Every multiplication is either with respect to lines, or angles, or figures. While the species travels in a medium of one rarity, as in what is wholly sky, and wholly fire, and wholly air, or wholly water, it is propagated in straight paths, because Aristotle says in the fifth book of the Metaphysics that nature works in the shorter way possible, and the straight line is the shortest of all. This fact is also made evident by the twentieth proposition of the first book of Euclid, which states that in every triangle two sides are longer than the third.

But when the second body is of another rarity and density, so that it is not wholly dense, but changes in some way the passage of the species, like water, which in one way is rare, and in another dense, and crystal similarly, and glass and the like, through the media of which we are able to see, then the species either impinges upon the second body perpendicularly, and still travels along the straight line as in the first medium; or if it does not fall perpendicularly, then of necessity it changes its straight path, and makes an angle on entering the second body, and its declination from the straight path is called refraction of the ray and the species. This is because the perpendicular is the stronger and shorter, and therefore nature works in a better way on it, as geometrical demonstrations show, of which mention will be made later more particularly in the proper place. But this refraction is twofold, since if the second body is denser, as is the case in descending from the sky to these lower objects, all the forces of the stars that do not fall perpendicularly on the globe of elements, are broken between the straight path and the perpendicular drawn from the place of refraction. If the second body is rarer, as is the case in ascending from water into the air, the straight path falls between the refracted ray and the perpendicular drawn from the place of refraction. And this is a wonderful diversity in the action of nature, but it is not strange, when countless wonders are performed by nature in accordance with the laws of these refractions; and by means of art aiding nature those things can be done which the world

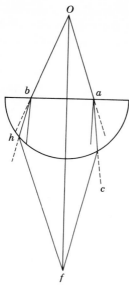

FIGURE 1

cannot receive, as I shall explain in perspective science. But it will be
driven by these means in the times of Antichrist to those things which
it will itself wish for in great part.

That, moreover, these things are true authorities teach, and all experts
know, and instruments can be made so that we may sensibly see propaga-
tions of this kind; but until we have instruments we can prove this by
natural effect without contradiction, as this figure shows (Figure 1).
Let us take then a hemisphere of crystal or a glass vessel, the lower part
of which is round and full of water. When, therefore, rays come from
the center of the sun to the body of crystal, or of glass, which is denser
than the air, those that are not perpendicular to such a body (and these
are the ones that do not pass through its center, as is clear from geometric
principles) are refracted between the straight path and the perpendicular
drawn from the point of refraction, as is the ray *ac*, which after passing
through the whole body of the vessel, comes obliquely to the air which
is of less density. Of necessity, therefore, it so travels that the straight
path is between the path of the ray and the perpendicular drawn to the
point of refraction, and therefore the ray will not travel to *c*, but bends
to *f*, on the principal perpendicular, which comes from the sun, that is,
ray *Of*. And in the same way at any other point, owing to the double
refraction, *hf* will pass through the same point *f* on the ray *Of*. But an
infinite number of rays come forth from every point on the sun to the

body; therefore an infinite number will meet in this same point by means of the double refraction. But a convergence of rays is the cause of heat. Therefore a burning heat will be produced at this point. And this is a fact, as is clear to the sense; for if a combustible be placed at this point, as wool, silk, or a piece of rag, it will be consumed. Since, therefore, there is combustion at this point and this cannot happen except through a convergence of rays, and the rays cannot assemble except through a double refraction, because a single refraction would not suffice and a third refraction is not required, therefore we must assume this kind of refraction, a wonderful thing in the eyes of men of science. For why is it that nature so acts? Surely nothing is pleasing to nature, or to her will, except what is remade by change; but the causes are hidden. We need not now investigate the causes, since we know this marvel by means of a very certain test, and in what follows other tests will be added.

When, however, the second body is so dense as in no way to permit the passage of the species,—I am speaking of a passage appreciated by human vision,—we say that the species is reflected. Yet according to Aristotle and Boetius the vision of the lynx penetrates walls. Therefore the species does actually pass through as a matter of fact; but human vision forms no judgment concerning this, but does concerning the reflection which of necessity takes place. For on account of the difficulty of passage through the dense medium, since in the air from which it came it finds an easy road, it multiplies itself more abundantly in the direction from which it came (Figure 2). And this in the first place can happen in general in two ways; for either the ray falls perpendicularly on the dense body and then returns upon itself wholly by the same path by which it came, and a ray is generated in the same place, as for example the ray ab falls perpendicularly, and this is in planes at right angles, as is shown in the eleventh book of geometry, just as in spherical shaped bodies when the ray passes through the center. And the reason for this is that the angles of incidence and reflection are always equal, as a manifold demonstration shows, and authorities maintain, and instru-

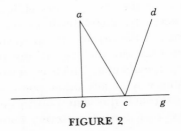

FIGURE 2

ments made for this purpose make clear to the eye. But there are only two right angles at the dense body in the case of *ab*. Therefore by these same angles the reflex ray will return upon itself and therefore in the same place. But the line *ac* which falls at oblique angles and not perpendicularly, does not return upon itself, but passes to *d*, because of the equality of the angles of incidence and reflection. Whenever the ray falls at oblique angles, the acute angle is called the angle of incidence; and from the obtuse angle an angle equal to the angle of incidence is cut off by the reflected line. The angle so formed is contained between the reflected line and the dense body, as is the angle *dcg*, and it is called the angle of reflection, which of necessity must equal the acute angle on the other side, and we prove this to the sight in mirrors. For we cannot see things, unless the eye is in the line of reflection, as if the eye be at *d* it will see *a;* and if not, it will not see by means of that reflected ray. These are known facts, and tests will be given adequately concerning this matter in what follows.

Moreover, an infinite number of rays can be assembled by reflection, just as by multiplication, so that strong combustions take place. But from a plain surface rays cannot converge to one point, because one goes to one point, another to another point. Nor can they do so from a convex mirror; but they can converge from a concave spherical mirror, or from one column-shaped, or pyramidal, or ring-shaped, or oval, and so too from others. If, therefore, a concave spherical mirror be exposed to the sun, an infinite number of rays will converge to one point by means of reflection. And therefore of necessity fire is kindled when a concave mirror is exposed to the sun, as is stated in the last proposition of the book on Mirrors, and the demonstration is there given. But an instrument might very well have been made for this purpose, and the phenomenon would then be visible to the eye, as we stated before in the case of refraction. Hence if a mirror should be made of good steel, or of silver, the combustion would occur more easily; but a combustion does not take place by all rays falling on a mirror, but by those only which fall on the circumference of a circle around the axis of the mirror, because all that fall in one circumference fall at equal angles, and therefore are reflected to a point on the axis, because the angles of the reflected rays are equal, and those that fall in another circle are reflected to another point, and those in a third circle to a third point, and the same statement may be made of an infinite number of circles imagined around the axis of the mirror; for of necessity rays falling on different circumferences travel to different points, because they do not fall at equal angles. Those falling in a smaller circle are reflected higher, and those in the greatest circle are reflected to the lowest point, namely to the pole of the sphere, or to the end of the axis. But neither nature nor art is content with combustion of this kind, nay, they wish so to fashion bodies that all the rays falling on the whole surface of the mirror may converge to a single point; and what is more at every distance we desire. This is the ultimate which the power of geometry can do. For this mirror would burn fiercely everything on which it could be focused. We are to believe that Antichrist will use these mirrors to burn up cities and camps and armies. Since if a moderate convergence of rays by refraction or by a concave mirror burns perceptibly, how much more so without limit, when rays without number converge by means of this mirror. Scientists reckon that this is a necessary consequence. And an author in a book on burning mirrors shows how this instrument is made, but without sufficient reason hid in that book much respecting the artifice, and states that he has placed the lacking information in another book, which has not been translated by the Latins. But there are Latins who because of the ill favor of that author in concealing the perfection of his knowledge, have studied this wonderful secret of nature, because that author stimulates greatly men skilled in science to perfect what is lacking, and he shows that the mirror must be nearly ring-shaped or oval, as if the cones of an egg were cut off, the figure would be ring-shaped; if, however, one cone remains, it is oval. Now in such a figure properly constructed all the rays falling on the whole surface must fall at equal angles, and therefore they must be reflected at like angles, and for this reason to one point. Moreover, the most skillful of the Latins is busily engaged on the construction of this mirror, and the glory of your Magnificence will be able to order him to complete it when he is known to you. This triple multiplication is said to be a principal one, because it comes from the agent itself.

But the fourth kind is more necessary to the world, although it is called accidental multiplication. For light is called accidental with respect to the principal light coming from an object, since it does not come from an agent, but from principal multiplications, as in a house the principal multiplication falls through the window from the sun, but in a corner of the house the accidental light comes from the ray of the window. Moreover, the bodies of mortals would not be able to be exposed always to principal species without destruction, and for this reason God has tempered all things by means of accidental species of this kind.

The fifth kind is different from the others, for it does not follow the common laws of nature, but claims for itself a special privilege. This multiplication does not take place except in an animated medium, as in the nerves of the senses; for the species follows the tortuous course of the nerve, and pays no attention to the straight path. This happens through the force of the vital principle regulating the path of the species, as the actions of an animated being require. Concerning this propagation something will be said in the truths of perspective. The first four in respect to which nature delights to work are common to the inanimate things of the world; the fifth is known to pertain to sensation.

Chapter III

In Which Multiplication Is Given as Respects Figures

We must next consider how multiplication takes place with respect to figures. Multiplication of necessity takes place in the form of a sphere. For the agent multiplies itself equally in every direction, and with respect to all diameters, and all differences of position, namely, above, below, before, behind, to the right, and to the left. Therefore everywhere the lines go forth in every direction from the agent as from a center: but lines traveling everywhere from one place cannot terminate except on the concave surface of a sphere. And this is clear, because the eye sees only by means of the coming species, but if an infinite number of eyes were placed everywhere, all would see the same thing; therefore the species goes forth by means of an infinite number of lines; but an infinite number of lines terminate only on a spherical surface. If it should be said that light entering through a large triangular opening or through one of another polygonal figure does not fall in spherical form, but does so when it enters through a small opening, we must state that the sides of the small opening are not far apart and therefore the light in a short distance is able to regain its figure, but when it passes through a large figure, it cannot do so easily, but it will do so at some sufficient distance, if obstacles are removed. This principle is made evident by the fourteenth and fifteenth propositions of the first book of the elements of Euclid, as the figure shows (Figure 3). For let the rays be drawn as far from the intersection as from the intersection to the sun, by the propositions mentioned the bases of the triangles must be equal. But those bases are the diameters of the lights. Therefore the diameter of the species is necessarily equal to the diameter of the sun at some one distance, and consequently the mul-

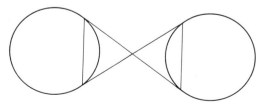

FIGURE 3

tiplication will be an equal spherical one, and can be varied according to difference of distance, but it will always be of spherical form. Nor is the light of fire a case in point, which ascends in the form of a pyramid; because this is not a multiplication from the proper nature of light, but is owing to the motion of the body of the fire itself, of which light is an accident, and the accident moves in accordance with the motion of its subject, like the light of the sun in the sun. Now fire must ascend in pyramidal form, since the interior parts are removed from the surrounding cold, and therefore they are less impeded and extricate themselves more quickly than the parts on the outside, and for this reason rise higher, and the remaining parts the nearer they are to these, the more quickly do they extricate themselves, and they attach themselves to the ones in the interior, failing somewhat to reach the height of the inmost parts, and so in regular gradation the remoter ones reach a lesser height, because they are more impeded by the contrary force surrounding them; and therefore a pyramid must necessarily be formed. But in the sphere all regular figures can be inscribed, as is clear from the fifteenth book of the elements of Euclid, among which figures is the pyramid.

And although according to the principle of inscribing geometrical figures irregular ones cannot be inscribed, nor round figures, nevertheless all figures can be produced and marked on the sphere. And therefore not only in spherical multiplication shall we find pyramids with sides, which can be inscribed in a sphere, but also round pyramids, which can be marked and drawn in spherical multiplication. And it is this figure that nature especially selects in every multiplication and action, and not any pyramid at all, but that one whose base is the surface of the agent and whose vertex falls on some point of the surface acted on, because

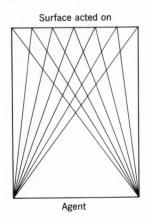

FIGURE 4

in this way can the species of the agent come to each point of the surface acted on by means of an infinite number of separate pyramids, as is clear in the figure (Figure 4).

For from each point of the surface acted on there are an infinite number of rays and therefore they can be combined infinitely to form an infinite number of round pyramids with one common base, namely, the surface of the whole agent; and to every part of the surface acted on there comes an apex of a pyramid, so that force comes from the whole agent to each point of the surface acted on, and not from some limited part, to the end that the force may come complete and as a whole, not partial and imperfect, so that the action may be complete, because nature acts in accordance with what is better.

* * * *

PART SIX OF THIS PLEA

Chapter I

Having laid down fundamental principles of the wisdom of the Latins so far as they are found in language, mathematics, and optics, I now wish to unfold the principles of experimental science, since without experience nothing can be sufficiently known. For there are two modes of acquiring knowledge, namely, by reasoning and experience. Reasoning draws a conclusion and makes us grant the conclusion, but does not make the conclusion certain, nor does it remove doubt so that the mind may rest on the intuition of truth, unless the mind discovers it by the path of experience; since many have the arguments relating to what can be known, but because they lack experience they neglect the arguments, and neither avoid what is harmful nor follow what is good. For if a man who has never seen fire should prove by adequate reasoning that fire burns and injures things and destroys them, his mind would not be satisfied thereby, nor would he avoid fire, until he placed his hand or some combustible substance in the fire, so that he might prove by experience that which reasoning taught. But when he has had actual experience of combustion his mind is made certain and rests in the full light of truth. Therefore reasoning does not suffice, but experience does.

This is also evident in mathematics, where proof is most convincing. But the mind of one who has the most convincing proof in regard to the equilateral triangle will never cleave to the conclusion without experience, nor will he heed it, but will disregard it until experience is offered him by the intersection of two circles, from either intersection of which two lines may be drawn to the extremities of the given line; but then the man accepts the conclusion without any question. Aristotle's statement, then, that proof is reasoning that causes us to know is to be understood with the proviso that the proof is accompanied by its appropriate experience, and is not to be understood of the bare proof. His statement also in the first book of the Metaphysics that those who understand the reason and the cause are wiser than those who have empiric knowledge of a fact, is spoken of such as know only the bare truth without the cause. But I am here speaking of the man who knows the reason and the cause through experience. These men are perfect in their wisdom, as Aristotle maintains in the sixth book of the Ethics, whose simple statements must be accepted as if they offered proof, as he states in the same place.

He therefore who wishes to rejoice without doubt in regard to the truths underlying phenomena must know how to devote himself to experiment. For authors write many statements, and people believe them through reasoning which they formulate without experience. Their reasoning is wholly false. For it is generally believed that the diamond cannot be broken except by goat's blood, and philosophers and theologians misuse this idea. But fracture by means of blood of this kind has never been verified, although the effort has been made; and without that blood it can be broken easily. For I have seen this with my own eyes, and this is necssary, because gems cannot be carved except by fragments of this stone. Similarly it is generally believed that the castors employed by physicians are the testicles of the male animal. But this is not true, because the beaver has these under its breast, and both the male and female produce testicles of this kind. Besides these castors the male beaver has its testicles in their natural place; and therefore what is subjoined is a dreadful lie, namely, that when the hunters pursue the beaver, he himself knowing what they are seeking cuts out with his teeth these glands. Moreover, it is generally believed that hot water freezes more quickly than cold water in vessels, and the argument in support of this is advanced that contrary is excited by contrary, just like enemies meeting each other. But it is certain that cold water freezes more quickly for any one who makes the experiment. People attribute this to Aristotle in the second book of the Meteorologics; but he certainly does not make this statement, but he does make one like it, by which they have been deceived, namely, that if cold water and hot water are poured on a cold place, as upon ice, the hot water freezes more quickly, and this is true. But if hot water and cold are placed in two vessels, the cold will freeze more quickly. Therefore all things must be verified by experience.

But experience is of two kinds; one is gained through our external senses, and in this way we gain our experience of those things that are in the heavens by instruments made for this purpose, and of those things here below by means attested by our vision. Things that do not belong in our part of the world we know through other scientists who have had experience of them. As, for example, Aristotle on the authority of Alexander sent two thousand men through different parts of the world to gain experimental knowledge of all things that are on the surface of the earth, as Pliny bears witness in his Natural History. This experience is both human and philosophical, as far as man can act in accordance with the grace given him; but this experience does not suffice him, because it does not give full attestation in regard to things corporeal owing to its difficulty, and does not touch at all on things spiritual. It is necessary, therefore, that the intellect of man should be otherwise aided, and for this reason the holy patriarchs and prophets, who first gave sciences to the world, received illumination within and were not dependent on sense alone. The same is true of many believers since the time of Christ. For the grace of faith illuminates greatly, as also do divine inspirations, not only in things spiritual, but in things corporeal and in the sciences of philosophy; as Ptolemy states in the Centilogium, namely, that there are two roads by which we arrive at the knowledge of facts, one through the experience of philosophy, the other through divine inspiration, which is far the better way, as he says.

Moreover, there are seven stages of this internal knowledge, the first of which is reached through illuminations relating purely to the sciences. The second consists in the virtues. For the evil man is ignorant, as Aristotle says in the second book of the Ethics. Moreover, Algazel says in his Logic that the soul disfigured by sins is like a rusty mirror, in which the species of objects cannot be seen clearly; but the soul adorned with virtues is like a well-polished mirror, in which the forms of objects are clearly seen. For this reason true philosophers have labored more in morals for the honor of virtue, concluding in their own case that they cannot perceive the causes of things unless they have souls free from sins. Such is the statement of Augustine in regard to Socrates in the eighth book of the City of God, chapter III. Wherefore the Scripture says, "in a malevolent soul, etc." For it is not possible that the soul should rest in the light of truth while it is stained with sins, but like a parrot or magpie it will repeat the words of another which it has learned by long practice. The proof of this is that the beauty of truth known in its splendor attracts men to the love of it, but the proof of love is the display of a work of love. Therefore he who acts contrary to the truth must necessarily be ignorant of it, although he may know how to compose very elegant phrases, and quote the opinions of other people, like an animal that imitates the words of human beings, and like an ape that relies on the aid of men to perform its part, although it does not understand their reason. Virtue, therefore, clarifies the mind, so that a man comprehends more easily not only moral but scientific truths. I have proved this carefully in the case of many pure young men, who because of innocency of soul have attained greater proficiency than can be stated, when they have had sane advice in regard to their study. Of this number is the bearer of this present treatise, whose fundamental knowledge very few of the Latins have acquired. For since he is quite young, about twenty years of age, and very poor, nor has he been able to have teachers, nor has he spent one year in learning his great store of knowledge, nor is he a man of great genius nor of a very retentive memory, there can be no other cause except the grace of God, which owing to the purity of his soul has granted to him those things that it has as a rule refused to show to all other students. For as a spotless virgin he has departed from me, nor have I found in him any kind of mortal sin, although I have examined him carefully, and he has, therefore, a soul so bright and clear that with very little instruction he has learned more than can be estimated. And I have striven to aid in bringing it about that these two young men should be useful vessels in God's Church, to the end that they may reform by the grace of God the whole course of study of the Latins.

The third stage consists in the seven gifts of the Holy Spirit, which Isaiah enumerates. The fourth consists in the beatitudes, which the Lord defines in the Gospels. The fifth consists in the spiritual senses. The sixth consists in fruits, of which is the peace of God which passes all understanding. The seventh consists in raptures and their states according to the different ways in which people are caught up to see many things of which it is not lawful for a man to speak. And he who has had diligent training in these experiences or in several of them is able to assure himself and others not only in regard to things spiritual, but also in regard to all human sciences. Therefore since all the divisions of speculative philosophy proceed by arguments, which are either based on a point from authority or on the other points of argumentation except this division which I am now examining, we find necessary the science that is called experimental. I wish to explain it, as it is useful not only to philosophy, but to the knowledge of God, and for the direction of the whole world; just as in the preceding divisions I showed the relationship of the languages and sciences to their end, which is the divine wisdom by which all things are disposed.

Chapter II

Since this Experimental Science is wholly unknown to the rank and file of students, I am therefore unable to convince people of its utility

unless at the same time I disclose its excellence and its proper signification. This science alone, therefore, knows how to test perfectly what can
be done by nature, what by the effort of art, what by trickery, what the
incantations, conjurations, invocations, deprecations, sacrifices, that belong to magic, mean and dream of, and what is in them, so that all falsity
may be removed and the truth alone of art and nature may be retained.
This science alone teaches us how to view the mad acts of magicians, that
they may be not ratified but shunned, just as logic considers sophistical
reasoning.

This science has three leading characteristics with respect to other sciences. The first is that it investigates by experiment the notable conclusions of all those sciences. For the other sciences know how to discover
their principles by experiments, but their conclusions are reached by
reasoning drawn from the principles discovered. But if they should have
a particular and complete experience of their own conclusions, they must
have it with the aid of this noble science. For it is true that mathematics
has general experiments as regards its conclusions in its figures and calculations, which also are applied to all sciences and to this kind of experiment because no science can be known without mathematics. But if
we give our attention to particular and complete experiments and such
as are attested wholly by the proper method, we must employ the principles of this science which is called experimental. I give as an example
the rainbow and phenomena connected with it, of which nature are the
circle around the sun and the stars, the streak [virga] also lying at the
side of the sun or of a star, which is apparent to the eye in a straight line,
and is called by Aristotle in the third book of the Meteorologics a perpendicular, but by Seneca a streak, and the circle is called a corona, phenomena which frequently have the colors of the rainbow. The natural
philosopher discusses these phenomena, and the writer on Perspective
has much to add pertaining to the mode of vision that is necessary in this
case. But neither Aristotle nor Avicenna in their Natural Histories has
given us a knowledge of phenomena of this kind, nor has Seneca, who
composed a special book on them. But Experimental Science attests them.

*   *   *   *

[IN CHAPTERS III-XIII, BACON PRODUCES THE PROMISED DEMONSTRATIONS, THEN
CONCLUDES:]

Hence, reasoning does not attest these matters, but experiments on a
large scale made with instruments and by various necessary means are
required. Therefore no discussion can give an adequate explanation in
these matters, for the whole subject is dependent on experiment. For

this reason I do not think that in this matter I have grasped the whole truth, because I have not yet made all the experiments that are necessary, and because in this work I am proceeding by the method of persuasion and of demonstration of what is required in the study of science, and not by the method of compiling what has been written on this subject. Therefore it does not devolve on me to give at this time an attestation possible for me, but to treat the subject in the form of a plea for the study of science. . . .

Chapter on the Second Prerogative of Experimental Science

This mistress of the speculative sciences alone is able to give us important truths within the confines of the other sciences, which those sciences can learn in no other way. Hence these truths are not connected with the discussion of principles but are wholly outside of these, although they are within the confines of these sciences, since they are neither conclusions nor principles. Clear examples in regard to these matters can be given; but in what follows the man without experience must not seek a reason in order that he may first understand, for he will never have this reason except after experiment. Hence in the first place there should be readiness to believe, until in the second place experiment follows, so that in the third reasoning may function. For if a man is without experience that a magnet attracts iron, and has not heard from others that it attracts, he will never discover this fact before an experiment. Therefore in the beginning he must believe those who have made the experiment, or who have reliable information from experimenters, nor should he reject the truth, because he is ignorant of it, and because he does not arrive at it by reasoning.

*   *   *   *

Chapter on the Third Prerogative or the Dignity of the Experimental Art

But there is a third dignity of this science. It arises from those properties through which it has no connection with the other sciences, but by its own power investigates the secrets of nature. This consists in two things; namely, in the knowledge of the future, the past, and the present, and in wonderful works by which it excels in the power of forming judgments the ordinary astronomy dealing with judgments. For Ptolemy in the book introductory to the Almagest says that there is a more certain road than that through the ordinary astronomy, and this is the pathway of experiment, which follows the course of nature, to which many of the philosophers who are believers are turning, just like Aristotle and a host of the authors of judgments formed from the stars, as he himself says, and as we know by proper practice, which cannot be gainsaid. This science was discovered as a complete remedy for human ignorance and inadvertence; for it is difficult to get accurate astronomical instruments, and it is more difficult to get verified tables, especially those in which the motion of the planets is equalized. The use, moreover, of these tables is difficult, but still more difficult is the use of the instruments. But this science has discovered the definitions and the means by which it can answer easily every question, as far as the power of a single branch of philosophy can do so, and by which it can show us the forms of the celestial forces, and the influences of the heavenly bodies on this world without the difficulty of the ordinary astronomy. This part of the science relating to judgments has four principal divisions or secret sciences.

Moreover, certain bear witness that activities of this science which display philosophy consist in changing the character of a region, so that the habits of its people are changed. One of such witnesses was Aristotle himself, the most learned of philosophers. When Alexander asked him in regard to the nations which he had discovered, whether he should exterminate them because of the ferocity of their character, or should permit them to live, he replied in the book of Secrets, "If you can alter the air of those nations, permit them to live; if you cannot, then kill them." For he maintained that the air of these nations could be changed advantageously, so that the complexions of their bodies would be changed, and then their minds influenced by their complexions would choose good morals in accordance with the freedom of the will. This is one of the secrets.

Moreover, certain assert that change is effected by the sun. There is, as an illustration, the example of Aristotle when he said to Alexander, "Give a hot drink from the seed of a plant to whomsoever you wish, and he will obey you for the rest of your life." Some maintain that an army may be stupefied and put to flight. Of this number is Aristotle, who says to Alexander, "Take such a stone, and every army will flee from you." They bear witness that these statements and innumerable others of this kind are true, not meaning that violence is done to the freedom of the will, since Aristotle, who maintains this view, says in the Ethics that the will cannot be coerced. The body, moreover, can be changed by the influence of things, and the minds of people are then aroused and influenced to desire voluntarily that to which they are directed; just as we see in the book of Medicine that through potions and many medicines people can be changed in body and in the passions of the soul and in the inclination of the will.

There are, moreover, other inventions belonging more to nature which do not have as their object a marvelous change in the will, and they are diversified in character. Some of these possess an excellence of wisdom with other advantages, as, for example, perpetual baths most suitable for human use that do not require any artificial renewal; and ever-burning lamps. For we see many things that cannot be impaired by fire, nay, that are purified by fire, like the skin of the salamander and many other things of this kind, which also can be so prepared that they are externally luminous of themselves, and retain the power of fire, and give forth flame and light. Moreover, against foes of the state they have discovered important arts, so that without a sword or any weapon requiring physical contact they could destroy all who offer resistance. There are many kinds of these inventions. Some of these are perceived by no one of the senses, or by smell alone, and of these inventions Aristotle's book explains that of altering the air, but not those of which I spoke above. These last are of a different character, since they act by means of an infection. There are others also that change some one of the senses, and they are diversified in accordance with all the senses.

Certain of these work a change by contact only and thus destroy life. For malta, which is a kind of bitumen and is plentiful in this world, when cast upon an armed man burns him up. The Romans suffered severe loss of life from this in their conquests, as Pliny states in the second book of the Natural History, and as the histories attest. Similarly yellow petroleum, that is, oil springing from the rock, burns up whatever it meets if it is properly prepared. For a consuming fire is produced by this which can be extinguished with difficulty; for water cannot put it out. Certain inventions disturb the hearing to such a degree that, if they are set off suddenly at night with sufficient skill, neither city nor army can endure them. No clap of thunder could compare with such noises. Certain of these strike such terror to the sight that the coruscations of the clouds disturb it incomparably less. Gideon is thought to have employed inventions similar to these in the camp of the Midianites. We have an example of this in that toy of children which is made in many parts of the world, namely, an instrument as large as the human thumb. From the force of the salt called saltpeter so horrible a sound is produced at the bursting of so small a thing, namely, a small piece of parchment, that we perceive it exceeds the roar of sharp thunder, and the flash exceeds the greatest brilliancy of the lightning accompanying the thunder.

There are also very many things that slay every poisonous animal by the gentlest touch, and if a circle is made around these animals with things of this kind the animals cannot get out, but die, although they are not touched. But if a man is bitten by a poisonous animal, by the application of the powder of such things he can be healed, as Bede states in his Ecclesiastical History and as we know by experience. And thus there are innumerable things that have strange virtues, whose potencies we are ignorant of solely from our neglect of experiment.

But there are other inventions which do not possess such advantage for the state, but are to be looked upon as miracles of nature, such as experiments with the magnet, not only on iron, but on gold and other metals. Moreover, if the experiment on iron were not known, it would be viewed as a great miracle. And surely in respect to the action of the magnet on iron there are phenomena unknown to those who use the magnet which show in a wonderful way the dissolutions of nature. Just as also from these the faithful experimenter knows how to experiment on the mutual attraction of other things, as, for example, the stone that passes to the acid, and bitumen that ignites from fire placed at a distance from it, as Pliny states in the second book of the Natural History; and certain other things that are mutually attracted although locally separated. This is truly wonderful beyond all that I have seen and heard. For after I saw this, there has been nothing difficult for my intellect to believe, provided it had a trustworthy authority. And that this fact may not be hidden from your Reverence, this phenomenon occurs in the parts of plants divided and locally separated. For if a sapling of one year's growth is taken, which springs forth beside the roots of the hazel, and is divided longitudinally, and the divided parts separated by the space of a palm or four fingers, and one person holds on one side the extremities of the two parts, and another similarly on the other side, always with an equal and gentle grasp, so that the parts are kept opposite each other in the same position they had before the division, within the time of a half mile's walk the parts of the twig begin to approach each other gradually, but with greater force at the end of the experiment, so that at length they meet and are united. The ends, however, remain apart, because they are prevented from meeting owing to the force exerted by those holding the parts. This is a very wonderful thing. For this reason magicians perform this experiment, repeating different incantations, and they believe that the phenomenon is caused by virtue of the incantations. I have disregarded the incantations and have discovered the wonderful action of nature, which is similar to that of the magnet on iron. For just as the one attracts the other because of the similar nature of the iron and the magnet, so do the parts in this case. Hence the natural force, which is similar in both parts of the twig, causes them to unite. If they were arranged in the required way, they would meet at the extremities just as in the middle and more quickly, as, for example, if the ends were minutely pierced and threads passed through the ends, so that they could be suspended in the air without hindrance. This is true not only of hazel saplings but of many others, as in the case of willows and perhaps in that of all saplings if they were arranged in the required manner. But since in such matters the mind thinks more aptly than the pen writes, I forbear for the present. I am here merely writing down the statements of scientists and noting their achievements. The genius of these men I admire more than I understand.

Concluding thus the subject of this science experimental without restriction, I shall now show its advantage to theology, as I have done similarly in the case of the other sciences. Since I have now shown the intrinsic nature of this science, it is evident to all that next to moral philosophy this science is the most useful, and it is so in the first place to theology itself in its unrestricted sense because of the literal and spiritual meaning in which it consists. For I showed above that the literal meaning consists in expressing the truth in regard to created things by means of their definitions and descriptions, and I likewise showed that reasoning does not arrive at this truth, but that experiment does. Wherefore this science next to moral philosophy will present the literal truth of Scripture most effectively, so that through suitable adaptations and similitudes the spiritual sense may be derived, owing to the peculiar nature of the sacred Scripture and in accordance with the methods employed by the sacred writers and by all sages.

Then this science as regards the commonwealth of believers is useful, as we saw in its special knowledge of the future, present, and past, and in its display of wonderful works on behalf of Church and state, so that all useful activities are promoted and the opposite are hindered both in the few and in the multitude, as was explained. And if we proceed to the conversion of unbelievers, it is evidently of service in two main ways with numerous subdivisions, since a plea for the faith can be effectively made through this science, not by arguments but by works, which is the more effective way. For to the man who denies the truth of the faith because he cannot understand it I shall state the mutual attraction of things in nature, just as I described it. Likewise I shall tell him that a jar may be broken without human force, and the wine contained in it remain motionless and without flow for three days; and that gold and silver in a pouch, and a sword in its scabbard may be consumed without injury to their containers, as Seneca states in the book of Natural Questions. I shall tell him, moreover, that the birds called kingfisher in the depth of winter compel the stormy sea to be calm and restrain itself until they have laid their eggs and brought forth their young, as Basil and Ambrose in the Hexaemeron and philosophers and poets state. For these facts and similar ones ought to influence a man and urge him to accept the divine verities. Since if in the vilest creatures verities are found by which the pride of the human intellect ought to be subdued so that it may believe them although it does not understand them, conviction should follow, or injury will be done to infallible truth, since a man ought rather to humble his mind to the glorious truths of God. Surely there is no comparison.

But there is still another very useful way; since the formation of judgments, as I have said, is a function of this science, in regard to what can happen by nature or be effected in art, and what not. This science, moreover, knows how to separate the illusions of magic and to detect all their errors in incantations, invocations, conjurations, sacrifices, and cults. But unbelievers busy themselves in these mad acts and trust in them, and have believed that the Christians used such means in working their miracles. Wherefore this science is of the greatest advantage in persuading men to accept the faith, since this branch alone of philosophy happens to proceed in this way, because this is the only branch that considers matters of this kind, and is able to overcome all falsehood and superstition and error of unbelievers in regard to magic, such as incantations and the like already mentioned. How far, moreover, it may serve to reprobate obstinate unbelievers is already shown by the violent means that have just been touched upon, and therefore I pass on.

We must consider, however, that although other sciences do many wonders, as in the case of practical geometry, which produces mirrors that burn up every opposing object, and so too in the other sciences, yet all things of such wonderful utility in the state belong chiefly to this science. For this science has the same relation to the other sciences as the science of navigation to the carpenter's art and the military art to that of the engineer. For this science teaches how wonderful instruments may be made, and uses them when made, and also considers all secret things owing to the advantages they may possess for the state and for individuals; and it directs other sciences as its handmaids, and therefore the whole power of speculative science is attributed especially to this science. And now the wonderful advantage derived from these three sciences in this world on behalf of the Church of God against the enemies of the faith is manifest, who should be destroyed rather by the discoveries of science than by the warlike arms of combatants. Antichrist will use these means freely and effectively, in order that he may crush and confound the power of this world; and by these means tyrants in times past brought the world under their sway. This has been shown by examples without end.

But I now cite the one example of Alexander the Great in place of all other examples that might be cited, who when he set out from Greece to conquer the world had only 32,000 foot soldiers and 4500 horsemen, as Orosius states to Augustine in his book Ormesta Mundi, bringing war with so small a force upon the whole world. It is uncertain which is the more wonderful, that he conquered or that he ventured the attack. In his first battle with King Darius he overcame 600,000 Persians with a loss in his army of 120 horsemen and nine foot soldiers. In the second battle he conquered 400,000 men, and of his own army 130 foot soldiers and 150 horsemen fell. After this he easily subdued the rest of the world, which had become terrified. But Orosius says that he conquered not less by skill than by the valor of the Macedonians. Nor is it to be wondered at, since Aristotle was with him in these wars, as we read in the life of Aristotle. Seneca, moreover, states in the Natural Questions that Alexander conquered the world under the guidance of Aristotle and Callisthenes, who were his teachers in all knowledge. But Aristotle was his chief teacher; and it is easily apparent from what has been said how by the paths of knowledge Aristotle was able to hand over the world to Alexander. Moreover, the Church should consider the employment of these inventions against unbelievers and rebels, in order that it may spare Christian blood, and especially should it do so because of future perils in the times of Antichrist, which with the grace of God it would be easy to meet, if prelates and princes promoted study and investigated the secrets of nature and of art.

7

JEAN BURIDAN

Inevitably, the details of Jean Buridan's life have not survived. Probably he was born in northern France, and apparently the date fell shortly before 1300. Medieval philosophy was then at its height, and Buridan was fortunate to study in its leading center, the University of Paris, under one of its undoubted masters, William of Ockham. Buridan himself went on to a highly successful career as a teacher in the same university, serving twice as its rector, and on one occasion defending its interests before the Papal court in Rome. A circle of able students, including Nicole Oresme and Albert of Saxony, gathered about him and extended the scope and the influence of his ideas. Beyond that, the story consists of rumors now largely discredited—that he founded the University of Vienna, and that he was the lover of the Queen of France. The latter, if true, would have been a unique achievement in the history of science. His death, like his birth, is uncertain, but apparently he died in 1358.

Buridan's role in the history of science focuses upon the question of motion. Like every medieval philosopher, he found his starting point in Aristotle but, unlike most, he objected to "the philosopher's" doctrine and offered a substantial alternative. Both because of their importance in the history of mechanics, and because of their necessity for the under-standing of Buridan, passages on motion from Aristotle are included in the selection. Basic to Aristotle's treatment is the proposition that any body in motion must be moved by another with which it is in contact. Behind the proposition was a conception of motion deliberately broad enough to include, not only the local motion of bodies, but also such phenomena as the growth of trees and the education of youth. That is, motion was a process affecting the essence of things. Aristotle held that there must be a proportion, on the one hand, between the moving force and the rate of the motion that it causes, and equally a proportion between the rate of motion and the resistance. The two proportions implied a mathematical description of motion utterly different from that yielded by the equations that we now employ.

Aristotle's conception of motion adequately expressed the facts of common phenomena such as a galley pulled by oars or a cart drawn by an ox. Greeks also threw the discus, however, and with projectiles such as the discus problems arose. What keeps them in motion once they have parted from the mover? Moreover, Aristotle's proportions between motion, moving force, and resistance suggested that bodies should fall with a uniform velocity, whereas they manifestly do not. Buridan's discussion of motion is addressed to these problems. The answer that he gave (which, to be sure, was not entirely original with him) has been interpreted from two points of view. One interpretation contends that it embodies the essence of the modern idea of inertia. The other replies that, for all its disagreement with Aristotle, it repeats in another form the fundamentals of his conception of motion.

7

Aristotle: *The Physics*

BOOK IV

Chapter 8

Let us return to the demonstration that vacuum with the independent existence that some assign to it does not really exist.

For if each of the elementary bodies has a natural trend of its own—fire upwards, and earth downwards and towards the centre—it is clear that vacancy cannot be the cause of these trends. Of what kind of motion-change, then, can it be the cause? For it is just of this local movement that it is supposed to be the cause and that it is not.

Again, if, when there is vacancy, there is something that might be called a place bereft of any material content, whither shall the body placed in it move? Clearly not anywhere-or-everywhere. And the same argument applies to those who hold that "place" is itself something that exists apart from matter, into which the travelling body is carried. For how can the body placed in it either move or stay still? And it is nothing astonishing that the same argument should occur positively with respect to the up-and-downness of place as we conceive it (which makes vacancy superfluous as the condition of movement of the elements) and with reference to the supposed nature of vacancy itself (which precludes all possibility of its being such a cause in any case); for our adversaries reduce both place and void to mere abstract dimensionality. And indeed how can anything be *in* either "place" so conceived or void, in the proper local sense of "in"? But when (as with us) the place of a body is external to itself and has material existence of its own as its contents come and go, this is not what happens but the parts of it exist in it as parts exist in the whole, not as the content in the continent. Finally, in whatever

---

Reprinted by permission of the publishers and The Loeb Classical Library from Aristotle, *The Physics*, P. H. Wicksteed and F. M. Cornford, trs., Cambridge, Mass.: Harvard University Press, 1929 and 1934.

sense the void is identified with "place," when "place" in that sense is shown not to exist the void vanishes with it.

But indeed on reflection we see that the assertion "motion is impossible except into vacancy" is not only untrue but the contradiction of the truth, for it is impossible for there to be any motion at all if there be a circumambient void. Just as it has been asserted that the earth is at rest by the law of symmetry, so must it be in vacancy, since no preference can be given to one line of motion more than to another, inasmuch as the void, as such, is incapable of differentiation.

To begin with, every motion must be either natural or forced, and there can be no such thing as forced movement if there is no natural movement (for forced movement is movement counter to that which is natural, and the unnatural presupposes the natural); so that, unless every natural body has a natural movement, there cannot be any other movement at all. But how can there be any natural movement in the undifferentiated limitless void? For *qua* limitless it can have no top or bottom or middle, and *qua* vacancy it can have no differentiated directions of up and down (since the non-existent can no more be differentiated than "nothing" can, and the void is conceived as not being a thing, but as mere shortage); whereas natural trends are differentiated and differentiate the substances that manifest them. So it follows either that nothing has any natural trend in any direction or (since this is not so) that the supposed vacancy-as-conditioning-movement is a fiction.

In the second place, projectiles move when the body that impelled them is no longer in contact with them, whether this be due (as some suppose) to a circulating thrust, or to the air being set by the original impact in more rapid motion than that of the natural movement of the missile towards the place proper to it. But in vacancy neither of these agencies would be operation, so that nothing could go on moving unless it were carried. Nor (if it did move) could a reason be assigned why the projectile should ever stop—for why here more than there? It must therefore either not move at all, or continue its movement without limit, unless some stronger force impedes it.

Yet again, we are told that things go *into* vacant spaces because they offer no resistance; but *in* vacancy there is no resistance in any direction, so that, as to direction of movement, it would be a case of one-as-good-as-another.

A further proof of our thesis is this: We see that the velocity of a moving weight or mass depends on two conditions: (1) the distinctive nature of the medium—water, earth, or air—through which the motion occurs, and (2) the comparative gravity or levity of the moving body itself, other conditions being equal.

(1) Now the medium reduces velocity all the more if it is itself moving in the opposite direction, but it also reduces it, though in a lesser degree, if it is quiescent; and this impedium of motion is proportional to the resistance offers to cleavage, which is to say its density. Thus, if one medium is easier to cleave than another, the time taken in travelling a given distance through it will be proportionately less. *E.g.*, if the media are water and air, the ratio of air's cleavableness and unsubstantiality to that of water will give the ratio of the velocity of the passage through air to that through water.

Velocity in air : velocity in water =
Cleavability of air : cleavability of water.

So, if air is twice as easy to cleave as water, the passage through air will be twice as swift, and the time taken in covering a given distance half as long in air as in water. According to this universal principle, then, the velocity will in every case be greater in proportion to the unsubstantiality and diminished power of impeding and easier cleavability of the medium.

But the nonexistent substantiality of vacuity cannot bear any ratio whatever to the substantiality of any material substance, any more than zero can bear a ratio to a number. For if we divide a constant quantity c (that which exceeds) into two variable parts, a (the excess) and b (the exceeded), then, as a increases, b will decrease and the ratio $a : b$ will increase; but when the whole of c is in section a there will be none of c for section b; and it is absurd to speak of "none of c" as "a part of c." So the ratio $a : b$ will cease to exist, because b has ceased to exist and only a is left, and there is no proportion between something and nothing. (And in the same way there is no such thing as the proportion between a line and a point, because, since a point is no part of a line, taking a point is not taking any of the line.) And in like manner there is not any ratio that can express the excess of the resistance of a plenum over that of a vacuum, or of the consequential velocity in the vacuum over that in the plenum; but if movement through the finest medium covers a given distance in a given time, movement through the void is out of all proportion.

For if we take D_1 and D_2 to represent the densities of any two media, and T_1 and T_2 to represent the length of time occupied by a body under otherwise similar conditions in passing through equal spaces in the respective media, then if there be any proportion that expresses the ratio of the velocity through vacancy, let it be that which covers the constant distance in T_3, less than T_2 but standing to it in a certain ratio. Now take a medium with a density D_3 that stands to D_2 in the inverse proportion of T_3 to T_2

$$D_3 : D_2 :: T_2 : T_3$$

T_3 will represent the time taken to traverse the constant distance through the medium of D_3. But the time occupied if there were no medium at all should be less than T_3, whereas T_3 was taken as that time itself. Thus a body would pass through a plenum and a vacuum with equal velocity. Which is impossible. Evidently, then, if any period of time be assigned for the passage of any selected distance you may choose through vacancy, we shall be landed in this impossible consequence; for the assumption will involve the passage of a body through a material medium and through vacancy at the same velocity, since one may always take a medium whose density bears such a proportion to that of a standard medium as will correspond to the proportion of the supposed transit through vacancy to that of the standard transit.

To sum up. The principle that leads to our conclusion is that there must always be a ratio between any two velocities (for they are both measured by time, and between two determinate periods of time there must be ratio); but there is no such ratio of densities between vacancy and any kind of fullness.

This is how velocities are affected by the media through which the movement occurs. But (2) as to differences that depend on the moving bodies themselves, we see that of two bodies of similar formation the one that has the stronger trend downward by weight or upward by buoyancy, as the case may be, will be carried more quickly than the other through a given space in proportion to the greater strength of this trend. And this should hold in vacancy as elsewhere. But it cannot; for what reason can be assigned for this greater velocity? If the passage is through a medium, there must be such a difference; for when there is anything there to cleave, the body superior in force of its thrust will necessarily cleave the medium faster, since either its more suitable shape or the natural thrust it exercises, whether following its natural movement or being thrown, makes it cleave the better. Where there is nothing to cleave, therefore, all bodies will move at the same velocity; which is impossible.

It is obvious, then, that the hypothesis of "the void" leads to conclusions the precise opposite of those in support of which it was invented by its advocates.

BOOK VIII

Chapter 10

. . . But before discussing rotating bodies it will be well to examine a certain question concerning bodies in locomotion. If everything that is in motion is being moved by something, how comes it that certain things, missiles for example, that are not self-moving nevertheless continue their motion without a break when no longer in contact with the agent that gave them motion? Even if that agent at the same time that he puts the missile in motion also sets something else (say air) in motion, which something when itself in motion has power to move other things, still when the prime agent has ceased to be in contact with this secondary agent and has therefore ceased to be moving it, it must be just as impossible for it as for the missile to be in motion: missile and secondary agent must all be in motion simultaneously, and must have ceased to be in motion the instant the prime mover ceases to move them; and this holds good even if the prime agent is like the magnet, which has power to confer upon the iron bar it moves the power of moving another iron bar. We are forced, therefore, to suppose that the prime mover conveys to the air (or water, or other such intermediary as is naturally capable both of moving and conveying motion) a power of conveying motion, but that this power is not exhausted when the intermediary ceases to be moved itself. Thus the intermediary will cease to be moved itself as soon as the prime mover ceases to move it, but will still be able to move something else. Thus this something else will be put in motion after the prime mover's action has ceased, and will itself continue the series. The end of it all will approach as the motive power conveyed to each successive secondary agent wanes, till at last there comes one which can only move its neighbour without being able to convey motive force to it. At this point the last active intermediary will cease to convey motion, the passive intermediary that has no active power will cease to be in motion, and the missile will come to a stand, at the same instant. Now this movement occurs in things that are sometimes in motion and sometimes stationary, and it is not continuous, though it appears to be. For there is a succession of contiguous agents, since there is no one motor concerned but a series, one following upon another. And so there comes about both in air and water the kind of motion that some have called *antiperistasis*. But whereas the only possible solution of the problem it suggests is that which has just been explained, the theory of those who call it *antiperistasis* would involve the simultaneity of the action of every motor and the passion of every mobile in the series, and the simultaneity of their cessation. Whereas the fact is that the supposed continuity of the movement of the single mobile which sets us inquiring after the motor is only apparent; for in fact it is not impelled by one and the same motor throughout its course.

Now we have seen that there must be a continuous movement somewhere in the sum of things, and that it must be uniform, and that such uniform motion must be that of some dimensional magnitude (for that which is not dimensional cannot move), and that such magnitude must be unitary and must be kept in motion by a unitary motor (for otherwise the motion would not be continuous, but would be resolved into a series of successive motions), and that this single motor must itself be either in motion or unmoving. Now if it is in motion (and is therefore a physical magnitude) it will have to follow up that which it is moving, and therefore be itself locally changing, and moreover must be referred back to some motor that causes its motion. This leaves us where we were, and the perpetual recession can only be arrested by supposing a motor that is not in motion. Such a motor need not undergo any change to preserve a constant relation with the mobile, but can exercise its kinetic power without ever being exhausted (for suchlike conveying of motion is not toilsome); and such motion or change as it directly causes must be uniform either uniquely or in the primary and supreme sense, for the motor is subject to no change. And for the motion to be uniform, the disposition of the mobile to the motor must also be without change. Now the action of this unmoving cause must be felt either at the centre or the periphery, for these are the determining principles; and since the swiftest movements must be those of the parts closest to the moving force, and the movement of the outermost sphere is such, it is there that the motive influence is felt.

The question arises, however, whether it may not be possible for a motor which itself is in motion to cause a continuous movement in something else, not with the specious continuity of a succession of thrusts, but genuinely. Well, in such a case either (i.) the prime motor itself must all the time directly thrust or draw the mobile (or both thrust and draw it), or (ii.) there must be some continuous succession of intermediaries other than the prime motor, as we just now supposed to be the fact in the case of missiles, and if these intermediaries are constituted by an easily divisible substance, such as air or water, what is causing the movement at any time will be the particular division of that substance which at the time being is in motion. In both cases (i.) and (ii.), therefore, the movement is not one and unbroken, but successional. The only continuous movement, therefore, is that which is caused by the motionless motor, which ever maintains its own uniformity of disposition and will therefore maintain a uniform and continuous relation to the mobile.

Questions on the Four Books on the Heavens and the World of Aristotle

1. Whether natural motion ought to be swifter in the end than the beginning. . . . With respect to this question it ought to be said that it is a conclusion not to be doubted factually, for, as it has been said, all people perceive that the motion of a heavy body downward is continually accelerated, it having been posited that it falls through a uniform medium. For everybody perceives that by the amount that a stone descends over a greater distance and falls on a man, by that amount does it more seriously injure him.

2. But the great difficulty in this question is why this [acceleration] is so. Concerning this matter there have been many different opinions. The Commentator (Averroës) in the second book [of his commentary on the *De caelo*] ventures some obscure statements on it, declaring that a heavy body approaching the end is moved more swiftly because of a great desire for the end and because of the heating action of its motion. From these statements two opinions have sprouted.

3. The first opinion was that motion produces heat, as it is said in the second book [of the *De caelo*], and, therefore, a heavy body descending swiftly through the air makes that air hot, and consequently it becomes rarefied. The air, thus rarefied, is more easily divisible and less resistant. Now, if the resistance is diminished, it is reasonable that the movement becomes swifter.

But this argument is insufficient. In the first place, because the air in the summer is noticeably hotter than in the winter, and yet the same stone falling an equal distance in the summer and in the winter is not moved with appreciably greater speed in the summer than in the winter; nor does it strike harder. Furthermore, the air does not become hot

Translated from the Latin by Marshall Clagett in *The Science of Mechanics in the Middle Ages*, Madison: The University of Wisconsin Press, 1959, pp. 557-562. Reprinted by permission of The Regents of the University of Wisconsin.

through movement unless it is previously moved and divided. Therefore, since the air resists before there has been movement or division, the resistance is not diminished by its heating. Furthermore, a man moves his hand just as swiftly as a stone falls toward the beginning of its movement. This is apparent, because striking another person hurts him more than the falling stone, even if the stone is harder. And yet a man so moving his hand does not heat the air sensibly, since he would perceive that heating. Therefore, in the same way the stone, at least from the beginning of the case, does not thus sensibly heat the air to the extent that it ought to produce so manifest an acceleration as is apparent at the end of the movement.

4. The other opinion which originated from the statements of the Commentator is this: Place is related to the thing placed as a final cause, as Aristotle implies and the Commentator explains in the fourth book of the *Physics*. And some say, in addition to this, that place is the cause moving the heavy body by a method of attraction, just as a magnet attracts iron. By whichever of these methods it takes place, it seems reasonable that the heavy body is moved more swiftly by the same amount that it is nearer to its natural place. This is because, if place is the moving cause, then it can move that body more strongly when the body is nearer to it, for an agent acts more strongly on something near to it than on something far away from it. And if place were nothing but the final cause which the heavy body seeks naturally and for the attainment of which the body is moved, then it seems reasonable that that natural appetite for that end is increased more from it as that end is nearer. And so it seems in every way reasonable that a heavy body is moved more swiftly by the amount that it is nearer to its downward place. But in descending continually it ought to be moved more and more swiftly.

But this opinion cannot stand up. In the first place, it is against Aristotle and against the Commentator in the first book of the *De caelo*, where they assert that, if there were several worlds, the earth of the other world would be moved to the middle of this world. . . .

Furthermore, this opinion is against manifest experience, for you can lift the same stone near the earth just as easily as you can in a high place if that stone were there, for example, at the top of a tower. This would not be so if it had a stronger inclination toward the downward place when it was low than when it was high. It is responded that actually there is a greater inclination when the stone is low than when it is high, but it is not great enough for the senses to perceive. This response is not valid, because if that stone falls continually from the top of the tower to the earth, a double or triple velocity and a double or triple injury would be sensed near the earth than would be sensed higher up near the beginning of the movement. Hence, there is a double or triple cause of the velocity. And so it follows that that inclination which you posit not to be sensible or notable is not the cause of such an increase of velocity.

Again, let a stone begin to fall from a high place to the earth and another similar stone begin to fall from a low place to the earth. Then these stones, when they should be at a distance of one foot from the earth, ought to be moved equally fast and one ought not be swifter than the other if the greater velocity should arise only from nearness to their natural place, because they should be equally near to their natural place. Yet it is manifest to the senses that the body which should fall from the high point would be moved much more quickly than that which should fall from the low point, and it would kill a man while the other stone would not hurt him.

Again, if a stone falls from an exceedingly high place through a space of ten feet and then encountering there an obstacle comes to rest, and if a similar stone descends from a low point to the earth, also through a distance of ten feet, neither of these movements will appear to be any swifter than the other, even though one is nearer to the natural place of earth than the other.

I conclude, therefore, that the accelerated natural movements of heavy and light bodies do not arise from greater proximity to their natural place, but from something else that is either near or far, but which is varied by reason of the length of the motion. Nor is the case of the magnet and the iron similar, because if the iron is nearer to the magnet, it immediately will begin to be moved more swiftly than if it were farther away. But such is not the case with a heavy body in relation to its natural place.

5. The third opinion was that the more the heavy body descends, by so much less is there air beneath it, and the less air then can resist less. And if the resistance is decreased and the moving gravity remains the same, it follows that the heavy body ought to be moved more swiftly.

But this opinion falls into the same inconsistency as the preceding one, because, as was said before, if two bodies similar throughout begin to fall, one from an exceedingly high place and the other from a low place such as a distance of ten feet from the earth, those bodies in the beginning of their motion are moved equally fast, notwithstanding the fact that one of them has a great deal of air beneath it and the other has only a little. Hence, throughout, the greater velocity does not arise from greater proximity to the earth or because the body has less air beneath it, but from the fact that that moving body is moved from a longer distance and through a longer space.

Again, it is not true that the less air in the aforementioned case resists less. This is because, when a stone is near the earth, there is still just as much air laterally as if it were farther from the earth. Hence, it is just as difficult for the divided air to give way and flee laterally [near the earth] as it was when the stone was farther from the earth. And, in addition, it is equally difficult or more difficult, when the stone is nearer the earth, for the air underneath to give way in a straight line, because the earth, which is more resistant than the air, is in the way. Hence, the imagined solution is not valid.

6. With the [foregoing] methods of solving this question set aside, there remains, it seems to me, one necessary solution. It is my supposition that the natural gravity of this stone remains always the same and similar before the movement, after the movement, and during the movement. Hence the stone is found to be equally heavy after the movement as it was before it. I suppose also that the resistance which arises from the medium remains the same or is similar, since, as I have said, it does not appear to me that the air lower and near to the earth should be less resistant than the superior air. Rather the superior air perhaps ought to be less resistant because it is more subtle. Third, I suppose that if the moving body is the same, the total mover is the same, and the resistance also is the same or similar, the movement will remain equally swift, since the proportion of mover to moving body and to the resistance will remain [the same]. Then I add that in the movement downward of the heavy body the movement does not remain equally fast but continually becomes swifter.

From these [suppositions] it is concluded that another moving force concurs in that movement beyond the natural gravity which was moving the body from the beginning and which remains always the same. Then finally I say that this other mover is not the place which attracts the heavy body as the magnet does the iron; nor is it some force existing in the place and arising either from the heavens or from something else, because it would immediately follow that the same heavy body would begin to be moved more swiftly from a low place than from a high one, and we experience the contrary of this conclusion. . . .

From these [reasons] it follows that one must imagine that a heavy body not only acquires motion unto itself from its principal mover, i.e., its gravity, but that it also acquires unto itself a certain impetus with that motion. This impetus has the power of moving the heavy body in conjunction with the permanent natural gravity. And because that impetus is acquired in common with motion, hence the swifter the motion is, the greater and stronger the impetus is. So, therefore, from the beginning the heavy body is moved by its natural gravity only; hence it is moved slowly. Afterwards it is moved by that same gravity and by the impetus acquired at the same time; consequently, it is moved more swiftly. And because the movement becomes swifter, therefore the impetus also becomes greater and stronger, and thus the heavy body is moved by its natural gravity and by that greater impetus simultaneously, and so it will again be moved faster; and thus it will always and continually be accelerated to the end. And just as the impetus is acquired in common with motion, so it is decreased or becomes deficient in common with the decrease and deficiency of the motion.

And you have an experiment [to support this position]: If you cause a large and very heavy smith's mill [i.e., a wheel] to rotate and you then cease to move it, it will still move a while longer by this impetus it has acquired. Nay, you cannot immediately bring it to rest, but on account of the resistance from the gravity of the mill, the impetus would be continually diminished until the mill would cease to move. And if the mill would last forever without some diminution or alteration of it, and there were no resistance corrupting the impetus, perhaps the mill would be moved perpetually by that impetus.

7. And thus one could imagine that it is unnecessary to posit intelligences as the movers of celestial bodies since the Holy Scriptures do not inform us that intelligences must be posited. For it could be said that when God created the celestial spheres, He began to move each of them as He wished, and they are still moved by the impetus which He gave to them because, there being no resistance, the impetus is neither corrupted nor diminished.

You should note that some people have called that impetus "accidental gravity" and they do so aptly, because names are for felicity of expression. Whence this name appears to be harmonious with Aristotle and the Commentator in the first book of the De caelo, where they say that gravity would be infinite if a heavy body were moved infinitely, because by the amount that it is moved more, by that same amount is it moved more swiftly; and by the amount that it is moved more swiftly, by that amount is the gravity greater. If this is true, therefore, it is necessary that a heavy body in moving acquires continually more gravity, and that gravity is not of the same constitution or nature as the first natural gravity, because the first gravity remains always, even with the movement stopped, while the acquired gravity does not remain. All of these statements will appear more to be true and necessary when the violent movements of projectiles and other things are investigated. . . .

8

GALILEO GALILEI

Son of the late Italian Renaissance, Galileo Galilei was born in Pisa in
1564. First as a professor of mathematics in the universities of Pisa and
of Padua, and then in Florence as mathematician and philosopher in
the court of the Medici, Galileo passed his life in the intellectual centers
of his day. In the end, he was to become as well a central figure in the
intellectual crisis of the late Renaissance, when the rising movement of
modern scientific thought met and clashed with the growing rigidity
of the Counter-Reformation. As the professed champion of the Copernican revolution in astronomy, Galileo had the misfortune to espouse the
cause of Copernicanism at the time when the Catholic Church, after
more than half a century of neutrality, decided to crush it. The result
was Galileo's trial before the Inquisition in Rome and his condemnation
to house arrest for the remainder of his life. There he died in 1642.

Galileo's *Systeme of the World in Four Dialogues,* from which the
following selection is taken, provided the specific occasion of his trial.
Behind a pretense of impartial discussion, it vigorously argued the case
for Copernican astronomy. By the time the *Dialogues* were published,
the Copernican system was nearly a century old, but the number of its
avowed adherents remained minute. Not only did Copernican astronomy
imply the negation of several positions embedded in the philosophic
tradition of the Western world, but it also challenged the plain dictates
of common sense. In nothing did it appear more paradoxical than in
its central proposition that the earth moves, whereas experience daily
affirmed its stability. The *Dialogues* were not a work of technical astronomy; they were, instead, a polemic against the dictates of common
sense and their refinements in the philosophic tradition, which seemed
to proclaim the impossibility of the Copernican system.

The center of the argument was the problem of motion. According
to the accepted idea of motion, the assertion that the earth turns daily
on its axis was absurd. Any body in motion, it was held following
Aristotle, requires the constant action of a mover. A heavy body dropped

from a tower would fall vertically to the earth if the earth were at rest. But if the earth turns on its axis, the heavy body would cease to move with the tower once it was released, and as the tower moves to the east, the body would appear to fall well to the west. In the *Dialogues,* Galileo solved the basic dilemma of Copernican astronomy by proposing a new conception of motion. Although his conception of motion was to become the foundation on which the structure of modern science has rested, Galileo did not propose it in exactly the form that modern science was to accept. Galileo's concern with the problem of a rotating earth led to a peculiarity in his conception of motion, as the selection indicates.

8

Systeme of the World in Four Dialogues

SALV. Leaving the general contemplation of the whole [world], let us descend to the consideration of its parts, which Aristotle, in his first division, makes two, and they very different and almost contrary to one another; namely the Coelestial and the Elementary: the former ungenerated, incorruptible, unalterable, unpassable, &c. and the latter exposed to a continual alteration, mutation, &c. Which difference, as from its original principle, he derives from the diversity of local motions, and in this method he proceeds.

Leaving the sensible, if I may so speak, and retiring into the Ideal World, he begins Architectonically to consider that, nature being the principle of motion, it followeth that natural bodies be imbued with local motion. Next he declares local motion to be of three kinds, namely, circular, straight, and mixt of straight and circular: and the first two he calleth simple, for that of all lines, the circular and straight are the only simple ones. And here somewhat restraining himself, he defineth anew of simple motions; one to be circular, namely that which is made about the center, and the other namely the straight; upwards and downwards, upwards that which moveth from the center and downwards that which goeth towards the center. And from hence he infers, as he may by necessary consequence, that all simple motions are confined to these three kinds, namely, to the center, from the center, and about the center; the which corresponds, saith he, with what hath been said before of a body, that it is perfected by three things, and so is its motion. Having confirmed these motions, he proceeds saying, that of natural bodies some being simple, and some composed of them (and he calleth simple bodies those that have a principle of motion from nature, as the Fire and Earth) it follows that simple motions belong to simple bodies, and mixt to the compound; yet in such sort, that the compounded incline to the part predominant in the composition.

Translated from the Italian by Thomas Salusbury, London, 1665. The editors are grateful to the William Andrews Clark Memorial Library of the University of California at Los Angeles for permission to reproduce from its copy of this translation.

SAGR. Pray you hold a little Salviatus, for I find so many doubts to spring up on all sides in this discourse, that I shall be constrained, either to communicate them if I would attentively hearken to what you shall add, or to take off my attention from the things spoken, if I would remember objections.

SALV. I will very willingly stay, for that I also run the same hazard, and am ready at every step to lose my self whilst I sail between Rocks, and boisterous Waves, that make me, as they say, to lose my Compass; therefore before I make them more, propound your difficulties.

SAGR. You and Aristotle together would at first take me a little out of the sensible World, to tell me of the Architecture, wherewith it ought to be fabricated, and very appositely begin to tell me, that a natural body is by nature moveable, nature being (as elsewhere it is defined) the principle of motion. But here I am somewhat doubtful why Aristotle said not that of natural bodies, some are moveable by nature, and others immoveable, for that in the definition, nature is said to be the principle of Motion, and Rest; for if natural bodies have all a principle of motion, either he might have omitted the mention of Rest in the definition of nature, or not have introduced such a definition in the first place. Next, as to the declaration of what Aristotle intends by simple motions, and how by Spaces he determines them (calling those simple that are made by simple lines, which are only the straight and circular) I entertain it willingly; nor do I desire to tender the instance of the Helix about the cylinder, which, in that it is in every part like to itself, might seemingly be numbered among simple lines. But herein I cannot concur, that he should so restrain simple motions (whilst he seems to go about to repeat the same definition in other words) as to call one of them the motion about the center, the others *Sursum* & *Deorsum*, namely upwards and downwards, which terms are not to be used of the World fabricated, but imply it not only made, but already inhabited by us; for if the straight motion be simple, by the simplicity of the straight line, and if the simple motion be natural, it is made on every side—to wit, upwards, downwards, backwards, forwards, to the right, to the left, and, if any other way can be imagined, provided it be straight, it shall agree to any simple natural body; or if not so, then the supposition of Aristotle is defective. It appears, moreover, that Aristotle hinteth but one circular motion alone to be in the World, and consequently but one only Center, to which alone the motions of upwards and downwards refer. All which are apparent proofs that Aristotle's aim is to make white black, and to accommodate Architecture to the building, and not to model the building according to the precepts of Architecture: for if I should say that Nature in Universal may have a thousand Circular Motions, and by consequence a thousand Centers, there would be also a thousand motions upwards, and downwards. Again he makes as hath been said, a simple motion, and a mixt motion, calling simple, the circular and straight, and mixt, the compound of them two: of natural bodies he calls some simple (namely those that have a natural principle to simple motion) and others compound: and simple motions he attributes to simple bodies, and the compounded to the compound; but by compound motion he doth no longer understand the mixt of straight and circular, which may be in the World; but introduceth a mixt motion as impossible, as it is impossible to mixe opposite motions made in the same straight line, so as to produce from them a motion partly upwards, partly downwards, and, to moderate such an absurdity, and impossibility, he asserts that such mixt bodies move according to the simple part predominant: which necessitates others to say, that even the motion made by the same straight line is sometimes simple, and sometimes also compound: so that the simplicity of the motion is no longer dependent only on the simplicity of the line.

SIMPL. How? Is it not difference sufficient, that the simple and absolute are more swift than that which proceeds from predominion? and how much faster doth a piece of pure Earth descend, than a piece of Wood?

SAGR. Well, Simplicius; But if the simplicity for this cause was changed, besides the fact that there would be a hundred thousand mixt motions, you would not be able to determine the simple; nay farther, if the greater or lesser velocity be able to alter the simplicity of the motion, no simple body should move with a simple motion; since in all natural straight motions, the velocity is ever increasing, and by consequence still changing the simplicity, which as it is simplicity, ought of consequence to be immutable; and that which more importeth, you charge Aristotle with another thing, that in the definition of motions compounded, he hath not made mention of tardity nor velocity, which you now insert for a necessary and essential point. Again you can draw no advantage from this rule, for that there will be amongst the mixt bodies some, (and that not a few) that will move more swiftly, and others more slowly than the simple, as for example, Lead, and Wood, in comparison of earth; and therefore amongst these motions, which call you the simple, and which the mixt?

SIMPL. I would call that simple motion, which is made by a simple body, and mixt, that of a compound body.

SAGR. Very well, and yet, Simplicius, a little before you said that the simple and compound motions discovered which were mixt and which were simple bodies; now you will have me by simple and mixt bodies, come to know which is the simple, and which is the compound motion:

an excellent way to keep us ignorant, both of motions and bodies. More-over, you have also a little above declared, how that a greater velocity did not suffice, but you seek a third condition for the definement of simple motion, for which Aristotle contented himself with one alone, namely, of the simplicity of the Space, or Medium: But now according to you, the simple motion, shall be that which is made upon a simple line, with a certain determinate velocity, by a body simply moveable. Now be it as you please, and let us return to Aristotle, who defineth the mixt motion to be that compounded of the straight, and circular, but pro-duceth not any body, which naturally moveth with such a motion.

SALV. I come again to Aristotle, who having very well and Method-ically begun his discourse, but having a greater aim to rest at, and hit a marke predesigned in his minde, than that to which his method led him, digressing from the purpose, he comes to assert as a thing known and manifest, that as to the motions directly upwards or downwards, they naturally agree to Fire, and Earth; and that therefore it is necessary, that besides these bodies, which are near unto us, there must be in nature another, to which the circular motion may agree: which shall be so much the more excellent by how much the circular motion is more perfect, than the straight; but how much more perfect the former is than the latter, he determines from the greatness of the circular line's perfec-tion above the straight line; calling the one perfect, the other imperfect; imperfect, because if infinite it wanteth a termination and end: and if it be finite, there is yet something beyond which it may be prolonged. This is the basis, ground work, and master-stone of all the Fabrick of the Aristotelian World, upon which they superstruct all their other properties, of neither heavy nor light, of ingenerable, incorruptible exemption from all motions, save only the local, &c. And all these passions he affirmeth to be proper to a simple body that is moved cir-cularly; and the contrary qualities of gravity, levity, corruptibility, &c. he assigns to bodies naturally moveable in a straight line. For that if we have already discovered defects in the foundation, we may rationally question what soever may be farther built thereon. I deny not, that this which Aristotle hitherto hath introduced, with a general discourse dependent upon universal primary principles, hath been since in process of time, re-inforced with particular reasons, and experiments; all which it would be necessary distinctly to consider and weigh; but because what hath been said hitherto presents to such as consider the same many and no small difficulties, (and yet it would be necessary that the primary principles and fundamentals be certain, firm, and established, that so they might with more confidence be built upon) it would not be amiss before we farther multiply doubts, to see if haply (as I conjecture) betaking ourselves to other ways, we may not light upon a more direct and secure method, and with better considered principles of Architecture lay out primary fundamentals. Therefore suspending for the present the method of Aristotle, (which we will re-affirme again in its proper place, and particularly examine;) I say, that in the things hitherto affirmed by him, I agree with him, and admit that the World is a body enjoying all dimension, and therefore most perfect, and I add, that as such, it is necessarily most ordered, that is, having parts between themselves with exquisite and most perfect order disposed, which assumption I think is not to be denied, neither by you or any other.

SIMPL. Who can deny it? the first particular (of the world's dimensions) is taken from Aristotle himself, and its denomination as ordered seems only to be assumed from the order which it most exactly keeps.

SALV. This principle then established, one may immediately conclude, that if the entire parts of the World should be by their nature moveable, it is impossible that their motions should be straight, or other than circular; and the reason is sufficiently easie, and manifest; for that whatsoever moveth with a straight motion, changeth place; and continuing to move, doth by degrees more and more remove from the place from whence it departed, and from all the places through which it successively passed; and if such motion naturally suited with it, then it was not at the beginning in its proper place; and so the parts of the World were not disposed with perfect order. But we suppose them to be perfectly ordered; therefore as such, it is impossible that they should by nature change place, and consequently move in a straight motion. Again, the straight motion being by nature infinite, for that the straight line is infinite and indeterminate, it is impossible that anything moveable can have a natural principle of moving in a straight line; namely toward the place whither it is impossible to arrive, there being no praefinite end; and nature, as Aristotle himself saith well, never attempts to do that which can never be done, nor essayes to move whither it is impossible to arrive. And if any one should yet object, that albeit the straight line, and consequently the motion by it, is producible *in infinitum,* that is to say, is interminate; yet nevertheless Nature, as one may say, arbitrarily hath assigned them some ends, and given natural instincts to its natural bodies to move unto the same; I will reply, that this might perhaps be fabled to have come to pass in the first Chaos, where indistinct matters confusedly and inordinately wandered; to regulate which, Nature very appositely made use of straight motions, by which, like as the well-constituted in moving disorder themselves, so were they which were before depravedly disposed by this motion ranged in order: but after their exquisite distribution and collocation, it is impossible that there should remain natural inclinations in them of longer moving in a straight motion, from which now would ensue their removal from their proper and natural place, that is to say, their disordering; we may therefore say that the straight motion serves to conduct the matter to erect the work; but that once erected, it is to rest immoveable, or if moveable, to move itself only circularly.

*   *   *   *

SALV. For the present we will return to our first proposal, going on there where we made digression; which if I well remember, was about the proving the motion by a straight line of no use in the ordered parts of the World; and we did proceed to say, that it was not so in circular motions, of which that which is made by the moveable in itself, still retains it in the same place, and that which carrieth the moveable by the circumference of a circle about its fixed centre, neither puts itself, nor those about it in disorder, for that such a motion primarily is finite and terminate (though not yet finished and determined): but there is no point in the circumference that is not the first and last term in the circulation; and continuing it in the circumference assigned it, it leaveth all the rest, within and without that, free for the use of others, without ever impeding or disordering them. This being a motion that makes the moveable continually leave, and continually arrive at the end, it alone therefore can primarily be uniform; for that acceleration of motion is made in the moveable, when it goeth towards the place to which it hath inclination; and the retardation happens by the repugnance that it hath to leave and part from the same place; and because in circular motion, the moveable continually leaves the natural place, and continually moveth towards the same, therefore, in it, the repugnance and inclination are always of equal force: from which equality results a velocity, neither retarded nor accelerated, i.e. an uniformity in motion. From this conformity, and from the being terminate, may follow the perpetual continuation by successively reiterating the circulations; which in an undetermined line, and in a motion continually retarded or accelerated, cannot naturally be. I say, naturally; because the straight motion which is retarded, is the violent, which cannot be perpetual; and the accelerated arriveth necessarily at the end, if one there be; and if there be none, it cannot be moved to it, because nature moves not whither it is impossible to attain. I conclude therefore, that the circular motion can only naturally consist with natural bodies, parts of the universe, and constituted in an excellent order; and that the straight, at the most that can be said for it, is assigned by nature to its bodies, and their parts, at such time as they shall be out of their proper places, constituted in a depraved order, and for that cause needing to be reduced by the shortest way to their natural state. Hence, methinks, it may rationally be concluded that for maintenance of perfect order amongst the parts of the World, it is necessary to say, that moveables are moveable only circularly; and if there be any that move not circularly, these of necessity are immoveable, there being nothing but rest and circular motion apt to the conservation of order. And I do not a little wonder with myself, that Aristotle, who held that the Terrestrial globe was placed in the center of the World, and there remained immoveable, should not say, that of natural bodies some are moveable by nature, and others immoveable; especially having before defined Nature, to be the principle of Motion and Rest.

SIMPL. Aristotle, though of a very perspicacious wit, would not strain it further than needed: holding in all his argumentations that sensible experiments were to be preferred before any reasons founded upon strength of wit, and saying that those which should deny the testimony of sense deserved to be punished with the loss of the sense; now who is so blind that sees not the parts of the Earth and Water to move, as being heavy, naturally downwards, namely, towards the center of the Universe, assigned by nature herself for the end and term of straight motion *deorsum*; and doth not likewise see the Fire and Air to move straight upwards towards the Concave of the Lunar Orb, as to the natural end of motion *sursum?* And this being so manifestly seen, and we being certain, that *eadem est ratio totius & partium*, why may we not assert it for a true and manifest proposition, that the natural motion of the Earth is the straight motion *ad medium*, and that of the Fire, the straight *à medio?*

SALV. The most that you can pretend from this your Discourse, were it granted to be true, is that, like as the parts of the Earth removed from the whole (namely, from the place where they naturally rest, that is, in short, reduced to a depraved and disordered disposition) return to their place spontaneously, and therefore naturally in a straight motion, (it being granted, that *eadem sit ratio totius & partium*) so it may be inferred, that were the Terrestrial Globe removed violently from the place assigned it by nature, it would return by a straight line. This, as I have said, is the most that can be granted you, and that only for want of examination; but he that shall with exactness revise these things, will first deny, that the parts of the Earth, in returning to its whole, move in a straight line, and not by a circular or mixt; and really you would have enough to do to demonstrate the contrary, as you shall plainly see in the answers to the particular reasons and experiments alledged by

Ptolemy and Aristotle. Secondly, if another should say that the parts of the Earth, go not in their motion towards the Center of the World, but to unite with its Whole; and that for that reason they naturally incline towards the center of the Terrestrial Globe, by which inclination they conspire to form and preserve it, what other All, or what other Center would you find for the World, to which the whole Terrene Globe, being thence removed, would seek to return, that so the reason of the Whole might be like to that of its parts? It may be added, that neither Aristotle nor you can ever prove that the Earth *de facto* is in the center of the Universe; but if any Center may be assigned to the Universe, we shall rather find the Sun placed in it, as by the sequel you shall understand.

Now, like as from the consentaneous conspiration of all the parts of the Earth to form its whole doth follow that they with equal inclination concur thither from all parts; and to unite themselves as much as is possible together, they there spherically adapt themselves; why may we not believe that the Sun, Moon, and other mundane Bodies be also of a round figure, not by other than a concordant instinct, and natural concourse of all the parts composing them? Of which, if any, at any time, by any violence were separated from the whole, is it not reasonable to think, that they would spontaneously and by natural instinct return? and in this manner to infer, that the straight motion agreeth with all mundane bodies alike.

*   *   *   *

SALV. Let our contemplation begin therefore with this consideration, that whatsoever motion may be ascribed to the Earth, it is necessary that it be to us (as inhabitants upon it, and consequently partakers of the same) altogether imperceptible, and as if it were not at all, so long as we have regard only to terrestrial things; but yet it is on the contrary, as necessary that the same motion do seem common to all other bodies, and visible objects, that being separated from the Earth participate not of the same. So that the true method to find whether any kind of motion may be ascribed to the Earth, and that found, to know what it is, is to consider and observe if in bodies separated from the Earth, one may discover any appearance of motion, which equally suiteth to all the rest; for a motion that is only seen, *v.gr.* in the Moon, and that hath nothing to do with Venus or Jupiter, or any other Stars, cannot any way belong to the Earth, or to any other save the Moon alone. Now there is a most general and grand motion above all others, and it is that by which the Sun, the Moon, the other Planets, and the Fixed Stars, and in a word, the whole Universe, the Earth only excepted, appeareth in our thinking to move from the East towards the West, in the space of twenty four hours; and this, as to this first appearance, hath no obstacle to hinder it, that it may not belong to the Earth alone, as well as to all the World besides, the Earth excepted; for the same aspects will appear in the one position, as in the other. Hence it is that Aristotle and Ptolemy, as having hit upon this consideration in going about to prove the Earth to be immoveable, argue not against any other than this Diurnal Motion, save only that Aristotle hinteth something in obscure terms against another Motion ascribed to it by an Ancient, of which we shall speak in its place.

SAGR. I very well perceive the necessity of your conclusion: but I meet with a doubt which I know not how to free myself from, and this it is: that Copernicus assigning to the Earth another motion beside the Diurnal (which, according to the rule even now laid down, ought to be to us as to appearance imperceptible in the Earth but visible in all the rest of the World) methinks I may necessarily infer either that he hath manifestly erred in assigning the Earth a motion, to which there appears not a general correspondence in Heaven, or else that if there be such a congruity therein, Ptolemy on the other hand hath been deficient in not confuting this, as he hath done the other.

SALV. You have good cause for your doubt: and when we come to treat of the other Motion, you shall see how far Copernicus excelled Ptolemy in clearness and sublimity of wit, in that he saw what the other did not, I mean the admirable harmony wherein that Motion agreed with all the other Coelestial Bodies. But for the present we will suspend this particular, and return to our first consideration; touching which I will proceed to propose (beginning with things more general) those reasons which seem to favour the mobility of the Earth, and then wait the answers which Simplicius shall make thereto. And first, if we consider only the immense magnitude of the Starry Sphere, compared to the smallness of the Terrestrial Globe, contained therein so many millions of times; and moreover weigh the velocity of the motion which must in a day and night make an entire revolution thereof, I cannot perswade myself, that there is any man who believes it more reasonable and credible, that the Coelestial Sphere turneth round, and the Terrestrial Globe stands still.

SAGR. If from the universality of effects, which may in nature have dependence upon such like motions, there should indifferently follow all the same consequences to an hair, as well in one Hypothesis as in the other; yet I for my part, as to my first and general apprehension, would esteem that he which should hold it more rational to make the whole Universe move, and thereby to save the Earth's immobility, is more unreasonable than he that being got to the top of your Turret, should desire, to the end only that he might behold the City and the Fields about it, that the whole Country might turn round, that so he might not be put to the trouble to stir his head. And yet doubtless the advantages would be many and great which the Copernican Hypothesis is attended with, above those of the Ptolemaique, which in my opinion resembleth, nay surpasseth that other folly; so that all this makes me think the former far more probable than the latter. But haply Aristotle, Ptolemy, and Simplicius may find the advantages of their Systeme, which they would do well to communicate to us also, if any such there be; or else declare to me, that there neither are or can be any such things.

SALV. For my part, as I have not been able, as much as I have thought upon it, to find any diversity therein; so I think I have found that no such diversity can be in them; in so much that I esteem it to no purpose to seek farther after it. Therefore observe: Motion is so far Motion, and as Motion operateth, by how far it hath relation to things which lack Motion: but in those things which all equally partake thereof it hath nothing to do, and is as if it never were. And thus the Merchandises with which a ship is laden, so far move, by how far leaving London, they pass by France, Spain, Italy, and sail to Aleppo, which London, France, Spain &c. stand still, not moving with the ship: but as to the Chests, Bales and other Parcels, wherewith the ship is stow'd and laden, and in respect of the ship itself, the Motion from London to Syria is as much as nothing; and nothing altereth the relation which is between them: and this, because it is common to all, and is participated by all alike: and of the Cargo which is in the ship, if a Bale were romag'd from a Chest but one inch only, this alone would be in that Cargo, a greater Motion in respect of the Chest, than the whole Voyage of above three thousand miles, made by them as they were stow'd together.

SIMPL. This Doctrine is good, sound, and altogether Peripatetick.

SALV. I hold it to be much more antient: and suspect that Aristotle in receiving it from some good School, did not fully understand it, and that therefore, having delivered it with some alteration, it hath been an occasion of confusion amongst those, who would defend whatever he saith. And when he writ, that whatsoever moveth, doth move upon something immoveable, I suppose that he equivocated, and meant that whatever moveth, moveth in respect to something immoveable; which proposition admitteth no doubt, and the other many.

SAGR. Pray you make no digression, but proceed in the dissertation you began.

SALV. It being therefore manifest, that the motion which is common to many moveables, is idle, and as it were, null as to the relation of those moveables between themselves, because that among themselves they have made no change: and that it is operative only in the relation that those moveables have to other things, which want that motion, among which the habitude is changed: and we having divided the Universe into two parts, one of which is necessarily moveable, and the other immoveable; for the obtaining of whatsoever may depend upon, or be required from such a motion, it may as well be done by making the Earth alone, as by making all the rest of the World to move: for that the operation of such a motion consists in nothing else, save in the relation or habitude which is between the Coelestial Bodies and the Earth, the which relation is all that is changed. Now if for the obtaining of the same effect *ad unguem*, it be all one whether the Earth alone moveth, the rest of the Universe standing still, or that the Earth only standing still, the whole Universe moveth with one and the same motion; who would believe, that Nature (which by common consent, doth not that by many things, which may be done by few) hath chosen to make an innumerable number of most vast bodies move, and that with an unconceivable velocity, to perform that which might be done by the moderate motion of one alone about its own Center?

SIMPL. I do not well understand how this grand motion signifieth nothing as to the Sun, as to the Moon, as to the other Planets, and as to the innumerable multitude of fixed stars: or why you should say that it is to no purpose for the Sun to pass from one Meridian to another; to rise above this Horizon, to set beneath that other; to make it one while day, another while night: the like variations are made by the Moon, the other Planets, and the fixed stars themselves.

SALV. All these alterations instanced by you, are nothing, save only in relation to the Earth: and that this is true, do but imagine the Earth to move, and there will be no such thing in the World as the rising or set- ting of the Sun or Moon, nor Horizons, nor Meridians, nor days, nor nights; nor, in a word, will such a motion cause any mutation between the Moon and Sun, or any other star whatsoever, whether fixed or er- ratick; but all these changes have relation to the Earth: which all do yet in sum import no other than as if the Sun should shew itself now to China, anon to Persia, then to Egypt, Greece, France, Spain, America, &c. and the like holdeth in the Moon, and the rest of the Coelestial Bodies: which self-same effect falls out exactly in the same manner, if, without troubling so great a part of the Universe, the Terrestrial Globe be made to revolve in itself. But we will augment the difficulty by the addition of this other, which is a very great one, namely, that if you will ascribe this Great Motion to Heaven, you must of necessity make it con- trary to the particular motion of all the Orbs of the Planets, each of which without controversie hath its peculiar motion from the West towards the East, and this but very easie and moderate: and then you make them to be hurried to the contrary part, i.e. from the East to West, by this most furious diurnal motion: whereas, on the contrary, making the Earth to move in itself, the contrariety of motions is taken away, and the only motion from West to East is accommodated to all appearances, and exactly satisfieth every Phoenomenon.

SIMPL. As to the contrariety of Motions it would import little, for Aristotle demonstrateth, that circular motions, are not contrary to one another, and that theirs cannot be truly called contrariety.

SALV. Doth Aristotle demonstrate this, or doth he not rather barely affirm it, as serving to some certain design of his? If contraries be those things that destroy one another, as he himself affirmeth, I do not see how two moveables that encounter each other in a circular line, should less prejudice one another, than if they interfered in a straight line.

SAGR. Hold a little, I pray you. Tell me Simplicius, when two Knights encounter each other, tilting in open field, or when two whole Squadrons, or two Fleets at Sea, make up to grapple, and are broken and sunk, do you call these encounters contrary to one another?

SIMPL. Yes, we say they are contrary.

SAGR. How then, is there no contrariety in circular motion? These motions, being made upon the superficies of the Earth or Water, which are, as you know, spherical, come to be circular. Can you tell, Simplicius, which those circular motions be, that are not contrary to each other? They are (if I mistake not) those of two circles, which touching one another without, one thereof being turn'd round, naturally maketh the other move the contrary way; but if one of them shall be within the other, it is impossible that their motion being made towards different points, they should not justle one another.

SALV. But be they contrary, or not contrary, these are but alterations of words, and I know that upon the matter it would be far more proper and agreeable with Nature, if we could save all with one motion only, than to introduce two that are (if you will not call them contrary) opposite; yet do I not censure this introduction (of contrary motions) as impossible, nor pretend I from the denial thereof, to infer a necessary Demonstration, but only a greater probability, of the other. A third reason which maketh the Ptolemaique Hypothesis less probable is that it most unreasonably confoundeth the order which we assuredly see to be amongst those Coelestial Bodies, the circumgyration of which is not questionable, but most certain. And that Order is, that according as an Orb is greater, it finisheth its revolution in a longer time, and the lesser, in shorter. And thus Saturn describing a greater Circle than all the other

Planets, compleateth the same in thirty yeares: Jupiter finisheth his, that is lesse, in twelve years: Mars in two: The Moon runneth through hers, so much lesse than the rest, in a Month only. Nor do we less sensibly see that one of the Medicean Stars which is nearest to Jupiter, to make its revolution in a very short time, that is, in four and forty hours, or thereabouts; the next to that in three days and an half, the third in seven days, and the most remote in sixteen. And this rate holdeth well enough, nor will it at all alter, whilst we assign the motion of 24 hours to the Terrestrial Globe, for it to move round its own center in that time; but if you would have the Earth immoveable, it is necessary, that when you have past from the short period of the Moon, to the others successively bigger, until you come to that of Mars in two years, and from thence to that of the bigger Sphere of Jupiter in twelve years, and from this to the other yet bigger of Saturn, whose period is of thirty years, it is necessary, I say, that you pass to another Sphere incomparably greater still than that, and make this to accomplish an entire revolution in twenty four hours. And this yet is the least disorder that can follow. For if any one should pass from the Sphere of Saturn to the Starry Orb, and make it so much bigger than that of Saturn, as proportion would require, in respect of its very slow motions, of many thousands of years, then it must needs be a Step much more absurd, to skip from this to another bigger, and to make it convertible in twenty four hours. But the motion of the Earth being granted, the order of the periods will be exactly observed, and from the very slow Sphere of Saturn, we come to the fixed Stars, which are wholly immoveable, and so avoid a fourth difficulty; which we must of necessity admit if the Starry Sphere be supposed moveable, and that is the immense disparity between the motions of those stars themselves; of which some would come to move most swiftly in most vast circles, others most slowly in circles very small, according as they should be found nearer, or more remote from the Poles; which still is accompanied with an inconvenience, as well because we see those, of whose motion there is no question to be made, to move all in very immense circles, as also, because it seems to be an act done with no good consideration, to constitute bodies, that are designed to move circularly, at immense distances from the center, and afterwards to make them move in very small circles.

*   *   *   *

SALV. All, for the strongest reason, alledge that of heavy bodies, which falling downwards from on high, move by a straight line, that is perpendicular to the surface of the Earth, an argument which is held undeniably to prove that the Earth is immoveable: for in case it should have the diurnal motion, a Tower, from the top of which a stone is let fall, being carried along by the conversion of the Earth, in the time that the stone spends in falling, would be transported many hundreds yards Eastward, and so far distant from the Towers foot would the stone come to ground. The which effect they back with another experiment; to wit, by letting a bullet of lead fall from the round top of a Ship, that lieth at anchor, and observing the mark it makes where it lights, which they find to be near the foot of the Mast; but if the same bullet be let fall from the same place when the ship is under sail, it shall light as far from the former place, as the ship hath run in the time of the leads descent; and this for no other reason, than because the natural motion of the ball being at liberty is by a straight line towards the center of the Earth. They fortifie this argument with the experiment of a projectile shot on high at a very great distance, as for example, a ball sent out of a Cannon, erected perpendicular to the horizon, the which spendeth so much time in ascending and falling, that in our parallel the Cannon and we both should be carried by the Earth many miles towards the East, so that the ball in its return could never come near the Cannon, but would fall as far West, as the Earth had run East. They againe adde a third, and very evident experiment, *scilicet,* that shooting a bullet point blank (or as Gunners say neither above nor under metal) out of a Culverin towards the East, and afterwards another, with the same charge, and at the same elevation or disport towards the West, the range towards the West should be very much greater than the other towards the East: for that whilst the ball goeth Westward, the Cannon is carried along by the Earth Eastward and the ball will fall from the Cannon as far distant as is the aggregate of the two motions, one made by itself towards the West, and the other by the Cannon carried about by the Earth towards the East; and on the contrary, from the range of the ball shot Eastward you are to substract the space the Cannon moved, being carried after it. Now suppose, for example, that the range of the ball shot West were five miles, and that the Earth in the same parallel and in the time of the Ball's ranging should remove three miles; the Ball in this case would fall eight miles distant from the Culverin, namely, its own five Westward, and the Culverin's three miles Eastward: but the range of the shot towards the East would be but two miles long, for so much is the remainder, after you have subtracted from the five miles of the range, the three miles which the Cannon had moved towards the same part. But experience sheweth the Ranges to be equal, therefore the Culverin, and consequently the Earth are immoveable. And the stability of the Earth is no less confirmed by two other shots made North and South; for they would never hit the mark, but the Ranges would be always wide, or towards the West, by means of the remove the mark would make, being carried along with the Earth towards the East, whilst the ball is flying. And not only shots made by the Meridians, but also those aimed East or West would prove uncertain; for those aimed East would be too high, and those directed West too low, although they were shot point blank, as I said. For the Range of the Ball in both the shots being made by the Tangent, that is, by a line parallel to the Horizon, and being that in the diurnal motion, if it be of the Earth, the Horizon goeth continually descending towards the East, and rising from the West (therefore the Oriental Stars seem to rise, and the Occidental to decline) so that the Oriental mark would descend below the aim, and thereupon the shot would fly too high, and the ascending of the Western mark would make the shot aimed that way range too low, so that the Cannon would never carry true towards any point; and for that experience telleth us the contrary, it is requisite to say, that the Earth is immoveable.

*   *   *   *

SALV. Therefore we may proceed to the fourth, upon which it's requisite that we stay some time, by reason it is founded upon that experiment from whence the greater part of the remaining arguments derive all their strength. Aristotle saith therefore, that it is a most convincing argument of the Earth's immobility, to see that projectiles thrown or shot upright, return perpendicularly by the same line unto the same place from whence they were shot or thrown. And this holdeth true, although the motion be of a very great height; which could never come to pass, did the Earth move: for in the time that the projected body is moving upwards and downwards in a state of separation from the Earth, the place from whence the motion of the projection began would be past, by means of the Earth's revolution, a great way towards the East, and however great that space was, so far from that place would the projected body in its descent come to the ground. So that hither may be referred the argument taken from a bullet shot from a Cannon directly upwards, as also that other used by Aristotle and Ptolemy, of the heavy bodies that falling from on high are observed to descend by a direct and perpendicular line to the surface of the Earth. Now that I may begin to untie these knots, I demand of Simplicius that in case one should deny to Ptolemy and Aristotle that weights in falling freely from on high, descend by a straight and perpendicular line, that is, directly to the center, what means he would use to prove it?

SIMPL. The means of the senses, the which assureth us, that the Tower or other altitude, is upright and perpendicular, and sheweth us that that stone, or other heavy body, doth slide along the Wall, without inclining a hair's breadth to one side or another, and light at the foot there of just under the place from whence it was let fall.

SALV. But if it should happen that the Terrestrial Globe did move round, and consequently carry the Tower also along with it, and that the stone did then also grate and slide along the side of the Tower, what must its motion be then?

SIMPL. In this case we may rather say its motions: for it would have one wherewith to descend from the top of the Tower to the bottom, and should necessarily have another to follow the course of the said Tower.

SALV. So that its motion should be compounded of two, to wit, of that wherewith it measureth the Tower, and of that other wherewith it followeth the same: From which composition would follow, that the stone would no longer describe that simple straight and perpendicular line, but one transverse and perhaps not straight.

SIMPL. I can say nothing of its non-rectitude, but this I know very well, that it would of necessity be transverse, and different from the other directly perpendicular, which it doth describe, the Earth standing still.

SALV. You see then, that upon the mere observing the falling stone to glide along the Tower, you cannot certainly affirm that it describeth a line which is straight and perpendicular, unless you first suppose that the Earth standeth still.

SIMPL. True; for if the Earth should move, the stone's motion would be transverse, and not perpendicular.

SALV. Behold then the Paralogism of Aristotle and Ptolemy to be evident and manifest, and discovered by you yourself, wherein that is supposed as known, which is intended to be demonstrated.

SIMPL. How can that be? To me it appeareth that the Syllogism is rightly demonstrated without *petitionem principii.*

SALV. You shall see how it is; answer me a little. Doth he not lay down the conclusion as unknown?

SIMPL. Unknown; why otherwise the demonstrating it would be superfluous.

SALV. But the middle term, ought not that to be known?

SIMPL. It's necessary that it should, for otherwise it would be a proving *ignotum per aequè ignotum.*

SALV. Our conclusion which is to be proved, and which is unknown, is it not the stability of the Earth?

SIMPL. It is the same.

SALV. The middle term, which ought to be known, is it not the straight and perpendicular descent of the stone?

SIMPL. It is so.

SALV. But was it not just now concluded, that we can have no certain knowledge whether that same shall be direct and perpendicular, unless we first know that the Earth stands still? Therefore, in your Syllogism the certainty of the middle term is assumed from the uncertainty of the conclusion. You may see then, what and how great the Paralogism is.

SAGR. I would, in favour of Simplicius, defend Aristotle if it were possible, or at least better satisfie myself concerning the strength of your conclusion. You say, that the seeing the stone rake along the Tower, is not sufficient to assure us, that its motion is perpendicular (which is the middle term of the Syllogism) unless it be presupposed, that the Earth standeth still, which is the conclusion to be proved: For that if the Tower did move together with the Earth, and the stone did slide along the same, the motion of the stone would be transverse, and not perpendicular. But I shall answer, that should the Tower move, it would be impossible that the stone should fall gliding along the side of it, and therefore from its falling in that manner the stability of the Earth is inferred.

SIMPL. It is so, for if you would have the stone in descending to grate upon the Tower, though it were carried round by the Earth, you must allow the stone two natural motions, to wit, the straight motion towards the Center; and the circular about the Center, the which is impossible.

SALV. Aristotle's defense then consisteth in the impossibility, or at least in his esteeming it an impossibility, that the stone should move with a motion mixt of straight and circular: for if he did not hold it impossible that the stone could move to the Center and about the Center at once, he must have understood, that it might come to pass that the falling stone might in its descent, rake the Tower as well when it moved as when it stood still; and consequently he must have perceived, that from this grating nothing could be inferred touching the mobility or immobility of the Earth. But this doth not any way excuse Aristotle; as well because he ought to have exprest it, if he had had such a conceit, it being so material a part of his Argument, as also because it can neither be said that such an effect is impossible, nor that Aristotle did esteem it so. The first cannot be affirmed, for that by and by I shall shew that it is not only possible, but necessary: nor much less can the second be averred, for that Aristotle himself granteth fire to move naturally upwards in a straight line, and to move about with the diurnal motion, imparted by Heaven to the whole Element of Fire and the greater part of the Air: If therefore he held it not impossible to mix the straight motion upwards, with the circular communicated to the Fire and Air from the concave of the Moon, much less ought he to account impossible the mixture of the

straight motion downwards of the stone, with the circular which we presuppose natural to the whole Terrestrial Globe, of which the stone is a
part.

SIMPL. I see no such thing: for if the element of Fire revolve round together with the Air, it is a very easie, yea a necessary thing, that a spark
of fire which from the Earth mounts upwards, in passing through the
moving air, should receive the same motion, being a body so thin, light,
and easie to be moved: but that a very heavy stone or a Cannon bullet,
that descendeth from on high and that is at liberty to move whither it
will, should suffer itself to be transported either by the air or any other
thing, is altogether incredible. Besides that, we have the Experiment,
which is so proper to our purpose, of the stone let fall from the round
top of the Mast of a ship, which when the ship lyeth still, falleth at the
Foot of the Mast, but when the ship saileth, falls so far distant from that
place, by how far the ship in the time of the stone's falling had run forward; which will not be a few fathoms, when the ship's course is swift.

SALV. There is great disparity between the case of the Ship and that of
the Earth, if the Terrestrial Globe be supposed to have a diurnal motion. For it is a thing very manifest, that the motion of the Ship, as it is
not natural to it, so the motion of all those things that are in it is accidental; whence it is no wonder that the stone which was retained in the
round top, being left at liberty, descendeth downwards without any obli-
gation to follow the motion of the Ship. But the diurnal conversion is
ascribed to the Terrestrial Globe for its proper and natural motion, and
consequently, it is so to all the parts of the said Globe; and, as being
impressed by nature, is indelible in them; and therefore that stone that
is on the top of the Tower hath an intrinsick inclination of revolving
about the Center of it completely in twenty four hours, and this same
natural instinct it exerciseth eternally, be it placed in any state whatsoever. And to be assured of the truth of this, you have no more to do but
to alter an antiquated impression made in your mind; and to say, Like
as in that I hitherto, holding it to be the property of the Terrestrial
Globe to rest immoveable about its Center, did never doubt or question
but that all whatsoever particles thereof do also naturally remain in the
same state of rest: So it is reason, in case the Terrestrial Globe did move
round by natural instinct in twenty-four hours, that the intrinsick and
natural inclination of all its parts should also be, not to stand still, but
to follow the same revolution. And thus without running into any inconvenience, one may conclude that the motion conferred by the force
of Oars on the Ship, and by it on all the things that are contained within
her, is not natural but foreign: it is very reasonable that the stone, it

being separated from the ship, do reduce itself to its natural disposure, and return to exercise its pure simple instinct given it by nature. To this I add, that it's necessary, that at least that part of the Air which is beneath the greater heights of mountains, should be transported and carried round by the roughness of the Earth's surface; or that, as being mixt with many Vapours, and terrene Exhalations, it do naturally follow the diurnal motion, which occurreth not in the Air about the ship rowed by Oars: So that your arguing from the ship to the Tower hath not the force of an inference; because that stone which falls from the round top of the Mast, entereth into a medium, which is unconcerned in the motion of the ship: but that which departeth from the top of the Tower, finds a medium that hath a motion in common with the whole Terrestrial Globe; so that without being hindered, rather being assisted by the motion of the air, it may follow the universal course of the Earth.

SIMPL. I cannot conceive that the air can imprint in a very great stone, or in a gross Globe of Wood or Ball of Lead, as suppose of two hundred weight, the motion wherewith itself is moved, and which it doth perhaps communicate to feathers, snow, and other very light things: nay, I see that a weight of that nature, being exposed to even the most impetuous wind, is not thereby removed an inch from its place; now consider with yourself whether the air will carry it along therewith.

SALV. There is great difference between your experiment and our case. You introduce the wind blowing against that stone, supposed in a state of rest, and we expose to the air, which already moveth, the stone which doth also move with the same velocity; so that the air is not to confer a new motion upon it, but only to maintain, or to speak better, not to hinder the motion already acquired: you would drive the stone with a strange and preternatural motion, and we desire to conserve it in its natural. If you would produce a more pertinent experiment, you should say, that it is observed, if not with the eye of the forehead, yet with that of the mind, what would happen, if an eagle that is carried by the course of the wind, should let a stone fall from its talons; which, assuming that at its being let go, it went along with the wind, and after it was let fall it entered into a medium that moved with equal velocity, I am very confident that it would not be seen to descend in its fall perpendicularly, but that following the course of the wind, and adding thereto that of its particular gravity, it would move with a transverse motion.

SIMPL. But it would first be known how such an experiment may be made; and then one might judge according to the event. In the mean time the effect of the ship doth hitherto incline to favor our opinion.

SALV. Well said you hitherto, for perhaps it may anon change countenance. And that I may no longer hold you in suspense, tell me, Simplicius, do you really believe that the Experiment of the ship squares so very well with our purpose that it ought to be believed, that that which we see happen in it, ought also to happen in the Terrestrial Globe?

SIMPL. As yet I am of that opinion; and though you have alledged some small disparities, I do not think them of so great moment, as that they should make me change my judgment.

SALV. I rather desire that you would continue therein, and hold for certain, that the effect of the Earth would exactly answer that of the ship: provided, that when it shall appear prejudicial to your cause, you would not be humorous and alter your thoughts. You may haply say, Forasmuch as when the ship stands still, the stone falls at the foot of the Mast, and when she is under sail, it lights far from thence, that therefore by conversion, from the stone's falling at the foot is argued the ship's standing still, and from its falling far from thence is argued her moving; and because that which occurreth to the ship, ought likewise to befall the Earth: that therefore from the falling of the stone at the foot of the Tower is necessarily inferred the immobility of the Terrestrial Globe. Is not this your argumentation?

SIMPL. It is; and reduced into such conciseness, as that it is become most easie to be apprehended.

SALV. Now tell me, if the stone let fall from the Roundtop, when the ship is in a swift course, should fall exactly in the same place of the ship, in which it falleth when the ship is at anchor, what service would these experiments do you, in order to the ascertaining whether the vessel doth stand still or move?

SIMPL. Just none: Like as, for example, from the beating of the pulse one cannot know whether a person be asleep or awake, seeing that the pulse beateth after the same manner in sleeping as in waking.

SALV. Very well. Have you ever tryed the experiment of the Ship?

SIMPL. I have not; but yet I believe that those Authors which alledge the same, have accurately observed it; besides that the cause of the disparity is so manifestly known, that it admits of no question.

SALV. That it is possible that those Authors instance in it, without having made tryal of it, you yourself are a good testimony, who without having examined it, alledge it as certain, and in a credulous way remit it to their authority; as it is now not only possible, but very probable that they likewise did; I mean, did remit the same to their Predecessors, without ever arriving at one that had made the experiment: for whoever shall examine the same, shall find the event succeed quite contrary to what hath been written of it: that is, he shall see the stone fall at all times in the same place of the Ship, whether it stand still, or move with any whatsoever velocity. So that the same holding true in the Earth, as in the Ship, one cannot from the stone's falling perpendicularly at the foot of the Tower, conclude anything touching the motion or rest of the Earth.

SIMPL. If you should refer me to any other means than to experience, I verily believe our Disputations would not come to an end in haste, for this seemeth to me a thing so remote from all human reason, as that it leaveth not the least place for credulity or probability.

SALV. And yet it hath left place in me for both.

SIMPL. How is this? You have not made an hundred, no nor one proof thereof, and do you so confidently affirm it for true? I for my part will return to my incredulity, and to the confidence I had that the Experiment hath been tried by the principal Authors who made use thereof, and that the event succeeded as they affirm.

SALV. I am assured that the effect will ensue as I tell you; for so it is necessary that it should: and I farther add, that you know yourself that it cannot fall out otherwise, however you feign or seem to feign that you know it not. Yet I am so good at taming of wits, that I will make you confess the same whether you will or no. But Sagredus stands very mute, and yet, if I mistake not, I saw him make an offer to speak somewhat.

SAGR. I had an intent to say something, but to tell you true, I know not what it was, for the curiosity that you have moved in me, by promising that you would force Simplicius to discover the knowledge which he would conceal from us, hath made me to depose all other thoughts: therefore I pray you to make good your vaunt.

SALV. Provided that Simplicius do consent to reply to what I shall ask him, I will not fail to do it.

SIMPL. I will answer what I know, assured that I shall not be much put to it, for that of those things which I hold to be false, I think nothing can be known, in regard that Science respecteth truths and not falsehoods.

SALV. I desire not that you should say or reply, that you know anything, save that which you most assuredly know. Therefore tell me; If you had here a flat superficies as smooth as a Looking glass, and of a substance as hard as steel, and that it were not parallel to the Horizon, but somewhat inclining, and that upon it you did put a Ball perfectly spherical, and of a substance heavy and hard, as suppose of brass; what think you it would do being let go? do not you believe (as for my part I do) that it would lie still?

SIMPL. If that superficies were inclining?

SALV. Yes; for so I have already supposed.

SIMPL. I cannot conceive how it should be still: nay, I am confident that it would move towards the declivity spontaneously.

SALV. Take good heed what you say, Simplicius, for I am confident that it would lie still in what ever place you should lay it.

SIMPL. So long as you make use of such suppositions, Salviatus, I shall cease to wonder if you infer most absurd conclusions.

SALV. Are you assured, then, that it would freely move towards the declivity?

SIMPL. Who doubts it?

SALV. And this you verily believe, not because I told you so, (for I endeavoured to perswade you to think the contrary) but of yourself, and upon your natural judgment.

SIMPL. Now I see what you would be at; you spoke not this as really believing the same; but to try me, and to wrest matter out of my own mouth wherewith to condemn me.

SALV. You are in the right. And how long would that Ball move, and with what velocity? But take notice that I instanced in a Ball exactly round, and a plane exquisitely polished, that all external and accidental impediments might be taken away. And so would I have you remove all obstructions caused by the Air's resistance to division, and all other casual obstacles, if any other there can be.

SIMPL. I very well understand your meaning, and as to your demand, I answer, that the Ball would continue to move *in infinitum*, if the inclination of the plain should so long last, and continually with an accelerating motion; for such is the nature of ponderous moveables, that *vires acquirans eundo:* and the greater the declivity was, the greater the velocity would be.

SALV. But if one should require that that Ball should move upwards on that same superficies, do you believe that it would so do?

SIMPL. Not spontaneously; but being drawn, or violently thrown, it may.

SALV. And in case it were thrust forward by the impression of some violent impetus from without, what and how great would its motion be?

SIMPL. The motion would go continually decreasing and retarding, as being contrary to nature; and would be longer or shorter, according to the greater or less impulse, and according to the greater or less acclivity.

SALV. It seems, then, that hitherto you have explained to me the accidents of a moveable upon two different Planes; and that in the inclining plane, the heavy moveable doth spontaneously descend, and goeth continually accelerating, and that to retain it in rest, force must be used therein: but that on the ascending plane, there is required a force to thrust it forwards, and also to stay it in rest, and that the motion impressed goeth continually diminishing, till that in the end it cometh to nothing. You say yet farther, that in both the one and the other case, there do arise differences from the planes having a greater or less declivity or acclivity; so that the greater inclination is attended with the greater velocity; and contrariwise, upon the ascending plane, the same moveable thrown with the same force, moveth a greater distance, by how much the elevation is less. Now tell me, what would befall the same moveable upon a superficies that had neither acclivity nor declivity?

SIMPL. Here you must give me a little time to consider of an answer. There being no declivity, there can be no natural inclination to motion: and there being no acclivity, there can be no resistance to being moved; so that there would arise an indifference between propension and resistance of motion; therefore, methinks it ought naturally to stand still. But I had forgot myself: it was but even now that Sagredus gave me to understand that it would so do.

SALV. So I think, provided one did lay it down gently: but if it had an impetus given it towards any part, what would follow?

SIMP. There would follow, that it should move towards that part.

SALV. But with what kind of motion? with the continually accelerated, as in declining planes, or with the successively retarded, as in those ascending.

SIMP. I cannot tell how to discover any cause of acceleration or retardation, there being no declivity or acclivity.

SALV. Well: but if there be no cause of retardation, much less ought there to be any cause of rest. How long therefore would you have the moveable to move?

SIMP. As long as that superficies, neither inclined nor declined shall last.

SALV. Therefore if such a space were interminate, the motion upon the same would likewise have no termination, that is, would be perpetual?

SIMP. I think so, if so be the moveable be of a matter durable.

SALV. That hath been already supposed, when it was said, that all external and accidental impediments were removed, and the brittlenesse of the moveable in this our case, is one of those impediments accidental. Tell me now, what do you think is the cause that that same Ball moveth spontaneously upon the inclining plane, and not without violence upon the erected?

SIMP. Because the inclination of heavy bodies is to move towards the center of the Earth, and only by violence upwards towards the circumference; and the inclining superficies is that which acquireth vicinity to the center, and the ascending one, remoteness.

SALV. Therefore a superficies which should be neither declining nor ascending ought in all its parts to be equally distant from the center. But is there any such superficies in the World?

SIMP. There is no want thereof: Such is our Terrestrial Globe, if it were more even, and not as it is rough and mountainous; but you have that of the Water, at such time as it is calm and still.

SALV. Then a ship which moveth in a calm at Sea, is one of those moveables, which run along one of those superficies that are neither declining nor ascending, and therefore disposed, in case all obstacles external and accidental were removed, to move with the impulse once imparted incessantly and uniformly.

SIMPL. It should seem to be so.

SALV. And that stone which is on the round top, doth not it move, as being together with the ship carried about by the circumference of a Circle about the Center, and therefore consequently by a motion in it indelible, if all external obstacles be removed? And is not this motion as swift as that of the ship?

SIMPL. Hitherto all is well. But what followeth?

SALV. Then in good time recant, I pray you, your last conclusion, if you are satisfied with the truth of all the premises.

SIMPL. By my last conclusion, you mean, That that same stone moving with a motion indelibly impressed upon it, is not to leave, nay rather is to follow the ship, and in the end to light in the self-same place, where it falleth when the ship lyeth still; and so I also grant it would do, in case there were no outward impediments that might disturb the stone's motion after its being let go. But the impediments are two: the one is the moveable's inability to break through the air with its mere impetus only, it being deprived of that of the strength of Oars, of which it had been partaker, as part of the ship, at the time that it was upon the Mast; the other is the new motion of descent, which also must needs be an hinderance of that other progressive motion.

SALV. As to the impediment of the Air, I do not deny it you; and if the thing falling were a light matter, as a feather, or a lock of wool, the retardation would be very great, but in an heavy stone is very exceeding small. And you yourself but even now did say that the force of the most impetuous wind sufficeth not to stir a great stone from its place; now do but consider what the calmer air is able to do, being encountred by a stone no more swift than the whole ship. Neverthelesse, as I said before, I do allow you this small effect that may depend upon such an impediment, like as I know that you will grant to me that if the air should move with the same velocity that the ship and stone hath, then the impediment would be nothing at all. As to the other of the additional motion downwards, in the first place it is manifest that these two, I mean the circular about the center and the straight towards the center, are not contraries, or destructive to one another, or incompatible. Because that as to the moveable, it hath no repugnance at all to such motions, for you yourself have already confest the repugnance to be against the motion which removeth from the center, and the inclination to be towards the motion which approacheth to the center. Whence it doth of necessity follow that the moveable hath neither repugnance nor propension to the motion which neither approacheth, nor goeth from the center, nor consequently is there any cause for the diminishing in it the faculty impressed. And forasmuch as the moving cause is not one alone, which must wear itself out by the new operation, but that there are two, distinct from each other (of which, the gravity attends only to the drawing of the moveable towards the center, and the vertue impressed attends to the conducting it about the center), there remaineth no occasion of impediment.

*   *   *   *

SALV. And here for a final proof of the nullity of all the experiments before alledged, I conceive it now a time and place convenient to demonstrate a way how to make an exact trial of them all. Shut yourself up with some friend in the grand Cabbin between the decks of some large Ship and there procure gnats, flies, and such other small winged creatures: get also a great tub (or other vessel) full of water, and within it put certain fishes, let also a certain bottle be hung up, which drop by drop letteth forth its water into another bottle placed underneath, having a narrow neck: and, the Ship lying still, observe diligently how those small winged animals fly with like velocity towards all parts of the Cabin; how the fishes swim indifferently towards all sides; and how the distilling drops all fall into the bottle placed underneath. And casting anything towards your friend, you need not throw it with more force one way then another, provided the distances be equal: and leaping, as the saying is, with your feet closed, you will reach as far one way as another. Having observed all these particulars, though no man doubteth that so long as the vessel stands still they ought to succeed in this manner; make the Ship to move with what velocity you please; for (so long as the motion is uniforme, and not fluctuating this way and that way) you shall not discern any the least alteration in all the forenamed effects; nor can you gather by any of them whether the Ship doth move or stand still. In leaping you shall reach as far upon the floor, as before; nor for that the Ship moveth shall you make a greater leap towards the poop than towards the prow; howbeit in the time that you staid in the Air, the floor under your feet shall have run the contrary way to that of your jump; and throwing any thing to your companion you shall not need to cast it with more strength that it may reach him, if he shall be towards the prow and you towards the poop, than if you stood in a contrary situation; the drops shall all distill as before into the inferior bottle, and not so much as one shall fall towards the poop, albeit whilst the drop is in the Air, the Ship shall have run many feet; the Fishes in their water shall not swim with more trouble towards the fore-part, than towards the hinder part of the tub; but shall with equal velocity make to the bait placed on any side of the tub; and lastly, the flies and gnats shall continue their flight indifferently towards all parts; nor shall they ever happen to be driven together towards the side of the Cabbin next the poop, as if they were wearied with following the swift course of the Ship, from which through their suspension in the Air, they had been long separated; and if burning a few graines of incense you make a little smoke, you shall see it ascend on high, and there in manner of a cloud suspend itself and move indifferently, not inclining more to one side than another: and of this correspondence of effects the cause is for that the Ship's motion is common to all the things contained in it and to the Air also; I mean if those things be shut up in the Cabbin: but in case those things were above deck in the open Air, and not obliged to follow the course of the Ship, differences more or less notable would be observed in some of the fore-named effects, and there is no doubt but that the smoke would stay behind as much as the Air itself; the flies also and the gnats being hindered by the Air would not be able to follow the motion of the Ship if they were separated at any distance from it. But keeping near thereto, because the Ship itself as being an unfractuous Fabrick, carrieth along with it part of its nearest Air, they would follow the said Ship without any pains or difficulty. And for the like reason we see sometimes in riding post, that the troublesome flies and hornets do follow the horses flying sometimes to one, sometimes to another part of the body. But in the falling drops the difference would be very small; and in the jumps, and projections of heavy bodies altogether imperceptible.

9

WILLIAM HARVEY

Born in 1578, son of a minor merchant who destined his eldest son for a learned career, William Harvey matriculated at Gonville and Caius College in Cambridge in 1593. Already he had determined to follow medicine, and after taking his degree from Cambridge, he proceeded to further study with the leading medical faculty in Europe at the University of Padua. His residence in Padua fell within the period when Galileo occupied the university's chair in mathematics. On his return to England, Harvey settled down to a successful career in London, where he quickly rose to a position of prominence in the Royal College of Physicians. For more than forty years, he delivered their Lumleian Lectures in surgery. Harvey also won the attention of the crown, serving first as Physician Extraordinary to James I and then as Physician in Ordinary to Charles I. When the Civil War broke out in 1642, Harvey followed the fortunes of the king and suffered loss for his loyalty when the royal cause went down in defeat. He died in London during the interregnum, in 1657.

De motu cordis, Harvey's masterpiece, appeared in 1628. Chronologically, it appeared during the period that witnessed the publication of the works of Galileo and Descartes, which became the foundations of the mechanical philosophy of nature. Its subject matter, however, belonged to the realm of biological science, and fell outside the normal precincts of the mechanical philosophy. To be sure, Descartes attempted to bring biology within his conception of nature, and in the *Discourse* he gave a mechanical exposition of Harvey's principal discovery. Nevertheless, biology in the 17th century generally resisted the effort wholly to mechanize it, and students of biological science generally saw, in living beings, evidence of vital principles that refused to be reduced to particles of matter in motion. One of the interesting questions that the student of Harvey must face is the extent of mechanistic influence on his work.

The immediate background of Harvey's book, however, lies more in the tradition of anatomical research associated with the university in which he studied. *De fabrica corporis humanae* (1543) of Andrea Vesalius, who occupied the Paduan chair of anatomy, is generally taken as the origin of modern anatomy, and worthy successors in the chair, including Harvey's teacher Fabricius of Aquapendente, carried the tradition on. Basing their work on the direct observation of the human body in dissection to an extent never done before, the Paduan anatomists inevitably discovered errors in the accepted teachings of Galen. Some of the discoveries, especially those concerned with the vascular system (such as the impervious solidity of the septum dividing the heart and the valve-like structures in the veins), implicitly raised questions about Galen's physiology as well. It was William Harvey, English heir of the Paduan school, who made the implicit questions explicit, and went on to draw the conclusions that mark the first steps toward modern physiology.

9

On the Motion of the Heart
and Blood in Animals

Chapter II

On the Motions of the Heart as Seen in the Dissection of Living Animals

In the first place, then, when the chest of a living animal is laid open and the capsule that immediately surrounds the heart is slit up or removed, the organ is seen now to move, now to be at rest; there is a time when it moves, and a time when it is motionless.

These things are more obvious in the colder animals, such as toads, frogs, serpents, small fishes, crabs, shrimps, snails, and shell-fish. They also become more distinct in warm-blooded animals, such as the dog and hog, if they be attentively noted when the heart begins to flag, to move more slowly, and, as it were, to die: the movements then become slower and rarer, the pauses longer, by which it is made much more easy to perceive and unravel what the motions really are, and how they are performed. In the pause, as in death, the heart is soft, flaccid, exhausted, lying, as it were, at rest.

In the motion, and interval in which this is accomplished, three principal circumstances are to be noted:

1. That the heart is erected, and rises upwards to a point, so that at this time it strikes against the breast and the pulse is felt externally.

2. That it is everywhere contracted, but more especially towards the sides so that it looks narrower, relatively longer, more drawn together. The heart of an eel taken out of the body of the animal and placed upon the table or the hand, shows these particulars; but the same things are manifest in the hearts of all small fishes and of those colder animals where the organ is more conical or elongated.

3. The heart being grasped in the hand, is felt to become harder dur-

Translated from the Latin by Robert Willis, London, 1847.

ing its action. Now this hardness proceeds from tension, precisely as when the forearm is grasped, its tendons are perceived to become tense and resilient when the fingers are moved.

4. It may further be observed in fishes, and the colder blooded animals, such as frogs, serpents, etc., that the heart, when it moves, becomes of a paler color, when quiescent of a deeper blood-red color.

From these particulars it appears evident to me that the motion of the heart consists in a certain universal tension—both contraction in the line of its fibres, and constriction in every sense. It becomes erect, hard, and of diminished size during its action; the motion is plainly of the same nature as that of the muscles when they contract in the line of their sinews and fibres; for the muscles, when in action, acquire vigor and tenseness, and from soft become hard, prominent, and thickened: and in the same manner the heart.

We are therefore authorized to conclude that the heart, at the moment of its action, is at once constricted on all sides, rendered thicker in its parietes and smaller in its ventricles, and so made apt to project or expel its charge of blood. This, indeed, is made sufficiently manifest by the preceding fourth observation in which we have seen that the heart, by squeezing out the blood that it contains, becomes paler, and then when it sinks into repose and the ventricle is filled anew with blood, that the deeper crimson colour returns. But no one need remain in doubt of the fact, for if the ventricle be pierced the blood will be seen to be forcibly projected outwards upon each motion or pulsation when the heart is tense.

These things, therefore, happen together or at the same instant: the tension of the heart, the pulse of its apex, which is felt externally by its striking against the chest, the thickening of its parietes, and the forcible expulsion of the blood it contains by the constriction of its ventricles.

Hence the very opposite of the opinions commonly received appears to be true; inasmuch as it is generally believed that when the heart strikes the breast and the pulse is felt without, the heart is dilated in its ventricles and is filled with blood; but the contrary of this is the fact, and the heart, when it contracts (and the impulse of the apex is conveyed through the chest wall), is emptied. Whence the motion which is generally regarded as the diastole of the heart, is in truth its systole. And in like manner the intrinsic motion of the heart is not the diastole but the systole; neither is it in the diastole that the heart grows firm and tense, but in the systole, for then only, when tense, is it moved and made vigorous.

Neither is it by any means to be allowed that the heart only moves in the lines of its straight fibres, although the great Vesalius giving this notion countenance, quotes a bundle of osiers bound in a pyramidal heap in illustration; meaning, that as the apex is approached to the base, so are the sides made to bulge out in the fashion of arches, the cavities to dilate, the ventricles to acquire the form of a cupping-glass and so to suck in the blood. But the true effect of every one of its fibres is to constringe the heart at the same time they render it tense; and this rather with the effect of thickening and amplifying the walls and substance of the organ than enlarging its ventricles. And, again, as the fibres run from the apex to the base, and draw the apex towards the base, they do not tend to make the walls of the heart bulge out in circles, but rather the contrary; inasmuch as every fibre that is circularly disposed, tends to become straight when it contracts; and is distended laterally and thickened, as in the case of muscular fibres in general, when they contract, that is, when they are shortened longitudinally, as we see them in the bellies of the muscles of the body at large. To all this let it be added, that not only are the ventricles contracted in virtue of the direction and condensation of their walls, but farther, that those fibres, or bands, styled nerves by Aristotle, which are so conspicuous "in the ventricles" of the larger animals, and contain all the straight fibres (the parietes of the heart containing only circular ones), when they contract simultaneously by an admirable adjustment all the internal surfaces are drawn together as if with cords, and so is the charge of blood expelled with force.

Neither is it true, as vulgarly believed, that the heart by any dilatation or motion of its own, has the power of drawing the blood into the ventricles; for when it acts and becomes tense, the blood is expelled; when it relaxes and sinks together it receives the blood in the manner and wise which will by-and-by be explained.

*   *   *   *

Chapter V

Of the Motion, Action and Office of the Heart

From these and other observations of a similar nature, I am persuaded it will be found that the motion of the heart is as follows:

First of all, the auricle contracts, and in the course of its contraction forces the blood (which it contains in ample quantity as the head of the veins, the store-house and cistern of the blood) into the ventricle, which, being filled, the heart raises itself straightway, makes all its fibres tense, contracts the ventricles, and performs a beat, by which it immediately sends the blood supplied to it by the auricle into the arteries. The right ventricle sends its charge into the lungs by the vessel which is called vena arteriosa, but which in structure and function, and all other respects, is an artery. The left ventricle sends its charge into the aorta, and through this by the arteries to the body at large.

These two motions, one of the ventricles, the other of the auricles, take place consecutively, but in such a manner that there is a kind of harmony or rhythm preserved between them, the two concurring in such wise that but one motion is apparent, especially in the warmer blooded animals, in which the movements in question are rapid. Nor is this for any other reason than it is in a piece of machinery, in which, though one wheel gives motion to another, yet all the wheels seem to move simultaneously; or in that mechanical contrivance which is adapted to firearms, where, the trigger being touched, down comes the flint, strikes against the steel, elicits a spark, which falling among the powder, ignites it, when the flame extends, enters the barrel, causes the explosion, propels the ball, and the mark is attained—all of which incidents, by reason of the celerity with which they happen, seem to take place in the twinkling of an eye. So also in deglutition: by the elevation of the root of the tongue, and the compression of the mouth, the food or drink is pushed into the fauces, when the larynx is closed by its muscles and by the epiglottis. The pharynx is then raised and opened by its muscles in the same way as a sac that is to be filled is lifted up and its mouth dilated. Upon the mouthful being received, it is forced downwards by the transverse muscles, and then carried farther by the longitudinal ones. Yet all these motions, though executed by different and distinct organs, are performed harmoniously, and in such order that they seem to constitute but a single motion and act, which we call deglutition.

Even so does it come to pass with the motions and action of the heart, which constitute a kind of deglutition, a transfusion of the blood from the veins to the arteries. And if anyone, bearing these things in mind, will carefully watch the motions of the heart in the body of a living animal, he will perceive not only all the particulars I have mentioned, viz., the heart becoming erect, and making one continuous motion with its auricles; but farther, a certain obscure undulation and lateral inclination in the direction of the axis of the right ventricle, as if twisting itself slightly in performing its work. And indeed everyone may see, when a horse drinks, that the water is drawn in and transmitted to the stomach at each movement of the throat, which movement produces a sound and yields a pulse both to the ear and the touch; in the same way it is with each motion of the heart, when there is the delivery of a quantity of blood from the veins to the arteries a pulse takes place, and can be heard within the chest.

The motion of the heart, then, is entirely of this description, and the one action of the heart is the transmission of the blood and its distribution, by means of the arteries, to the very extremities of the body; so that the pulse which we feel in the arteries is nothing more than the impulse of the blood derived from the heart.

Whether or not the heart, besides propelling the blood, giving it motion locally, and distributing it to the body, adds anything else to it—heat, spirit, perfection,—must be inquired into by-and-by, and decided upon other grounds. So much may suffice at this time, when it is shown that by the action of the heart the blood is transfused through the ventricles from the veins to the arteries, and distributed by them to all parts of the body.

The above, indeed, is admitted by all, both from the structure of the heart and the arrangement and action of its valves. But still they are like persons purblind or groping about in the dark, for they give utterance to various, contradictory, and incoherent sentiments, delivering many things upon conjecture, as we have already shown.

The grand cause of doubt and error in this subject appears to me to have been the intimate connexion between the heart and the lungs. When men saw both the pulmonary artery and the pulmonary veins losing themselves in the lungs, of course it became a puzzle to them to know how or by what means the right ventricle should distribute the blood to the body, or the left draw it from the venæ cavæ. This fact is borne witness to by Galen, whose words, when writing against Erasistratus in regard to the origin and use of the veins and the coction of the blood, are the following: "You will reply," he says, "that the effect is so; that the blood is prepared in the liver, and is thence transferred to the heart to receive its proper form and last perfection; a statement which does not appear devoid of reason; for no great and perfect work is ever accomplished at a single effort, or receives its final polish from one instrument. But if this be actually so, then show us another vessel which draws the absolutely perfect blood from the heart, and distributes it as the arteries do the spirits over the whole body." Here then is a reasonable opinion not allowed, because, forsooth, besides not seeing the true means of transit, he could not discover the vessel which should transmit the blood from the heart to the body at large!

But had anyone been there in behalf of Erasistratus, and of that opinion which we now espouse, and which Galen himself acknowledges in other respects consonant with reason, to have pointed to the aorta as the vessel which distributes the blood from the heart to the rest of the body, I wonder what would have been the answer of that most ingenious and learned man? Had he said that the artery transmits spirits and not blood, he would indeed sufficiently have answered Erasistratus, who imagined that the arteries contained nothing but spirits; but then he would have contradicted himself, and given a foul denial to that for which he had keenly contended in his writings against this very Erasistratus, to wit, that blood in substance is continued in the arteries, and not spirits; a fact which he demonstrated not only by many powerful arguments, but by experiments.

But if the divine Galen will here allow, as in other places he does, "that all the arteries of the body arise from the great artery, and that this takes its origin from the heart; that all these vessels naturally contain and carry blood; that the three semilunar valves situated at the orifice of the aorta prevent the return of the blood into the heart, and that nature never connected them with this, the most noble viscus of the body, unless for some important end"; if, I say, this father of physicians concedes all these things,—and I quote his own words,—I do not see how he can deny that the great artery is the very vessel to carry the blood, when it has attained its highest term of perfection, from the heart for distribution to all parts of the body. Or would he perchance still hesitate, like all who have come after him, even to the present hour, because he did not perceive the route by which the blood was transferred from the veins to the arteries, in consequence, as I have already said, of the intimate connexion between the heart and the lungs? And that this difficulty puzzled anatomists not a little, when in their dissections they found the pulmonary artery and left ventricle full of thick, black, and clotted blood, plainly appears, when they felt themselves compelled to affirm that the blood made its way from the right to the left ventricle by transuding through the septum of the heart. But this fancy I have already refuted. A new pathway for the blood must therefore be prepared and thrown open, and being once exposed, no further difficulty will, I believe, be experienced by anyone in admitting what I have already proposed in regard to the pulse of the heart and arteries, viz., the passage of the blood from the veins to the arteries, and its distribution to the whole of the body by means of these vessels.

Chapter VI

Of the Course by Which the Blood Is Carried from the Vena Cava into the Arteries, or from the Right into the Left Ventricle of the Heart

Since the intimate connexion of the heart with the lungs, which is apparent in the human subject, has been the probable cause of the errors that have been committed on this point, they plainly do amiss who, pretending to speak of the parts of animals generally, as anatomists for the most part do, confine their researches to the human body alone, and that when it is dead. They obviously do not act otherwise than he who, having studied the forms of a single commonwealth, should set about the composition of a general system of polity; or who, having taken cognizance of the nature of a single field, should imagine that he had mastered the science of agriculture; or who, upon the ground of one particular proposition, should proceed to draw general conclusions.

Had anatomists only been as conversant with the dissection of the lower animals as they are with that of the human body, the matters that have hitherto kept them in a perplexity of doubt would, in my opinion, have met them freed from every kind of difficulty.

And first, in fishes, in which the heart consists of but a single ventricle, being devoid of lungs, the thing is sufficiently manifest. Here the sac, which is situated at the base of the heart, and is the part analogous to the auricle in man, plainly forces the blood into the heart, and the heart, in its turn, conspicuously transmits it by a pipe or artery, or vessel analogous to an artery; these are facts which are confirmed by simple ocular inspection, as well as by a division of the vessel, when the blood is seen to be projected by each pulsation of the heart.

The same thing is also not difficult of demonstration in those animals that have, as it were, no more than a single ventricle to the heart, such as toads, frogs, serpents, and lizards, which have lungs in a certain sense, as they have a voice. I have many observations by me on the admirable structure of the lungs of these animals, and matters appertaining, which, however, I cannot introduce in this place. Their anatomy plainly shows us that the blood is transferred in them from the veins to the arteries in the same manner as in higher animals, viz., by the action of the heart; the way, in fact, is patent, open, manifest; there is no difficulty, no room for doubt about it; for in them the matter stands precisely as it would in man were the septum of his heart perforated or removed, or one ventricle made out of two; and this being the case, I imagine that no one will doubt as to the way by which the blood may pass from the veins into the arteries.

But as there are actually more animals which have no lungs than there are furnished with them, and in like manner a greater number which have only one ventricle than there are with two, it is open to us to conclude, judging from the mass or multitude of living creatures, that for the major part, and generally, there is an open way by which the blood is transmitted from the veins through the sinuses or cavities of the heart into the arteries.

I have, however, cogitating with myself, seen further, that the same thing obtained most obviously in the embryos of those animals that have lungs; for in the fœtus the four vessels belonging to the heart, viz., the vena cava, the pulmonary artery, the pulmonary vein, and the great artery or aorta, are all connected otherwise than in the adult, a fact sufficiently known to every anatomist. The first contact and union of the vena cava with the pulmonary veins, which occurs before the cava opens properly into the right ventricle of the heart, or gives off the coronary vein, a little above its escape from the liver, is by a lateral anastomosis; this is an ample foramen, of an oval form, communicating between the cava and the pulmonary vein, so that the blood is free to flow in the greatest abundance by that foramen from the vena cava into the pulmonary vein, and left auricle, and from thence into the left ventricle. Farther, in this foramen ovale, from that part which regards the pulmonary vein, there is a thin tough membrane, larger than the opening, extended like an operculum or cover; this membrane in the adult blocking up the foramen, and adhering on all sides, finally closes it up, and almost obliterates every trace of it. In the fœtus, however, this membrane is so contrived that falling loosely upon itself, it permits a ready access to the lungs and heart, yielding a passage to the blood which is streaming from the cava, and hindering the tide at the same time from flowing back into that vein. All things, in short, permit us to believe that in the embryo the blood must constantly pass by this foramen from the vena cava into the pulmonary vein, and from thence into the left auricle of the heart; and having once entered there, it can never regurgitate.

Another union is that by the pulmonary artery, and is effected when that vessel divides into two branches after its escape from the right ventricle of the heart. It is as if to the two trunks already mentioned a third were superadded, a kind of arterial canal, carried obliquely from the pulmonary artery, to perforate and terminate in the great artery or aorta. So that in the dissection of the embryo, as it were, two aortas, or two roots of the great artery, appear springing from the heart. This canal shrinks gradually after birth, and after a time becomes withered, and finally almost removed, like the umbilical vessels.

The arterial canal contains no membrane or valve to direct or impede the flow of blood in this or in that direction: for at the root of the pulmonary artery, of which the arterial canal is the continuation in the fœtus, there are three semilunar valves, which open from within outwards, and oppose no obstacle to the blood flowing in this direction or from the right ventricle into the pulmonary artery and aorta; but they prevent all regurgitation from the aorta or pulmonic vessels back upon the right ventricle; closing with perfect accuracy, they oppose an effectual obstacle to everything of the kind in the embryo. So that there is also reason to believe that when the heart contracts, the blood is regularly propelled by the canal or passage indicated from the right ventricle into the aorta.

What is commonly said in regard to these two great communications, to wit, that they exist for the nutrition of the lungs, is both improbable and inconsistent; seeing that in the adult they are closed up, abolished, and consolidated, although the lungs, by reason of their heat and motion, must then be presumed to require a larger supply of nourishment. The same may be said in regard to the assertion that the heart in the embryo does not pulsate, that it neither acts nor moves, so that nature was forced to make these communications for the nutrition of the lungs. This is plainly false; for simple inspection of the incubated egg, and of embryos just taken out of the uterus, shows that the heart moves in them precisely as in adults, and that nature feels no such necessity. I have myself repeatedly seen these motions, and Aristotle is likewise witness of their reality. "The pulse," he observes, "inheres in the very constitution of the heart, and appears from the beginning as is learned both from the dissection of living animals and the formation of the chick in the egg." But we further observe that the passages in question are not only pervious up to the period of birth in man, as well as in other animals, as anatomists in general have described them, but for several months subsequently, in some indeed for several years, not to say for the whole course of life; as, for example, in the goose, snipe, and various birds and many of the smaller animals. And this circumstance it was, perhaps, that imposed upon Botallus, who thought he had discovered a new passage for the blood from the vena cava into the left ventricle of the heart; and I own that when I met with the same arrangement in one of the larger members of the mouse family, in the adult state, I was myself at first led to something of a like conclusion.

From this it will be understood that in the human embryo, and in the embryos of animals in which the communications are not closed, the same thing happens, namely, that the heart by its motion propels the blood by obvious and open passages from the vena cava into the aorta through the cavities of both the ventricles, the right one receiving the blood from the auricle, and propelling it by the pulmonary artery and its continuation, named the ductus arteriosus, into the aorta; the left, in like manner, charged by the contraction of its auricle, which has received its supply through the foramen ovale from the vena cava, contracting, and projecting the blood through the root of the aorta into the trunk of that vessel.

In embryos, consequently, whilst the lungs are yet in a state of inaction, performing no function, subject to no motion any more than if they had not been present, nature uses the two ventricles of the heart as if they formed but one, for the transmission of the blood. The condition of the embryos of those animals which have lungs, whilst these organs are yet in abeyance and not employed, is the same as that of those animals which have no lungs.

So it clearly appears in the case of the fœtus that the heart by its action transfers the blood from the vena cava into the aorta, and that by a route as obvious and open, as if in the adult the two ventricles were made to communicate by the removal of their septum. We therefore find that in the greater number of animals—in all, indeed, at a certain period of their existence—the channels for the transmission of the blood through the heart are conspicuous. But we have to inquire why in some creatures—those, namely, that have warm blood, and that have attained to the adult age, man among the number—we should not conclude that the same thing is accomplished through the substance of the lungs, which in the embryo, and at a time when the function of these organs is in abeyance, nature effects by the direct passages described, and which, indeed, she seems compelled to adopt through want of a passage by the lungs; or why it should be better (for nature always does that which is best) that she should close up the various open routes which she had formerly made use of in the embryo and fœtus, and still uses in all other animals. Not only does she thereby open up no new apparent channels for the passages of the blood, but she even shuts up those which formerly existed.

And now the discussion is brought to this point, that they who inquire into the ways by which the blood reaches the left ventricle of the heart and pulmonary veins from the vena cava, will pursue the wisest course if they seek by dissection to discover the causes why in the larger and more perfect animals of mature age nature has rather chosen to make the blood percolate the parenchyma of the lungs, than, as in other instances, chosen a direct and obvious course—for I assume that no other path or mode of transit can be entertained. It must be because the larger and more perfect animals are warmer, and when adult their heat greater—ignited, as I might say, and requiring to be damped or mitigated, that the blood is sent through the lungs, in order that it may be tempered by the air that is inspired, and prevented from boiling up, and so becoming extinguished, or something else of the sort. But to determine these matters, and explain them satisfactorily, were to enter on a speculation in regard to the office of the lungs and the ends for which they exist. Upon such a subject, as well as upon what pertains to respiration, to the necessity and use of the air, etc., as also to the variety and diversity of organs that exist in the bodies of animals in connexion with these matters, although I have made a vast number of observations, I shall not speak till I can more conveniently set them forth in a treatise apart, lest I should be held as wandering too wide of my present purpose, which is the use and motion of the heart, and be charged with speaking of things beside the question, and rather complicating and quitting than illustrating it. And now returning to my immediate subject, I go on with what yet remains for demonstration, viz., that in the more perfect and warmer adult animals, and man, the blood passes from the right ventricle of the heart by the pulmonary artery, into the lungs, and thence by the pulmonary veins into the left auricle, and from there into the left ventricle of the heart. And, first, I shall show that this may be so, and then I shall prove that it is so in fact.

* * * *

Chapter VIII

Of the Quantity of Blood Passing Through the Heart from the Veins to the Arteries; and of the Circular Motion of the Blood

Thus far I have spoken of the passage of the blood from the veins into the arteries, and of the manner in which it is transmitted and distributed by the action of the heart; points to which some, moved either by the authority of Galen or Columbus, or the reasonings of others, will give in their adhesion. But what remains to be said upon the quantity and source of the blood which thus passes is of a character so novel and unheard-of that I not only fear injury to myself from the envy of a few, but I tremble lest I have mankind at large for my enemies, so much doth wont and custom become a second nature. Doctrine once sown strikes deep its root, and respect for antiquity influences all men. Still the die is cast, and my trust is in my love of truth and the candour of cultivated minds. And sooth to say, when I surveyed my mass of evidence, whether derived from vivisections, and my various reflections on them, or from the study of the ventricles of the heart and the vessels that enter into and issue from them, the symmetry and size of these conduits,—for nature doing nothing in vain, would never have given them so large a relative size without a purpose,—or from observing the arrangement and intimate structure of the valves in particular, and of the other parts of the heart in general, with many things besides, I frequently and seriously bethought me, and long revolved in my mind, what might be the quantity of blood which was transmitted, in how short a time its passage might be effected, and the like. But not finding it possible that this could be supplied by the juices of the ingested aliment without the veins on the one hand becoming drained, and the arteries on the other getting ruptured through the excessive charge of blood, unless the blood should somehow find its way from the arteries into the veins, and so return to the right side of the heart, I began to think whether there might not be a MOTION, AS IT WERE, IN A CIRCLE. Now, this I afterwards found to be true; and I finally saw that the blood, forced by the action of the left ventricle into the arteries, was distributed to the body at large, and its several parts, in the same manner as it is sent through the lungs, impelled by the right ventricle into the pulmonary artery, and that it then passed through the veins and along the vena cava, and so round to the left ventricle in the manner already indicated. This motion we may be allowed to call circular, in the same way as Aristotle says that the air and the rain emulate the circular motion of the superior bodies; for the moist earth, warmed by the sun, evaporates; the vapours drawn upwards are condensed, and descending in the form of rain, moisten the earth again. By this arrangement are generations of living things produced; and in like manner are tempests and meteors engendered by the circular motion, and by the approach and recession of the sun.

And similarly does it come to pass in the body, through the motion of the blood, that the various parts are nourished, cherished, quickened by the warmer, more perfect, vaporous, spirituous, and, as I may say, alimentive blood; which, on the other hand, owing to its contact with these parts, becomes cooled, coagulated, and so to speak effete. It then returns to its sovereign, the heart, as if to its source, or to the inmost home of the body, there to recover its state of excellence or perfection. Here it renews its fluidity, natural heat, and becomes powerful, fervid, a kind of treasury of life, and impregnated with spirits, it might be said with balsam. Thence it is again dispersed. All this depends on the motion and action of the heart.

The heart, consequently, is the beginning of life; the sun of the microcosm, even as the sun in his turn might well be designated the heart of the world; for it is the heart by whose virtue and pulse the blood is moved, perfected, and made nutrient, and is preserved from corruption and coagulation; it is the household divinity which, discharging its function, nourishes, cherishes, quickens the whole body, and is indeed the foundation of life, the source of all action. But of these things we shall speak more opportunely when we come to speculate upon the final cause of this motion of the heart.

As the blood-vessels, therefore, are the canals and agents that transport the blood, they are of two kinds, the cava and the aorta; and this not by reason of there being two sides of the body, as Aristotle has it, but because of the difference of office, not, as is commonly said, in consequence of any diversity of structure, for in many animals, as I have said, the vein does not differ from the artery in the thickness of its walls, but solely in virtue of their distinct functions and uses. A vein and an artery, both styled veins by the ancients, and that not without reason, as Galen has remarked, for the artery is the vessel which carries the blood from the heart to the body at large, the vein of the present day bringing it back from the general system to the heart; the former is the conduit from, the latter the channel to, the heart; the latter contains the cruder, effete blood, rendered unfit for nutrition; the former transmits the digested, perfect, peculiarly nutritive fluid.

Chapter IX

That There Is a Circulation of the Blood Is Confirmed from the First Proposition

But lest anyone should say that we give them words only, and make mere specious assertions without any foundation, and desire to innovate without sufficient cause, three points present themselves for confirmation, which, being stated, I conceive that the truth I contend for will follow necessarily, and appear as a thing obvious to all. First, the blood is incessantly transmitted by the action of the heart from the vena cava to the arteries in such quantity that it cannot be supplied from the ingesta, and in such a manner that the whole must very quickly pass through the organ; second, the blood under the influence of the arterial pulse enters and is impelled in a continuous, equable, and incessant stream through every part and member of the body, in much larger quantity than were sufficient for nutrition, or than the whole mass of fluids could supply; third, the veins in like manner return this blood incessantly to the heart from parts and members of the body. These points proved, I conceive it will be manifest that the blood circulates, revolves, propelled and then returning, from the heart to the extremities, from the extremities to the heart, and thus that it performs a kind of circular motion.

Let us assume, either arbitrarily or from experiment, the quantity of blood which the left ventricle of the heart will contain when distended, to be, say, two ounces, three ounces, or one ounce and a half—in the dead body I have found it to hold upwards of two ounces. Let us assume further how much less the heart will hold in the contracted than in the dilated state; and how much blood it will project into the aorta upon each contraction; and all the world allows that with the systole something is always projected, a necessary consequence demonstrated in the third chapter, and obvious from the structure of the valves; and let us suppose as approaching the truth that the fourth, or fifth, or sixth, or even but the eighth part of its charge is thrown into the artery at each contraction; this would give either half an ounce, or three drachms, or one drachm of blood as propelled by the heart at each pulse into the aorta; which quantity, by reason of the valves at the root of the vessel, can by no means return into the ventricle. Now, in the course of half an hour, the heart will have made more than one thousand beats, in some as many as two, three, and even four thousand. Multiplying the number of drachms propelled by the number of pulses, we shall have either one thousand half ounces, or one thousand times three drachms, or a like proportional quantity of blood, according to the amount which we assume as propelled with each stroke of the heart, sent from this organ into the artery—a larger quantity in every case than is contained in the whole body! In the same way, in the sheep or dog, say but a single scruple of blood passes with each stroke of the heart, in one half-hour we should have one thousand scruples, or about three pounds and a half, of blood injected into the aorta; but the body of neither animal contains above four pounds of blood, a fact which I have myself ascertained in the case of the sheep.

Upon this supposition, therefore, assumed merely as a ground for reasoning, we see the whole mass of blood passing through the heart, from the veins to the arteries, and in like manner through the lungs.

But let it be said that this does not take place in half an hour, but in an hour, or even in a day; any way, it is still manifest that more blood passes through the heart in consequence of its action, than can either be supplied by the whole of the ingesta, or than can be contained in the veins at the same movement.

Nor can it be allowed that the heart in contracting sometimes propels and sometimes does not propel, or at most propels but very little, a mere nothing, or an imaginary something: all this, indeed, has already been refuted, and is, besides, contrary both to sense and reason. For if it be a necessary effect of the dilatation of the heart that its ventricles become filled with blood, it is equally so that, contracting, these cavities should expel their contents; and this not in any trifling measure. For neither are the conduits small, nor the contractions few in number, but frequent, and always in some certain proportion, whether it be a third or a sixth, or an eighth, to the total capacity of the ventricles, so that a like proportion of blood must be expelled, and a like proportion received with each stroke of the heart, the capacity of the ventricle contracted always bearing a certain relation to the capacity of the ventricle when dilated. And since, in dilating, the ventricles cannot be supposed to get filled with nothing, or with an imaginary something, so in contracting they never expel nothing or aught imaginary, but always a certain something, viz., blood, in proportion to the amount of the contraction. Whence it is to be concluded that if at one stroke the heart of man, the ox, or the sheep, ejects but a single drachm of blood and there are one thousand strokes in half an hour, in this interval there will have been ten pounds five ounces expelled; if with each stroke two drachms are expelled, the quantity would, of course, amount to twenty pounds and ten ounces; if half an ounce, the quantity would come to forty-one pounds and eight ounces; and were there one ounce, it would be as much as eighty-three pounds and four ounces; the whole of which, in the course of one-half hour, would have been transfused from the veins to the arteries. The actual quantity of blood expelled at each stroke of the heart, and the circumstances under which it is either greater or less than ordinary, I leave for particular determination afterwards, from numerous observations which I have made on the subject.

Meantime this much I know, and would here proclaim to all, that the blood is transfused at one time in larger, at another in smaller, quantity; and that the circuit of the blood is accomplished now more rapidly, now more slowly, according to the temperament, age, etc., of the individual, to external and internal circumstances, to naturals and non-naturals—sleep, rest, food, exercise, affections of the mind, and the like. But, supposing even the smallest quantity of blood to be passed through the heart and the lungs with each pulsation, a vastly greater amount would still be thrown into the arteries and whole body than could by any possibility be supplied by the food consumed. It could be furnished in no other way than by making a circuit and returning.

This truth, indeed, presents itself obviously before us when we consider what happens in the dissection of living animals; the great artery need not be divided, but a very small branch only (as Galen even proves in regard to man), to have the whole of the blood in the body, as well that of the veins as of the arteries, drained away in the course of no long time—some half-hour or less. Butchers are well aware of the fact and can bear witness to it; for, cutting the threat of an ox and so dividing the vessels of the neck, in less than a quarter of an hour they have all the vessels bloodless—the whole mass of blood has escaped. The same thing also occasionally occurs with great rapidity in performing amputations and removing tumors in the human subject.

Nor would this argument lose of its force, did any one say that in killing animals in the shambles, and performing amputations, the blood escaped in equal, if not perchance in larger quantity by the veins than by the arteries. The contrary of this statement, indeed, is certainly the truth: the veins, in fact, collapsing, and being without any propelling power, and further, because of the impediment of the valves, as I shall show immediately, pour out but very little blood; whilst the arteries spout it forth with force abundantly, impetuously, and as if it were propelled by a syringe. And then the experiment is easily tried of leaving the vein untouched and only dividing the artery in the neck of a sheep or dog, when it will be seen with what force, in what abundance, and how quickly, the whole blood in the body, of the veins as well as of the arteries, is emptied. But the arteries receive blood from the veins in no other way than by transmission through the heart, as we have already seen; so that if the aorta be tied at the base of the heart, and the carotid or any other artery be opened, no one will now be surprised to find it empty, and the veins only replete with blood.

And now the cause is manifest, why in our dissections we usually find so large a quantity of blood in the veins, so little in the arteries; why there is much in the right ventricle, little in the left, which probably led the ancients to believe that the arteries (as their name implies) contained nothing but spirits during the life of an animal. The true cause of the difference is perhaps this, that as there is no passage to the arteries, save through the lungs and heart, when an animal has ceased to breathe and the lungs to move, the blood in the pulmonary artery is prevented from passing into the pulmonary veins, and from thence into the left ventricle of the heart; just as we have already seen the same transit prevented in the embryo, by the want of movement in the lungs and the alternate opening and shutting of their hidden and invisible porosities and apertures. But the heart not ceasing to act at the same precise moment as the lungs, but surviving them and continuing to pulsate for a time, the left ventricle and arteries go on distributing their blood to the body at large and sending it into the veins; receiving none from the lungs, however, they are soon exhausted, and left, as it were empty. But even this fact confirms our views, in no trifling manner, seeing that it can be ascribed to no other than the cause we have just assumed.

Moreover, it appears from this that the more frequently or forcibly the arteries pulsate, the more speedily will the body be exhausted of its blood during hemorrhage. Hence, also, it happens, that in fainting fits and in states of alarm, when the heart beats more languidly and less forcibly, hemorrhages are diminished and arrested.

Still further, it is from this, that after death, when the heart has ceased to beat, it is impossible, by dividing either the jugular or femoral veins and arteries, by any effort, to force out more than one-half of the whole mass of the blood. Neither could the butchers ever bleed the carcass effectually did he neglect to cut the throat of the ox which he has knocked on the head and stunned, before the heart had ceased beating.

Finally, we are now in a condition to suspect wherefore it is that no one has yet said anything to the purpose upon the anastomosis of the veins and arteries, either as to where or how it is effected, or for what purpose. I now enter upon the investigation of the subject.

* * * *

Chapter XI

The Second Position Is Demonstrated

That this may the more clearly appear to everyone, I have here to cite certain experiments, from which it seems obvious that the blood enters a limb by the arteries, and returns from it by the veins; that the arteries are the vessels carrying the blood from the heart, and the veins the returning channels of the blood to the heart; that in the limbs and extreme parts of the body the blood passes either immediately by anastomosis from the arteries into the veins, or mediately by the porosities of the flesh, or in both ways, as has already been said in speaking of the passage of the blood through the lungs whence it appears manifest that in the circuit the blood moves from that place to this place, and from that point to this one; from the centre to the extremities, to wit; and from the extreme parts back to the centre. Finally, upon grounds of calculation, with the same elements as before, it will be obvious that the quantity can neither be accounted for by the ingesta, nor yet be held necessary to nutrition.

The same thing will also appear in regard to ligatures, and wherefore they are said to *draw*; though this is neither from the heat, nor the pain, nor the vacuum they occasion, nor indeed from any other cause yet thought of; it will also explain the uses and advantages to be derived from ligatures in medicine, the principle upon which they either suppress or occasion hemorrhage; how they induce sloughing and more extensive mortification in extremities; and how they act in the castration of animals and the removal of warts and fleshly tumours. But it has come to pass, from no one having duly weighed and understood the cause and rationale of these various effects, that though almost all, upon the faith of the old writers, recommend ligatures in the treatment of disease, yet very few comprehend their proper employment, or derive any real assistance from them in effecting cures.

Ligatures are either very tight or of medium tightness. A ligature I designate as tight or perfect when it so constricts an extremity that no vessel can be felt pulsating beyond it. Such a ligature we use in amputations to control the flow of blood; and such also are employed in the castration of animals and the ablation of tumours. In the latter instances, all afflux of nutriment and heat being prevented by the ligature, we see the testes and large fleshy tumours dwindle, die, and finally fall off.

Ligatures of medium tightness I regard as those which compress a limb firmly all round, but short of pain, and in such a way as still suffers a certain degree of pulsation to be felt in the artery beyond them. Such a ligature is in use in blood-letting, an operation in which the fillet applied above the elbow is not drawn so tight but that the arteries at the wrist may still be felt beating under the finger.

Now let anyone make an experiment upon the arm of a man, either using such a fillet as is employed in blood-letting, or grasping the limb lightly with his hand, the best subject for it being one who is lean, and who has large veins, and the best time after exercise, when the body is warm, the pulse is full, and the blood carried in larger quantity to the extremities, for all then is more conspicuous; under such circumstances let a ligature be thrown about the extremity, and drawn as tightly as can be borne, it will first be perceived that beyond the ligature, neither in the wrist nor anywhere else, do the arteries pulsate, at the same time that immediately above the ligature the artery begins to rise higher at each diastole, to throb more violently, and to swell in its vicinity with a kind of tide, as if it strove to break through and overcome the obstacle to its current; the artery here, in short, appears as if it were preternaturally full. The hand under such circumstances retains its natural colour and appearance; in the course of time it begins to fall somewhat in temperature, indeed, but nothing is *drawn* into it.

After the bandage has been kept on for some short time in this way, let it be slackened a little, brought to that state or term of medium tightness which is used in bleeding, and it will be seen that the whole hand and arm will instantly become deeply coloured and distended, and the veins show themselves tumid and knotted; after ten or twelve pulses of the artery, the hand will be perceived excessively distended, injected, gorged with blood, *drawn,* as it is said, by this medium ligature, without pain, or heat, or any horror of a vacuum, or any other cause yet indicated.

If the finger be applied over the artery as it is pulsating by the edge of the fillet, at the moment of slackening it, the blood will be felt to glide through, as it were, underneath the finger; and he, too, upon whose arm the experiment is made, when the ligature is slackened, is distinctly conscious of a sensation of warmth, and of something, viz., a stream of blood suddenly making its way along the course of the vessels and diffusing itself through the hand, which at the same time begins to feel hot, and becomes distended.

As we had noted, in connexion with the tight ligature, that the artery above the bandage was distended and pulsated, not below it, so, in the case of the moderately tight bandage, on the contrary, do we find that the veins below, never above, the fillet, swell, and become dilated, whilst the arteries shrink; and such is the degree of distension of the veins here, that it is only very strong pressure that will force the blood beyond the fillet, and cause any of the veins in the upper part of the arm to rise.

From these facts it is easy for every careful observer to learn that the blood enters an extremity by the arteries; for when they are effectually compressed nothing is *drawn* to the member; the hand preserves its colour; nothing flows into it, neither is it distended; but when the pressure is diminished, as it is with the bleeding fillet, it is manifest that the blood is instantly thrown in with force, for then the hand begins to swell; which is as much as to say, that when the arteries pulsate the blood is flowing through them, as it is when the moderately tight ligature is applied; but where they do not pulsate, as, when a tight ligature is used, they cease from transmitting anything, they are only distended above the part where the ligature is applied. The veins again being compressed, nothing can flow through them; the certain indication of which is, that below the ligature they are much more tumid than above it, and than they usually appear when there is no bandage upon the arm.

It therefore plainly appears that the ligature prevents the return of the blood through the veins to the parts above it, and maintains those beneath it in a state of permanent distension. But the arteries, in spite of its pressure, and under the force and impulse of the heart, send on the blood from the internal parts of the body to the parts beyond the ligature. And herein consists the difference between the tight and the medium ligature, that the former not only prevents the passage of the blood in the veins, but in the arteries also; the latter, however, whilst it does not prevent the force of the pulse from extending beyond it, and so propelling the blood to the extremities of the body, compresses the veins, and greatly or altogether impedes the return of the blood through them.

Seeing, therefore, that the moderately tight ligature renders the veins turgid and distended, and the whole hand full of blood, I ask, whence is this? Does the blood accumulate below the ligature coming through the veins, or through the arteries, or passing by certain hidden porosities? Through the veins it cannot come; still less can it come through invisible channels; it must needs, then, arrive by the arteries, in conformity with all that has been already said. That it cannot flow in by the veins appears plainly enough from the fact that the blood cannot be forced towards the heart unless the ligature be removed; when this is done suddenly all the veins collapse, and disgorge themselves of their contents into the superior parts, the hand at the same time resumes its natural pale colour, the tumefaction and the stagnating blood having disappeared.

Moreover, he whose arm or wrist has thus been bound for some little time with the medium bandage, so that it has not only got swollen and livid but cold, when the fillet is undone is aware of something cold making its way upwards along with the returning blood, and reaching the elbow or the axilla. And I have myself been inclined to think that this cold blood rising upwards to the heart was the cause of the fainting that often occurs after blood-letting: fainting frequently supervenes even in robust subjects, and mostly at the moment of undoing the fillet, as the vulgar say, from the turning of the blood.

Farther, when we see the veins below the ligature instantly swell up and become gorged, when from extreme tightness it is somewhat relaxed, the arteries meantime continuing unaffected, this is an obvious indication that the blood passes from the arteries into the veins, and not from the veins into the arteries, and that there is either an anastomosis of the two orders of vessels, or porosities in the flesh and solid parts generally that are permeable to the blood. It is farther an indication that the veins have frequent communications with one another, because they all become turgid together, whilst under the medium ligature applied above the elbow; and if any single small vein be pricked with a lancet, they all speedily shrink, and disburthening themselves into this they subside almost simultaneously.

These considerations will enable anyone to understand the nature of the attraction that is exerted by ligatures, and perchance of fluxes generally; how, for example, when the veins are compressed by a bandage of medium tightness applied above the elbow, the blood cannot escape, whilst it still continues to be driven in, by the forcing power of the heart, by which the parts are of necessity filled, gorged with blood. And how should it be otherwise? Heat and pain and a vacuum draw, indeed; but in such wise only that parts are filled, not preternaturally distended or gorged, and not so suddenly and violently overwhelmed with the charge of blood forced in upon them, that the flesh is lacerated and the vessels ruptured. Nothing of the kind as an effect of heat, or pain, or the vacuum force, is either credible or demonstrable.

Besides, the ligature is competent to occasion the afflux in question without either pain, or heat, or a vacuum. Were pain in any way the cause, how should it happen that, with the arm bound above the elbow, the hand and fingers should swell below the bandage, and their veins become distended? The pressure of the bandage certainly prevents the blood from getting there by the veins. And then, wherefore is there neither swelling nor repletion of the veins, nor any sign or symptom of attraction or afflux, above the ligature? But this is the obvious cause of the preternatural attraction and swelling below the bandage, and in the hand and fingers, that the blood is entering abundantly, and with force, but cannot pass out again.

Now is not this the cause of all tumefaction, as indeed Avicenna has it, and of all oppressive redundancy in parts, that the access to them is open, but the egress from them is closed? Whence it comes that they are gorged and tumefied. And may not the same thing happen in local inflammations, where, so long as the swelling is on the increase, and has not reached its extreme term, a full pulse is felt in the part, especially when the disease is of the more acute kind, and the swelling usually takes place most rapidly. But these are matters for after discussion. Or does this, which occurred in my own case, happen from the same cause? Thrown from a carriage upon one occasion, I struck my forehead a blow upon the place where a twig of the artery advances from the temple, and immediately, within the time in which twenty beats could have been made I felt a tumour the size of an egg developed, without either heat or any great pain: the near vicinity of the artery had caused the blood to be effused into the bruised part with unusual force and velocity.

And now, too, we understand why in phlebotomy we apply our ligature above the part that is punctured, not below it; did the flow come from above, not from below, the constriction in this case would not only be of no service, but would prove a positive hindrance; it would have to be applied below the orifice, in order to have the flow more free, did the blood descend by the veins from superior to inferior parts; but as it is elsewhere forced through the extreme arteries into the extreme veins, and the return in these last is opposed by the ligature, so do they fill and swell, and being thus filled and distended, they are made capable of projecting their charge with force, and to a distance, when any one of them is suddenly punctured; but the ligature being slackened, and the returning channels thus left open, the blood forthwith no longer escapes, save by drops; and, as all the world knows, if in performing phlebotomy the bandage be either slackened too much or the limb be bound too tightly, the blood escapes without force, because in the one case the returning channels are not adequately obstructed; in the other the channels of influx, the arteries, are impeded.

* * * *

Chapter XIII

The Third Position Is Confirmed: And the Circulation of the Blood Is Demonstrated from It

Thus far we have spoken of the quantity of blood passing through the heart and the lungs in the centre of the body, and in like manner from the arteries into the veins in the peripheral parts and the body at large. We have yet to explain, however, in what manner the blood finds its way back to the heart from the extremities by the veins, and how and in what way these are the only vessels that convey the blood from the external to the central parts; which done, I conceive that the three fundamental propositions laid down for the circulation of the blood will be so plain, so well established, so obviously true, that they may claim general credence. Now the remaining position will be made sufficiently clear from the valves which are found in the cavities of the veins themselves, from the uses of these, and from experiments cognizable by the senses.

The celebrated Hieronymus Fabricius of Aquapendente, a most skilful anatomist, and venerable old man, or, as the learned Riolan will have it, Jacobus Silvius, first gave representations of the valves in the veins, which consist of raised or loose portions of the inner membranes of these vessels, of extreme delicacy, and a sigmoid or semilunar shape. They are situated at different distances from one another, and diversely in different individuals; they are connate at the sides of the veins; they are directed upwards towards the trunks of the veins; the two—for there are for the most part two together—regard each other, mutually touch, and are so ready to come into contact by their edges, that if anything attempts to pass from the trunks into the branches of the veins, or from the greater vessels into the less, they completely prevent it; they are farther so arranged, that the horns of those that succeed are opposite the middle of the convexity of those that precede, and so on alternately.

The discoverer of these valves did not rightly understand their use, nor have succeeding anatomists added anything to our knowledge: for their office is by no means explained when we are told that it is to hinder the blood, by its weight, from all flowing into inferior parts; for the edges of the valves in the jugular veins hang downwards, and are so contrived that they prevent the blood from rising upwards; the valves, in a word, do not invariably look upwards, but always toward the trunks of the veins, invariably towards the seat of the heart. I, and indeed others, have sometimes found valves in the emulgent veins, and in those of the mesentery, the edges of which were directed towards the vena cava and vena portæ. Let it be added that there are no valves in the arteries, and that dogs, oxen, etc., have invariably valves at the divisions of their crural veins, in the veins that meet towards the top of the os sacrum, and in those branches which come from the haunches, in which no such effect of gravity from the erect position was to be apprehended. Neither are there valves in the jugular veins for the purpose of guarding against apoplexy, as some have said; because in sleep the head is more apt to be influenced by the contents of the carotid arteries. Neither are the valves present, in order that the blood may be retained in the divarications or smaller trunks and minuter branches, and not be suffered to flow entirely into the more open and capacious channels; for they occur where there are no divarications; althought it must be owned that they are most frequent at the points where branches join. Neither do they exist for the purpose of rendering the current of blood more slow from the centre of the body; for it seems likely that the blood would be disposed to flow with sufficient slowness of its own accord, as it would have to pass from larger into continually smaller vessels, being separated from the mass and fountain head, and attaining from warmer into colder places.

But the valves are solely made and instituted lest the blood should pass from the greater into the lesser veins, and either rupture them or cause them to become varicose; lest, instead of advancing from the extreme to the central parts of the body, the blood should rather proceed along the veins from the centre to the extremities; but the delicate valves, while they readily open in the right direction, entirely prevent all such contrary motion, being so situated and arranged, that if any-thing escapes, or is less perfectly obstructed by the cornua of the one above, the fluid passing, as it were, by the chinks between the cornua, it is immediately received on the convexity of the one beneath, which is placed transversely with reference to the former, and so is effectually hindered from getting any farther.

And this I have frequently experienced in my dissections of the veins: if I attempted to pass a probe from the trunk of the veins into one of the smaller branches, whatever care I took I found it impossible to introduce it far any way, by reason of the valves; whilst, on the contrary, it was most easy to push it along in the opposite direction, from without in-wards, or from the branches towards the trunks and roots. In many places two valves are so placed and fitted, that when raised they come exactly together in the middle of the vein, and are there united by the contact of their margins; and so accurate is the adaptation, that neither by the eye nor by any other means of examination, can the slightest chink along the line of contact be perceived. But if the probe be now introduced from the extreme towards the more central parts, the valves, like the floodgates of a river, give way, and are most readily pushed aside. The effect of this arrangement plainly is to prevent all motion of the blood from the heart and vena cava, whether it be upwards towards the head, or downwards towards the feet, or to either side towards the arms, not a drop can pass; all motion of the blood, beginning in the larger and tending towards the smaller veins, is opposed and resisted by them; whilst the motion that proceeds from the lesser to end in the larger branches is favoured, or, at all events, a free and open passage is left for it.

But that this truth may be made the more apparent, let an arm be tied up above the elbow as if for phlebotomy. At intervals in the course of the veins, especially in labouring people and those whose veins are large, certain knots or elevations will be perceived, and this not only at the places where a branch is received, but also where none enters: these knots or risings are all formed by valves, which thus show themselves externally. And now if you press the blood from the space above one of the valves, and keep the point of a finger upon the vein inferiorly, you will see no influx of blood from above; the portion of the vein between the point of the finger and the valve will be obliterated; yet will the vessel continue sufficiently distended above the valve. The blood being thus pressed out, and the vein emptied, if you now apply a finger of the other hand upon the distended part of the vein above the valve and press downwards, you will find that you cannot force the blood through or beyond the valve; but the greater effort you use, you will only see the portion of vein that is between the finger and the valve become more distended, that portion of the vein which is below the valve remaining all the while empty.

It would therefore appear that the function of the valves in the veins is the same as that of the three sigmoid valves which we find at the commencement of the aorta and pulmonary artery, viz., to prevent all reflux of the blood that is passing over them.

Farther, the arm being bound as before, and the veins looking full and distended, if you press at one part in the course of a vein with the point of a finger, and then with another finger streak the blood upwards beyond the next valve, you will perceive that this portion of the vein continues empty, and that the blood cannot retrograde, precisely as we have already seen the case to be; but the finger first applied, being removed, immediately the vein is filled from below. That the blood in the veins therefore proceeds from inferior or more remote parts, and towards the heart, moving in these vessels in this and not in the contrary direction, appears most obviously. And although in some places the valves, by not acting with such perfect accuracy, or where there is but a single valve, do not seem totally to prevent the passage of the blood from the centre, still the greater number of them plainly do so; and then, where things appear contrived more negligently, this is compensated either by the more frequent occurrence or more perfect action of the succeeding valves, or in some other way: the veins in short, as they are the free and open conduits of the blood returning *to* the heart, so are they effectually prevented from serving as its channels of distribution *from* the heart.

But this other circumstance has to be noted: The arm being bound, and the veins made turgid, and the valves prominent, as before, apply the thumb or finger over a vein in the situation of one of the valves in such a way as to compress it, and prevent any blood from passing upwards from the hand; then, with a finger of the other hand, streak the blood in the vein upwards till it has passed the next valve above, the vessel now remains empty; but the finger being removed for an instant, the vein is immediately filled from below; apply the finger again, and having in the same manner streaked the blood upwards, again remove the finger below, and again the vessel becomes distended as before; and this repeat, say a thousand times, in a short space of time. And now compute the quantity of blood which you have thus pressed up beyond the valve, and then multiplying the assumed quantity by one thousand, you will find that so much blood has passed through a certain portion of the vessel; and I do now believe that you will find yourself convinced of the circulation of the blood, and of its rapid motion. But if in this experiment you say that a violence is done to nature, I do not doubt but that, if you proceed in the same way, only taking as great a length of vein as possible, and merely remark with what rapidity the blood flows upwards, and fills the vessel from below, you will come to the same conclusion.

Chapter XIV

Conclusion of the Demonstration of the Circulation

And now I may be allowed to give in brief my view of the circulation of the blood, and to propose it for general adoption.

Since all things, both argument and ocular demonstration, show that the blood passes through the lungs, and heart by the force of the ventricles, and is sent for distribution to all parts of the body, where it makes its way into the veins and porosities of the flesh, and then flows by the veins from the circumference on every side to the centre, from the lesser to the greater veins, and is by them finally discharged into the vena cava and right auricle of the heart, and this in such a quantity or in such a flux and reflux thither by the arteries, hither by the veins, as cannot possibly be supplied by the ingesta, and is much greater than can be required for mere purposes of nutrition; it is absolutely necessary to conclude that the blood in the animal body is impelled in a circle, and is in a state of ceaseless motion; that this is the act or function which the heart performs by means of its pulse; and that it is the sole and only end of the motion and contraction of the heart.

10

RENÉ DESCARTES

René Descartes was born in 1596 in central France, to an old and established family of the minor nobility. His elder brother, who followed the career of his father as a counsellor to the Parlement of Brittany, always regarded René, who published books, as a disgrace to the family. He studied for eight years in the Jesuit school of La Flèche, one of the leading educational institutions in Europe at the beginning of the 17th century, and then in Paris. Descartes was determined to see the world, however. First as a soldier and then without that excuse, he travelled over much of the continent, before settling down in the Netherlands, the age's haven of intellectual freedom. There, in twenty years of extraordinary philosophical endeavor, he built the structure of Cartesian philosophy. Renown brought problems in its train. Queen Christina of Sweden induced him to come to Stockholm to instruct her in his philosophy. The combined rigors of the northern winter and the royal penchant to receive instruction at 5:00 A.M. were more than a Gallic philosophic constitution could bear, and he died of inflammation of the lungs early in 1650.

Descartes was less a scientist than a philosopher, if the distinction has meaning for the 17th century, but he was a philosopher who shaped the structure of modern scientific thought perhaps more than any other man. The *Discourse on Method,* his intellectual autobiography, explains a great deal about his role in the history of science. Descartes lived during what has been called the sceptical crisis. At a time when religious revolution at home and exploration abroad were shattering the traditional foundations of intellectual life in western Christendom, recovery of the writings of the ancient sceptics provided a rationale for the questioning of any and all certainty. The beginnings of modern science in the new astronomy of Copernicus and Kepler, with its implicit questioning of Aristotelian cosmology, also contributed. Appalled by the implications of scepticism, Descartes attempted to construct a new foundation for certainty. From the perspective of the 20th century, we can say that he failed, but in his effort he left behind a judgment on the philosophic and scientific tradition of Europe which is one of the best expressions of an attitude toward the past that was shared by the entire scientific revolution.

If the first parts of the *Discourse* face the past, the final parts turn toward the future, sketching in the outlines of a new conception of nature to replace Aristotle's. As a consistent system it failed, just as Cartesian epistemology failed in its reply to the challenge of scepticism. In the broad outlines of its picture of nature as a machine, however, Cartesian philosophy exercised a profound influence on the emerging structure of modern science. Through the mechanical philosophy, Descartes helped to shape the framework of thought that determined what type of question a scientist in the 17th century would ask and what type of answer he would accept.

10

Discourse on Method

PART I

Good sense is, of all things among men, the most equally distributed; for every one thinks himself so abundantly provided with it, that those even who are the most difficult to satisfy in everything else, do not usually desire a larger measure of this quality than they already possess. And in this it is not likely that all are mistaken: the conviction is rather to be held as testifying that the power of judging aright and of distinguishing Truth from Error, which is properly what is called Good Sense or Reason, is by nature equal in all men; and that the diversity of our opinions, consequently, does not arise from some being endowed with a larger share of Reason than others, but solely from this, that we conduct our thoughts along different ways, and do not fix our attention on the same objects. For to be possessed of a vigorous mind is not enough; the prime requisite is rightly to apply it. The greatest minds, as they are capable of the highest excellencies, are open likewise to the greatest aberrations; and those who travel very slowly may yet make far greater progress, provided they keep always to the straight road, than those who, while they run, forsake it.

For myself, I have never fancied my mind to be in any respect more perfect than those of the generality; on the contrary, I have often wished that I were equal to some others in promptitude of thought, or in clearness and distinctness of imagination, or in fulness and readiness of memory. And besides these, I know of no other qualities that contribute to the perfection of the mind; for as to the Reason or Sense, inasmuch as it is that alone which constitutes us men, and distinguishes us from the brutes, I am disposed to believe that it is to be found complete in each individual; and on this point to adopt the common opinion of philosophers, who say that the difference of greater and less holds only among the *accidents*, and not among the *forms* or *natures* of *individuals* of the same *species*.

Translated from the French by John Veitch, London, 1850.

I will not hesitate, however, to avow my belief that it has been my singular good fortune to have very early in life fallen in with certain tracks which have conducted me to considerations and maxims, of which I have formed a Method that gives me the means, as I think, of gradually augmenting my knowledge, and of raising it by little and little to the highest point which the mediocrity of my talents and the brief duration of my life will permit me to reach. For I have already reaped from it such fruits that, although I have been accustomed to think lowly enough of myself, and although when I look with the eye of a philosopher at the varied courses and pursuits of mankind at large, I find scarcely one which does not appear vain and useless, I nevertheless derive the highest satisfaction from the progress I conceive myself to have already made in the search after truth, and cannot help entertaining such expectations of the future as to believe that if, among the occupations of men as men, there is any one really excellent and important, it is that which I have chosen.

After all, it is possible I may be mistaken; and it is but a little copper and glass, perhaps, that I take for gold and diamonds. I know how very liable we are to delusion in what relates to ourselves, and also how much the judgments of our friends are to be suspected when given in our favour. But I shall endeavour in this Discourse to describe the paths I have followed, and to delineate my life as in a picture, in order that each one may be able to judge of them for himself, and that in the general opinion entertained of them, as gathered from current report, I myself may have a new help towards instruction to be added to those I have been in the habit of employing.

My present design, then, is not to teach the Method which each ought to follow for the right conduct of his Reason, but solely to describe the way in which I have endeavoured to conduct my own. They who set themselves to give precepts must of course regard themselves as possessed of greater skill than those to whom they prescribe; and if they err in the slightest particular, they subject themselves to censure. But as this Tract is put forth merely as a history, or, if you will, as a tale, in which, amid some examples worthy of imitation, there will be found, perhaps, as many more which it were advisable not to follow, I hope it will prove useful to some without being hurtful to any, and that my openness will find some favour with all.

From my childhood, I have been familiar with letters; and as I was given to believe that by their help a clear and certain knowledge of all that is useful in life might be acquired, I was ardently desirous of instruction. But as soon as I had finished the entire course of study, at the close of which it is customary to be admitted into the order of the learned, I completely changed my opinion. For I found myself involved in so many doubts and errors, that I was convinced I had advanced no farther in all my attempts at learning, than the discovery at every turn of my own ignorance. And yet I was studying in one of the most celebrated Schools in Europe, in which I thought there must be learned men, if such were anywhere to be found. I had been taught all that others learned there; and not contented with the sciences actually taught us, I had, in addition, read all the books that had fallen into my hands, treating of such branches as are esteemed the most curious and rare. I knew the judgment which others had formed of me; and I did not find that I was considered inferior to my fellows, although there were among them some who were already marked out to fill the places of our instructors. And, in fine, our age appeared to me as flourishing, and as fertile in powerful minds as any preceding one. I was thus led to take the liberty of judging of all other men by myself, and of concluding that there was no science in existence that was of such a nature as I had previously been given to believe.

I still continued, however, to hold in esteem the studies of the Schools. I was aware that the Languages taught in them are necessary to the understanding of the writings of the ancients; that the grace of Fable stirs the mind; that the memorable deeds of History elevate it; and, if read with discretion, aid in forming the judgment; that the perusal of all excellent books is, as it were, to interview with the noblest men of past ages, who have written them, and even a studied interview, in which are discovered to us only their choicest thoughts; that Eloquence has incomparable force and beauty; that Poesy has its ravishing graces and delights; that in the Mathematics there are many refined discoveries eminently suited to gratify the inquisitive, as well as further all the arts and lessen the labour of man; that numerous highly useful precepts and exhortations to virtue are contained in treatises on Morals; that Theology points out the path to heaven; that Philosophy affords the means of discoursing with an appearance of truth on all matters, and commands the admiration of the more simple; that Jurisprudence, Medicine, and the other Sciences, secure for their cultivators honours and riches; and, in fine, that it is useful to bestow some attention upon all, even upon those abounding the most in superstition and error, that we may be in a position to determine their real value, and guard against being deceived.

But I believed that I had already given sufficient time to Languages, and likewise to the reading of the writings of the ancients, to their Histories and Fables. For to hold converse with those of other ages and to travel, are almost the same thing. It is useful to know something of the manners of different nations, that we may be enabled to form a more correct judgment regarding our own, and be prevented from thinking that everything contrary to our customs is ridiculous and irrational—a conclusion usually come to by those whose experience has been limited to their own country. On the other hand, when too much time is occupied in travelling, we become strangers to our native country; and the over curious in the customs of the past are generally ignorant of those of the present. Besides, fictitious narratives lead us to imagine the possibility of many events that are impossible; and even the most faithful histories, if they do not wholly misrepresent matters, or exaggerate their importance to render the account of them more worthy of perusal, omit, at least, almost always the meanest and least striking of the attendant circumstances; hence it happens that the remainder does not represent the truth, and that such as regulate their conduct by examples drawn from this source, are apt to fall into the extravagances of the knight-errants of Romance, and to entertain projects that exceed their powers.

I esteemed Eloquence highly, and was in raptures with Poesy; but I thought that both were gifts of nature rather than fruits of study. Those in whom the faculty of Reason is predominant, and who most skilfully dispose their thoughts with a view to render them clear and intelligible, are always the best able to persuade others of the truth of what they lay down, though they should speak only in the language of Lower Brittany, and be wholly ignorant of the rules of Rhetoric; and those whose minds are stored with the most agreeable fancies, and who can give expression to them with the greatest embellishment and harmony, are still the best poets, though unacquainted with the Art of Poetry.

I was especially delighted with the Mathematics, on account of the certitude and evidence of their reasonings: but I had not as yet a precise knowledge of their true use; and thinking that they but contributed to the advancement of the mechanical arts, I was astonished that foundations, so strong and solid, should have had no loftier superstructure reared on them. On the other hand, I compared the disquisitions of the ancient Moralists to very towering and magnificent palaces with no better foundation than sand and mud: they laud the virtues very highly, and exhibit them as estimable far above anything on earth; but they give us no adequate criterion of virtue, and frequently that which they designate with so fine a name is but apathy, or pride, or despair, or parricide.

I revered our Theology, and aspired as much as any one to reach heaven: but being given assuredly to understand that the way is not less open to the most ignorant than to the most learned, and that the revealed truths which lead to heaven are above our comprehension, I did not presume to subject them to the impotency of my Reason; and I thought that in order competently to undertake their examination, there was need of some special help from heaven, and of being more than man.

Of Philosophy I will say nothing, except that when I saw that it had been cultivated for many ages by the most distinguished men, and that yet there is not a single matter within its sphere which is not still in dispute, and nothing, therefore, which is above doubt, I did not presume to anticipate that my success would be greater in it than that of others; and further, when I considered the number of conflicting opinions touching a single matter that may be upheld by learned men, while there can be but one true, I reckoned as well-nigh false all that was only probable.

As to the other Sciences, inasmuch as these borrow their principles from Philosophy, I judged that no solid superstructures could be reared on foundations so infirm; and neither the honour nor the gain held out by them was sufficient to determine me to their cultivation: for I was not, thank Heaven, in a condition which compelled me to make merchandise of Science for the bettering of my fortune; and though I might not profess to scorn glory as a Cynic, I yet made very slight account of that honour which I hoped to acquire only through fictitious titles. And, in fine, of false Sciences I thought I knew the worth sufficiently to escape being deceived by the professions of an alchemist, the predictions of an astrologer, the impostures of a magician, or by the artifices and boasting of any of those who profess to know things of which they are ignorant.

For these reasons, as soon as my age permitted me to pass from under the control of my instructors, I entirely abandoned the study of letters, and resolved no longer to seek any other science than the knowledge of myself, or of the great book of the world. I spent the remainder of my youth in travelling, in visiting courts and armies, in holding intercourse with men of different dispositions and ranks, in collecting varied experience, in proving myself in the different situations into which fortune threw me, and, above all, in making such reflection on the matter of my experience as to secure my improvement. For it occurred to me that I should find much more truth in the reasonings of each individual with reference to the affairs in which he is personally interested, and the issue of which must presently punish him if he has judged amiss, than in those conducted by a man of letters in his study, regarding speculative matters that are of no practical moment, and followed by no consequences to himself, farther, perhaps, than that they foster his vanity the better the more remote they are from common sense; requiring, as they must in this case, the exercise of greater ingenuity and art to render them probable. In addition, I had always a most earnest desire to know how to distinguish the true from the false, in order that I might be able clearly to discriminate the right path in life, and proceed in it with confidence.

It is true that, while busied only in considering the manners of other men, I found here, too, scarce any ground for settled conviction, and remarked hardly less contradiction among them than in the opinions of the philosophers. So that the greatest advantage I derived from the study consisted in this, that, observing many things which, however extravagant and ridiculous to our apprehension, are yet by common consent received and approved by other great nations, I learned to entertain too decided a belief in regard to nothing of the truth of which I had been persuaded merely by example and custom: and thus I gradually extricated myself from many errors powerful enough to darken our Natural Intelligence, and incapacitate us in great measure from listening to Reason. But after I had been occupied several years in thus studying the book of the world, and in essaying to gather some experience, I at length resolved to make myself an object of study, and to employ all the powers of my mind in choosing the paths I ought to follow; an undertaking which was accompanied with greater success than it would have been had I never quitted my country or my books.

PART II

I was then in Germany, attracted thither by the wars in that country, which have not yet been brought to a termination; and as I was returning to the army from the coronation of the Emperor, the setting in of winter arrested me in a locality where, as I found no society to interest me, and was besides fortunately undisturbed by any cares or passions, I remained the whole day in seclusion, with full opportunity to occupy my attention with my own thoughts. Of these one of the very first that occurred to me was, that there is seldom so much perfection in works composed of many separate parts, upon which different hands have been employed, as in those completed by a single master. Thus it is observable that the buildings which a single architect has planned and executed, are generally more elegant and commodious than those which several have attempted to improve, by making old walls serve for purposes for which they were not originally built. Thus also, those ancient cities which, from being at first only villages, have become, in course of time, large towns, are usually but ill laid out compared with the regularly constructed towns which a professional architect has freely planned on an open plain; so that although the several buildings of the former may often equal or surpass in beauty those of the latter, yet when one observes their indiscriminate juxtaposition, there a large one and here a small, and the consequent crookedness and irregularity of the streets, one is disposed to allege that chance rather than any human will guided by reason, must have led to such an arrangement. And if we consider that nevertheless there have been at all times certain officers whose duty it was to see that private buildings contributed to public ornament, the difficulty of reaching high perfection with but the materials of others to operate on, will be readily acknowledged. In the same way I fancied that those nations which, starting from a semi-barbarous state and advancing to civilisation by slow degrees, have had their laws successively determined, and, as it were, forced upon them simply by experience of the hurtfulness of particular crimes and disputes, would by this process come to be possessed of less perfect institutions than those, which, from the commencement of their association as communities, have followed the appointments of some wise legislator. It is thus quite certain that the constitution of the true religion, the ordinances of which are derived from God, must be incomparably superior to that of every other. And, to speak of human affairs, I believe that the past preëminence of Sparta was due not to the goodness of each of its laws in particular, for many of these were very strange, and even opposed to good morals, but to the circumstance that, originated by a single individual, they all tended to a single end. In the same way I thought that the sciences contained in books, (such of them at least as are made up of probable reasonings, without demonstrations,) composed as they are of the opinions of many different individuals massed together, are farther removed from truth than the simple inferences which a man of good sense using his natural and unprejudiced judgment draws respecting the matters of his experience. And because we have all to pass through a state of infancy to manhood, and have been of necessity, for a length of time, governed by our desires and preceptors, (whose dictates were frequently conflicting, while neither perhaps always counselled us for the best,) I farther concluded that it is almost impossible that our judgments can be so correct or solid as they would have been, had our Reason been mature from the moment of our birth, and had we always been guided by it alone.

It is true, however, that it is not customary to pull down all the houses of a town with the single design of rebuilding them differently, and thereby rendering the streets more handsome; but it often happens that a private individual takes down his own with the view of erecting it anew, and that people are even sometimes constrained to this when their houses are in danger of falling from age, or when the foundations are insecure. With this before me by way of example, I was persuaded that it would indeed be preposterous for a private individual to think of reforming a state by fundamentally changing it throughout, and overturning it in order to set it up amended; and the same I thought was true of any similar project for reforming the body of the Sciences, or the order of teaching them established in the Schools: but as for the opinions which up to that time I had embraced, I thought that I could not do better than resolve at once to sweep them wholly away, that I might afterwards be in a position to admit either others more correct, or even perhaps the same when they had undergone the scrutiny of Reason. I firmly believed that in this way I should much better succeed in the conduct of my life, than if I built only upon old foundations, and leant upon principles which, in my youth, I had taken upon trust. For although I recognised various difficulties in this undertaking, these were not, however, without remedy, nor once to be compared with such as attend the slightest reformation in public affairs. Large bodies, if once overthrown, are with great difficulty set up again, or even kept erect when once seriously shaken, and the fall of such is always disastrous. Then if there are any imperfections in the constitutions of states, (and that many such exist the diversity of constitutions is alone sufficient to assure us,) custom has without doubt materially smoothed their inconveniencies, and has even managed to steer altogether clear of, or insensibly corrected a number which sagacity could not have provided against with equal effect; and, in fine, the defects are almost always more tolerable than the change necessary for their removal; in the same manner that highways which wind among mountains, by being much frequented, become gradually so smooth and commodious, that it is much better to follow them than to seek a straighter path by climbing over the tops of rocks and descending to the bottoms of precipices.

Hence it is that I cannot in any degree approve of those restless and busy meddlers who, called neither by birth nor fortune to take part in the management of public affairs, are yet always projecting reforms; and if I thought that this Tract contained aught which might justify the suspicion that I was a victim of such folly, I would by no means permit its publication. I have never contemplated anything higher than the reformation of my own opinions, and basing them on a foundation wholly my own. And although my own satisfaction with my work has led me to present here a draft of it, I do not by any means therefore recommend to every one else to make a similar attempt. Those whom God has endowed with a larger measure of genius will entertain, perhaps, designs still more exalted; but for the many I am much afraid lest even the present undertaking be more than they can safely venture to imitate. The single design to strip one's self of all past beliefs is one that ought not to be taken by every one. The majority of men is composed of two classes, for neither of which would this be at all a befitting resolution: in the *first* place, of those who with more than a due confidence in their own powers, are precipitate in their judgments and want the patience requisite for orderly and circumspect thinking; whence it happens, that if men of this class once take the liberty to doubt of their accustomed opinions, and quit the beaten highway, they will never be able to thread the byeway that would lead them by a shorter course, and will lose themselves and continue to wander for life; in the *second* place, of those who, possessed of sufficient sense or modesty to determine that there are others who excel them in the power of discriminating between truth and error, and by whom they may be instructed, ought rather to content themselves with the opinions of such than trust for more correct to their own Reason.

For my own part, I should doubtless have belonged to the latter class, had I received instruction from but one master, or had I never known the diversities of opinion that from time immemorial have prevailed among men of the greatest learning. But I had become aware, even so early as during my college life, that no opinion, however absurd and incredible, can be imagined, which has not been maintained by some one of the philosophers; and afterwards in the course of my travels I remarked that all those whose opinions are decidedly repugnant to ours are not on that account barbarians and savages, but on the contrary that many of these nations make an equally good, if not a better, use of their Reason than we do. I took into account also the very different character which a person brought up from infancy in France or Germany exhibits, from that which, with the same mind originally, this individual would have possessed had he lived always among the Chinese or with savages, and the circumstance that in dress itself the fashion which pleased us ten years ago, and which may again, perhaps, be received into favour before ten years have gone, appears to us at this moment extravagant and ridiculous. I was thus led to infer that the ground of our opinions is far more custom and example than any certain knowledge. And, finally, although such be the ground of our opinions, I remarked that a plurality of suffrages is no guarantee of truth where it is at all of difficult discovery, as in such cases it is much more likely that it will be found by one than by many. I could, however, select from the crowd no one whose opinions seemed worthy of preference, and thus I found myself constrained, as it were, to use my own Reason in the conduct of my life.

But like one walking alone and in the dark, I resolved to proceed so slowly and with such circumspection, that if I did not advance far, I would at least guard against falling. I did not even choose to dismiss summarily any of the opinions that had crept into my belief without having been introduced by Reason, but first of all took sufficient time carefully to satisfy myself of the general nature of the task I was setting myself, and ascertain the true Method by which to arrive at the knowledge of whatever lay within the compass of my powers.

Among the branches of Philosophy, I had, at an earlier period, given some attention to Logic, and among those of the Mathematics to Geometrical Analysis and Algebra—three Arts or Sciences which ought, as I conceived, to contribute something to my design. But, on examination, I found that, as for Logic, its syllogisms and the majority of its other precepts are of avail rather in the communication of what we already know, or even as the Art of Lully, in speaking without judgment of things of which we are ignorant, than in the investigation of the unknown; and although this Science contains indeed a number of correct and very excellent precepts, there are, nevertheless, so many others, and these either injurious or superfluous, mingled with the former, that it is almost quite as difficult to effect a severance of the true from the false as it is to extract a Diana or a Minerva from a rough block of marble. Then as to the Analysis of the ancients and the Algebra of the moderns, besides that they embrace only matters highly abstract, and, to appearance, of no use, the former is so exclusively restricted to the consideration of figures, that it can exercise the Understanding only on condition of greatly fatiguing the Imagination; and, in the latter, there is so complete a subjection to certain rules and formulas, that there results an art full of confusion and obscurity calculated to embarrass, instead of a science fitted to cultivate the mind. By these considerations I was induced to seek some other Method which would comprise the advantages of the three and be exempt from their defects. And as a multitude of laws often only hampers justice, so that a state is best governed when, with few laws, these are rigidly administered; in like manner, instead of the great number of precepts of which Logic is composed, I believed that the four following would prove perfectly sufficient for me, provided I took the firm and unwavering resolution never in a single instance to fail in observing them.

The *first* was never to accept anything for true which I did not clearly know to be such; that is to say, carefully to avoid precipitancy and prejudice, and to comprise nothing more in my judgment than what was presented to my mind so clearly and distinctly as to exclude all ground of doubt.

The *second*, to divide each of the difficulties under examination into as many parts as possible, and as might be necessary for its adequate solution.

The *third*, to conduct my thoughts in such order that, by commencing with objects the simplest and easiest to know, I might ascend by little and little, and, as it were, step by step, to the knowledge of the more complex; assigning in thought a certain order even to those objects which in their own nature do not stand in a relation of antecedence and sequence.

And the *last*, in every case to make enumerations so complete, and reviews so general, that I might be assured that nothing was omitted.

The long chains of simple and easy reasonings by means of which geometers are accustomed to reach the conclusions of their most difficult demonstrations, had led me to imagine that all things, to the knowledge of which man is competent, are mutually connected in the same way, and that there is nothing so far removed from us as to be beyond our reach, or so recondite that we cannot discover it, provided only we abstain from accepting the false for the true, and always preserve in our thoughts the order necessary for the deduction of one truth from another. And I had little difficulty in determining the objects with which it was necessary to commence, for I was already persuaded that it must be with the simplest and easiest to know, and, considering that of all those who have hitherto sought truth in the Sciences, the mathematicians alone have been able to find any demonstrations, that is, any certain and evident reasons, I did not doubt but that such must have been the rule of their investigations. I resolved to commence, therefore, with the examination of the simplest objects, not anticipating, however, from this any other advantage than that to be found in accustoming my mind to the love and nourishment of truth, and to a distaste for all such reasonings as were unsound. But I had no intention on that account of attempting to master all the particular Sciences commonly denominated Mathematics: but observing that, however different their objects, they all agree in considering only the various relations or proportions subsisting among those objects, I thought it best for my purpose to consider these proportions in the most general form possible, without referring them to any objects in particular, except such as would most facilitate the knowledge of them, and without by any means restricting them to these, that afterwards I might thus be the better able to apply them to every other class of objects to which they are legitimately applicable. Perceiving further, that in order to understand these relations I should sometimes have to consider them one by one, and sometimes only to bear them in mind, or embrace them in the aggregate, I thought that, in order the better to consider them individually, I should view them as subsisting between straight lines, than which I could find no objects more simple, or capable of being more distinctly represented to my imagination and senses; and on the other hand, that in order to retain them in the memory, or embrace an aggregate of many, I should express them by certain characters the briefest possible. In this way I believed that I could borrow all that was best both in Geometrical Analysis and in Algebra, and correct all the defects of the one by help of the other.

And, in point of fact, the accurate observance of these few precepts gave me, I take the liberty of saying, such ease in unravelling all the questions embraced in these two sciences, that in the two or three months I devoted to their examination, not only did I reach solutions of questions I had formerly deemed exceedingly difficult, but even as regards questions of the solution of which I continued ignorant, I was enabled, as it appeared to me, to determine the means whereby, and the extent to which, a solution was possible; results attributable to the circumstance that I commenced with the simplest and most general truths, and that thus each truth discovered was a rule available in the discovery of subsequent ones. Nor in this perhaps shall I appear too vain, if it be considered that, as the truth on any particular point is one, whoever apprehends the truth, knows all that on that point can be known. The child, for example, who has been instructed in the elements of Arithmetic, and has made a particular addition, according to rule, may be assured that he has found, with respect to the sum of the numbers before him, all that in this instance is within the reach of human genius. Now, in conclusion, the Method which teaches adherence to the true order, and an exact enumeration of all the conditions of the thing sought includes all that gives certitude to the rules of Arithmetic.

But the chief ground of my satisfaction with this Method, was the assurance I had of thereby exercising my reason in all matters, if not with absolute perfection, at least with the greatest attainable by me: besides, I was conscious that by its use my mind was becoming gradually habituated to clearer and more distinct conceptions of its objects; and I hoped also, from not having restricted this Method to any particular matter, to apply it to the difficulties of the other Sciences, with not less success than to those of Algebra. I should not, however, on this account have ventured at once on the examination of all the difficulties of the Sciences which presented themselves to me, for this would have been contrary to the order prescribed in the Method, but observing that the knowledge of such is dependent on principles borrowed from Philosophy, in which I found nothing certain, I thought it necessary first of all to endeavour to establish its principles. And because I observed, besides, that an inquiry of this kind was of all others of the greatest moment, and one in which precipitancy and anticipation in judgment were most to be dreaded, I thought that I ought not to approach it till I had reached a more mature age, (being at that time but twenty-three,) and had first of all employed much of my time in preparation for the work, as well by eradicating from my mind all the erroneous opinions I had up to that moment accepted, as by amassing variety of experience to afford materials for my reasonings, and by continually exercising myself in my chosen Method with a view to increased skill in its application.

*   *   *   *

PART IV

I am in doubt as to the propriety of making my first meditations in the place above mentioned matter of discourse; for these are so meta-physical, and so uncommon, as not, perhaps, to be acceptable to every one. And yet, that it may be determined whether the foundations that I have laid are sufficiently secure, I find myself in a measure constrained to advert to them. I had long before remarked that, in relation to prac-tice, it is sometimes necessary to adopt, as if above doubt, opinions which we discern to be highly uncertain, as has been already said; but as I then desired to give my attention solely to the search after truth, I thought that a procedure exactly the opposite was called for, and that I ought to reject as absolutely false all opinions in regard to which I could suppose the least ground for doubt, in order to ascertain whether after that there remained aught in my belief that was wholly indubitable. Accordingly, seeing that our senses sometimes deceive us, I was willing to suppose that there existed nothing really such as they presented to us; and because some men err in reasoning, and fall into paralogisms, even on the simplest matters of Geometry, I, convinced that I was as open to error as any other, rejected as false all the reasonings I had hitherto taken for demonstrations; and finally, when I considered that the very same thoughts (presentations) which we experience when awake may also be experienced when we are asleep, while there is at that time not one of them true, I supposed that all the objects (presentations) that had ever entered into my mind when awake, had in them no more truth than the illusions of my dreams. But immediately upon this I observed that, whilst I thus wished to think that all was false, it was absolutely necessary that I, who thus thought, should be somewhat; and as I ob-served that this truth, *I think, hence I am,* was so certain and of such evidence, that no ground of doubt, however extravagant, could be alleged by the Sceptics capable of shaking it, I concluded that I might, without scruple, accept it as the first principle of the Philosophy of which I was in search.

In the next place, I attentively examined what I was, and as I observed that I could suppose that I had no body, and that there was no world nor any place in which I might be; but that I could not therefore suppose that I was not; and that, on the contrary, from the very circumstance that I thought to doubt of the truth of other things, it most clearly and certainly followed that I was; while, on the other hand, if I had only ceased to think, although all the other objects which I had ever imagined had been in reality existent, I would have had no reason to believe that I existed; I thence concluded that I was a substance whose whole essence or nature consists only in thinking, and which, that it may exist, has need of no place, nor is dependent on any material thing; so that "I," that is to say, the mind by which I am what I am, is wholly distinct from the body, and is even more easily known than the latter, and is such, that although the latter were not, it would still continue to be all that it is.

After this I inquired in general into what is essential to the truth and certainty of a proposition; for since I had discovered one which I knew to be true, I thought that I must likewise be able to discover the ground of this certitude. And as I observed that in the words *I think, hence I am,* there is nothing at all which gives me assurance of their truth beyond this, that I see very clearly that in order to think, it is necessary to exist, I concluded that I might take, as a general rule, the principle, that all the things which we very clearly and distinctly conceive are true, only observing, however, that there is some difficulty in rightly determining the objects which we distinctly conceive.

In the next place, from reflecting on the circumstance that I doubted, and that consequently my being was not wholly perfect, (for I clearly saw that it was a greater perfection to know than to doubt,) I was led to inquire whence I had learned to think of something more perfect than myself; and I clearly recognised that I must hold this notion from some Nature which in reality was more perfect. As for the thoughts of many other objects external to me, as of the sky, the earth, light, heat, and a thousand more, I was less at a loss to know whence these came; for since I remarked in them nothing which seemed to render them superior to myself, I could believe that, if these were true, they were dependencies on my own nature, in so far as it possessed a certain perfection, and, if they were false, that I held them from nothing, that is to say, that they were in me because of a certain imperfection of my nature. But this could not be the case with the idea of a Nature more perfect than myself; for to receive it from nothing was a thing manifestly impossible; and, because it is not less repugnant that the more perfect should be an effect of, and dependence on the less perfect, than that something should proceed from nothing, it was equally impossible that I could hold it from myself: accordingly, it but remained that it had been placed in me by a Nature which was in reality more perfect than mine, and which even possessed within itself all the perfections of which I could form any idea; that is to say, in a single word, which was God. And to this I added that, since I knew some perfections which I did not possess, I was not the only being in existence, (I will here, with your permission, freely use the terms of the schools) ; but, on the contrary, that there was of necessity some other more perfect Being upon whom I was dependent, and from whom I had received all that I possessed; for if I had existed alone, and independently of every other being, so as to have had from myself all the perfection, however little, which I actually possessed, I should have been able, for the same reason, to have had from myself the whole remainder of perfection, of the want of which I was conscious, and thus could of myself have become infinite, eternal, immutable, omniscient, all-powerful, and, in fine, have possessed all the perfections which I could recognise in God. For in order to know the nature of God, (whose existence has been established by the preceding reasonings,) as far as my own nature permitted, I had only to consider in reference to all the properties of which I found in my mind some idea, whether their possession was a mark of perfection; and I was assured that no one which indicated any imperfection was in him, and that none of the rest was awanting. Thus I perceived that doubt, inconstancy, sadness, and such like, could not be found in God, since I myself would have been happy to be free from them. Besides, I had ideas of many sensible and corporeal things; for although I might suppose that I was dreaming, and that all which I saw or imagined was false, I could not, nevertheless, deny that the ideas were in reality in my thoughts. But, because I had already very clearly recognised in myself that the intelligent nature is distinct from the corporeal, and as I observed that all composition is an evidence of dependency, and that a state of dependency is manifestly a state of imperfection, I therefore determined that it could not be a perfection in God to be compounded of these two natures, and that consequently he was not so compounded; but that if there were any bodies in the world, or even any intelligences, or other natures that were not wholly perfect, their existence depended on his power in such a way that they could not subsist without him for a single moment.

I was disposed straightway to search for other truths; and when I had represented to myself the object of the geometers, which I conceived to be a continuous body, or a space indefinitely extended in length, breadth, and height or depth, divisible into divers parts which admit of different figures and sizes, and of being moved or transposed in all manner of ways, (for all this the geometers suppose to be in the object they contemplate,) I went over some of their simplest demonstrations. And, in the first place, I observed, that the great certitude which by common consent is accorded to these demonstrations, is founded solely upon this, that they are clearly conceived in accordance with the rules I have already laid down. In the next place, I perceived that there was nothing at all in these demonstrations which could assure me of the existence of their object: thus, for example, supposing a triangle to be given, I distinctly perceived that its three angles were necessarily equal to two right angles, but I did not on that account perceive anything which could assure me that any triangle existed: while, on the contrary, recurring to the examination of the idea of a Perfect Being, I found that the existence of the Being was comprised in the idea in the same way that the equality of its three angles to two right angles is comprised in the idea of a triangle, or as in the idea of a sphere, the equidistance of all points on its surface from the centre, or even still more clearly; and that consequently it is at least as certain that God, who is this Perfect Being, is, or exists, as any demonstration of Geometry can be.

But the reason which leads many to persuade themselves that there is a difficulty in knowing this truth, and even also in knowing what their mind really is, is that they never raise their thoughts above sensible objects, and are so accustomed to consider nothing except by way of imagination, which is a mode of thinking limited to material objects, that all that is not imaginable seems to them not intelligible. The truth of this is sufficiently manifest from the single circumstance, that the philosophers of the Schools accept as a maxim that there is nothing in the Understanding which was not previously in the Senses, in which however it is certain that the ideas of God and of the soul have never been; and it appears to me that they who make use of their imagination to comprehend these ideas do exactly the same thing as if, in order to hear sounds or smell odours, they strove to avail themselves of their eyes; unless indeed that there is this difference, that the sense of sight does not afford us an inferior assurance to those of smell or hearing; in place of which, neither our imagination nor our senses can give us assurance of anything unless our Understanding intervene.

Finally, if there be still persons who are not sufficiently persuaded of the existence of God and of the soul, by the reasons I have adduced, I am desirous that they should know that all the other propositions, of the truth of which they deem themselves perhaps more assured, as that we have a body, and that there exist stars and an earth, and such like, are less certain; for, although we have a moral assurance of these things, which is so strong that there is an appearance of extravagance in doubting of their existence, yet at the same time no one, unless his intellect is impaired, can deny, when the question relates to a metaphysical certitude, that there is sufficient reason to exclude entire assurance, in the observation that when asleep we can in the same way imagine ourselves possessed of another body and that we see other stars and another earth, when there is nothing of the kind. For how do we know that the thoughts which occur in dreaming are false rather than those other which we experience when awake, since the former are often not less vivid and distinct than the latter? And though men of the highest genius study this question as long as they please, I do not believe that they will be able to give any reason which can be sufficient to remove this doubt, unless they presuppose the existence of God. For, in the first place, even the principle which I have already taken as a rule, viz., that all the things which we clearly and distinctly conceive are true, is certain only because God is or exists, and because he is a Perfect Being, and because all that we possess is derived from him: whence it follows that our ideas or notions, which to the extent of their clearness and distinctness are real, and proceed from God, must to that extent be true. Accordingly, whereas we not unfrequently have ideas or notions in which some falsity is contained, this can only be the case with such as are to some extent confused and obscure, and in this proceed from nothing, (participate of negation,) that is, exist in us thus confused because we are not wholly perfect. And it is evident that it is not less repugnant that falsity or imperfection, in so far as it is imperfection, should proceed from God, than that truth or perfection should proceed from nothing. But if we did not know that all which we possess of real and true proceeds from a Perfect and Infinite Being, however clear and distinct our ideas might be, we should have no ground on that account for the assurance that they possessed the perfection of being true.

But after the knowledge of God and of the soul has rendered us certain of this rule, we can easily understand that the truth of the thoughts we experience when awake, ought not in the slightest degree to be called in question on account of the illusions of our dreams. For if it happened that an individual, even when asleep, had some very distinct idea, as, for example, if a geometer should discover some new demonstration, the circumstance of his being asleep would not militate against its truth; and as for the most ordinary error of our dreams, which consists in their representing to us various objects in the same way as our external senses, this is not prejudicial, since it leads us very properly to suspect the truth of the ideas of sense; for we are not unfrequently deceived in the same manner when awake; as when persons in the jaundice see all objects yellow, or when the stars or bodies at a great distance appear to us much smaller than they are. For, in fine, whether awake or asleep, we ought never to allow ourselves to be persuaded of the truth of anything unless on the evidence of our Reason. And it must be noted that I say of our *Reason*, and not of our imagination or of our senses: thus, for example, although we very clearly see the sun, we ought not therefore to determine that it is only of the size which our sense of sight presents; and we may very distinctly imagine the head of a lion joined to the body of a goat, without being therefore shut up to the conclusion that a chimæra exists; for it is not a dictate of Reason that what we thus see or imagine is in reality existent; but it plainly tells us that all our ideas or notions contain in them some truth; for otherwise it could not be that God, who is wholly perfect and veracious, should have placed them in us. And because our reasonings are never so clear or so complete during sleep as when we are awake, although sometimes the acts of our imagination are then as lively and distinct, if not more so than in our waking moments, Reason further dictates that, since all our thoughts cannot be true because of our partial imperfection, those possessing truth must infallibly be found in the experience of our waking moments rather than in that of our dreams.

PART V

I would here willingly have proceeded to exhibit the whole chain of truths which I deduced from these primary; but as with a view to this it would have been necessary now to treat of many questions in dispute among the learned, with whom I do not wish to be embroiled, I believe that it will be better for me to refrain from this exposition, and only mention in general what these truths are, that the more judicious may be able to determine whether a more special account of them would conduce to the public advantage. I have ever remained firm in my original resolution to suppose no other principle than that of which I have recently availed myself in demonstrating the existence of God and of the soul, and to accept as true nothing that did not appear to me more clear and certain than the demonstrations of the geometers had formerly appeared; and yet I venture to state that not only have I found means to satisfy myself in a short time on all the principal difficulties which are usually treated of in Philosophy, but I have also observed certain laws established in nature by God in such a manner, and of which he has impressed on our minds such notions, that after we have reflected sufficiently upon these, we cannot doubt that they are accurately observed in all that exists or takes place in the world: and farther, by considering the concatenation of these laws, it appears to me that I have discovered many truths more useful and more important than all I had before learned, or even had expected to learn.

But because I have essayed to expound the chief of these discoveries in a Treatise which certain considerations prevent me from publishing, I cannot make the results known more conveniently than by here giving a summary of the contents of this Treatise. It was my design to comprise in it all that, before I set myself to write it, I thought I knew of the nature of material objects. But like the painters who, finding themselves unable to represent equally well on a plain surface all the different faces of a solid body, select one of the chief, on which alone they make the light fall, and throwing the rest into the shade, allow them to appear only in so far as they can be seen while looking at the principal one; so, fearing lest I should not be able to comprise in my discourse all that was in my mind, I resolved to expound singly, though at considerable length, my opinions regarding light; then to take the opportunity of adding something on the sun and the fixed stars, since light almost wholly proceeds from them; on the heavens since they transmit it; on the planets, comets, and earth, since they reflect it; and particularly on all the bodies that are upon the earth, since they are either coloured, or transparent, or luminous; and finally on man, since he is the spectator of these objects. Further, to enable me to cast this variety of subjects somewhat into the shade, and to express my judgment regarding them with greater freedom, without being necessitated to adopt or refute the opinions of the learned, I resolved to leave all the people here to their disputes, and to speak only of what would happen in a new world, if God were now to create somewhere in the imaginary spaces matter suffi-cient to compose one, and were to agitate variously and confusedly the different parts of this matter, so that there resulted a chaos as disorded as the poets ever feigned, and after that did nothing more than lend his ordinary concurrence to nature, and allow her to act in accordance with the laws which he had established. On this supposition, I, in the first place, described this matter, and essayed to represent it in such a manner that to my mind there can be nothing clearer and more intelligible, ex-cept what has been recently said regarding God and the soul; for I even expressly supposed that it possessed one of those forms or qualities which are so debated in the Schools, nor in general anything the knowledge of which is not so natural to our minds that no one can so much as imagine himself ignorant of it. Besides, I have pointed out what are the laws of nature; and, with no other principle upon which to found my reasonings except the infinite perfection of God, I endeavoured to demonstrate all those about which there could be any room for doubt, and to prove that they are such, that even if God had created more worlds, there could have been none in which these laws were not observed. Thereafter, I showed how the greatest part of the matter of this chaos must, in ac-cordance with these laws, dispose and arrange itself in such a way as to present the appearance of heavens; how in the meantime some of its parts must compose an earth and some planets and comets, and others a sun and fixed stars. And, making a digression at this stage on the subject of light, I expounded at considerable length what the nature of that light must be which is found in the sun and the stars, and how thence in an instant of time it traverses the immense spaces of the heavens, and how from the planets and comets it is reflected towards the earth. To this I likewise added much respecting the substance, the situation, the motions, and all the different qualities of these heavens and stars; so that I thought I had said enough respecting them to show that there is nothing observable in the heavens or stars of our system that must not, or at least may not appear precisely alike in those of the system which I described. I came next to speak of the earth in particular, and to show how, even though I had expressly supposed that God had given no weight to the matter of which it is composed, this should not prevent all its parts from tending exactly to its centre; how with water and air on its surface, the disposition of the heavens and heavenly bodies, more especially of the moon, must cause a flow and ebb, like in all its circumstances to that observed in our seas, as also a certain current both of water and air from east to west, such as is likewise observed between the tropics; how the mountains, seas, fountains, and rivers might naturally be formed in it, and the metals produced in the mines, and the plants grow in the fields; and in general, how all the bodies which are commonly denominated mixed or composite might be generated: and, among other things in the discoveries alluded to, inasmuch as besides the stars, I knew nothing except fire which produces light, I spared no pains to set forth all that pertains to its nature—the manner of its production and support, and to explain how heat is sometimes found without light, and light without heat; to show how it can induce various colours upon different bodies and other diverse qualities; how it reduces some to a liquid state and hardens others; how it can consume almost all bodies, or convert them into ashes and smoke; and finally, how from these ashes, by the mere intensity of its action, it forms glass: for as this transmutation of ashes into glass appeared to me as wonderful as any other in nature, I took a special pleasure in describing it.

I was not, however, disposed, from these circumstances, to conclude that this world had been created in the manner I described; for it is much more likely that God made it at the first such as it was to be. But this is certain, and an opinion commonly received among theologians, that the action by which he now sustains it is the same with that by which he originally created it; so that even although he had from the beginning given it no other form than that of chaos, provided only he had established certain laws of nature, and had lent it his concurrence to enable it to act as it is wont to do, it may be believed, without discredit to the miracle of creation, that, in this way alone, things purely material might, in course of time, have become such as we observe them at present; and their nature is much more easily conceived when they are beheld coming in this manner gradually into existence, than when they are only considered as produced at once in a finished and perfect state.

From the description of inanimate bodies and plants, I passed to animals, and particularly to man. But since I had not as yet sufficient knowledge to enable me to treat of these in the same manner as of the rest, that is to say, by deducing effects from their causes, and by showing from what elements and in what manner Nature must produce them, I remained satisfied with the supposition that God formed the body of man wholly like to one of ours, as well in the external shape of the members as in the internal conformation of the organs, of the same matter with that I had described, and at first placed in it no Rational Soul, nor any other principle, in room of the Vegetative or Sensitive Soul, beyond kindling in the heart one of those fires without light, such as I had already described, and which I thought was not different from the heat in hay that has been heaped together before it is dry, or that which causes fermentation in new wines before they are run clear of the fruit. For, when I examined the kind of functions which might, as consequences of this supposition, exist in this body, I found precisely all those which may exist in us independently of all power of thinking, and consequently without being in any measure owing to the soul; in other words, to that part of us which is distinct from the body, and of which it has been said above that the nature distinctively consists in thinking—functions in which the animals void of Reason may be said wholly to resemble us; but among which I could not discover any of those that, as dependent on thought alone, belong to us as men, while, on the other hand, I did afterwards discover these as soon as I supposed God to have created a Rational Soul, and to have annexed it to this body in a particular manner which I described.

But, in order to show how I there handled this matter, I mean here to give the explication of the motion of the heart and arteries, which, as the first and most general motion observed in animals, will afford the means of readily determining what should be thought of all the rest. And that there may be less difficulty in understanding what I am about to say on this subject, I advise those who are not versed in Anatomy, before they commence the perusal of these observations, to take the trouble of getting dissected in their presence the heart of some large animal possessed of lungs, (for this is throughout sufficiently like the human,) and to have shewn to them its two ventricles or cavities: in the first place, that in the right side, with which correspond two very ample tubes, viz., the hollow vein, (*vena cava,*) which is the principal receptacle of the blood, and the trunk of the tree, as it were, of which all the other veins in the body are branches; and the arterial vein, (*vena arteriosa,*) inappropriately so denominated, since it is in truth only an artery, which, taking its rise in the heart, is divided, after passing out from it, into many branches which presently disperse themselves all over the lungs; in the second place, the cavity in the left side, with which correspond in the same manner two canals in size equal to or larger than the preceding, viz., the venous artery, (*arteria venosa,*) likewise inappropriately thus designated, because it is simply a vein which comes from the lungs, where it is divided into many branches, interlaced with those of the arterial vein, and those of the tube called the windpipe, through which the air we breathe enters; and the great artery which, issuing from the heart, sends its branches all over the body. I should wish also that such persons were carefully shewn the eleven pellicles which, like so many small valves, open and shut the four orifices that are in these two cavities, viz., three at the entrance of the hollow vein, where they are disposed in such a manner as by no means to prevent the blood which it contains from flowing into the right ventricle of the heart, and yet exactly to prevent its flowing out; three at the entrance to the arterial vein, which, arranged in a manner exactly the opposite of the former, readily permit the blood contained in this cavity to pass into the lungs, but hinder that contained in the lungs from returning to this cavity; and, in like manner, two others at the mouth of the venous artery, which allow the blood from the lungs to flow into the left cavity of the heart, but preclude its return; and three at the mouth of the great artery, which suffer the blood to flow from the heart, but prevent its reflux. Nor do we need to seek any other reason for the number of these pellicles beyond this that the orifice of the venous artery being of an oval shape from the nature of its situation, can be adequately closed with two, whereas the others being round are more conveniently closed with three. Besides, I wish such persons to observe that the grand artery and the arterial vein are of much harder and firmer texture than the venous artery and the hollow vein; and that the two last expand before entering the heart, and there form, as it were, two pouches denominated the auricles of the heart, which are composed of a substance similar to that of the heart itself; and that there is always more warmth in the heart than in any other part of the body; and, finally, that this heat is capable of causing any drop of blood that passes into the cavities rapidly to expand and dilate, just as all liquors do when allowed to fall drop by drop into a highly heated vessel.

For, after these things, it is not necessary for me to say anything more with a view to explain the motion of the heart, except that when its cavities are not full of blood, into these the blood of necessity flows,— from the hollow vein into the right, and from the venous artery into the left; because these two vessels are always full of blood, and their orifices, which are turned towards the heart, cannot then be closed. But as soon as two drops of blood have thus passed, one into each of the cavities, these drops which cannot but be very large, because the orifices through which they pass are wide, and the vessels from which they come full of blood, are immediately rarefied, and dilated by the heat they meet with. In this way they cause the whole heart to expand, and at the same time press home and shut the five small valves that are at the entrances of the two vessels from which they flow, and thus prevent any more blood from coming down into the heart, and becoming more and more rarefied, they push open the six small valves that are in the orifices of the other two vessels, through which they pass out, causing in this way all the branches of the arterial vein and of the grand artery to expand almost simultaneously with the heart—which immediately thereafter begins to contract, as do also the arteries, because the blood that has entered them has cooled, and the six small valves close, and the five of the hollow vein and of the venous artery open anew and allow a passage to other two drops of blood, which cause the heart and the arteries again to expand as before. And, because the blood which thus enters into the heart passes through these two pouches called auricles, it thence happens that their motion is the contrary of that of the heart, and that when it expands they contract. But lest those who are ignorant of the force of mathematical demonstrations, and who are not accustomed to distinguish true reasons from mere verisimilitudes, should venture, without examination, to deny what has been said, I wish it to be considered that the motion which I have now explained follows as necessarily from the very arrangement of the parts, which may be observed in the heart by the eye alone, and from the heat which may be felt with the fingers, and from the nature of the blood as learned from experience, as does the motion of a clock from the power, the situation, and shape of its counterweights and wheels.

But if it be asked how it happens that the blood in the veins, flowing in this way continually into the heart, is not exhausted, and why the arteries do not become too full, since all the blood which passes through the heart flows into them, I need only mention in reply what has been written by a physician of England, who has the honour of having broken the ice on this subject, and of having been the first to teach that there are many small passages at the extremities of the arteries, through which the blood received by them from the heart passes into the small branches of the veins, whence it again returns to the heart; so that its course amounts precisely to a perpetual circulation. Of this we have abundant proof in the ordinary experience of surgeons, who, by binding the arm with a tie of moderate straitness above the part where they open the vein, cause the blood to flow more copiously than it would have done without any ligature; whereas quite the contrary would happen were they to bind it below; that is, between the hand and the opening, or were to make the ligature above the opening very tight. For it is manifest that the tie, moderately straitened, while adequate to hinder the blood already in the arm from returning towards the heart by the veins, cannot on that account prevent new blood from coming forward through the arteries, because these are situated below the veins, and their coverings, from their greater consistency, are more difficult to compress; and also that the blood which comes from the heart tends to pass through them to the hand with greater force than it does to return from the hand to the heart through the veins. And since the latter current escapes from the arm by the opening made in one of the veins, there must of necessity be certain passages below the ligature, that is, towards the extremities of the arm through which it can come thither from the arteries. This physician likewise abundantly establishes what he has advanced respecting the motion of the blood, from the existence of certain pellicles, so disposed in various places along the course of the veins, in the manner of small valves, as not to permit the blood to pass from the middle of the body towards the extremities, but only to return from the extremities to the heart; and farther, from experience which shows that all the blood which is in the body may flow out of it in a very short time through a single artery that has been cut, even although this had been closely tied in the immediate neighbourhood of the heart, and cut between the heart and the ligature, so as to prevent the supposition that the blood flowing out of it could come from any other quarter than the heart.

But there are many other circumstances which evince that what I have alleged is the true cause of the motion of the blood: thus, in the first place, the difference that is observed between the blood which flows from the veins, and that from the arteries, can only arise from this, that being rarefied, and, as it were, distilled by passing through the heart, it is thinner, and more vivid, and warmer immediately after leaving the heart, in other words, when in the arteries, than it was a short time before passing into either, in other words, when it was in the veins; and if attention be given, it will be found that this difference is very marked only in the neighbourhood of the heart; and is not so evident in parts more remote from it. In the next place, the consistency of the coats of which the arterial vein and the great artery are composed, sufficiently shows that the blood is impelled against them with more force than against the veins. And why should the left cavity of the heart and the great artery be wider and larger than the right cavity and the arterial vein, were it not that the blood of the venous artery, having only been in the lungs after it has passed through the heart, is thinner, and rarefies more readily, and in a higher degree, than the blood which proceeds immediately from the hollow vein? And what can physicians conjecture from feeling the pulse unless they know that according as the blood changes its nature it can be rarefied by the warmth of the heart, in a higher or lower degree, and more or less quickly than before? And if it be inquired how this heat is communicated to the other members, must it not be admitted that this is effected by means of the blood, which, passing through the heart, is there heated anew, and thence diffused over all the body? Whence it happens, that if the blood be withdrawn from any part, the heat is likewise withdrawn by the same means; and although the heart were as hot as glowing iron, it would not be capable of warming the feet and hands as at present, unless it continually sent thither new blood. We likewise perceive from this, that the true use of respiration is to bring sufficient fresh air into the lungs, to cause the blood which flows into them from the right ventricle of the heart, where it has been rarefied and, as it were, changed into vapours, to become thick, and to convert it anew into blood, before it flows into the left cavity, without which process it would be unfit for the nourishment of the fire that is there. This receives confirmation from the circumstance, that it is observed of animals destitute of lungs that they have also but one cavity in the heart, and that in children who cannot use them while in the womb, there is a hole through which the blood flows from the hollow vein into the left cavity of the heart, and a tube through which it passes from the arterial vein into the grand artery without passing through the lung. In the next place, how could digestion be carried on in the stomach unless the heart communicated heat to it through the arteries, and along with this certain of the more fluid parts of the blood, which assist in the dissolution of the food that has been taken in? Is not also the operation which converts the juice of food into blood easily comprehended, when it is considered that it is distilled by passing and repassing through the heart perhaps more than one or two hundred times in a day? And what more need be adduced to explain nutrition, and the production of the different humours of the body, beyond saying, that the force with which the blood, in being rarefied, passes from the heart towards the extremities of the arteries, causes certain of its parts to remain in the members at which they arrive, and there occupy the place of some others expelled by them; and that according to the situation, shape, or smallness of the pores with which they meet, some rather than others flow into certain parts, in the same way that some sieves are observed to act, which, by being variously perforated, serve to separate different species of grain? And, in the last place, what above all is here worthy of observation, is the generation of the animal spirits, which are like a very subtle wind, or rather a very pure and vivid flame which, continually ascending in great abundance from the heart to the brain, thence penetrates through the nerves into the muscles, and gives motion to all the members; so that to account for other parts of the blood which, as most agitated and penetrating, are the fittest to compose these spirits, proceeding towards the brain, it is not necessary to suppose any other cause, than simply, that the arteries which carry them thither proceed from the heart in the most direct lines, and that, according to the rules of Mechanics, which are the same with those of Nature, when many objects tend at once to the same point where there is not sufficient room for all, (as is the case with parts of the blood which flow forth from the left cavity of the heart and tend towards the brain,) the weaker and less agitated parts must necessarily be driven aside from that point by the stronger which alone in this way reach it.

I had expounded all these matters with sufficient minuteness in the Treatise which I formerly thought of publishing. And after these, I had shewn what must be the fabric of the nerves and muscles of the human body to give the animal spirits contained in it the power to move the members, as when we see heads shortly after they have been struck off still move and bite the earth, although no longer animated; what changes must take place in the brain to produce waking, sleep, and dreams; how light, sounds, odours, tastes, heat, and all the other qualities of external objects impress it with different ideas by means of the senses; how hunger, thirst, and the other internal affections can likewise impress upon it divers ideas; what must be understood by the common sense (*sense communis*) in which these ideas are received, by the memory which retains them, by the fantasy which can change them in various ways, and out of them compose new ideas, and which, by the same means, distributing the animal spirits through the muscles, can cause the members of such a body to move in as many different ways, and in a manner as suited, whether to the objects that are presented to its senses or to its internal affections, as can take place in our own case apart from the guidance of the will. Nor will this appear at all strange to those who are acquainted with the variety of movements performed by the different automata, or moving machines fabricated by human industry, and that with help of but few pieces compared with the great multitude of bones, muscles, nerves, arteries, veins, and other parts that are found in the body of each animal. Such persons will look upon this body as a machine made by the hands of God, which is incomparably better arranged, and adequate to movements more admirable than is any machine of human invention. And here I specially stayed to show that, were there such machines exactly resembling in organs and outward form an ape or any other irrational animal, we could have no means of knowing that they were in any respect of a different nature from these animals; but if there were machines bearing the image of our bodies, and capable of imitating our actions as far as it is morally possible, there would still remain two most certain tests whereby to know that they were not therefore really men. Of these the first is that they could never use words or other signs arranged in such a manner as is competent to us in order to declare our thoughts to others: for we may easily conceive a machine to be so constructed that it emits vocables, and even that it emits some correspondent to the action upon it of external objects which cause a change in its organs; for example, if touched in a particular place it may demand what we wish to say to it; if in another it may cry out that it is hurt, and such like; but not that it should arrange them variously so as appositely to reply to what is said in its presence, as men of the lowest grade of intellect can do. The second test is, that although such machines might execute many things with equal or perhaps greater perfection than any of us, they would, without doubt, fail in certain others from which it could be discovered that they did not act from knowledge, but solely from the disposition of their organs: for while Reason is an universal instrument that is alike available on every occasion, these organs, on the contrary, need a particular arrangement for each particular action; whence it must be morally impossible that there should exist in any machine a diversity of organs sufficient to enable it to act in all the occurrences of life, in the way in which our reason enables us to act. Again, by means of these two tests we may likewise know the difference between men and brutes. For it is highly deserving of remark, that there are no men so dull and stupid, not even idiots, as to be incapable of joining together different words, and thereby constructing a declaration by which to make their thoughts understood; and that on the other hand, there is no other animal, however perfect or happily circumstanced which can do the like. Nor does this inability arise from want of organs: for we observe that magpies and parrots can utter words like ourselves, and are yet unable to speak as we do, that is, so as to show that they understand what they say; in place of which men born deaf and dumb, and thus not less, but rather more than the brutes, destitute of the organs which others use in speaking, are in the habit of spontaneously inventing certain signs by which they discover their thoughts to those who, being usually in their company, have leisure to learn their language. And this proves not only that the brutes have less Reason than man, but that they have none at all: for we see that very little is required to enable a person to speak; and since a certain inequality of capacity is observable among animals of the same species, as well as among men, and since some are more capable of being instructed than others, it is incredible that the most perfect ape or parrot of its species, should not in this be equal to the most stupid infant of its kind, or at least to one that was crack-brained, unless the soul of brutes were of a nature wholly different from ours. And we ought not to confound speech with the natural movements which indicate the passions, and can be imitated by machines as well as manifested by animals; nor must it be thought with certain of the ancients, that the brutes speak, although we do not understand their language. For if such were the case, since they are endowed with many organs analogous to ours, they could as easily communicate their thoughts to us as to their fellows. It is also very worthy of remark, that, though there are many animals which manifest more industry than we in certain of their actions, the same animals are yet observed to show none at all in many others: so that the circumstance that they do better than we does not prove that they are endowed with mind, for it would thence follow that they possessed greater Reason than any of us, and could surpass us in all things; on the contrary, it rather proves that they are destitute of Reason, and that it is Nature which acts in them according to the disposition of their organs: thus it is seen, that a clock composed only of wheels and weights can number the hours and measure time more exactly than we with all our skill.

I had after this described the Reasonable Soul, and shewn that it could by no means be educed from the power of matter, as the other things of which I had spoken, but that it must be expressly created; and that it is not sufficient that it be lodged in the human body exactly like a pilot in a ship, unless perhaps to move its members, but that it is necessary for it to be joined and united more closely to the body, in order to have sensations and appetites similar to ours, and thus constitute a real man. I here entered, in conclusion, upon the subject of the soul at considerable length, because it is of the greatest moment: for after the error of those who deny the existence of God, an error which I think I have already sufficiently refuted, there is none that is more powerful in leading feeble minds astray from the straight path of virtue than the supposition that the soul of the brutes is of the same nature with our own; and consequently that after this life we have nothing to hope for or fear, more than flies and ants; in place of which, when we know how far they differ we much better comprehend the reasons which establish that the soul is of a nature wholly independent of the body, and that consequently it is not liable to die with the latter; and, finally, because no other causes are observed capable of destroying it, we are naturally led thence to judge that it is immortal.

11

ISAAC NEWTON

Isaac Newton was born on Christmas day in 1642, the year of Galileo's death. The two men symbolize the shifting geographical focus of European science: Galileo was one of the last representatives of the long Mediterranean leadership which stretched back all the way to the flowering of Greek civilization; by Newton's age the torch had been passed north and west to the nations facing the Atlantic. Even before he completed his bachelor's degree at Cambridge University, Newton was moving beyond the existing frontiers of science. Already he had discovered the infinitesimal calculus, and he had begun the work in celestial mechanics that led eventually to the law of universal gravitation. He also had made his basic discovery in optics. Following his graduation, Newton stayed on at Cambridge as a professor, and the investigation in optics was the first work that he carried to completion, although in the end it was the last that he published fully. Newton lived until 1727, but his creative work in science had ceased before the *Opticks* appeared in 1704.

Thirty years earlier, a letter (which constitutes half of this selection) published in the *Philosophical Transactions* of the Royal Society had stated the central idea of Newton's contribution to optics. Its subject was color. The question of color, in turn, involved a crucial difference between the Aristotelian philosophy of nature and the mechanical philosophy of the 17th century. To the Aristotelian, nature was fundamentally qualitative; bodies really possessed the qualities, such as heat or color, that the senses perceived. To the mechanical philosophy, on the other hand, nature was quantitative, and particular qualities were only peculiar sensations caused by particles of matter impinging on the nerves. Light was merely matter in motion, and colors were particular modifications of the motion. Descartes and those who followed him held that light, in its pure condition, as it comes from the sun, appears white. When its motion is modified by refraction or reflection, the sensation it causes in the eye is also changed, and the phenomena of colors appear.

Newton's theory of color mounted a direct attack on the Cartesian theory.

Another question in 17th century optics was the nature of light. If all of nature were only matter in motion, two general possibilities alone existed. One was upheld by Descartes, who asserted that light is a motion transmitted through matter. He employed the analogy of the stick with which a blind man "sees." When the end of the stick strikes an obstacle, a motion is transmitted through the stick to his hand, and he perceives the obstacle. The immense velocity of light would be comprehensible in such terms, Descartes argued. No body has to move from the object to the perceiver; when the end of the stick strikes a stone, the other end moves at the same instant in the blind man's hand. Descartes' discussion of light was the first step toward what we now call the wave theory of light. Another possibility existed, however, and Newton embraced it. In Query 28 in the *Opticks,* the second part of this selection, he detailed his reasons for rejecting conceptions of light similar to Descartes'.

11

A Letter of Mr. Isaac Newton, Professor of Mathematics in the University of Cambridge; Containing his New Theory of Light and Colours

Sir—To perform my late promise to you, I shall without further ceremony acquaint you, that in the beginning of the year 1666 (at which time I applied myself to the grinding of optic glasses of other figures than spherical,) I procured a triangular glass prism, to try therewith the celebrated phænomena of colours. And for that purpose having darkened my chamber, and made a small hole in my window shuts, to let in a convenient quantity of the sun's light, I placed my prism at his entrance, that it might be thereby refracted to the opposite wall. It was at first a very pleasing diversion to view the vivid and intense colours produced thereby; but after a while applying myself to consider them more circumspectly, I was surprised to see them in an oblong form; which, according to the received laws of refraction, I expected would have been circular. They were terminated at the sides with strait lines, but at the ends, the decay of light was so gradual, that it was difficult to determine justly what was their figure; yet they seemed semicircular (Figure 1).

Comparing the length of this coloured spectrum with its breadth, I found it about five times greater; a disproportion so extravagant, that it excited me to a more than ordinary curiosity of examining from whence it might proceed. I could scarce think, that the various thickness of the glass, or the termination with shadow or darkness, could have any influence on light to produce such an effect; yet I thought it not amiss, first to examine those circumstances, and so tried what would happen by transmitting light through parts of the glass of divers thicknesses, or

Published in *The Philosophical Transactions of the Royal Society*, London, 1672/3. Sent by the author to the editor from Cambridge, February 6, 1671–1672; to be communicated to the Royal Society.

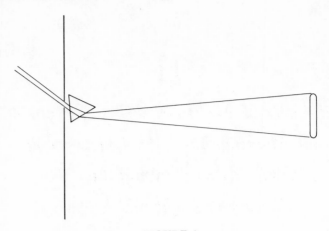

FIGURE 1

through holes in the window of divers sizes, or by setting the prism without, so that the light might pass through it, and be refracted before it
was terminated by the hole; but I found none of those circumstances
material. The fashion of the colours was in all these cases the same.

Then I suspected, whether by any unevenness in the glass, or other
contingent irregularity, these colours might be thus dilated. And to try
this, I took another prism like the former, and so placed it, that the
light, passing through them both, might be refracted contrary ways, and
so by the latter returned into that course from which the former had
diverted it. For, by this means, I thought the regular effects of the first
prism would be destroyed by the second, but the irregular ones more
augmented, by the multiplicity of refractions. The event was, that the
light, which by the first prism was diffused into an oblong form, was by
the second reduced into an orbicular one, with as much regularity as
when it did not at all pass through them. So that, whatever was the cause
of that length, it was not any contingent irregularity.

I then proceeded to examine more critically, what might be effected
by the difference of the incidence of rays coming from divers parts of the
sun; and to that end measured the several lines and angles, belonging
to the image. Its distance from the hole or prism was 22 feet; its utmost
length $13\frac{1}{4}$ inches; its breath $2\frac{5}{8}$; the diameter of the hole $\frac{1}{4}$ of an inch;
the angle, which the rays, tending towards the middle of the image, made
with those lines in which they would have proceeded without refraction,
was 44° 56′. And the vertical angle of the prism, 63° 12′. Also the refractions on both sides the prism, that is, of the incident and emergent rays,
were as near as I could make them equal, and consequently about 54° 4′.

And the rays fell perpendicularly upon the wall. Now subducting the diameter of the hole from the length and breadth of the image, there remains 13 inches the length, and 2⅜ the breadth, comprehended by those rays, which passed through the centre of the said hole; and consequently the angle of the hole, which that breadth subtended, was about 31', answerable to the sun's diameter; but the angle which its length subtended, was more than five such diameters, namely 2° 49'.

Having made these observations, I first computed from them the refractive power of that glass, and found it measured by the ratio of the sines, 20 to 31. And then, by that ratio, I computed the refractions of two rays flowing from opposite parts of the sun's discus, so as to differ 31' in their obliquity of incidence, and found that the emergent rays should have comprehended an angle of about 31', as they did, before they were incident. But because this computation was founded on the hypothesis of the proportionality of the sines of incidence and refraction, which though, by my own experience, I could not imagine to be so erroneous as to make that angle but 31', which in reality was 2° 49'; yet my curiosity caused me again to take my prism. And having placed it at my window, as before, I observed, that by turning it a little about its axis to and fro, so as to vary its obliquity to the light, more than an angle of 4 or 5 degrees, the colours were not thereby sensibly translated from their place on the wall, and consequently by that variation of incidence, the quantity of refraction was not sensibly varied. By this experiment therefore, as well as by the former computation, it was evident, that the difference of the incidence of rays, flowing from divers parts of the sun, could not make them, after a decussation, diverge at a sensibly greater angle, than that at which they before converged; which being at most but about 31 or 32 minutes, there still remained some other cause to be found out, from whence it could be 2° 49'.

Then I began to suspect whether the rays, after their trajection through the prism, did not move in curve lines, and according to their more or less curvity tend to divers parts of the wall. And it increased my suspicion, when I remembered that I had often seen a tennis ball, struck with an oblique racket, describe such a curve line. For, a circular as well as a progressive motion being communicated to it by that stroke, its parts on that side, where the motions conspire, must press and beat the contiguous air more violently than on the other, and there excite a reluctancy and reaction of the air proportionably greater. And for the same reason, if the rays of light should possibly be globular bodies, and by their oblique passage out of one medium into another acquire a circulating motion, they ought to feel the greater resistance from the ambient æther, on that side where the motions conspire, and thence be continually bowed to

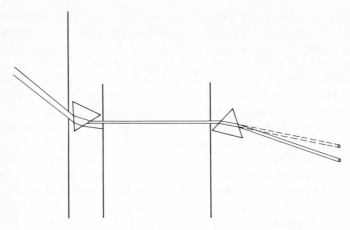

FIGURE 2

the other. But notwithstanding this plausible ground of suspicion, when I came to examine it, I could observe no such curvity in them. And besides (which was enough for my purpose) I observed, that the difference between the length of the image and diameter of the hole, through which the light was transmitted, was proportionable to their distance.

The gradual removal of these suspicions, at length led me to the experimentum crucis, which was this: I took two boards, and placed one of them close behind the prism at the window, so that the light might pass through a small hole, made in it for the purpose, and fall on the other board, which I placed at about 12 feet distance, having first made a small hole in it also, for some of that incident light to pass through (Figure 2). Then I placed another prism behind this second board, so that the light, trajected through both the boards, might pass through that also, and be again refracted before it arrived at the wall. This done, I took the first prism in my hand, and turned it to and fro slowly about its axis, so much as to make the several parts of the image, cast on the second board, successively pass through the hole in it, that I might observe to what places on the wall the second prism would refract them. And I saw, by the variation of those places, that the light tending to that end of the image, towards which the refraction of the first prism was made, did in the second prism suffer a refraction considerably greater than the light tending to the other end. And so the true cause of the length of that image was detected to be no other, than that light consists of rays differently refrangible, which, without any respect to a difference in their incidence, were, according to their degrees of refrangibility, transmitted towards divers parts of the wall.

When I understood this, I left off my aforesaid glass works; for I saw, that the perfection of telescopes was hitherto limited, not so much for want of glasses truly figured according to the prescriptions of optic authors, (which all men have hitherto imagined,) as because that light itself is a heterogeneous mixture of differently refrangible rays. So that, were a glass so exactly figured, as to collect any one sort of rays into one point, it could not collect those also into the same point, which having the same incidence upon the same medium are apt to suffer a different refraction. Nay, I wondered, that seeing the difference of refrangibility was so great, as I found it, telescopes should arrive to that perfection they are now at. For measuring the refractions in one of my prisms, I found, that supposing the common sine of incidence upon one of its planes was 44 parts, the sine of refraction of the utmost rays on the red end of the colours, made out of the glass into the air, would be 68 parts, and the sine of refraction of the utmost rays on the other end 69 parts: so that the difference is about a 24th or 25th part of the whole refraction: and consequently, the object glass of any telescope cannot collect all the rays which come from one point of an object, so as to make them convene at its focus in less room than in a circular space, whose diameter is the 50th part of the diameter of its aperture; which is an irregularity, some hundreds of times greater than a circularly figured lens, of so small a section as the object glasses of long telescopes are, would cause by the unfitness of its figure, were light uniform.

This made me take reflections into consideration; and finding them regular, so that the angle of reflection of all sorts of rays was equal to their angle of incidence, I understood that by their mediation optic instruments might be brought to any degree of perfection imaginable, provided a reflecting substance could be found, which would polish as finely as glass, and reflect as much light as glass transmits, and the art of communicating to it a parabolic figure be also attained. But there seemed very great difficulties, and I have almost thought them insuperable, when I further considered, that every irregularity in a reflecting superficies makes the rays stray 5 or 6 times more out of their due course, than the like irregularities in a refracting one: so that a much greater curiosity would be here requisite, than in figuring glasses for refraction.

Amidst these thoughts I was forced from Cambridge by the intervening plague, and it was more than two years before I proceeded further. But then having thought on a tender way of polishing, proper for metal, whereby, as I imagined, the figure also would be corrected to the last, I began to try what might be effected in this kind, and by degrees so far perfected an instrument (in the essential parts of it like that I sent to London,) by which I could discern Jupiter's 4 concomitants, and showed them divers times to two others of my acquaintance. I could also discern the moon-like phase of Venus, but not very distinctly, nor without some niceness in disposing the instrument.

From that time I was interrupted till this last autumn, when I made the other. And as that was sensibly better than the first (especially for day objects,) so I doubt not, but they will be still brought to a much greater perfection by their endeavours, who, as you inform me, are taking care about it at London.

I have sometimes thought to make a microscope, which in like manner should have, instead of an object glass, a reflecting piece of metal. And this I hope they will also take into consideration. For those instruments seem as capable of improvement as telescopes, and perhaps more, because but one reflective piece of metal is requisite in them.

But to return from this digression, I told you, that light is not similar, or homogeneal, but consists of difform rays, some of which are more refrangible than others: so that of those, which are alike incident on the same medium, some shall be more refracted than others, and that not by any virtue of the glass, or other external cause, but from a predisposition, which every particular ray has to suffer a particular degree of refraction.

I shall now proceed to acquaint you with another more notable difformity in its rays, wherein the origin of colours is unfolded: concerning which I shall lay down the doctrine first, and then, for its examination, give you an instance or two of the experiments, as a specimen of the rest. The doctrine you will find comprehended and illustrated in the following propositions:

1. As the rays of light differ in degrees of refrangibility, so they also differ in their disposition to exhibit this or that particular colour. Colours are not qualifications of light, derived from refractions, or reflections of natural bodies (as it is generally believed,) but original and connate properties, which in divers rays are divers. Some rays are disposed to exhibit a red colour, and no other; some a yellow, and no other; some a green, and no other; and so of the rest. Nor are there only rays proper and particular to the more eminent colours, but even to all their intermediate gradations.

2. To the same degree of refrangibility ever belongs the same colour, and to the same colour ever belongs the same degree of refrangibility. The least refrangible rays are all disposed to exhibit a red colour, and contrarily, those rays which are disposed to exhibit a red colour, are all the least refrangible: so the most refrangible rays are all disposed to exhibit a deep violet colour, and contrarily, those which are apt to exhibit such a violet colour, are all the most refrangible. And so to all the intermediate colours, in a continued series, belong intermediate degrees of

refrangibility. And this analogy betwixt colours, and refrangibility, is very precise and strict; the rays always either exactly agreeing in both, or proportionally disagreeing in both.

3. The species of colour, and degree of refrangibility proper to any particular sort of rays, is not mutable by refraction, nor by reflection from natural bodies, nor by any other cause, that I could yet observe. When any one sort of rays has been well parted from those of other kinds, it has afterwards obstinately retained its colour, notwithstanding my utmost endeavours to change it. I have refracted it with prisms, and reflected it with bodies, which in day-light were of other colours; I have intercepted it with the coloured film of air interceding two compressed plates of glass; transmitted it through coloured mediums, and through mediums irradiated with other sorts of rays, and diversely terminated it; and yet could never produce any new colour out of it. It would, by contracting or dilating, become more brisk, or faint, and by the loss of many rays, in some cases very obscure and dark; but I could never see it change in specie.

4. Yet seeming transmutations of colours may be made, where there is any mixture of divers sorts of rays. For in such mixtures, the component colours appear not, but, by their mutual allaying each other, constitute a middling colour. And therefore, if by refraction, or any other of the aforesaid causes, the difform rays, latent in such a mixture, be separated, there shall emerge colours different from the colour of the composition. Which colours are not new generated, but only made apparent by being parted; for if they be again entirely mixed and blended together, they will again compose that colour, which they did before separation. And for the same reason, transmutations made by the convening of divers colours are not real; for when the difform rays are again severed, they will exhibit the very same colours, which they did before they entered the composition; as you see, blue and yellow powders, when finely mixed, appear to the naked eye green, and yet the colours of the component corpuscles are not thereby really transmuted, but only blended. For, when viewed with a good microscope, they still appear blue and yellow interspersedly.

5. There are therefore two sorts of colours. The one original and simple, the other compounded of these. The original or primary colours are, red, yellow, green, blue, and a violet-purple, together with orange, indigo, and an indefinite variety of intermediate gradations.

6. The same colours in specie with these primary ones may be also produced by composition: for a mixture of yellow and blue makes green; of red and yellow makes orange; of orange and yellowish green makes yellow. And in general, if any two colours be mixed, which in the series

of those, generated by the prism, are not too far distant one from another, they by their mutual alloy compound that colour, which in the
said series appears in the midway between them. But those which are
situated at too great a distance, do not so. Orange and indigo produce
not the intermediate green, nor scarlet and green the intermediate yellow.

7. But the most surprising and wonderful composition was that of
whiteness. There is no one sort of rays which alone can exhibit this. It
is ever compounded, and to its composition are requisite all the aforesaid
primary colours, mixed in a due proportion. I have often with admiration beheld, that all the colours of the prism being made to converge,
and thereby to be again mixed as they were in the light before it was
incident upon the prism, reproduced light, entirely and perfectly white,
and not at all sensibly differing from a direct light of the sun, unless
when the glasses, I used, were not sufficiently clear; for then they would
a little incline it to their colour.

8. Hence therefore it comes to pass, that whiteness is the usual colour
of light; for, light is a confused aggregate of rays indued with all sorts of
colours, as they are promiscuously darted from the various parts of luminous bodies. And of such a confused aggregate, as I said, is generated
whiteness, if there be a due proportion of the ingredients; but if any one
predominate, the light must incline to that colour; as it happens in the
blue flame of brimstone; the yellow flame of a candle; and the various
colours of the fixed stars.

9. These things considered, the manner how colours are produced by
the prism, is evident. For, of the rays constituting the incident light,
since those which differ in colour, proportionally differ in refrangibility,
they by their unequal refractions must be severed and dispersed into an
oblong form in an orderly succession, from the least refracted scarlet, to
the most refracted violet. And for the same reason it is that objects, when
looked upon through a prism, appear coloured. For the difform rays, by
their unequal refractions, are made to diverge towards several parts of
the retina, and there express the images of things coloured, as in the
former case they did the sun's image upon a wall. And by this inequality
of refractions they become not only coloured, but also very confused and
indistinct.

10. Why the colours of the rainbow appear in falling drops of rain, is
also from hence evident. For, those drops which refract the rays disposed
to appear purple, in greatest quantity to the spectator's eye, refract the
rays of other sorts so much less, as to make them pass beside it; and such
are the drops on the inside of the primary bow, and on the outside of
the secondary or exterior one. So those drops, which refract in greatest
plenty the rays apt to appear red, towards the spectator's eye, refract

those of other sorts so much more, as to make them pass beside it; and such are the drops on the exterior part of the primary, and interior part of the secondary bow.

11. The odd phænomena of an infusion of lignum nephriticum, leaf gold, fragments of coloured glass, and some other transparently coloured bodies, appearing in one position of one colour, and of another in another, are on these grounds no longer riddles. For, those are substances apt to reflect one sort of light, and transmit another; as may be seen in a dark room, by illuminating them with similar or uncompounded light. For, then they appear of that colour only, with which they are illuminated, but yet in one position more vivid and luminous than in another, accordingly as they are disposed more or less to reflect or transmit the incident colour.

12. From hence also is manifest the reason of an unexpected experiment, which Mr. Hook, somewhere in his micrography, relates to have made with two wedge-like transparent vessels, filled the one with red, the other with a blue liquor: namely, that though they were severally transparent enough, yet both together became opaque; for, if one transmitted only red, and the other only blue, no rays could pass through both.

13. I might add more instances of this nature; but I shall conclude with this general one, that the colours of all natural bodies have no other origin than this, that they are variously qualified to reflect one sort of light in greater plenty than another. And this I have experimented in a dark room, by illuminating those bodies with uncompounded light of divers colours. For, by that means, any body may be made to appear of any colour. They have there no appropriate colour, but ever appear of the colour of the light cast upon them, but yet with this difference, that they are most brisk and vivid in the light of their own day-light colour. Minium appears there of any colour indifferently, with which it is illustrated, but yet most luminous in red; and so bise appears indifferently of any colour with which it is illustrated, but yet most luminous in blue. And therefore minium reflects rays of any colour, but most copiously, those indued with red; and consequently when illustrated with daylight, that is, with all sorts of rays promiscuously blended, those qualified with red shall abound most in the reflected light, and by their prevalence cause it to appear of that colour. And for the same reason bise, reflecting blue most copiously shall appear blue by the excess of those rays in its reflected light; and the like of other bodies. And that this is the entire and adequate cause of their colours, is manifest, because they have no power to change or alter the colours of any sort of rays, incident apart, but put on all colours indifferently, with which they are enlightened.

These things being so, it can be no longer disputed, whether there be colours in the dark, nor whether they be the qualities of the objects we see; no, nor perhaps whether light be a body. For since colours are the qualities of light, having its rays for their entire and immediate subject, how can we think those rays qualities also, unless one quality may be the subject of and sustain another; which in effect is to call it substance. We should not know bodies for substances, were it not for their sensible qualities, and the principal of those being now found due to something else, we have as good reason to believe that to be a substance also.

Besides, whoever thought any quality to be a heterogeneous aggregate, such as light is discovered to be? But, to determine more absolutely what light is, after what manner refracted, and by what modes or actions it produces in our minds the phantasms of colours, is not so easy. And I shall not mingle conjectures with certainties.

Reviewing what I have written, I see the discourse itself will lead to divers experiments sufficient for its examination, and therefore I shall not trouble you further, than to describe one of those which I have already insinuated.

In a darkened room make a hole in the shut of a window, whose diameter may conveniently be about a third part of an inch, to admit a convenient quantity of the sun's light; and there place a clear and colourless prism, to refract the entering light towards the further part of the room, which, as I said, will thereby be diffused into an oblong coloured image. Then place a lens of about three feet radius (suppose a broad object glass of a three foot telescope,) at the distance of about four or five feet from thence, through which all those colours may at once be transmitted, and made by its refraction to convene at a further distance of about ten or twelve feet. If at that distance you intercept this light with a sheet of white paper, you will see the colours converted into whiteness again by being mingled. But it is requisite, that the prism and lens be placed steady, and that the paper on which the colours are cast be moved to and fro; for by such motion, you will not only find at what distance the whiteness is most perfect, but also see how the colours gradually convene, and vanish into whiteness, and afterwards having crossed one another in that place where they compound whiteness, are again dissipated and severed, and in an inverted order retain the same colours which they had before they entered the composition. You may also see, that if any of the colours at the lens be intercepted, the whiteness will be changed into the other colours. And therefore that the composition of whiteness be perfect, care must be taken that none of the colours fall beside the lens.

In the annexed design of this experiment (Figure 3), ABC expresses

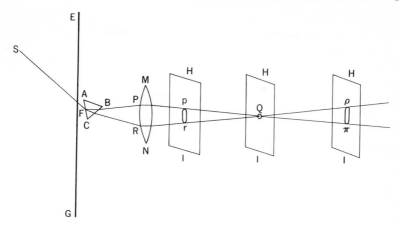

FIGURE 3

the prism set end-wise to sight, close by the hole F of the window EG. Its vertical angle ACB may conveniently be about 60 degrees: MN designs the lens. Its breadth 2½ or 3 inches. SF one of the straight lines, in which difform rays may be conceived to flow successively from the sun. FP and FR two of those rays unequally refracted, which the lens makes to converge towards Q, and after decussation to diverge again. And HI the paper, at divers distances, on which the colours are projected; which in Q constitute whiteness, but are red and yellow in R, r, and ρ, and blue and purple in P, p, and π.

If you proceed further to try the impossibility of changing any uncompounded colour, (which I have asserted in the 3d and 13th propositions) it is requisite that the room be made very dark, lest any scattering light mixing with the colour disturb and allay it, and render it compound, contrary to the design of the experiment. It is also requisite, that there be a perfecter separation of the colours than, after the manner above described, can be made by the refraction of one single prism, and how to make such further separations, will scarcely be difficult to them that consider the discovered laws of refractions. But if trial shall be made with colours not thoroughly separated, there must be allowed changes proportionable to the mixture. Thus, if compound yellow light fall upon blue bise, the bise will not appear perfectly yellow but rather green, because there are in the yellow mixture many rays indued with green, and green being less remote from the usual blue colour of bise than yellow, is the more copiously reflected by it.

In like manner, if any one of the prismatic colours, suppose red, be intercepted, on design to try the asserted impossibility of reproducing that colour out of the others which are pretermitted; it is necessary, either that the colours be very well parted before the red be intercepted, or that together with the red the neighboring colours, into which any red is secretly dispersed, (that is, the yellow, and perhaps green too) be intercepted, or else, that allowance be made for the emerging of so much red out of the yellow green, as may possibly have been diffused, and scatteringly blended in those colours. And if these things be observed, the new production of red, or any intercepted colour, will be found impossible.

This I conceive is enough for an introduction to experiments of this kind; which if any of the Royal Society shall be so curious as to prosecute, I should be very glad to be informed with what success; that if any thing seem to be defective, or to thwart this relation, I may have an opportunity of giving further direction about it, or of acknowledging my errors, if I have committed any.

Opticks

Qu. 28. Are not all Hypotheses erroneous, in which Light is supposed to consist in Pression or Motion, propagated through a fluid Medium? For in all these Hypotheses, the Phenomena of Light have been hitherto explain'd by supposing that they arise from new Modifications of the Rays; which is an erroneous Supposition.

If Light consisted only in Pression propagated without actual Motion, it would not be able to agitate and heat the Bodies which refract and reflect it. If it consisted in Motion propagated to all distances in an instant, it would require an infinite force every moment, in every shining Particle, to generate that Motion. And if it consisted in Pression or Motion, propagated either in an instant or in time, it would bend into the Shadow. For Pression or Motion cannot be propagated in a Fluid in straight Lines beyond an Obstacle which stops part of the Motion, but will bend and spread every way into the quiescent Medium which lies beyond the Obstacle. Gravity tends downwards, but the Pressure of Water arising from Gravity tends every way with equal force, and is propagated as readily, and with as much force sideways as downwards, and through crooked passages as through strait ones. The Waves on the Surface of stagnating Water, passing by the sides of a broad Obstacle which stops part of them, bend afterwards and dilate themselves gradually into the quiet Water behind the Obstacle. The Waves, Pulses or Vibrations of the Air, wherein Sounds consist, bend manifestly, though not so much as the Waves of Water. For a Bell or a Canon may be heard beyond a Hill which intercepts the sight of the sounding Body, and Sounds are propagated as readily through crooked Pipes as through straight ones. But Light is never known to follow crooked Passages nor to bend into the Shadow. For the fix'd Stars by the Interposition of any of the Planets cease to be seen. And so do the Parts of the Sun by the Interposition of the Moon, *Mercury* or *Venus*. The Rays which pass very near to the edges of any Body, are bent a little by the action of the Body, as we shew'd above; but this bending is not towards but from the Shadow, and is perform'd only in the passage of the Ray by the Body, and at a very small distance from it. So soon as the Ray is past the Body, it goes right on.

First published in the second English edition, London, 1717.

To explain the unusual Refraction of Island Crystal by Pression or Motion propagated, has not hitherto been attempted (to my knowledge) except by *Huygens*, who for that end supposed two several vibrating Mediums within that Crystal. But when he tried the Refractions in two successive pieces of that Crystal, and found them such as is mention'd above: He confessed himself at a loss for explaining them. For Pressions or Motions, propagated from a shining Body through an uniform Medium, must be on all sides alike; whereas by those Experiments it appears, that the Rays of Light have different Properties in their different Sides. He suspected that the Pulses of *Æther* in passing through the first Crystal might receive certain new Modifications, which might determine them to be propagated in this or that Medium within the second Crystal, according to the Position of that Crystal. But what Modifications those might be he could not say, nor think of any thing satisfactory in that Point. And if he had known that the unusual Refraction depends not on new Modifications, but on the original and unchangeable Dispositions of the Rays, he would have found it as difficult to explain how those Dispositions which he supposed to be impress'd on the Rays by the first Crystal, could be in them before their Incidence on that Crystal; and in general, how all Rays emitted by shining Bodies, can have those Dispositions in them from the beginning. To me, at least, this seems inexplicable, if Light be nothing else than Pression or Motion propagated through *Æther*.

And it is as difficult to explain by these Hypotheses, how Rays can be alternately in Fits of easy Reflexion and easy Transmission; unless perhaps one might suppose that there are in all Space two Æthereal vibrating Mediums, and that the Vibrations of one of them constitute Light, and the Vibrations of the other are swifter, and as often as they overtake the Vibrations of the first, put them into those Fits. But how two *Æthers* can be diffused through all Space, one of which acts upon the other, and by consequence is re-acted upon, without retarding, shattering, dispersing and confounding one anothers Motions, is inconceivable. And against filling the Heavens with fluid Mediums, unless they be exceeding rare, a great Objection arises from the regular and very lasting Motions of the Planets and Comets in all manner of Courses through the Heavens. For thence it is manifest, that the Heavens are void of all sensible Resistance, and by consequence of all sensible Matter.

For the resisting Power of fluid Mediums arises partly from the Attrition of the Parts of the Medium, and partly from the *Vis inertiæ* of the Matter. That part of the Resistance of a spherical Body which arises from the Attrition of the Parts of the Medium is very nearly as the

Diameter, or, at the most, as the *Factum* of the Diameter, and the Velocity of the spherical Body together. And that part of the Resistance which arises from the *Vis inertiæ* of the Matter, is as the Square of that *Factum*. And by this difference the two sorts of Resistance may be distinguish'd from one another in any Medium; and these being distinguish'd, it will be found that almost all the Resistance of Bodies of a competent Magnitude moving in Air, Water; Quick-silver, and such like Fluids with a competent Velocity, arises from the *Vis inertiæ* of the Parts of the Fluid.

Now that part of the resisting Power of any Medium which arises from the Tenacity, Friction or Attrition of the Parts of the Medium, may be diminish'd by dividing the Matter into smaller Parts, and making the Parts more smooth and slippery: But that part of the Resistance which arises from the *Vis inertiæ*, is proportional to the Density of the Matter, and cannot be diminish'd by dividing the Matter into smaller Parts, nor by any other means than by decreasing the Density of the Medium. And for these Reasons the Density of fluid Mediums is very nearly proportional to their Resistance. Liquors which differ not much in Density, as Water, Spirit of Wine, Spirit of Turpentine, hot Oil, differ not much in Resistance. Water is thirteen or fourteen times lighter than Quick-silver, and by consequence thirteen or fourteen times rarer, and its Resistance is less than that of Quick-silver in the same Proportion, or thereabouts, as I have found by Experiments made with Pendulums. The open Air in which we breathe is eight or nine hundred times lighter than Water, and by consequence eight or nine hundred times rarer, and accordingly its Resistance is less than that of Water in the same Proportion, or thereabouts; as I have also found by Experiments made with Pendulums. And in thinner Air the Resistance is still less, and at length, by rarifying the Air, becomes insensible. For small Feathers falling in the open Air meet with great Resistance, but in a tall Glass well emptied of Air, they fall as fast as Lead or Gold, as I have seen tried several times. Whence the Resistance seems still to decrease in proportion to the Density of the Fluid. For I do not find by any Experiments, that Bodies moving in Quick-silver, Water or Air, meet with any other sensible Resistance than what arises from the Density and Tenacity of those sensible Fluids, as they would do if the Pores of those Fluids, and all other Spaces, were filled with a dense and subtile Fluid. Now if the Resistance in a Vessel well emptied of Air, was but an hundred times less than in the open Air, it would be about a million of times less than in Quick-silver. But it seems to be much less in such a Vessel, and still much less in the Heavens, at the height of three or four hundred Miles from the Earth, or above. For Mr. *Boyle* has shew'd that Air may be rarefied above ten thousand times in Vessels of Glass; and the Heavens are much emptier of Air than any *Vacuum* we can make below. For since the Air is compress'd by the weight of the incumbent Atmosphere, and the Density of Air is proportional to the Force compressing it, it follows by Computation, that at the height of about seven *English* Miles from the Earth, the Air is four times rarer than at the Surface of the Earth; and at the height of 14 Miles, it is sixteen times rarer than that at the Surface of the Earth; and at the height of 21, 28, or 35 Miles, it is respectively 64, 256, or 1024 times rarer, or thereabouts; and at the height of 70, 140, 210 Miles, it is about 1000000, 1000000000000 or 1000000000000000000 times rarer; and so on.

Heat promotes Fluidity very much, by diminishing the Tenacity of Bodies. It makes many Bodies fluid which are not fluid in cold, and increases the Fluidity of tenacious Liquids, as of Oil, Balsam and Honey, and thereby decreases their Resistance. But it decreases not the Resistance of Water considerably, as it would do if any considerable part of the Resistance of Water arose from the Attrition or Tenacity of its Parts. And therefore the Resistance of Water arises principally and almost entirely from the *Vis inertiæ* of its Matter; and by consequence, if the Heavens were as dense as Water, they would not have much less Resistance than Water; if as dense as Quick-silver, they would not have much less Resistance than Quick-silver; if absolutely dense, or full of Matter without any *Vacuum*, let the Matter be never so subtile and fluid, they would have a greater Resistance than Quick-silver. A solid Globe in such a Medium would lose above half its Motion in moving three times the length of its Diameter, and a Globe not solid (such as are the Planets) would be retarded sooner. And therefore to make way for the regular and lasting Motions of the Planets and Comets, it's necessary to empty the Heavens of all Matter, except perhaps some very thin Vapours, Steams or Effluvia, from the Atmospheres of the Earth, Planets and Comets, and from such an exceedingly rare Æthereal Medium as we described above. A dense Fluid can be of no use for explaining the Phænomena of Nature, the Motions of the Planets and Comets being better explain'd without it. It serves only to disturb and retard the Motions of those great Bodies, and make the Frame of Nature languish. And in the Pores of Bodies, it serves only to stop the vibrating Motion of their Parts, wherein their Heat and Activity consists. And as it is of no use, and hinders the Operations of Nature, and makes her languish, so there is no evidence for its Existence, and therefore it ought to be rejected. And if it be rejected, the Hypotheses that Light consists in Pression or Motion propagated through such a Medium, are rejected with it.

And for rejecting such a Medium, we have the Authority of those the oldest and most celebrated Philosophers of *Greece* and *Phœnicia*, who made a *Vacuum* and Atoms, and the Gravity of Atoms, the first Principles of their Philosophy; tacitly attributing Gravity to some other Cause than dense Matter. Later Philosophers banish the Consideration of such a Cause out of Natural Philosophy, feigning Hypotheses for explaining all things mechanically, and referring other Causes to Metaphysicks: Whereas the main Business of Natural Philosophy is to argue from Phænomena without feigning Hypotheses, and to deduce Causes from Effects, till we come to the very first Cause, which certainly is not mechanical; and not only to unfold the Mechanism of the World, but chiefly to resolve these and such like Questions. What is there in places almost empty of Matter, and whence is it that the Sun and Planets gravitate towards one another, without dense Matter between them? Whence is it that Nature doth nothing in vain; and whence arises all that Order and Beauty which we see in the World? To what end are Comets, and whence is it that Planets move all one and the same way in Orbs concentrick, while Comets move all manner of ways in Orbs very excentrick, and what hinders the fix'd Stars from falling upon one another? How came the Bodies of Animals to be contrived with so much Art, and for what ends were their several Parts? Was the Eye contrived without Skill in Opticks, and the Ear without Knowledge of Sounds? How do the Motions of the Body follow from the Will, and whence is the Instinct in Animals? Is not the Sensory of Animals that place to which the sensitive Substance is present, and into which the sensible Species of Things are carried through the Nerves and Brain, that there they may be perceived by their immediate presence to that Substance? And these things being rightly dispatch'd, does it not appear from Phænomena that there is a Being incorporeal, living, intelligent, omnipresent, who in infinite Space, as it were in his Sensory, sees the things themselves intimately, and thoroughly perceives them, and comprehends them wholly by their immediate presence to himself: Of which things the Images only carried through the Organs of Sense into our little Sensoriums, are there seen and beheld by that which in us perceives and thinks. And tho' every true Step made in this Philosophy brings us not immediately to the Knowledge of the first Cause, yet it brings us nearer to it, and on that account is to be highly valued.

2

ISAAC NEWTON

If Newton is well known for his contribution to optics, he is better known for the discovery of the calculus, and for his work in mechanics culminating in the law of universal gravitation. By completing a celestial mechanics, which explained how the planets are held in elliptical orbits around the sun, he filled in the major gap in the theoretical structure of heliocentric astronomy. The publication of his *Principia* (in English, *Mathematical Principles of Natural Philosophy*) instantly made him the leader of English science; and if, on the continent, some objected to his conclusions, none could ignore them. Newton was the first scientist in Europe to be knighted—a landmark, not in the history of science, but in the education of rulers to the recognition that military prowess is not the sole criterion of human achievement. When Newton died in 1727, he was more celebrated by his contemporaries than any scientist before him. That fact testifies, not only to Newton, but also to the role that natural science was beginning to play in European civilization.

Two major problems were involved in the concept of universal gravitation. One was technical and mathematical, relevant to the science of rational mechanics. The law of universal gravitation rested on Newton's demonstration of a precise correlation between the observed phenomena in the heavens and the laws of terrestrial mechanics. It is impossible adequately to present this aspect—the most central one of the *Principia*—in a book of selections. It is sufficient to say that Newton's *Principia* first stated the three laws of motion in the form still used, and that it embodied a gigantic step forward in the science of mechanics. The second law solved the basic problem of dynamics that had bedevilled the entire century before him: it defined force by the acceleration that it produces in a given mass.

Beyond the mathematical issue lay a metaphysical one. What is the nature of the action called gravitation? The natural philosophers of the Renaissance had believed in all sorts of influences of a psychic nature exercised by one body on another—what they often referred to as sympathies and antipathies. In reaction against such notions, the mechanical philosophers of the 17th century insisted that bodies can act on one another by physical contact alone. Nature consists of particles of matter in motion, and all of the phenomena of nature arise from their interactions by impact. Thus Descartes conceived that the planets are borne along in their orbits by a huge vortex of subtle matter, and that bodies appear heavy and fall to the earth because of the pressure of subtle invisible matter upon them. Newton's concept of gravitational attraction appeared to deny the basic premise of the mechanical philosophy of nature. Indeed, Newton believed that the phenomenon of gravity is similar to a whole range of other phenomena, and in the 31st Query in the *Opticks*, he discusses the metaphysical issue in regard to them all.

12

Opticks

Qu. 31. Have not the small Particles of Bodies certain Powers, Virtues or Forces, by which they act at a distance, not only upon the Rays of Light for reflecting, refracting and inflecting them, but also upon one another for producing a great part of the Phænomena of Nature? For it's well known that Bodies act one upon another by the Attractions of Gravity, Magnetism and Electricity; and these Instances shew the Tenor and Course of Nature, and make it not improbable but that there may be more attractive Powers than these. For Nature is very consonant and conformable to herself. How these Attractions may be perform'd, I do not here consider. What I call Attraction may be perform'd by impulse, or by some other means unknown to me. I use that Word here to signify only in general any Force by which Bodies tend towards one another, whatsoever be the Cause. For we must learn from the Phænomena of Nature what Bodies attract one another, and what are the Laws and Properties of the Attraction, before we enquire the Cause by which the Attraction is perform'd, The Attractions of Gravity, Magnetism and Electricity, reach to very sensible distances, and so have been observed by vulgar Eyes, and there may be others which reach to so small distances as hitherto escape Observation; and perhaps electrical Attraction may reach to such small distances, even without being excited by Friction.

For when Salt of Tartar runs *per deliquium,* is not this done by an Attraction between the Particles of the Salt of Tartar, and the Particles of the Water which float in the Air in the form of Vapours? And why does not common Salt, or Salt-petre, or Vitriol, run *per deliquium,* but for want of such an Attraction? Or why does not Salt of Tartar draw more Water out of the Air than in a certain Proportion to its quantity, but for want of an attractive Force after it is satiated with Water? And whence is it but from this attractive Power that Water which alone distils with a gentle lukewarm Heat, will not distil from Salt of Tartar without a great Heat? And is it not from the like attractive Power

---

First published in the second English edition, London, 1717.

between the Particles of Oil of Vitriol and the Particles of Water, that Oil of Vitriol draws to it a good quantity of Water out of the Air, and after it is satiated draws no more, and in Distillation lets go the Water very difficultly? And when Water and Oil of Vitriol poured successively into the same Vessel grow very hot in the mixing, does not this Heat argue a great Motion in the parts of the Liquors? And does not this Motion argue that the Parts of the two Liquors in mixing coalesce with Violence, and by consequence rush towards one another with an accelerated Motion? And when *Aqua fortis* or Spirit of Vitriol poured upon Filings of Iron, dissolves the Filings with a great Heat and Ebullition, is not this Heat and Ebullition effected by a violent Motion of the Parts, and does not that Motion argue that the acid Parts of the Liquor rush towards the Parts of the Metal with violence, and run forcibly into its Pores till they get between its outmost Particles and the main Mass of the Metal, and surrounding those Particles loosen them from the main Mass, and set them at liberty to float off into the Water? And when the acid Particles which alone would distil with an easy Heat, will not separate from the Particles of the Metal without a very violent Heat, does not this confirm the Attraction between them?

When Spirit of Vitriol poured upon common Salt or Salt-petre makes an Ebullition with the Salt and unites with it, and in Distillation the Spirit of the common Salt or Salt-petre comes over much easier than it would do before, and the acid part of the Spirit of Vitriol stays behind; does not this argue that the fix'd Alcaly of the Salt attracts the acid Spirit of the Vitriol more strongly than its own Spirit, and not being able to hold them both, lets go its own? And when Oil of Vitriol is drawn off from its weight of Nitre, and from both the Ingredients a compound Spirit of Nitre is distilled, and two parts of this Spirit are poured on one part of Oil of Cloves or Caraway Seeds, or of any ponderous Oil of vegetable or animal Substances, or Oil of Turpentine thicken'd with a little Balsam of Sulphur, and the Liquors grow so very hot in mixing, as presently to send up a burning Flame: Does not this very great and sudden Heat argue that the two Liquors mix with violence, and that their Parts in mixing run towards one another with an accelerated Motion, and clash with the greatest Force? And is it not for the same reason that well rectified Spirit of Wine poured on the same compound Spirit flashes; and that the *Pulvis fulminans*, composed of Sulphur, Nitre, and Salt of Tartar, goes off with a more sudden and violent Explosion than Gun-powder, the acid Spirits of the Sulphur and Nitre rushing towards one another, and towards the Salt of Tartar, with so great a violence, as by the shock to turn the whole at once into Vapour and Flame? Where the Dissolution is slow, it makes a slow Ebullition and a gentle Heat; and where it is quicker, it makes a greater Ebullition with more Heat; and where it is done at once, the Ebullition is contracted into a sudden Blast or violent Explosion, with a Heat equal to that of Fire and Flame. So when a Drachm of the above mention'd compound Spirit of Nitre was poured upon half a Drachm of Oil of Caraway Seeds *in vacuo*; the Mixture immediately made a flash like Gun-powder, and burst the exhausted Receiver, which was a Glass six Inches wide, and eight Inches deep. And even the gross Body of Sulphur powder'd, and with an equal weight of Iron Filings, and a little Water made into Paste, acts upon the Iron, and in five or six Hours grows too hot to be touch'd, and emits a Flame. And by these Experiments compared with the great quantity of Sulphur with which the Earth abounds, and the warmth of the interior Parts of the Earth, and hot Springs, and burning Mountains, and with Damps, mineral Coruscations, Earthquakes, hot suffocating Exhalations, Hurricanes and Spouts; we may learn that sulphureous Steams abound in the Bowels of the Earth and ferment with Minerals, and sometimes take Fire with a sudden Coruscation and Explosion; and if pent up in subterraneous Caverns, burst the Caverns with a great shaking of the Earth, as in springing of a Mine. And then the Vapour generated by the Explosion, expiring through the Pores of the Earth, feels hot and suffocates, and makes Tempests and Hurricanes, and sometimes causes the Land to slide, or the Sea to boil, and carries up the Water thereof in Drops, which by their weight fall down again in Spouts. Also some sulphureous Steams, at all times when the Earth is dry, ascending into the Air, ferment there with nitrous Acids, and sometimes taking fire cause Lightening and Thunder, and fiery Meteors. For the Air abounds with acid Vapours fit to promote Fermentations, as appears by the rusting of Iron and Copper in it, the kindling of Fire by blowing, and the beating of the Heart by means of Respiration. Now the above mention'd Motions are so great and violent as to shew that in Fermentations, the Particles of Bodies which almost rest, are put into new Motions by a very potent Principle, which acts upon them only when they approach one another, and causes them to meet and clash with great violence, and grow hot with the Motion, and dash one another into pieces, and vanish into Air, and Vapour, and Flame. . . .

When *Aqua fortis* dissolves Silver and not Gold, and *Aqua regia* dissolves Gold and not Silver, may it not be said that *Aqua fortis* is subtile enough to penetrate Gold as well as Silver, but wants the attractive Force to give it Entrance; and that *Aqua regia* is subtile enough to penetrate Silver as well as Gold, but wants the attractive Force to give it Entrance? For *Aqua regia* is nothing else than *Aqua fortis* mix'd with some Spirit of Salt, or with Sal-armoniac; and even common Salt dis-

solved in *Aqua fortis*, enables the *Menstruum* to dissolve Gold, though
the Salt be a gross Body. When therefore Spirit of Salt precipitates Silver
out of *Aqua fortis*, is it not done by attracting and mixing with the
Aqua fortis, and not attracting, or perhaps repelling Silver? And when
Water precipitates Antimony out of the Sublimate of Antimony and Sal-
armoniac, or out of Butter of Antimony, is it not done by its dissolving,
mixing with, and weakening the Sal-armoniac or Spirit of Salt, and its
not attracting, or perhaps repelling the Antimony? And is it not for
want of an attractive Virtue between the Parts of Water and Oil, of
Quick-silver and Antimony, of Lead and Iron, that these Substances do
not mix; and by a weak Attraction, that Quick-silver and Copper mix
difficultly; and from a strong one, that Quick-silver and Tin, Antimony
and Iron, Water and Salts, mix readily? And in general, is it not from
the same Principle that Heat congregates homogeneal Bodies, and
separates heterogeneal ones?

When Arsnick with Soap gives a Regulus, and with Mercury sublimate a volatile fusible Salt, like Butter of Antimony, doth not this
shew that Arsnick, which is a Substance totally volatile, is compounded
of fix'd and volatile Parts, strongly cohering by a mutual Attraction, so
that the volatile will not ascend without carrying up the fixed? And so,
when an equal weight of Spirit of Wine and Oil of Vitriol are digested
together, and in Distillation yield two fragrant and volatile Spirits which
will not mix with one another, and a fix'd black Earth remains behind;
doth not this shew that Oil of Vitriol is composed of volatile and fix'd
Parts strongly united by Attraction, so as to ascend together in form of
a volatile, acid, fluid Salt, until the Spirit of Wine attracts and separates
the volatile Parts from the fixed? And therefore, since Oil of Sulphur
per campanam is of the same Nature with Oil of Vitriol, may it not be
inferred, that Sulphur is also a mixture of volatile and fix'd Parts so
strongly cohering by Attraction, as to ascend together in Sublimation.
By dissolving Flowers of Sulphur in Oil of Turpentine, and distilling the
Solution, it is found that Sulphur is composed of an inflamable thick
Oil or fat Bitumen, an acid Salt, a very fix'd Earth, and a little Metal.
The three first were found not much unequal to one another, the fourth
in so small a quantity as scarce to be worth considering. The acid Salt
dissolved in Water, is the same with Oil of Sulphur *per campanam*, and
abounding much in the Bowels of the Earth, and particularly in
Markasites, unites itself to the other Ingredients of the Markasite, which
are, Bitumen, Iron, Copper and Earth, and with them compounds
Alume, Vitriol and Sulphur. With the Earth alone it compounds Alume;
with the Metal alone, or Metal and Earth together, it compounds Vitriol;
and with the Bitumen and Earth it compounds Sulphur. Whence it

comes to pass that Markasites abound with those three Minerals. And is it not from the mutual Attraction of the Ingredients that they stick together for compounding these Minerals, and that the Bitumen carries up the other Ingredients of the Sulphur, which without it would not sublime? And the same Question may be put concerning all, or almost all the gross Bodies in Nature. For all the Parts of Animals and Vegetables are composed of Substances volatile and fix'd, fluid and solid, as appears by their Analysis: and so are Salts and Minerals, so far as Chymists have been hitherto able to examine their Composition.

When Mercury sublimate is resublimed with fresh Mercury, and becomes *Mercurius dulcis,* which is a white tastless Earth scarce dissolvable in Water, and *Mercurius dulcis* resublimed with Spirit of Salt returns into Mercury sublimate; and when Metals corroded with a little acid turn into Rust, which is an Earth tastless and indissolvable in Water, and this Earth imbibed with more Acid becomes a metallick Salt; and when some Stones, as Spar of Lead, dissolved in proper *Menstruums* become Salts; do not these things shew that Salts are dry Earth and watry Acid united by Attraction, and that the Earth will not become a Salt without so much Acid as makes it dissolvable in Water? Do not the sharp and pungent Tastes of Acids arise from the strong Attraction whereby the acid Particles rush upon and agitate the Particles of the Tongue? And when Metals are dissolved in acid *Menstruums,* and the Acids in conjunction with the Metal act after a different manner, so that the Compound has a different taste much milder than before, and sometimes a sweet one; is it not because the Acids adhere to the metallick Particles, and thereby lose much of their Activity? And if the Acid be in too small a Proportion to make the Compound dissolvable in Water, will it not by adhering strongly to the Metal become unctive and lose its taste, and the Compound be a tastless Earth? For such things as are not dissolvable by the Moisture of the Tongue, act not upon the Taste.

As Gravity makes the Sea flow round the denser and weightier Parts of the Globe of the Earth, so the Attraction may make the watry Acid flow round the denser and compacter Particles of Earth for composing the Particles of Salt. For otherwise the Acid would not do the office of a Medium between the Earth and common Water, for making Salts dissolvable in the Water; nor would Salt of Tartar readily draw off the Acid from dissolved Metals, nor Metals the Acid from Mercury. Now as in the great Globe of the Earth and Sea, the densest Bodies by their Gravity sink down in Water, and always endeavour to go towards the Center of the Globe; so in Particles of Salt, the densest Matter may always endeavour to approach the Center of the Particle: So that a Particle of Salt may be compared to a Chaos; being dense, hard, dry, and earthy in the Center; and rare, soft, moist, and watry in the Circumference. And hence it seems to be that Salts are of a lasting nature, being scarce destroy'd, unless by drawing away their watry Parts by violence, or by letting them soak into the Pores of the central Earth by a gentle Heat in Putrefaction, until the Earth be dissolved by the Water, and separated into smaller Particles, which by reason of their smallness make the rotten Compound appear of a black Colour. Hence also it may be that the Parts of Animals and Vegetables preserve their several Forms, and assimilate their Nourishment; the soft and moist Nourishment easily changing its Texture by a gentle Heat and Motion, till it becomes like the dense, hard, dry, and durable Earth in the Center of each Particle. But when the Nourishment grows unfit to be assimilated, or the central Earth grows too feeble to assimilate it, the Motion ends in Confusion, Putrefaction and Death.

If a very small quantity of any Salt or Vitriol be dissolved in a great quantity of Water, the Particles of the Salt or Vitriol will not sink to the bottom, though they be heavier in Specie than the Water, but will evenly diffuse themselves into all the Water, so as to make it as saline at the top as the bottom. And does not this imply that the Parts of the Salt or Vitriol recede from one another, and endeavour to expand themselves, and get as far asunder as the quantity of Water in which they float, will allow? And does not this Endeavour imply that they have a repulsive Force by which they fly from one another, or at least, that they attract the Water more strongly than they do one another? For as all things ascend in Water which are less attracted than Water, by the gravitating Power of the Earth; so all the Particles of Salt which float in Water, and are less attracted than Water by any one Particle of Salt, must recede from that Particle, and give way to the more attracted Water.

When any saline Liquor is evaporated to a Cuticle and let cool, the Salt concretes in regular Figures; which argues, that the Particles of the Salt before they concreted, floated in the Liquor at equal distances in rank and file, and by consequence that they acted upon one another by some Power which at equal distances is equal, at unequal distances unequal. For by such a Power they will range themselves uniformly, and without it they will float irregularly, and come together as irregularly. And since the Particles of Island Crystal act all the same way upon the Rays of Light for causing the unusual Refraction, may it not be supposed that in the Formation of this Crystal, the Particles not only ranged themselves in rank and file for concreting in regular Figures, but also by some kind of polar Virtue turned their homogeneal Sides the same way.

The Parts of all homogeneal hard Bodies which fully touch one another, stick together very strongly. And for explaining how this may be, some have invented hooked Atoms, which is begging the Question; and others tell us that Bodies are glued together by rest, that is, by an occult Quality, or rather by nothing; and others, that they stick together by conspiring Motions, that is, by relative rest amongst themselves. I had rather infer from their Cohesion, that their Particles attract one another by some Force, which in immediate Contact is exceeding strong, at small distances performs the chymical Operations above mention'd, and reaches not far from the Particles with any sensible Effect.

All Bodies seem to be composed of hard Particles: For otherwise Fluids would not congeal; as Water, Oils, Vinegar, and Spirit or Oil of Vitriol do by freezing; Mercury by Fumes of Lead; Spirit of Nitre and Mercury, by dissolving the Mercury and evaporating the Flegm; Spirit of Wine and Spirit of Urine, by deflegming and mixing them; and Spirit of Urine and Spirit of Salt, by subliming them together to make Sal-armoniac. Even the Rays of Light seem to be hard Bodies; for otherwise they would not retain different Properties in their different Sides. And therefore Hardness may be reckon'd the Property of all uncompounded Matter. At least, this seems to be as evident as the universal Impenetrability of Matter. For all Bodies, so far as Experience reaches, are either hard, or may be harden'd; and we have no other Evidence of universal Impenetrability, besides a large Experience without an experimental Exception. Now if compound Bodies are so very hard as we find some of them to be, and yet are very porous, and consist of Parts which are only laid together; the simple Particles which are void of Pores, and were never yet divided, must be much harder. For such hard Particles being heaped up together, can scarce touch one another in more than a few Points, and therefore must be separable by much less Force than is requisite to break a solid Particle, whose Parts touch in all the Space between them, without any Pores or Interstices to weaken their Cohesion. And how such very hard Particles which are only laid together and touch only in a few Points, can stick together, and that so firmly as they do, without the assistance of something which causes them to be attracted or press'd towards one another, is very difficult to conceive.

The same thing I infer also from the cohering of two polish'd Marbles *in vacuo*, and from the standing of Quick-silver in the Barometer at the height of 50, 60 or 70 Inches, or above, when ever it is well purged of Air and carefully poured in, so that its Parts be every where contiguous both to one another and to the Glass. The Atmosphere by its weight presses the Quick-silver into the Glass, to the height of 29 or 30 Inches. And some other Agent raises it higher, not by pressing it into the Glass, but by making its Parts stick to the Glass, and to one another. For upon any discontinuation of Parts, made either by Bubbles or by shaking the Glass, the whole Mercury falls down to the height of 29 or 30 Inches.

And of the same kind with these Experiments are those that follow. If two plane polish'd Plates of Glass (suppose two pieces of a polish'd Looking-glass) be laid together, so that their sides be parallel and at a very small distance from one another, and then their lower edges be dipped into Water, the Water will rise up between them. And the less the distance of the Glasses is, the greater will be the height to which the Water will rise. If the distance be about the hundredth part of an Inch, the Water will rise to the height of about an Inch; and if the distance be greater or less in any Proportion, the height will be reciprocally proportional to the distance very nearly. For the attractive Force of the Glasses is the same, whether the distance between them be greater or less; and the weight of the Water drawn up is the same, if the height of it be reciprocally proportional to the height of the Glasses. And in like manner, Water ascends between two Marbles polish'd plane, when their polished sides are parallel, and at a very little distance from one another. And if slender Pipes of Glass be dipped at one end into stagnating Water, the Water will rise up within the Pipe, and the height to which it rises will be reciprocally proportional to the Diameter of the Cavity of the Pipe, and will equal the height to which it rises between two Planes of Glass, if the Semi-diameter of the Cavity of the Pipe be equal to the distance between the Planes, or thereabouts. And these Experiments succeed after the same manner *in vacuo* as in the open Air (as hath been tried before the Royal Society) and therefore are not influenced by the Weight or Pressure of the Atmosphere.

And if a large Pipe of Glass be filled with sifted Ashes well pressed together in the Glass, and one end of the Pipe be dipped into stagnating Water, the Water will rise up slowly in the Ashes, so as in the space of a Week or Fort-night to reach up within the Glass, to the height of 30 or 40 Inches above the stagnating Water. And the Water rises up to this height by the Action only of those Particles of the Ashes which are upon the Surface of the elevated Water; the Particles which are within the Water, attracting or repelling it as much downwards as upwards. And therefore the Action of the Particles is very strong. But the Particles of the Ashes being not so dense and close together as those of Glass, their Action is not so strong as that of Glass, which keeps Quick-silver suspended to the height of 60 or 70 Inches, and therefore acts with a Force which would keep Water suspended to the height of above 60 Feet.

By the same Principle, a Sponge sucks in Water, and the Glands in the Bodies of Animals, according to their several Natures and Dispositions, suck in various Juices from the Blood.

If two plane polish'd Plates of Glass three or four Inches broad, and twenty or twenty five long, be laid, one of them parallel to the Horizon, the other upon the first, so as at one of their ends to touch one another, and contain an Angle of about 10 or 15 Minutes, and the same be first moisten'd on their inward sides with a clean Cloth dipp'd into Oil of Oranges or Spirit of Turpentine, and a Drop or two of the Oil or Spirit be let fall upon the lower Glass at the other end; so soon as the upper Glass is laid down upon the lower so as to touch it at one end as above, and to touch the Drop at the other end, making with the lower Glass an Angle of about 10 or 15 Minutes; the Drop will begin to move towards the Concourse of the Glasses, and will continue to move with an accelerated Motion, till it arrives at that Concourse of the Glasses. For the two Glasses attract the Drop, and make it run that way towards which the Attractions incline. And if when the Drop is in motion you lift up that end of the Glasses where they meet, and towards which the Drop moves, the Drop will ascend between the Glasses, and therefore is attracted. And as you lift up the Glasses more and more, the Drop will ascend slower and slower, and at length rest, being then carried downward by its Weight, as much as upwards by the Attraction. And by this means you may know the Force by which the Drop is attracted at all distances from the Concourse of the Glasses.

Now by some Experiments of this kind, (made by Mr. *Hawksby*) it has been found that the Attraction is almost reciprocally in a duplicate Proportion of the distance of the middle of the Drop from the Concourse of the Glasses, *viz.* reciprocally in a simple Proportion, by reason of the spreading of the Drop, and its touching each Glass in a larger Surface; and again reciprocally in a simple Proportion, by reason of the Attractions growing stronger within the same quantity of attracting Surface. The Attraction therefore within the same quantity of attracting Surface, is reciprocally as the distance between the Glasses. And therefore where the distance is exceeding small, the Attraction must be exceeding great. By the Table in the second Part of the second Book, wherein the thicknesses of colour'd Plates of Water between two Glasses are set down, the thickness of the Plate where it appears very black, is three eighths of the ten hundred thousandth part of an Inch. And where the Oil of Oranges between the Glasses is of this thickness, the Attraction collected by the foregoing Rule, seems to be so strong, as within a Circle of an Inch in diameter, to suffice to hold up a Weight equal to that of a Cylinder of Water of an Inch in diameter, and two or three Furlongs in length. And where it is of a less thickness the Attraction may be proportionally greater, and continue to increase, until the thickness do not exceed that of a single Particle of the Oil. There are therefore

Agents in Nature able to make the Particles of Bodies stick together by very strong Attractions. And it is the Business of experimental Philosophy to find them out.

Now the smallest Particles of Matter may cohere by the strongest Attractions, and compose bigger Particles of weaker Virtue; and many of these may cohere and compose bigger Particles whose Virtue is still weaker, and so on for divers Successions, until the Progression end in the biggest Particles on which the Operations in Chymistry, and the Colours of natural Bodies depend, and which by cohering compose Bodies of a sensible Magnitude. If the Body is compact, and bends or yields inward to Pression without any sliding of its Parts, it is hard and elastick, returning to its Figure with a Force arising from the mutual Attraction of its Parts. If the Parts slide upon one another, the Body is malleable or soft. If they slip easily, and are of a fit size to be agitated by Heat, and the Heat is big enough to keep them in Agitation, the Body is fluid; and if it be apt to stick to things, it is humid; and the Drops of every Fluid affect a round Figure by the mutual Attraction of their Parts, as the Globe of the Earth and Sea affects a round Figure by the mutual Attraction of its Parts by Gravity.

Since Metals dissolved in Acids attract but a small quantity of the Acid, their attractive Force can reach but to a small distance from them. And as in Algebra, where affirmative Quantities vanish and cease, there negative ones begin; so in Mechanicks, where Attraction ceases, there a repulsive Virtue ought to succeed. And that there is such a Virtue, seems to follow from the Reflexions and Inflexions of the Rays of Light. For the Rays are repelled by Bodies in both these Cases, without the immediate Contact of the reflecting or inflecting Body. It seems also to follow from the Emission of Light; the Ray so soon as it is shaken off from a shining Body by the vibrating Motion of the Parts of the Body, and gets beyond the reach of Attraction, being driven away with exceeding great Velocity. For that Force which is sufficient to turn it back in Reflexion, may be sufficient to emit it. It seems also to follow from the Production of Air and Vapour. The Particles when they are shaken off from Bodies by Heat or Fermentation, so soon as they are beyond the reach of the Attraction of the Body, receding from it, and also from one another with great Strength, and keeping at a distance, so as sometimes to take up above a million of times more space than they did before in the form of a dense Body. Which vast Contraction and Expansion seems unintelligible; by feigning the Particles of Air to be springy and ramous, or rolled up like Hoops, or by any other means than a repulsive Power. The Particles of Fluids which do not cohere too strongly, and are of such a smallness as renders them most susceptible of those Agitations which keep Liquors in a Fluor, are most easily separated and rarified into Vapour, and in the Language of the Chymists, they are volatile, rarifying with an easy Heat, and condensing with Cold. But those which are grosser, and so less susceptible of Agitation, or cohere by a stronger Attraction, are not separated without a stronger Heat, or perhaps not without Fermentation. And these last are the Bodies which Chymists call fix'd, and being rarified by Fermentation, become true permanent Air: those Particles receding from one another with the greatest Force, and being most difficultly brought together, which upon Contact cohere most strongly. And because the Particles of permanent Air are grosser, and arise from denser Substances than those of Vapours, thence it is that true Air is more ponderous than Vapour, and that a moist Atmosphere is lighter than a dry one, quantity for quantity. From the same repelling Power it seems to be that Flies walk upon the Water without wetting their Feet; and that the Object-glasses of long Telescopes lie upon one another without touching; and that dry Powders are difficultly made to touch one another so as to stick together, unless by melting them, or wetting them with Water, which by exhaling may bring them together; and that two polish'd Marbles, which by immediate Contact stick together, are difficultly brought so close together as to stick.

And thus Nature will be very conformable to her self and very simple, performing all the great Motions of the heavenly Bodies by the Attraction of Gravity which intercedes those Bodies, and almost all the small ones of their Particles by some other attractive and repelling Powers which intercede the Particles. The *Vis inertiæ* is a passive Principle by which Bodies persist in their Motion or Rest, receive Motion in proportion to the Force impressing it, and resist as much as they are resisted. By this Principle alone there never could have been any Motion in the World. Some other Principle was necessary for putting Bodies into Motion; and now they are in Motion, some other Principle is necessary for conserving the Motion. For from the various Composition of two Motions, 'tis very certain that there is not always the same quantity of Motion in the World. For if two Globes joined by a slender Rod, revolve about their common Center of Gravity with an uniform Motion, while that Center moves on uniformly in a straight Line drawn in the Plane of their circular Motion; the Sum of the Motions of the two Globes, as often as the Globes are in the straight Line described by their common Center of Gravity, will be bigger than the Sum of their Motions, when they are in a Line perpendicular to that straight Line. By this Instance it appears that Motion may be got or lost. But by reason of the Tenacity of Fluids, and Attrition of their Parts, and the Weakness of Elasticity in Solids, Motion is much more apt to be lost than got, and is always upon the Decay. For Bodies which are either absolutely hard, or so soft as to be void of Elasticity, will not rebound from one another. Impenetrability makes them only stop. If two equal Bodies meet directly *in vacuo*, they will by the Laws of Motion stop where they meet, and lose all their Motion, and remain in rest, unless they be elastick, and receive new Motion from their Spring. If they have so much Elasticity as suffices to make them rebound with a quarter, or half, or three quarters of the Force with which they come together, they will lose three quarters, or half, or a quarter of their Motion. And this may be tried, by letting two equal Pendulums fall against one another from equal heights. If the Pendulums be of Lead or soft Clay, they will lose all or almost all their Motions: If of elastick Bodies they will lose all but what they recover from their Elasticity. If it be said, that they can lose no Motion but what they communicate to other Bodies, the consequence is, that *in vacuo* they can lose no Motion, but when they meet they must go on and penetrate one another's Dimensions. If three equal round Vessels be filled, the one with Water, the other with Oil, the third with molten Pitch, and the Liquors be stirred about alike to give them a vortical Motion; the Pitch by its Tenacity will lose its Motion quickly, the Oil being less tenacious will keep it longer, and the Water being less tenacious will keep it longest, but yet will lose it in a short time. Whence it is easy to understand, that if many contiguous Vortices of molten Pitch were each of them as large as those which some suppose to revolve about the Sun and fix'd Stars, yet these and all their Parts would, by their tenacity and stiffness, communicate their Motion to one another till they all rested among themselves. Vortices of Oil or Water, or some fluider Matter, might continue longer in Motion; but unless the Matter were void of all Tenacity and Attrition of Parts, and Communication of Motion, (which is not to be supposed) the Motion would constantly decay. Seeing therefore the variety of Motion which we find in the World is always decreasing, there is a necessity of conserving and recruiting it by active Principles, such as are the cause of Gravity, by which Planets and Comets keep their Motions in their Orbs, and Bodies acquire great Motion in falling; and the cause of Fermentation, by which the Heart and Blood of Animals are kept in perpetual Motion and Heat; the inward Parts of the Earth are constantly warm'd, and in some places grow very hot; Bodies burn and shine, Mountains take Fire, the Caverns of the Earth are blown up, and the Sun continues violently hot and lucid, and warms all things by his Light. For we meet with very little Motion in the World, besides what is owing to these active Principles. And if it were not for these Principles the Bodies of the Earth, Planets, Comets, Sun, and all things in them would grow cold and freeze, and become inactive Masses; and all Putrefaction, Generation, Vegetation and Life would cease, and the Planets and Comets would not remain in their Orbs.

All these things being consider'd, it seems probable to me, that God in the Beginning form'd Matter in solid, massy, hard, impenetrable, moveable Particles, of such Sizes and Figures, and with such other Properties, and in such Proportion to Space, as most conduced to the End for which he form'd them; and that these primitive Particles being Solids, are incomparably harder than any porous Bodies compounded of them; even so very hard, as never to wear or break in pieces: No ordinary Power being able to divide what God himself made one in the first Creation. While the Particles continue entire, they may compose Bodies of one and the same Nature and Texture in all Ages: But should they wear away, or break in pieces, the Nature of Things depending on them, would be changed. Water and Earth composed of old worn Particles and Fragments of Particles, would not be of the same Nature and Texture now, with Water and Earth composed of entire Particles, in the Beginning. And therefore that Nature may be lasting, the Changes of corporeal Things are to be placed only in the various Separations and new Associations and Motions of these permanent Particles; compound Bodies being apt to break, not in the midst of solid Particles, but where those Particles are laid together, and only touch in a few Points.

It seems to me farther, that these Particles have not only a *Vis inertiæ*, accompanied with such passive Laws of Motion as naturally result from that Force, but also that they are moved by certain active Principles, such as is that of Gravity, and that which causes Fermentation, and the Cohesion of Bodies. These Principles I consider not as occult Qualities, supposed to result from the specifick Forms of Things, but as general Laws of Nature, by which the Things themselves are form'd: their Truth appearing to us by Phænomena, though their Causes be not yet discover'd. For these are manifest Qualities, and their Causes only are occult. And the *Aristotelians* gave the Name of occult Qualities not to manifest Qualities, but to such Qualities only as they supposed to lie hid in Bodies, and to be the unknown Causes of manifest Effects: Such as would be the Causes of Gravity, and of magnetick and electrick Attractions, and of Fermentations, if we should suppose that these Forces or Actions arose from Qualities unknown to us, and uncapable of being discovered and made manifest. Such occult Qualities put a stop to the Improvement of natural Philosophy, and therefore of late Years have been rejected. To tell us that every Species of Things is endow'd with an occult specifick Quality by which it acts and produces manifest Effects, is to tell us nothing: But to derive two or three general Principles of Motion from Phænomena, and afterwards to tell us how the Properties and Actions of all corporeal Things follow from those manifest Principles, would be a very great step in Philosophy, though the Causes of those Principles were not yet discover'd: And therefore I scruple not to propose the Principles of Motion above mention'd, they being of very general Extent, and leave their Causes to be found out.

Now by the help of these Principles, all material Things seem to have been composed of the hard and solid Particles above mention'd, variously associated in the first Creation by the Counsel of an intelligent Agent. For it became him who created them to set them in order. And if he did so, it's unphilosophical to seek for any other Origin of the World, or to pretend that it might arise out of a Chaos by the mere Laws of Nature; though being once form'd, it may continue by those Laws for many Ages. For while Comets move in very excentrick Orbs in all manner of Positions, blind Fate could never make all the Planets move one and the same way in Orbs concentrick, some inconsiderable Irregularities excepted which may have risen from the mutual Actions of Comets and Planets upon one another, and which will be apt to increase, till this System wants a Reformation. Such a wonderful Uniformity in the Planetary System must be allowed the Effect of Choice. And so must the Uniformity in the Bodies of Animals, they having generally a right and a left side shaped alike, and on either side of their Bodies two Legs behind, and either two Arms, or two Legs, or two Wings before upon their Shoulders, and between their Shoulders a Neck running down into a Back-bone, and a Head upon it; and in the Head two Ears, two Eyes, a Nose, a Mouth and a Tongue, alike situated. Also the first Contrivance of those very artificial Parts of Animals, the Eyes, Ears, Brain, Muscles, Heart, Lungs, Midriff, Glands, Larynx, Hands, Wings, Swimming Bladders, natural Spectacles, and other Organs of Sense and Motion; and the Instinct of Brutes and Insects, can be the effect of nothing else than the Wisdom and Skill of a powerful ever-living Agent, who being in all Places, is more able by his Will to move the Bodies within his boundless uniform Sensorium, and thereby to form and reform the Parts of the Universe, than we are by our Will to move the Parts of our own Bodies. And yet we are not to consider the World as the Body of God, or the several Parts thereof, as the Parts of God. He is an uniform Being, void of Organs, Members or Parts, and they are his Creatures subordinate to him, and subservient to his Will; and he is no more the Soul of them, than the Soul of a Man is the Soul of the Species of Things carried through the Organs of Sense into the place of its Sensation, where it perceives them by means of its immediate Presence, without the Intervention of any third thing. The Organs of Sense are not for enabling the

Soul to perceive the Species of Things in its Sensorium, but only for conveying them thither; and God has no need of such Organs, he being every where present to the Things themselves. And since Space is divisible *in infinitum*, and Matter is not necessarily in all places, it may be also allow'd that God is able to create Particles of Matter of several Sizes and Figures, and in several Proportions to Space, and perhaps of different Densities and Forces, and thereby to vary the Laws of Nature, and make Worlds of several sorts in several Parts of the Universe. At least, I see nothing of Contradiction in all this.

As in Mathematicks, so in Natural Philosophy, the Investigation of difficult Things by the Method of Analysis, ought ever to precede the Method of Composition. This Analysis consists in making Experiments and Observations, and in drawing general Conclusions from them by Induction, and admitting of no Objections against the Conclusions, but such as are taken from Experiments, or other certain Truths. For Hypotheses are not to be regarded in experimental Philosophy. And although the arguing from Experiments and Observations by Induction be no Demonstration of general Conclusions; yet it is the best way of arguing which the Nature of Things admits of, and may be looked upon as so much the stronger, by how much the Induction is more general. And if no Exception occur from Phænomena, the Conclusion may be pronounced generally. But if at any time afterwards any Exception shall occur from Experiments, it may then begin to be pronounced with such Exceptions as occur. By this way of Analysis we may proceed from Compounds to Ingredients, and from Motions to the Forces producing them; and in general, from Effects to their Causes, and from particular Causes to more general ones, till the Argument end in the most general. This is the Method of Analysis: And the Synthesis consists in assuming the Causes discover'd, and establish'd as Principles, and by them explaining the Phænomena proceeding from them, and proving the Explanations.

In the two first Books of these Opticks, I proceeded by this Analysis to discover and prove the original Differences of the Rays of Light in respect of Refrangibility, Reflexibility, and Colour, and their alternate Fits of easy Reflexion and easy Transmission, and the Properties of Bodies, both opake and pellucid, on which their Reflexions and Colours depend. And these Discoveries being proved, may be assumed in the Method of Composition for explaining the Phænomena arising from them: An Instance of which Method I gave in the End of the first Book. In this third Book I have only begun the Analysis of what remains to be discover'd about Light and its Effects upon the Frame of Nature, hinting several things about it, and leaving the Hints to be examin'd and improved by the farther Experiments and Observations of such as are inquisitive. And if natural Philosophy in all its Parts, by pursuing this Method, shall at length be perfected, the Bounds of moral Philosophy will be also enlarged. For so far as we can know by natural Philosophy what is the first Cause, what Power he has over us, and what Benefits we receive from him, so far our Duty towards him, as well as that towards one another, will appear to us by the Light of Nature. And no doubt, if the Worship of false Gods had not blinded the Heathen, their moral Philosophy would have gone farther than to the four Cardinal Virtues; and instead of teaching the Transmigration of Souls, and to worship the Sun and Moon, and dead Heroes, they would have taught us to worship our true Author and Benefactor.

13

BENJAMIN FRANKLIN

Benjamin Franklin was the first American to contribute significantly to the development of modern science, and one of the small handful of Americans to do so before the middle of the 20th century. Born in Boston in 1706, tenth son of a prolific father, he was originally destined for the church by the paternal determination to tithe with all increase. Economic necessity dictated otherwise. Withdrawn from school, he was apprenticed to his half-brother, a printer, and from him learned the trade which made his fortune and his reputation. Moving to Philadelphia, Franklin soon acquired his own shop and installed himself as editor of his own newspaper. His famous almanacks circulated more widely than any other publication in the colonies. As Philadelphia's leading citizen, he was instrumental in organizing its first lending library, an academy from which grew the University of Pennsylvania, and the American Philosophical Society. On the eve of the War of Independence, Franklin represented Pennsylvania in London; later, he represented the Continental Congress in Paris, where he negotiated the treaty of alliance that helped to win American independence and the treaty of peace that recognized it. Franklin died in 1790, not long after participating in the Constitutional Convention.

The science of electricity was essentially a product of the first half of the 18th century. Before that period, only a few crude phenomena of static electricity were known; after that period, the science stood fully established. Franklin played a major role in the change. Until his time, the so-called effluvial theory constituted the basis of electrical investigation. Devised in the 17th century, when the science occupied an obscure corner of natural philosophy, the theory regarded electricity as streams of subtle matter caused to radiate from bodies, like vapor evaporating from water, by the heat caused by rubbing. Minor modifications adapted the theory to comprehend discoveries such as the transmission of electricity by wire over considerable distances. During the 1740's, increasingly spectacular experimentation rapidly moved electricity to the center of attention. Machines invaded the science, replacing the tiny charges on glass rods with other charges powerful enough to kill small animals and perhaps (as some experimenters learned to fear) even to kill men. The machines, together with the Leyden Jar, soon produced several manifest contradictions to the existing electrical theory. Franklin replaced it with a new conceptual scheme broad enough to embrace the new phenomena.

The new theory embodied familiar ingredients, however. Following the lead of the mechanical philosophies of nature, especially the modified version of them which Newton attached to the *Opticks* in his speculative "Queries", 18th century science was prone to explain various classes of phenomena by the concept of invisible fluids that pervaded the universe. Perhaps the best known was the fluid of heat. Although he was not professionally trained as a scientist, Franklin was well aware of the prevailing modes of physical explanation. In dealing with electricity, he expressed himself in the terms of his age.

13

New Experiments and Observations on Electricity

"LETTER TO PETER COLLINSON"

PHILADELPHIA, 11 JULY, 1747.

SIR: In my last I informed you that in pursuing our electrical inquiries we had observed some particular phenomena which we looked upon to be new, and of which I promised to give you some account, though I apprehended they might not possibly be new to you, as so many hands are daily employed in electrical experiments on your side the water, some or other of which would probably hit on the same observations.

The first is the wonderful effect of pointed bodies, both in *drawing off* and *throwing off* the electrical fire. For example:

Place an iron shot of three or four inches diameter on the mouth of a clean, dry glass bottle. By a fine silken thread from the ceiling, right over the mouth of the bottle, suspend a small cork ball about the bigness of a marble, the thread of such a length as that the cork ball may rest against the side of the shot. Electrify the shot, and the ball will be repelled to the distance of four or five inches, more or less, according to the quantity of electricity. When in this state, if you present to the shot the point of a long, slender, sharp bodkin, at six or eight inches' distance, the repellency is instantly destroyed, and the cork flies to the shot. A blunt body must be brought within an inch and draw a spark to produce the same effect. To prove that the electrical fire is *drawn off* by the point, if you take the blade of the bodkin out of the wooden handle and fix it in a stick of sealing-wax, and then present it at the distance aforesaid, or if you bring it very near, no such effect follows; but sliding one finger along the wax till you touch the blade, and the ball flies to the shot immediately. If you present the point in the dark you will see, sometimes at a foot distance and more, a light gather upon it, like that of a fire-fly or glow-worm; the less sharp the point the nearer you must bring it to observe the light, and at whatever distance you see the light you may draw off the electrical fire and destroy the repellency. If a cork ball so

---

From the second edition, London, 1754.

suspended be repelled by the tube, and a point be presented quick to it, though at a considerable distance, it is surprising to see how suddenly it flies back to the tube. Points of wood will do near as well as those of iron, provided the wood is not dry, for perfectly dry wood will no more conduct electricity than sealing-wax.

To show that points will *throw off* as well as *draw off* the electrical fire; lay a long sharp needle upon the shot, and you cannot electrize the shot so as to make it repel the cork ball. Or fix a needle to the end of a suspended gun-barrel, or iron rod, so as to point beyond it like a little bayonet, and while it remains there, the gun-barrel or rod cannot, by applying the tube to the other end, be electrized so as to give a spark, the fire continually running out silently at the point. In the dark you may see it make the same appearance as it does in the case before mentioned.

The repellency between the cork ball and the shot is likewise destroyed: 1st, by sifting fine sand on it—this does it gradually; 2dly, by breathing on it; 3dly, by making a smoke about it from burning wood[1]; 4thly, by candle-light, even though the candle is at a foot distance—these do it suddenly. The light of a bright coal from a wood fire, and the light of a red-hot iron do it likewise, but not at so great a distance. Smoke from dry rosin dropped on hot iron does not destroy the repellency, but is attracted by both shot and cork ball, forming proportionable atmospheres round them, making them look beautifully, somewhat like some of the figures in Burnet's or Whiston's *Theory of the Earth*.

N. B. This experiment should be made in a closet where the air is very still, or it will be apt to fail.

The light of the sun thrown strongly on both cork and shot by a looking-glass, for a long time together, does not impair the repellency in the least. This difference between fire-light and sun-light is another thing that seems new and extraordinary to us.

We had for some time been of opinion that the electrical fire was not created by friction, but collected, being really an element diffused among, and attracted by other matter, particularly by water and metals. We had even discovered and demonstrated its afflux to the electrical sphere, as well as its efflux, by means of little, light windmill-wheels made of stiff paper vanes fixed obliquely, and turning freely on fine wire axes; also

1 We suppose every particle of sand, moisture, or smoke, being first attracted and then repelled, carries off with it a portion of the electrical fire; but that the same still subsists in those particles till they communicate it to something else, and that it is never really destroyed. So, when water is thrown on common fire, we do not imagine the element is thereby destroyed or annihilated, but only dispersed, each particle of water carrying off in vapor its portion of the fire which it had attracted and attached to itself.

by little wheels of the same matter, but formed like water-wheels. Of the disposition and application of which wheels, and the various phenomena resulting, I could, if I had time, fill you a sheet. The impossibility of electrizing one's self (though standing on wax) by rubbing the tube, and drawing the fire from it; and the manner of doing it by passing the tube near a person or thing standing on the floor, &c., had also occurred to us some months before Mr. Watson's ingenious *Sequel* came to hand; and these were some of the new things I intended to have communicated to you. But now I need only mention some particulars not hinted in that piece, with our reasonings thereupon; though perhaps the latter might well enough be spared.

1. A person standing on wax and rubbing the tube, and another person on wax drawing the fire, they will both of them (provided they do not stand so as to touch one another) appear to be electrized to a person standing on the floor; that is, he will perceive a spark on approaching each of them with his knuckle.

2. But if the persons on wax touch one another during the exciting of the tube, neither of them will appear to be electrized.

3. If they touch one another after exciting the tube, and drawing the fire as aforesaid, there will be a stronger spark between them than was between either of them and the person on the floor.

4. After such strong spark neither of them discover any electricity.

These appearances we attempt to account for thus: We suppose, as aforesaid, that electrical fire is a common element, of which every one of the three persons above mentioned has his equal share, before any operation is begun with the tube. *A,* who stands on wax and rubs the tube, collects the electrical fire from himself into the glass; and, his communication with the common stock being cut off by the wax, his body is not again immediately supplied. *B* (who stands on wax likewise), passing his knuckle along the tube, receives the fire which was collected by the glass from *A;* and his communication with the common stock being likewise cut off, he retains the additional quantity received. To *C,* standing on the floor, both appear to be electrized; for he, having only the middle quantity of electrical fire, receives a spark upon approaching *B,* who has an over quantity; but gives one to *A,* who has an under quantity. If *A* and *B* approach to touch each other, the spark is stronger, because the difference between them is greater. After such touch there is no spark between either of them and *C,* because the electrical fire in all is reduced to the original equality. If they touch while electrizing, the equality is never destroyed, the fire only circulating. Hence have arisen some new terms among us: we say *B* (and bodies like circumstanced) is electrized *positively; A, negatively.* Or rather, *B* is electrized *plus; A, minus.* And we daily in our experiments electrize bodies *plus* or *minus,* as we think proper. To electrize *plus* or *minus,* no more needs to be known than this, that the parts of the tube or sphere that are rubbed, do, in the instant of the friction, attract the electrical fire, and therefore take it from the thing rubbing; the same parts immediately, as the friction upon them ceases, are disposed to give the fire they have received to any body that has less. Thus you may circulate it as Mr. Watson has shown; you may also accumulate or subtract it, upon or from any body, as you connect that body with the rubber, or with the receiver, the communication with the common stock being cut off. We think that ingenious gentleman was deceived when he imagined (in his *Sequel*) that the electrical fire came down the wire from the ceiling to the gun-barrel, thence to the sphere, and so electrized the machine and the man turning the wheel, &c. We suppose it was *driven off,* and not brought on through that wire; and that the machine and man, &c., were electrized *minus*— that is, had less electrical fire in them than things in common.

As the vessel is just upon sailing, I cannot give you so large an account of American electricity as I intended; I shall only mention a few particulars more. We find granulated lead better to fill the phial with than water, being easily warmed, and keeping warm and dry in damp air. We fire spirits with the wire of the phial. We light candles, just blown out, by drawing a spark among the smoke between the wire and snuffers. We represent lightning by passing the wire in the dark over a China plate that has gilt flowers, or applying it to gilt frames of looking glasses, &c. We electrize a person twenty or more times running, with a touch of the finger on the wire, thus: He stands on wax. Give him the electrized bottle in his hand (as in Figure 1). Touch the wire with your finger and then touch his hand or face; there are sparks every time.[1] We increase the force of the electrical kiss vastly, thus: Let *A* and *B* stand on wax, or *A* on wax and *B* on the floor; give one of them the electrized phial in hand; let the other take hold of the wire; there will be a small spark; but when their lips approach they will be struck and shocked. The same if another gentleman and lady, *C* and *D,* standing also on wax, and joining hands with *A* and *B,* salute or shake hands. We suspend by fine silk thread a counterfeit spider made of a small piece of burnt cork, with legs of linen thread, and a grain or two of lead stuck in him to give him more weight. Upon the table, over which he hangs, we stick a wire upright, as high as the phial and wire, four or five inches from

---

1 By taking a spark from the wire, the electricity within the bottle is diminished; the outside of the bottle then draws some from the person holding it, and leaves him in a negative state. Then when his hand or face is touched, an equal quantity is restored to him from the person touching.

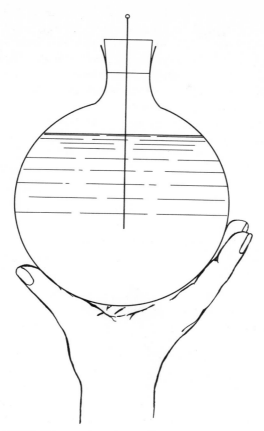

FIGURE 1   THE PHIAL (LEYDEN JAR).

the spider; then we animate him by setting the electrified phial at the same distance on the other side of him; he will immediately fly to the wire of the phial, bend his legs in touching it, then spring off and fly to the wire in the table, thence again to the wire of the phial, playing with his legs against both, in a very entertaining manner, appearing perfectly alive to persons unacquainted. He will continue this motion an hour or more in dry weather. We electrify, upon wax in the dark, a book that has a double line of gold round upon the covers, and then apply a knuckle to the gilding; the fire appears everywhere upon the gold like a flash of lightning; not upon the leather, nor if you touch the leather instead of the gold. We rub our tubes with buckskin and observe always to keep the same side to the tube and never to sully the tube by han-lling; thus they work readily and easily without the least fatigue, especially if kept in tight pasteboard cases lined with flannel, and sitting close to the tube. This I mention because the European papers on electricity frequently speak of rubbing the tubes as a fatiguing exercise. Our spheres are fixed on iron axes which pass through them. At one end of the axis there is a small handle with which you turn the sphere like a common grindstone. This we find very commodious, as the machine takes up but little room, is portable, and may be enclosed in a tight box when not in use. It is true the sphere does not turn so swift as when the great wheel is used; but swiftness we think of little importance, since a few turns will charge the phial, &c., sufficiently.

I am, &c.,

B. FRANKLIN.

"LETTER TO PETER COLLINSON"

PHILADELPHIA, 1 SEPTEMBER, 1747.

SIR: The necessary trouble of copying long letters, which perhaps, when they come to your hands, may contain nothing new, or worth your reading (so quick is the progress made with you in electricity), half discourages me of writing any more on that subject. Yet I cannot forbear adding a few observations on M. Muschenbroek's wonderful bottle.

1. The non-electric contained in the bottle differs, when electrized, from a non-electric electrized out of the bottle, in this: that the electrical fire of the latter is accumulated *on its surface,* and forms an electrical atmosphere round it of considerable extent; but the electrical fire is crowded *into the substance* of the former, the glass confining it.

2. At the same time that the wire and the top of the bottle, &c., is electrized *positively* or *plus,* the bottom of the bottle is electrized *negatively* or *minus,* in exact proportion; that is, whatever quantity of electrical fire is thrown in at the top, an equal quantity goes out of the bottom. To understand this, suppose the common quantity of electricity in each part of the bottle, before the operation begins, is equal to twenty; and at every stroke of the tube, suppose a quantity equal to one is thrown in; then, after the first stroke, the quantity contained in the wire and upper part of the bottle will be twenty-one, in the bottom nineteen; after the second, the upper part will have twenty-two, the lower eighteen; and so on, till after twenty strokes, the upper part will have a quantity of electrical fire equal to forty, the lower part none; and then the operation ends, for no more can be thrown into the upper part when no more can be driven out of the lower part. If you attempt to throw

more in, it is spewed back through the wire, or flies out in loud cracks through the sides of the bottle.

3. The equilibrium cannot be restored in the bottle by *inward* communication or contact of the parts; but it must be done by a communication formed *without* the bottle, between the top and bottom, by some non-electric, touching or approaching both at the same time; in which case it is restored with a violence and quickness inexpressible; or touching each alternately, in which case the equilibrium is restored by degrees.

4. As no more electrical fire can be thrown into the top of the bottle, when all is driven out of the bottom, so, in a bottle not yet electrized, none can be thrown into the top when none *can* get out at the bottom; which happens either when the bottom is too thick, or when the bottle is placed on an electric *per se*. Again, when the bottle is electrized, but little of the electrical fire can be *drawn out* from the top, by touching the wire, unless an equal quantity can at the same time *get in* at the bottom. Thus, place an electrized bottle on clean glass or dry wax, and you will not, by touching the wire, get out the fire from the top. Place it on a non-electric, and touch the wire, you will get it out in a short time—but soonest when you form a direct communication as above.

So wonderfully are these two states of electricity, the *plus* and *minus*, combined and balanced in this miraculous bottle! situated and related to each other in a manner that I can by no means comprehend! If it were possible that a bottle should in one part contain a quantity of air strongly compressed, and in another part a perfect vacuum, we know the equilibrium would be instantly restored *within*. But here we have a bottle containing at the same time a *plenum* of electrical fire and a *vacuum* of the same fire, and yet the equilibrium cannot be restored between them but by a communication *without*, though the *plenum* presses violently to expand, and the hungry vacuum seems to attract as violently in order to be filled.

5. The shock to the nerves (or convulsion rather) is occasioned by the sudden passing of the fire through the body in its way from the top to the bottom of the bottle. The fire takes the shortest course, as Mr. Watson justly observes. But it does not appear from experiment that, in order for a person to be shocked, a communication with the floor is necessary; for he that holds the bottle with one hand and touches the wire with the other, will be shocked as much, though his shoes be dry, or even standing on wax, as otherwise. And on the touch of the wire (or of the gun-barrel, which is the same thing), the fire does not proceed from the touching finger to the wire, as is supposed, but from the wire to the finger, and passes through the body to the other hand, and so into the bottom of the bottle.

Experiments Confirming the Above

EXPERIMENT 1

Place an electrized phial on wax; a small cork ball, suspended by a dry silk thread, held in your hand and brought near to the wire, will first be attracted and then repelled; when in this state of repellency, sink your hand that the ball may be brought towards the bottom of the bottle. It will be there instantly and strongly attracted till it has parted with its fire.

If the bottle had a *positive* electrical atmosphere, as well as the wire, an electrified cork would be repelled from one as well as from the other.

EXPERIMENT 2

Figure 2. From a bent wire (*a*) sticking in the table, let a small linen thread (*b*) hang down within half an inch of the electrized phial (*c*). Touch the wire or the phial repeatedly with your finger, and at every touch you will see the thread instantly attracted by the bottle. (This is best done by a vinegar-cruet, or some such bellied bottle.) As soon as

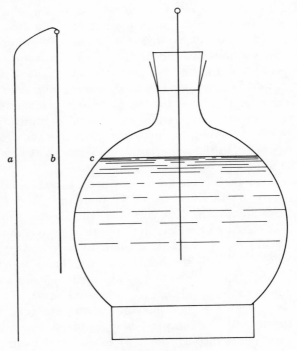

FIGURE 2

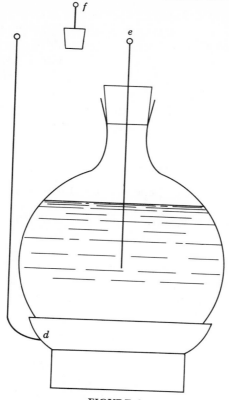

FIGURE 3

you draw any fire out from the upper part by touching the wire, the lower part of the bottle draws an equal quantity in by the thread.

EXPERIMENT 3

Figure 3. Fix a wire in the lead, with which the bottom of the bottle is armed (d), so as that, bending upwards, its ring-end may be level with the top or ring-end of the wire in the cork (e), and at three or four inches distance. Then electrize the bottle and place it on wax. If a cork, suspended by a silk thread (f), hang between these two wires, it will play incessantly from one to the other till the bottle is no longer electrized; that is, it fetches and carries fire from the top to the bottom of the bottle till the equilibrium is restored.

EXPERIMENT 4

Place an electrized phial on wax; take a wire in form of a C, the ends at such a distance, when bent, as that the upper may touch the wire of the bottle when the lower touches the bottom; stick the outer part on a stick of sealing-wax, which will serve as a handle; then apply the lower end to the bottom of the bottle, and gradually bring the upper end near the wire in the cork. The consequence is, spark follows spark till the equilibrium is restored. Touch the top first, and on approaching the bottom with the other end, you have a constant stream of fire from the wire entering the bottle. Touch the top and bottom together, and the equilibrium will instantly be restored, the crooked wire forming the communication.

EXPERIMENT 5

Let a ring of thin lead or paper surround a bottle, even at some distance from or above the bottom. From that ring let a wire proceed up till it touch the wire of the cork. A bottle so fixed cannot by any means be electrized; the equilibrium is never destroyed; for while the communication between the upper and lower parts of the bottle is continued by the outside wire, the fire only circulates; what is driven out at bottom is constantly supplied from the top. Hence a bottle cannot be electrized that is foul or moist on the outside, if such moisture continue up to the cork or wire.

EXPERIMENT 6

Place a man on a cake of wax, and present him the wire of the electrified phial to touch, you standing on the floor and holding it in your hand. As often as he touches it he will be electrified *plus;* and any one standing on the floor may draw a spark from him. The fire in this experiment passes out of the wire into him; and at the same time out of your hand into the bottom of the bottle.

EXPERIMENT 7

Give him the electrical phial to hold, and do you touch the wire; as often as you touch it he will be electrified *minus,* and may draw a spark from any one standing on the floor. The fire now passes from the wire to you, and from him into the bottom of the bottle.

EXPERIMENT 8

Lay two books on two glasses, back towards back, two or three inches distant. Set the electrified phial on one, and then touch the wire; that book will be electrified *minus,* the electrical fire being drawn out of it by the bottom of the bottle. Take off the bottle, and, holding it in your hand, touch the other with the wire; that book will be electrified *plus;*

the fire passing into it from the wire, and the bottle at the same time supplied from your hand. A suspended small cork ball will play between these books till the equilibrium is restored.

EXPERIMENT 9

When a body is electrized *plus,* it will repel a positively electrified feather or small cork ball. When *minus* (or when in the common state), it will attract them, but stronger when *minus* than when in the common state, the difference being greater.

EXPERIMENT 10

Though, as in *Experiment* VI, a man standing on wax may be electrized a number of times by repeatedly touching the wire of an electrized bottle (held in the hand of one standing on the floor), he receiving the fire from the wire each time; yet holding it in his own hand and touching the wire, though he draws a strong spark, and is violently shocked, no electricity remains in him, the fire only passing through him from the upper to the lower part of the bottle. Observe, before the shock, to let some one on the floor touch him to restore the equilibrium of his body; for in taking hold of the bottom of the bottle he sometimes becomes a little electrized *minus,* which will continue after the shock, as would also any *plus* electricity which he might have given him before the shock. For restoring the equilibrium in the bottle does not at all affect the electricity in the man through whom the fire passes; that electricity is neither increased nor diminished.

EXPERIMENT 11

The passing of the electrical fire from the upper to the lower part of the bottle, to restore the equilibrium, is rendered strongly visible by the following pretty experiment (Figure 4). Take a book whose covering is filleted with gold; bend a wire of eight or ten inches long, slip it on the end of the cover of the book, over the gold line, so as that the shoulder of it may press upon one end of the gold line, the ring up, but leaning towards the other end of the book. Lay the book on a glass or wax, and on the other end of the gold line set the bottle electrized; then bend the springing wire by pressing it with a stick of wax till its ring approaches the ring of the bottle wire; instantly there is a strong spark and stroke, and the whole line of gold, which completes the communication between the top and bottom of the bottle, will appear a vivid flame, like the sharpest lightning. The closer the contact between the shoulder of the wire and the gold at one end of the line, and between the bottom of the

FIGURE 4

bottle and the gold at the other end, the better the experiment succeeds. The room should be darkened. If you would have the whole filleting round the cover appear in fire at once, let the bottle and wire touch the gold in the diagonally opposite corners.

I am, &c.,

B. FRANKLIN.

"OPINIONS AND CONJECTURES CONCERNING THE PROPERTIES AND EFFECTS OF THE ELECTRICAL MATTER, AND THE MEANS OF PRESERVING BUILDINGS, SHIPS, &C., FROM LIGHTNING, ARISING FROM EXPERIMENTS AND OBSERVATIONS MADE AT PHILADELPHIA, 1749."

§ 1. The electrical matter consists of particles extremely subtile, since it can permeate common matter, even the densest metals, with such ease and freedom as not to receive any perceptible resistance.

2. If any one should doubt whether the electrical matter passes through the substance of bodies, or only over and along their surfaces, a shock from an electrified large glass jar, taken through his own body, will probably convince him.

3. Electrical matter differs from common matter in this, that the parts of the latter mutually attract, those of the former mutually repel, each other. Hence the appearing divergency in a stream of electrified effluvia.

4. But, though the particles of electrical matter do repel each other, they are strongly attracted by all other matter.

5. From these three things, the extreme subtility of the electrical matter, the mutual repulsion of its parts, and the strong attraction between them and other matter, arises this effect, that, when a quantity of electrical matter is applied to a mass of common matter, of any bigness or length, within our observation (which hath not already got its quantity), it is immediately and equally diffused through the whole.

6. Thus, common matter is a kind of sponge to the electrical fluid. And as a sponge would receive no water, if the parts of water were not smaller than the pores of the sponge; and even then but slowly, if there were not a mutual attraction between those parts and the parts of the sponge; and would still imbibe it faster, if the mutual attraction among the parts of the water did not impede, some force being required to separate them; and fastest, if, instead of attraction, there were a mutual repulsion among those parts, which would act in conjunction with the attraction of the sponge; so is the case between the electrical and common matter.

7. But in common matter there is (generally) as much of the electrical as it will contain within its substance. If more is added, it lies without upon the surface, and forms what we call an electrical atmosphere; and then the body is said to be electrified.

8. It is supposed, that all kinds of common matter do not attract and retain the electrical with equal strength and force, for reasons to be given hereafter. And that those called electrics *per se,* as glass, &c., attract and retain it strongest, and contain the greatest quantity.

9. We know, that the electrical fluid is *in* common matter, because we can pump it *out* by the globe or tube. We know that common matter has near as much as it can contain, because, when we add a little more to any portion of it, the additional quantity does not enter, but forms an electrical atmosphere. And we know, that common matter has not (generally) more than it can contain, otherwise all loose portions of it would repeal each other, as they constantly do when they have electric atmospheres.

10. The beneficial uses of this electric fluid in the creation we are not yet well acquainted with, though doubtless such there are, and those very considerable; but we may see some pernicious consequences that would attend a much greater proportion of it. For, had this globe we live on as much of it in proportion as we can give to a globe of iron, wood, or the like, the particles of dust and other light matters that get loose from it would, by virtue of their separate electrical atmospheres, not only repel each other, but be repelled from the earth, and not easily be brought to unite with it again; whence our air would continually be

more and more clogged with foreign matter and grow unfit for respiration. This affords another occasion of adoring that wisdom which has made all things by weight and measure!

11. If a piece of common matter be supposed entirely free from electrical matter, and a single particle of the latter be brought nigh, it will be attracted and enter the body, and take place in the centre, or where the attraction is every way equal. If more particles enter, they take their places where the balance is equal between the attraction of the common matter and their own mutual repulsion. It is supposed they form triangles, whose sides shorten as their number increases, till the common matter has drawn in so many that its whole power of compressing those triangles by attraction is equal to their whole power of expanding themselves by repulsion; and then will such a piece of matter receive no more.

12. When part of this natural proportion of electrical fluid is taken out of a piece of common matter, the triangles formed by the remainder are supposed to widen, by the mutual repulsion of the parts, until they occupy the whole piece.

13. When the quantity of electrical fluid taken from a piece of common matter is restored again, it enters the expanded triangles, being again compressed till there is room for the whole.

14. To explain this: take two apples, or two balls of wood or other matter, each having its own natural quantity of the electrical fluid. Suspend them by silk lines from the ceiling. Apply the wire of a well-charged phial, held in your hand, to one of them (A), and it will receive from the wire a quantity of the electrical fluid, but will not imbibe it, being already full. The fluid, therefore, will flow round its surface and form an electrical atmosphere. Bring A into contact with B, and half the electrical fluid is communicated, so that each has now an electrical atmosphere, and therefore they repel each other. Take away these atmospheres, by touching the balls, and leave them in their natural state; then, having fixed a stick of sealing-wax to the middle of the phial to hold it by, apply the wire to A, at the same time the coating touches B. Thus will a quantity of the electrical fluid be drawn out of B, and thrown on A. So that A will have a redundance of this fluid, which forms an atmosphere round, and B an exactly equal deficiency. Now, bring these balls again into contact, and the electrical atmosphere will not be divided between A and B, into two smaller atmospheres as before; for B will drink up the whole atmosphere of A, and both will be found again in their natural state.

15. The form of the electrical atmosphere is that of the body it surrounds. This shape may be rendered visible in a still air, by raising a smoke from dry rosin dropt into a hot tea-spoon under the electrified

body, which will be attracted, and spread itself equally on all sides, covering and concealing the body. And this form it takes, because it is attracted by all parts of the surface of the body, though it cannot enter the substance already replete. Without this attraction, it would not remain round the body, but dissipate in the air.

16. The atmosphere of electrical particles surrounding an electrified sphere is not more disposed to leave it, or more easily drawn off from any one part of the sphere than another, because it is equally attracted by every part. But that is not the case with bodies of any other figure. From a cube it is more easily drawn at the corners than at the plane sides, and so from the angles of a body of any other form, and still most easily from the angle that is most acute. Thus if a body shaped as *A, B, C, D, E.* in Figure 5, be electrified, or have an electrical atmosphere communicated to it, and we consider every side as a base on which the particles rest, and by which they are attracted, one may see, by imagining a line from *A* to *F,* and another from *E* to *G,* that the portion of the atmosphere included in *F, A, E, G,* has the line *A, E* for its basis. So the portion of atmosphere included in *H, A, B, I,* has the line *A, B* for its basis. And likewise the portion included in *K, B, C, L,* has *B, C* to rest on; and so on the other side of the figure. Now, if you will draw off this atmosphere with any blunt, smooth body, and approach the middle of the side *A, B,* you must come very near, before the force of your attractor exceeds the force or power with which that side holds the atmosphere. But there is a small portion between *I, B, K,* that has less of the surface to rest on, and to be attracted by, than the neighbouring portions, while at the same time there is a mutual repulsion between its particles and the particles of those portions; therefore here you can get it with more ease, or at a greater distance. Between *F, A, H,* there is a larger portion that has yet a less surface to rest on, and to attract it; here, therefore, you can get it away still more easily. But easiest of all, between *L, C, M,* where the quantity is largest, and the surface to attract and keep it back the least. When you have drawn away one of these angular portions of the fluid, another succeeds in its place from the nature of fluidity and the mutual repulsion before mentioned; and so the atmosphere con-

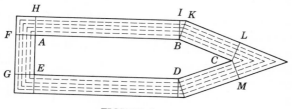

FIGURE 5

tinues flowing off at such angle, like a stream, till no more is remaining. The extremities of the portions of atmosphere over these angular parts are likewise at a greater distance from the electrified body, as may be seen by the inspection of the above figure; the point of the atmosphere of the angle *C* being much farther from *C,* than any other part of the atmosphere over the lines *C, B,* or *B, A;* and besides the distance arising from the nature of the figure, where the attraction is less, the particles will naturally expand to a greater distance by their mutual repulsion. On these accounts we suppose electrified bodies discharge their atmospheres upon unelectrified bodies more easily, and at a greater distance from their angles and points than from their smooth sides. Those points will also discharge into the air, when the body has too great an electrical atmosphere, without bringing any non-electric near to receive what is thrown off. For the air, though an electric *per se,* yet has always more or less water and other non-electric matters mixed with it; and these attract and receive what is so discharged.

17. But points have a property, by which they *draw on* as well as *throw off* the electrical fluid, at greater distances than blunt bodies can. That is, as the pointed part of an electrified body will discharge the atmosphere of that body, or communicate it farthest to another body, so the point of an unelectrified body will draw off the electrical atmosphere from an electrified body, farther than a blunter part of the same unelectrified body will do. Thus, a pin held by the head, and the point presented to an electrified body, will draw off its atmosphere at a foot distance; where, if the head were presented instead of the point, no such effect would follow. To understand this, we may consider that, if a person standing on the floor would draw off the electrical atmosphere from an electrified body, an iron crow and a blunt knitting-needle held alternately in his hand, and presented for that purpose, do not draw with different forces in proportion to their different masses. For the man, and what he holds in his hand, be it large or small, are connected with the common mass of unelectrified matter; and the force with which he draws is the same in both cases, it consisting in the different proportion of electricity in the electrified body and that common mass. But the force with which the electrified body retains its atmosphere by attracting it, is proportioned to the surface over which the particles are placed; that is, four square inches of that surface retain their atmosphere with four times the force that one square inch retains its atmosphere. And as in plucking the hairs from a horse's tail a degree of strength not sufficient to pull away a handful at once could yet easily strip it hair by hair, so a blunt body presented cannot draw off a number of particles at once, but a

pointed one, with no greater force, takes them away easily, particle by particle.

18. These explanations of the power and operation of points when they first occurred to me, and while they first floated in my mind, appeared perfectly satisfactory; but now I have written them, and considered them more closely, I must own I have some doubts about them; yet, as I have at present nothing better to offer in their stead, I do not cross them out; for, even a bad solution read, and its faults discovered, has often given rise to a good one, in the mind of an ingenious reader.

19. Nor is it of much importance to us to know the manner in which nature executes her laws; it is enough if we know the laws themselves. It is of real use to know that China left in the air unsupported will fall and break; but *how* it comes to fall, and *why* it breaks, are matters of speculation. It is a pleasure indeed to know them, but we can preserve our China without it.

20. Thus, in the present case, to know this power of points may possibly be of some use to mankind, though we should never be able to explain it. The following experiments, as well as those in my first paper, show this power. I have a large prime conductor, made of several thin sheets of clothier's pasteboard, formed into a tube, near ten feet long and a foot diameter. It is covered with Dutch embossed paper, almost totally gilt. This large metallic surface supports a much greater electrical atmosphere than a rod of iron of fifty times the weight would do. It is suspended by silk lines, and when charged will strike, at near two inches distance, a pretty hard stroke, so as to make one's knuckle ache. Let a person standing on the floor present the point of a needle, at twelve or more inches distance from it, and while the needle is so presented, the conductor cannot be charged, the point drawing off the fire as fast as it is thrown on by the electrical globe. Let it be charged, and then present the point at the same distance, and it will suddenly be discharged. In the dark you may see the light on the point, when the experiment is made. And if the person holding the point stands upon wax, he will be electrified by receiving the fire at that distance. Attempt to draw off the electricity with a blunt body, as a bolt of iron round at the end, and smooth (a silversmith's iron punch, inch thick, is what I use), and you must bring it within the distance of three inches before you can do it, and then it is done with a stroke and crack. As the pasteboard tube hangs loose on silk lines, when you approach it with the punch-iron, it likewise will move towards the punch, being attracted while it is charged; but if, at the same instant, a point be presented as before, it retires again, for the point discharges it. Take a pair of large brass scales, of two or more

feet beam, the cords of the scales being silk. Suspend the beam by a pack-thread from the ceiling, so that the bottom of the scales may be about a foot from the floor; the scales will move round in a circle by the untwist-ing of the pack-thread. Set the iron punch on the end upon the floor, in such a place as that the scales may pass over it in making their circle; then electrify one scale by applying the wire of a charged phial to it. As they move round, you see that scale draw nigher to the floor, and dip more when it comes over the punch; and if that be placed at a proper distance, the scale will snap and discharge its fire into it. But if a needle be stuck on the end of the punch, its point upward, the scale, instead of drawing nigh to the punch and snapping, discharges its fire silently through the point, and rises higher from the punch. Nay, even if the needle be placed upon the floor near the punch, its point upwards, the end of the punch, though so much higher than the needle, will not at-tract the scale and receive its fire, for the needle will get it and convey it away before it comes nigh enough for the punch to act. And this is constantly observable in these experiments, that the greater quantity of electricity on the pasteboard tube, the farther it strikes or discharges its fire, and the point likewise will draw it off at a still greater distance.

Now if the fire of electricity and that of lightning be the same, as I have endeavoured to show at large in a former paper, this pasteboard tube and these scales may represent electrified clouds. If a tube of only ten feet long will strike and discharge its fire on the punch at two or three inches distance, an electrified cloud of perhaps ten thousand acres may strike and discharge on the earth at a proportionably greater dis-tance. The horizontal motion of the scales over the floor may represent the motion of the clouds over the earth; and the erect iron punch, a hill or high building; and then we see how electrified clouds passing over hills or high buildings at too great a height to strike, may be attracted lower till within their striking distance. And lastly, if a needle fixed on the punch with its point upright, or even on the floor below the punch, will draw the fire from the scale silently at a much greater than the strik-ing distance, and so prevent its descending towards the punch; or if in its course it would have come nigh enough to strike, yet being first de-prived of its fire it cannot, and the punch is thereby secured from the stroke; I say, if these things are so, may not the knowledge of this power of points be of use to mankind in preserving houses, churches, ships, &c., from the stroke of lightning, by directing us to fix on the highest parts of those edifices upright rods of iron made sharp as a needle, and gilt to prevent rusting, and from the foot of those rods a wire down the outside of the building into the ground, or down round one of the shrouds of a ship, and down her side till it reaches the water? Would not these pointed rods probably draw the electrical fire silently out of a cloud before it came nigh enough to strike, and thereby secure us from that most sudden and terrible mischief?

21. To determine the question whether the clouds that contain lightning are electrified or not, I would propose an experiment to be tried where it may be done conveniently. On the top of some high tower or steeple, place a kind of sentry-box, big enough to contain a man and an electrical stand. From the middle of the stand let an iron rod rise and pass bending out of the door, and then upright twenty or thirty feet, pointed very sharp at the end. If the electrical stand be kept clean and dry, a man standing on it when such clouds are passing low might be electrified and afford sparks, the rod drawing fire to him from a cloud. If any danger to the man should be apprehended (though I think there would be none), let him stand on the floor of his box, and now and then bring near to the rod the loop of a wire that has one end fastened to the leads, he holding it by a wax handle; so the sparks, if the rod is electrified, will strike from the rod to the wire and not affect him. . . .

"LETTER TO PETER COLLINSON"

PHILADELPHIA, 19 OCTOBER, 1752.

SIR: As frequent mention is made in publick papers from Europe of the success of the Philadelphia experiment for drawing the electric fire from clouds by means of pointed rods of iron erected on high buildings, &c., it may be agreeable to the curious to be informed that the same experiment has succeeded in Philadelphia, though made in a different and more easy manner, which is as follows.

Make a small cross of two light strips of cedar, the arms so long as to reach to the four corners of a large thin silk handkerchief when extended; tie the corners of the handkerchief to the extremities of the cross, so you have the body of a kite; which, being properly accommodated with a tail, loop, and string, will rise in the air, like those made of paper; but this being of silk is fitter to bear the wet and wind of a thunder-gust without tearing. To the top of the upright stick of the cross is to be fixed a very sharp-pointed wire, rising a foot or more above the wood. To the end of the twine, next the hand, is to be tied a silk ribbon, and where the silk and twine join, a key may be fastened. This kite is to be raised when a thunder-gust appears to becoming on, and the person who holds the string must stand within a door or window, or under some cover, so that the silk ribbon may not be wet; and care must be taken that the twine does not touch the frame of the door or window. As soon as any of the thunder-clouds come over the kite, the pointed wire will draw the electric fire from them, and the kite, with all the twine, will be electrified, and the loose filaments of the twine will stand out every way, and be attracted by an approaching finger. And when the rain has wetted the kite and twine, so that it can conduct the electric fire freely, you will find it stream out plentifully from the key on the approach of your knuckle. At this key the phial may be charged; and from electric fire thus obtained spirits may be kindled, and all the other electric experiments be performed which are usually done by the help of a rubbed glass globe or tube, and thereby the sameness of the electric matter with that of lightning completely demonstrated.

B. FRANKLIN.

14

ANTOINE LAVOISIER

Antoine Lavoisier, the father of modern chemistry, was born in Paris, in 1743. He had access to the best education available, and in Paris he was able to sit at the feet of Europe's leading scientists. He proved to be an apt pupil. By the age of twenty-five, he had impressed his peers sufficiently to win election to the French Academy of Science. The royal government also recognized his ability and placed him in charge of its production of gunpowder; in this capacity, Lavoisier organized one of the early chemical industries: the manufacture of saltpetre which, until this time, had been mined. For the revolutionary government, he helped to reform the system of weights and measures, thus performing as midwife at the birth of the metric system. On the whole, however, the revolution found more reason to suspect Lavoisier than to applaud him. He had been intimately associated with the royal establishment, and he had participated as a partner in the notorious *ferme générale,* which contracted to collect the taxes of central France. In 1794, at the height of the terror, Lavoisier died on the scaffold, reaping with other members of the *ferme* the reward of an animosity built over long years.

Chemistry, the science to which Lavoisier devoted his life, had not prospered equally with physics during the scientific revolution of the 17th century. There had been much experimentation, and the corpus of chemical knowledge had expanded dramatically. Chemical theory, however, had failed to formulate the basic concepts from which a satisfactory chemical science could be constructed. The premise of the mechanical philosophy—that matter is differentiated only by the shape and motion of its particles, with the consequent conviction that matter is infinitely malleable, one substance transforming smoothly into another—may have stood in the way of a fruitful notion of chemical substance. Whatever the cause, chemistry was still searching for its peculiar level of generalization and its set of basic concepts when Lavoisier took up its study.

At that time, the problems surrounding the established doctrine of phlogiston were coming to a head. Considered as the material principle of combustion, phlogiston determined, by its presence, what substances would burn. The dissolution and destruction of bodies in combustion was explained as the liberation of phlogiston, which manifested itself as heat. The need to absorb the liberated phlogiston accounted for the recognized role of the air, but no one admitted the possibility that air could enter into the process of combustion or into any chemical reaction. The supreme achievement of the phlogiston theory had been its recognition of the essential identity of combustion and the calcination (or rusting) of metals. When the calxes of metals turned out to be heavier than the metals themselves, it could only be assumed that phlogiston had negative gravity—a perplexing conclusion in view of Newton's law of universal gravitation. The crucial step in the chemical revolution initiated by Lavoisier involved a reformulation of the associated notions of combustion and air.

14

Elements of Chemistry

. . . It will, no doubt, be a matter of surprise, that in a treatise upon the elements of chemistry, there should be no chapter on the constituent and elementary parts of matter; but I may here observe, that the fondness for reducing all the bodies in nature to three or four elements, proceeds from a prejudice which has descended to us from the Greek Philosophers. The notion of four elements, which by the variety of their proportions, compose all the known substances in nature, is a mere hypothesis, assumed long before the first principles of experimental philosophy or of chemistry had any existence. In those days, without possessing facts, they framed systems; while we, who have collected facts, seem determined to reject even these, when they do not agree with our prejudices. The authority of those fathers of human philosophy still carry great weight: and there is reason to fear that it will even bear hard upon generations yet to come.

It is remarkable, notwithstanding the number of philosophical chemists who have supported the doctrine of the four elements, that there is not one who has not been led, by the evidence of facts, to admit a greater number of elements into their theory. The first chemical authors, after the revival of letters, considered sulphur and salt as elementary substances, entering into the composition of a great number of bodies. Hence, instead of four, they admitted the existence of six elements. Beccher assumed the existence of three kinds of earth; from combinations of which, in different proportions, he supposed all the varieties of metallic substances to be produced. Stahl gave a new modification to this system: And succeeding chemists have taken the liberty to make or to imagine changes and additions of a similar nature. All these chemists were carried along by the genius of the age in which they lived, being satisfied with assertions instead of proofs; or, at least, often admitting as

Translated from the original French (1789) by Robert Kerr, Edinburgh, 1790 proofs the slightest degrees of probability, unsupported by that strictly rigorous analysis which is required by modern philosophy.

All that can be said upon the number and nature of elements is, in my opinion, confined to discussions entirely of a metaphysical nature. The subject only furnishes us with indefinite problems, which may be solved in a thousand different ways, not one of which, in all probability, is consistent with nature. I shall, therefore, only add upon this subject, that if, by the term *elements*, we mean to express those simple and indivisible atoms of which matter is composed, it is extremely probable we know nothing at all about them; but if we apply the term *elements* or *principles of bodies*, to express our idea of the last point which analysis is capable of reaching, we must admit, as elements, all the substances into which we are able to reduce bodies by decomposition. Not that we are entitled to affirm, that these substances which we consider as simple, may not themselves be compounded of two, or even of a greater number of more simple principles. But since these principles cannot be separated, or rather since we have not hitherto discovered the means of separating them, they act with regard to us as simple substances, and we ought never to suppose them compounded until experiment and observation have proved them to be so. . . .

Chapter I

Of the Combinations of Caloric, and the Formation of Elastic Aëriform Fluids

That every body, whether solid or fluid, is augmented in all its dimensions by any increase of its sensible heat, was long ago fully established as a physical axiom, or universal proposition, by the celebrated Boerhaave. Such facts as have been adduced, for controverting the generality of this principle, offer only fallacious results, or, at least, such as are so complicated with foreign circumstances, as to mislead the judgment. But, when we separately consider the effects, so as to deduce each from the cause to which they separately belong, it is easy to perceive, that the separation of particles by heat is a constant and general law of nature.

When we have heated a solid body to a certain degree, and have thereby caused its particles to separate from each other, if we allow the body to cool, its particles again approach each other in the same proportion in which they were separated by the increased temperature; the body returns by the same degrees of expansion through which it before extended; and, if brought back to the same temperature which it possessed at the commencement of the experiment, it recovers exactly the same dimensions which it formerly occupied. We are still very far

from being able to produce the degree of absolute cold, or total depriva-
tion of heat, being unacquainted with any degree of coldness which we
cannot suppose capable of still farther augmentation. Hence it follows,
that we are incapable of causing the ultimate particles of bodies to approach each other as near as possible, and that these particles of bodies
do not touch each other in any state hitherto known. Though this be a
very singular conclusion it is impossible to be denied.

It may be supposed, that, since the particles of bodies are thus continually impelled by heat to separate from each other, they would have
no connection between themselves; and that, of consequence, there could
be no solidity in nature, unless these particles were held together by
some other power which tended to unite them, and, so to speak, to
chain them together: This power, whatever be its cause or manner of
operation, is named Attraction.

Thus the particles of all bodies may be considered as subject to the
action of two opposite powers, Repulsion and Attraction, between which
they remain in equilibrio. So long as the attractive force remains
stronger, the body must continue in a state of solidity: but if, on the
contrary, heat has so far removed these particles from each other as to
place them beyond the sphere of attraction, they lose the cohesion they
before had with each other and the body ceases to be solid.

Water gives us a regular and constant example of these facts. Whilst
its temperature is below 32° of Fahrenheit's scale, it remains solid, and
is called ice. Above that degree of temperature, its particles being no
longer held together by reciprocal attraction, it becomes liquid; and,
when we raise its temperature above 212°, its particles, giving way to
the repulsion caused by the heat, assume the state of vapour or gas, and
the water is changed into an aëriform fluid.

The same may be affirmed of all bodies in nature: They are either
solid, or liquid, or in the state of elastic aëriform vapour, according to
the proportion which takes place between the attractive force inherent
in their particles, and the repulsive power of the heat acting upon these;
or, what amounts to the same thing, in proportion to the degrees of heat
to which they are exposed.

It is difficult to comprehend these phenomena, without admitting them
as the effects of a real and material substance, or very subtile fluid, which,
insinuating itself between the particles of bodies, separates them from
each other. Even allowing that the existence of this fluid may be hypothetical, we shall see in the sequel, that it explains the phenomena of
nature in a very satisfactory manner.

This substance, whatever it is, being the cause of heat, or, in other
words, the sensation which we call *warmth* being caused by the accumula-

tion of this substance, we cannot, in strict language, distinguish it by the term *heat*, because the same name would then very improperly express both cause and effect. For this reason, in the memoir which I published in 1777, I gave it the names of *igneous fluid*, and *matter of heat:* And since that time, in the work published by Mr. de Morveau, Mr. Berthollet, Mr. de Fourcroy, and myself, upon the reformation of chemical nomenclature, we thought it necessary to reject all periphrastic expressions, which both lengthen physical language, and render it less distinct, and which even frequently do not convey sufficiently just ideas of the object intended. Wherefore, we have distinguished the cause of heat, or that exquisitely elastic fluid which produces it, by the term of *caloric.* Besides that this expression fulfils our object in the system which we have adopted, it possesses this farther advantage, that it accords with every species of opinion; since, strictly speaking, we are not obliged to suppose this to be a real substance, it being sufficient, as will more clearly appear in the sequel of this work, that it be considered as the repulsive cause, whatever that may be, which separates the particles of matter from each other; so that we are still at liberty to investigate its effects in an abstract and mathematical manner.

In the present state of our knowledge, we are unable to determine whether light be a modification of caloric, or if caloric be, on the contrary, a modification of light. This, however, is indisputable, that in a system where only decided facts are admissible, and where we avoid, as far as possible, to suppose anything to be, that is not really known to exist, we ought provisionally to distinguish, by distinct terms, such things as are known to produce different effects. We therefore distinguish light from caloric; though we do not therefore deny that these have certain qualities in common, and that, in certain circumstances, they combine with other bodies almost in the same manner, and produce, in part, the same effects.

What I have already said, may suffice to determine the idea affixed to the word *caloric*; but there remains a more difficult attempt, which is, to give a just conception of the manner in which caloric acts upon other bodies. Since this subtile matter penetrates through the pores of all known substances; since there are no vessels through which it cannot escape; and, consequently, as there are none which are capable of retaining it, we can only come at the knowledge of its properties by effects which are fleeting and difficultly ascertainable. It is in those things which we neither see nor feel, that it is especially necessary to guard against the extravagancy of our imagination, which forever inclines to step beyond the bounds of truth, and is very difficultly restrained within the narrow limits of fact.

We have already seen, that the same body becomes solid, or fluid, or aëriform, according to the quantity of caloric by which it is penetrated; or, more strictly, according as the repulsive force exerted by the caloric is equal to, stronger, or weaker, than the attraction of the particles of the body it acts upon.

But, if these two powers only existed, bodies would become liquid at an indivisible degree of the thermometer, and would almost instantaneously pass from the solid state of aggregation to that of aëriform elasticity. Thus water, for instance, at the very instant when it ceases to be ice, would begin to boil, and would be transformed into an aëriform fluid, having its particles scattered indefinitely throughout the surrounding space. That this does not happen, must depend upon the action of some third power: The Pressure of the Atmosphere prevents this separation, and causes the water to remain in the liquid state until raised to the temperature indicated by 212° on the scale of Fahrenheit's thermometer; the quantity of caloric which it receives in the lower temperatures being insufficient to overcome the pressure of the atmosphere.

Whence it appears, that, without this atmospheric pressure, we should not have any permanent liquid, and should only see bodies in that state of existence in the very instant of melting; for the smallest additional caloric would then instantly separate their particles, and dissipate them through the surrounding medium. Besides, without this atmospheric pressure, we should not even have any proper aëriform fluids; because the moment the force of attraction is overcome by the repulsive power of the caloric, the particles of bodies would separate themselves indefinitely, having nothing to give limits to their expansion, unless their own gravity might collect them together, so as to form an atmosphere. . . .

We have already shewn, that the particles of every substance in nature exist in a certain state of equilibrium, between that attraction which tends to unite and keep the particles together, and the effects of the caloric which tends to separate them. Hence, caloric not only surrounds the particles of all bodies on every side, but fills up every interval which the particles of bodies leave between each other. We may form an idea of this, by supposing a vessel filled with small spherical leaden bullets, among which a quantity of fine sand is poured; this, insinuating itself into the intervals between the bullets, will fill up every void. The balls, in this comparison, are to the sand which surrounds them exactly in the same situation as the particles of bodies are with respect to the caloric; with this difference only, that the balls are supposed to touch each other, whereas the particles of bodies are not in contact, being retained at a small distance from each other by the caloric.

If, instead of spherical balls, we substitute solid bodies of a hexahedral, octohedral, or any other regular figure, the capacity of the intervals between them will be lessened, and consequently will no longer contain the same quantity of sand. The same thing takes place with respect to natural bodies; the intervals left between their particles are not of equal capacity, but vary in consequence of the different figures and magnitude of their particles, and of the distance at which these particles are maintained, according to the existing proportion between their inherent attraction, and the repulsive force exerted upon them by the caloric. . . .

It remains, before finishing this article, to say a few words concerning the cause of the elasticity of gases, and of liquids in the state of vapour. It is by no means difficult to perceive that this elasticity depends upon that of caloric, which seems to be the most eminently elastic body in nature. Nothing is more readily conceivable, than that one body should become elastic, by entering into combination with another body possessed of that quality. We must allow that this is only an explanation of elasticity, by an assumption of elasticity; we thus only remove the difficulty one step farther, and the reason for caloric being elastic still remains unexplained. Elasticity in the abstract is merely a supposable quality inherent in the particles of bodies, by virtue of which they recede from each other when forced together. This tendency in the particles of caloric to separate, takes place even at considerable distances. We shall be satisfied of this, when we consider that air is capable of undergoing great compression, which supposes that its particles were previously at a considerable distance from each other; for the power of approaching together certainly supposes a previous distance, at least equal to the degree of approximation: Consequently those particles of the air, which are already considerably distant from each other, tend to separate still farther. If we produce Boyle's vacuum in a large receiver of an air-pump, the last portion of air which remains extends itself uniformly through the whole capacity of the vessel, however large, filling it completely, and pressing everywhere against its sides: We cannot explain this fact, without supposing that the particles make an effort to separate themselves on every side; and we are quite ignorant at what distance, or in what degree of rarefaction, this effort ceases to act.

In the above experiments a true repulsion takes place between the particles of elastic fluids; at least, circumstances occur exactly as if such a repulsion actually existed; and we have a right to conclude that the particles of caloric mutually repel each other. When we are once permitted to suppose this repelling force, the theory of the formation of gases, or aëriform fluids, becomes perfectly simple; though we must, at the same time, allow, that it is extremely difficult to form an accurate conception how this repulsive force acts upon very minute particles placed at great distances from each other.

It is, perhaps, more natural to suppose, that the particles of caloric have a stronger mutual attraction than those of any other substance, and that these latter particles are torn asunder in consequence of this superior attraction of the particles of caloric, which forces them between the particles of other bodies, that they may be able to re-unite with each other. We may observe something analogous to this idea in the phenomena which occur when a dry sponge is dipt in water: The sponge swells; its particles separate from each other; and all its intervals are filled by the water. It is evident that the sponge, in the act of swelling, has acquired a greater capacity for containing water than it had when dry. But we cannot certainly maintain, that the introduction of water between the particles of the sponge has endowed them with a repulsive power, which tends to separate them from each other; on the contrary, the whole phenomena are produced by means of attractive powers: These are the gravity of the water, and the power which it exerts on every side, in common with all other fluids; The force of attraction, which takes place between the particles of the water, causing them to unite together; The mutual attraction of the particles of the sponge for each other; And, The reciprocal attraction which exists between the particles of the sponge and those of the water. It is easy to understand, that the explanation of this fact depends upon properly appreciating the intensity of, and connection between, these several powers. It is probable, therefore, that the separation of the particles of bodies, occasioned by caloric, depends in a similar manner upon a certain combination of different attractive powers, which, in conformity with the imperfection of our knowledge, we endeavour to express by saying that caloric communicates a power of repulsion to the particles of bodies.

*   *   *   *

Chapter III

Analysis of Atmospheric Air, and its Division into Two Elastic Fluids; the One Fit for Respiration; the Other Incapable of Being Respired

From what has been premised, it appears that our atmosphere is composed of a mixture of every substance capable of retaining the gaseous or aëriform state in the common temperatures, and under the usual degrees of pressure which it experiences. These fluids constitute a mass, in some measure homogeneous, extending from the surface of the earth to the greatest height hitherto attained, of which the density continually decreases in the inverse ratio of the superincumbent weight. But, as I have before observed, it is possible that this first stratum may be surmounted by several others consisting of different fluids.

Our business, in this place, is to endeavour to determine by experiments the nature of the elastic fluids which compose the inferior stratum of air which we inhabit. Modern chemistry has made great advances in this research; and it will appear, by the following details, that the analysis of atmospherical air has been more rigorously determined than that of any other substance of the class.

Chemistry affords two general methods of determining the constituent principles of bodies, the method of analysis, and that of synthesis. When, for instance, by combining water with alcohol, we form the species of liquor called, in commercial language, brandy, or spirit of wine, we certainly have a right to conclude, that brandy, or spirit of wine, is composed of alcohol combined with water. We can procure the same result by the analytical method; and in general it ought to be considered as a principle in chemical science, never to rest satisfied without both these species of proofs. We have this advantage in the analysis of atmospherical air; being able both to decompound it, and to form it anew in the most satisfactory manner. I shall, however, at present confine myself to recount such experiments as are most conclusive upon this head; and I may consider most of these as my own, having either first invented them, or having repeated those of others, intended for analyzing atmospherical air, in perfectly new points of view.

I took a container of about 36 cubical inches capacity, having a long neck of six or seven lines internal diameter, and having bent the neck to allow of its being placed in the furnace in such a manner that the extremity of its neck might be inserted under a bell-glass placed in a trough of quicksilver; I introduced four ounces of pure mercury into the container, and, by means of a syphon, exhausted the air in the receiver so as to raise the quicksilver to L L, and I carefully marked the height at which it stood, by pasting on a slip of paper. Having accurately noted the height of the thermometer and barometer, I lighted a fire in the furnace, which I kept up almost continually during twelve days, so as to keep the quicksilver always very near its boiling point. Nothing remarkable took place during the first day: The mercury, though not boiling, was continually evaporating, and covered the interior surface of the vessel with small drops, which gradually augmenting to a sufficient size, fell back into the mass at the bottom of the vessel. On the second day, small red particles began to appear on the surface of the mercury; these, during the four or five following days, gradually increased in size and number, after which they ceased to increase in either respect. At the end of twelve days, seeing that the calcination of the mercury did not at all increase, I extinguished the fire, and allowed the vessels to cool. The bulk of air in the body and neck of the container, and in the bell-glass, reduced to a medium of 28 inches of the barometer and 54.5° of the thermometer, at the commencement of the experiment was about 50 cubical inches. At the end of the experiment the remaining air, reduced to the same medium pressure and temperature, was only between 42 and 43 cubical inches; consequently it had lost about $\frac{1}{6}$ of its bulk. Afterwards, having collected all the red particles, formed during the experiment, from the running mercury in which they floated, I found these to amount to 45 grains.

I was obliged to repeat this experiment several times, as it is difficult, in one experiment, both to preserve the whole air upon which we operate, and to collect the whole of the red particles, or calx of mercury, which is formed during the calcination. It will often happen in the sequel, that I shall, in this manner, give in one detail the results of two or three experiments of the same nature.

The air which remained after the calcination of the mercury in this experiment, and which was reduced to $\frac{5}{6}$ of its former bulk, was no longer fit either for respiration or for combustion: animals being introduced into it were suffocated in a few seconds, and when a taper was plunged into it, it was extinguished, as if it had been immersed in water.

In the next place, I took the 45 grains of red matter formed during this experiment, which I put into a small glass retort, having a proper apparatus for receiving such liquid or gaseous product, as might be extracted: Having applied a fire to the retort in the furnace, I observed that, in proportion as the red matter became heated, the intensity of its colour augmented. When the retort was almost red hot, the red matter began gradually to decrease in bulk, and in a few minutes after it disappeared altogether; at the same time $41\frac{1}{2}$ grains of running mercury were collected in the recipient, and 7 or 8 cubical inches of elastic fluid, greatly more capable of supporting both respiration and combustion than atmospherical air, were collected in the bell-glass.

A part of this air being put into a glass-tube of about an inch diameter, shewed the following properties: A taper burned in it with a dazzling splendour; and charcoal, instead of consuming quietly, as it does in common air, burnt with a flame, attended with a decrepitating noise, like phosphorus, and threw out such a brilliant light that the eyes could hardly endure it. This species of air was discovered almost at the same time by Dr. Priestley, Mr. Scheele, and myself. Dr. Priestley gave it the name of *dephlogisticated air*; Mr. Scheele called it *empyreal air*; at first I named it *highly respirable air*, to which has since been substituted the term of *vital air*. We shall presently see what we ought to think of these denominations.

In reflecting upon the circumstances of this experiment, we readily perceive that the mercury, during its calcination, absorbs the salubrious and respirable part of the air, or, to speak more strictly, the base of this respirable part; that the remaining air is a species of mephitis, incapable of supporting combustion or respiration; and, consequently, that atmospheric air is composed of two elastic fluids of different and opposite qualities. As a proof of this important truth, if we recombine these two elastic fluids, which we have separately obtained in the above experiment, viz. the 42 cubical inches of mephitis, with the eight cubical inches of highly respirable air, we reproduce an air precisely similar to that of the atmosphere, and possessing nearly the same power of supporting combustion and respiration, and of contributing to the calcination of metals. . . .

Having filled a bell-glass of about six pints measure with pure air, or the highly respirable part of air, I transported this jar, by means of a very flat vessel, into a quicksilver bath, taking care to render the surface of the mercury perfectly dry, both within and without the jar, with blotting paper. I then provided a small cup of China-ware, very flat and open, in which I placed some small pieces of iron, turned spirally, and arranged in such a way as seemed most favourable for the combustion being communicated to every part. To the end of one of these pieces of iron was fixed a small morsel of tinder, to which was added about the sixteenth part of a grain of phosphorus; and, by raising the bell-glass a little, the china cup with its contents were introduced into the pure air. I know that, by this means, some common air must mix with the pure air in the glass; but this, when it is done dexterously, is so very trifling, as not to injure the success of the experiment. This being done, a part of the air was sucked out from the bell-glass by means of a syphon, so as to raise the mercury within the glass; and, to prevent the mercury from getting into the syphon, a small piece of paper was twisted round its extremity. In sucking out the air, if the motion of the lungs only be used, we cannot make the mercury rise above an inch or an inch and a half; but, by properly using the muscles of the mouth, we can, without difficulty, cause it to rise six or seven inches.

I next took an iron wire, properly bent for the purpose, and making it red hot in the fire, passed it through the mercury into the receiver, and brought it in contact with the small piece of phosphorus attached to the tinder. The phosphorus instantly took fire, which communicated to the tinder, and from that to the iron. When the pieces have been properly arranged, the whole iron burns, even to the last particle, throwing out a white brilliant light similar to that of Chinese fire-works. The great heat produced by this combustion melts the iron into round globules of different sizes, most of which fall into the China cup; but some are thrown out of it, and swim on the surface of the mercury. At the beginning of the combustion, there is a slight augmentation in the volume of the air in the bell-glass, from the dilation caused by the heat; but, presently afterwards, a rapid diminution of the air takes place, and the mercury rises in the glass, insomuch that, when the quantity of iron is sufficient, and the air operated upon is very pure, almost the whole air employed is absorbed. . . .

By this experiment, it is not possible to determine, at one time, both the additional weight acquired by the iron and the changes which have taken place in the air. If it is wished to ascertain what additional weight has been gained by the iron, and the proportion between that and the air absorbed, we must carefully mark upon the bell-glass with a diamond the height of the mercury, both before and after the experiment. After this, the syphon, guarded, as before, with a bit of paper to prevent its filling with mercury, is to be introduced under the bell-glass, having the thumb placed upon the extremity of the syphon, to regulate the passage of the air; and by this means the air is gradually admitted, so as to let the mercury fall to its level. This being done, the bell-glass is to be carefully removed; the globules of melted iron contained in the cup, and those which have been scattered about, and swim upon the mercury, are to be accurately collected, and the whole is to be weighted. The iron will be found in that state called *martial ethiops* by the old chemists, possessing a degree of metallic brilliancy, very friable, and readily reduced into powder, under the hammer, or with a pestle and mortar. If the experiment has succeeded well, from 100 grains of iron will be obtained 135 or 136 grains of ethiops, which is an augmentation of 35 *per cent.*

If all the attention has been made to this experiment which it deserves, the air will be found diminished in weight, exactly equal to what the iron has gained. Having therefore burnt 100 grains of iron, which has acquired an additional weight of 35 grains, the diminution of air will be found exactly 70 cubical inches; and it will be shewn, in the sequel, that the weight of vital air is very near half a grain for each cubical inch; so that, in effect, the augmentation of weight in the one exactly coincides with the loss of it in the other.

I shall observe here, once for all, that, in every experiment of this kind, the pressure and temperature of the air, both before and after the experiment, must be reduced by calculation to a common standard of 54° of the thermometer, and 28 inches of the barometer. Towards the end of this work, the manner of performing this very necessary reduction will be found accurately detailed.

If it be required to examine the nature of the air which remains after this experiment, we must operate in a somewhat different manner. After the combustion is finished, and the vessels have cooled, we first take out the cup, and the burnt iron, by introducing the hand through the quicksilver, under the bell-glass; we next introduce some solution of potash, or caustic alkali, or of the sulphuret of potash, or such other substances as are judged proper for examining their action upon the residuum of air. I shall, in the sequel, give an account of these methods of analyzing air, when I have explained the nature of these different substances, which are only here in a manner incidently mentioned. After this examination, so much water must be let into the glass as will displace the quicksilver, and then, by means of a shallow dish placed below the bell-glass, it is to be removed into the common water pneumato-chemical apparatus, where the air remaining may be examined at large, and with great facility.

When very soft and very pure iron has been employed in this experiment, and, when the combustion has been performed in the purest respirable or vital air, free from admixture of the noxious or mephitic part, the air which remains after the combustion will be found as pure as it was before: But it is difficult to find iron entirely free from a small portion of charry matter, which is chiefly abundant in steel; and it is likewise exceedingly difficult to procure pure air perfectly free from some admixture of mephitis, with which it is almost always contaminated: That species of noxious air does not, in the smallest degree, disturb the result of the experiment, as it is always found at the end exactly in the same quantity as at the beginning.

I mentioned before, that we have two ways of determining the constituent parts of atmospheric air, the method of analysis, and that by synthesis. The calcination of mercury has furnished us with an example of each of these methods, since, after having deprived it of the respirable part, by means of the mercury, we have restored it again, so as to recompose an air precisely similar to that of the atmosphere. But we can equally accomplish this synthetic composition of atmospheric air, by borrowing the materials of which it is formed from different kingdoms of nature. We shall see hereafter that, when animal substances are dissolved in the nitric acid, a great quantity of gas is disengaged, which extinguishes light, and is unfit for animal respiration, being exactly similar to the noxious or mephitic part of atmospheric air. And, if we take 73 parts, by weight, of this elastic fluid, and mix it with 27 parts of highly respirable air, procured from calcined mercury, we shall form an elastic fluid precisely similar to atmospheric air in all its properties. . . .

Chapter IV

Nomenclature of the Several Constituent Parts of Atmospheric Air

Hitherto I have been obliged to make use of circumlocution, to express the nature of the several substances which constitute our atmosphere, having provisionally used the terms of *respirable* and *noxious, or non-respirable, parts of the air.* But the investigations I mean to undertake require a more direct mode of expression; and, having now endeavoured to give simple and distinct ideas of the different substances which enter into the composition of the atmosphere, I shall henceforth express these ideas by words equally simple.

The temperature of our earth being very near to that at which water becomes solid, and at which reciprocally it changes from solid to fluid; and as this phenomenon takes place frequently under our observation, it has very naturally followed, that, in the languages of at least every climate subject to any degree of winter, a term has been used for signifying water in the state of solidity, or when deprived of its caloric. The same precision has not been found necessary with respect to water reduced to the state of vapour by an additional quantity of caloric. Those persons who do not make a particular study of objects of this kind, are still ignorant that water, when in a temperature only a little above the boiling heat, is changed into an elastic aëriform fluid, susceptible, like all other gases, of being received and contained in vessels, and of preserving its gaseous form so long as it remains at the temperature of 212°, and under a pressure not exceeding 28 inches of the mercurial barometer. As this phenomenon has not been very generally observed, no language has used a particular term for expressing water in this state; and the same thing occurs with all fluids, and all substances, which do not evaporate in the common temperature, and under the usual pressure of our atmosphere.

For similar reasons, names have not been given to the liquid or concrete states of most of the aëriform fluids: These were not known to arise from the combination of caloric with certain bases; and, as they had not been seen either in the liquid or solid states, their existence, under these forms, was even unknown to natural philosophers.

We have not pretended to make any alteration upon such terms as are sanctified by ancient custom; and, therefore, continue to use the words *water* and *ice* in their common acceptation. We likewise retain the word *air*, to express that collection of elastic fluids which composes our atmosphere: But we have not thought it necessary to preserve the same respect for modern terms, adopted by the later philosophers, having considered ourselves as at liberty to reject such as appeared liable to give erroneous ideas of the substances they are meant to express, and either to substitute new terms, or to employ the old ones, after having modified them in such a manner as to convey more determinate ideas. New words, when necessary, have been borrowed chiefly from the Greek language, in such a manner as to make their etymology convey some idea of what was meant to be represented by them; and we have always endeavoured to make these short, and of such a form as to admit of being changed into adjectives and verbs.

Following these principles, we have, after the example of Mr. Macquer, retained the term *gas*, employed by Vanhelmont; having arranged the numerous classes of elastic aëriform fluids under that name, excepting only atmospheric air. *Gas*, therefore, in our nomenclature, becomes a generic term, expressing the fullest degree of saturation in any body with caloric; being, in fact, a term expressive of a mode of existence. To distinguish the species of gas, we employ a second term derived from the name of the base, which, saturated with caloric, forms each particular gas. Thus, we name water combined to saturation with caloric, so as to form an elastic fluid, *aqueous gas;* ether, combined in the same manner, *ethereal gas;* the combination of alcohol with caloric becomes *alcoholic gas;* and, following the same principles, we have *muriatic acid gas, ammoniacal gas,* and so on of every substance susceptible of being combined with caloric, in such a manner as to assume the gaseous or elastic aëriform state.

We have already seen, that the atmospheric fluid, or common air, is composed of two gases or aëriform fluids; one of which is capable, by respiration, of contributing to support animal life; and in it metals are calcinable, and combustible bodies may burn: The other, on the contrary, is endowed with directly opposite qualities; it cannot be breathed by animals, neither will it admit of the combustion of inflammable bodies, nor of the calcination of metals. We have given to the base of the former, which is the respirable portion of atmospheric air, the name of *oxygen,* from ὀξυ *acidum,* and γεινομαι *gignor,* because one of the most general properties of this base is to form acids, by combining with many different substances. The union of this base with caloric, which is the same with what was formerly named *pure,* or *vital,* or *highly respirable air,* we now call *oxygen gas.* The weight of this gas, at the temperature of 54.50°, and under a pressure equal to 28 inches of the barometer, is half a grain for each cubical inch nearly, or one ounce and a half to each cubical foot.

The chemical properties of the noxious portion of atmospheric air being hitherto but little known, we have been satisfied to derive the name of its base from its known quality of killing such animals as are forced to breathe it, giving it the name of *azot*, from the Greek privative particle α and ζωὴ, *vita;* hence the name of the noxious part of the atmospheric air is *azotic gas*. The weight of this, in the same temperature, and under the same pressure, is 1 *oz*. 2 *drams* and 48 *grs.* to the cubical foot, or 0.4444 of a grain to the cubical inch. We cannot deny that this name appears somewhat extraordinary; but this must be the case with all new terms, which cannot be expected to become familiar until they have been some time in use. We long endeavoured to find a more proper designation without success: It was at first proposed to call it *alkaligen gas*, as, from the experiments of Mr. Berthollet, it appears to enter into the composition of ammoniac, or volatile alkali; but then we have as yet no proof of its making one of the constituent elements of the other alkalies; besides, it is proved to form a part of the nitric acid, which gives as good reason to have it called *nitrigen*. For these reasons, finding it necessary to reject any name upon systematic principles, we have considered that we ran no risk of mistake, in adopting the terms of *azot*, and *azotic gas*, which only express a matter of fact, or that property which it possesses, of depriving such animals as breathe it of their lives.

I should anticipate subjects more properly reserved for the subsequent chapters, were I in this place to enter upon the nomenclature of the several species of gases: It is sufficient, in this part of the work, to establish the principles upon which their denominations are founded. The principal merit of the nomenclature we have adopted is, that, when once the simple elementary subject is distinguished by an appropriate term, the names of all its compounds derive readily, and necessarily, from this first denomination. . . .

Chapter V

Of the Decomposition of Oxygen Gas by Sulphur, Phosphorus, and Charcoal—and of the Formation of Acids in General

. . . I have already shewn that phosphorus is changed by combustion into an extremely light, white, flakey matter. Its properties are likewise entirely altered by this transformation; from being insoluble in water, it becomes not only soluble, but so greedy of moisture, as to attract the humidity of the air with astonishing rapidity: By this means it is converted into a liquid, considerably more dense, and of more specific gravity, than water. In the state of phosphorus before combustion, it had scarcely any sensible taste; by its union with oxygen it acquires an extremely sharp and sour taste; in a word, from one of the class of combustible bodies, it is changed into an incombustible substance, and becomes one of those bodies called acids.

This property of a combustible substance to be converted into an acid, by the addition of oxygen, we shall presently find belongs to a great number of bodies: Wherefore, strict logic requires that we should adopt a common term for indicating all these operations which produce analogous results. This is the true way to simplify the study of science, as it would be quite impossible to bear all its specifical details in the memory, if they were not classically arranged. For this reason, we shall distinguish the conversion of phosphorus into an acid, by its union with oxygen, and in general every combination of oxygen with a combustible substance, by the term of *oxygenation*: From this I shall adopt the verb to *oxygenate*; and of consequence shall say, that in *oxygenating* phosphorus we convert it into an acid.

Sulphur is likewise a combustible body, or, in other words, it is a body which possesses the power of decomposing oxygen gas, by attracting the oxygen from the caloric with which it was combined. This can very easily be proved, by means of experiments quite similar to those we have given with phosphorus; but it is necessary to premise, that in these operations with sulphur, the same accuracy of result is not to be expected as with phosphorus; because the acid which is formed by the combustion of sulphur is difficultly condensible, and because sulphur burns with more difficulty, and is soluble in the different gases. But I can safely assert, from my own experiments, that sulphur in burning absorbs oxygen gas; that the resulting acid is considerably heavier than the sulphur burnt; that its weight is equal to the sum of the weights of the sulphur which has been burnt, and of the oxygen absorbed; and, lastly, that this acid is weighty, incombustible, and miscible with water in all proportions. The only uncertainty remaining upon this head, is with regard to the proportions of sulphur and of oxygen which enter into the composition of the acid.

Charcoal, which, from all our present knowledge regarding it, must be considered as a simple combustible body, has likewise the property of decomposing oxygen gas, by absorbing its base from the caloric: But the acid resulting from this combustion does not condense in the common temperature; under the pressure of our atmosphere, it remains in the state of gas, and requires a large proportion of water to combine with, or be dissolved in. This acid has, however, all the known properties of other acids though in a weaker degree, and combines, like them, with all the bases which are susceptible of forming neutral salts.

The combustion of charcoal in oxygen gas, may be effected like that of phosphorus in the bell-glass, placed over mercury: But, as the heat of red-hot iron is not sufficient to set fire to the charcoal, we must add a small morsel of tinder, with a minute particle of phosphorus, in the same manner as is directed in the experiment for the combustion of iron. By that experiment, it appears, that 28 parts by weight of carbon require 72 parts of oxygen for saturation, and that the aëriform acid produced is precisely equal in weight to the sum of the weights of the charcoal consumed and oxygen gas employed during the combustion. This aëriform acid was called fixed or fixable air by the chemists who first discovered it; they did not then know whether it was air resembling that of the atmosphere, or some other elastic fluid, vitiated and corrupted by combustion; but since it is now ascertained to be an acid, formed like all others by the oxygenation of its peculiar base, it is obvious that the name of fixed air is quite ineligible.

By burning charcoal, Mr. de la Place and I found that one *lib.* of charcoal melted 96.375 *libs.* of ice; that, during the combustion 2.5714 *libs.* of oxygen were absorbed, and that 3.5714 *libs.* of acid gas were formed. This gas weighs 0.695 parts of a grain for each cubical inch, in a common standard temperature and pressure mentioned above, so that 34242 cubical inches of acid gas are produced by the combustion of one pound of charcoal.

I might multiply these experiments, and show, by a numerous succession of facts, that all acids are formed by the combustion of certain substances; but I am prevented from doing so in this place, by the plan which I have laid down, of proceeding only from facts already ascertained to such as are unknown, and of drawing my examples only from circumstances already explained. In the mean time, however, the three examples above cited, may suffice for giving a clear and accurate conception of the manner in which acids are formed. By these, it may be clearly seen, that oxygen is an element common to them all, and which constitutes or produces their acidity; and that they differ from each other, according to the several natures of the oxygenated or acidified substances. We must, therefore, in every acid, carefully distinguish between the acidifiable base, which Mr. de Morveau calls the radical, and the acidifying principle, or oxygen.

*   *   *   *

Chapter XVII

Continuation of the Observations upon Salifiable Bases, and the Formation of Neutral Salts

. . . The known salifiable bases, or substances capable of being converted into neutral salts by union with acids, amounts to 24; viz. 3 alkalies, 4 earths, and 17 metallic substances; so that, in the present state of chemical knowledge, the whole possible number of neutral salts amounts to 1152. This number is upon the supposition that the metallic acids are capable of dissolving other metals, which is a new branch of chemistry, not hitherto investigated, upon which depends all the metallic combinations named *vitreous*. There is reason to believe that many of these supposable saline combinations are not capable of being formed, which must greatly reduce the real number of neutral salts producible by nature and art. Even if we suppose the real number to amount only to five or six hundred species of possible neutral salts, it is evident, that, were we to distinguish them, after the manner of the older chemists, either by the names of their first discoverers, or by terms derived from the substances from which they are procured, we should at least have such a confusion of arbitrary designations, as no memory could possibly retain. This method might be tolerable in the early ages of chemistry, or even till within these twenty years, when only about thirty species of salts were known; but in the present times, when the number is augmenting daily, when every new acid gives us 24 or 48 new salts, according as it is capable of one or two degrees of oxygenation, a new method is certainly necessary. The method here adopted, drawn from the nomenclature of the acids, is perfectly analogical, and, following Nature in the simplicity of her operations, gives a natural and easy nomenclature, applicable to every possible neutral salt.

In giving names to the different acids, we have expressed the common property by the generical term *acid*, and have distinguished each species by the name of its peculiar acidifiable base. Hence the acids formed by the oxygenation of sulphur, phosphorus, carbon, &c. are called *sulphuric acid, phosphoric acid, carbonic acid,* &c. We thought it proper likewise to indicate the different degrees of saturation with oxygen, by different terminations of the same specific names: Wherefore we distinguish between sulphurous and suphuric, and between phosphorous and phosphoric acids, &c.

By applying these principles to the nomenclature of neutral salts, we use a common term for all the neutral salts arising from the combinations of one acid, and distinguish the species by adding the name of the salifiable base. Thus, all the neutral salts having sulphuric acid in their composition are named *sulphats*; those formed by the phosphoric acid, *phosphats*, &c. The species being distinguished by the names of the salifiable bases gives us *sulphat of potash, sulphat of soda, sulphat of ammoniac, sulphat of lime, sulphat of iron*, &c. As we are acquainted with 24 salifiable bases, alkaline, earthy and metallic, we have consequently 24 sulphats, as many phosphats, and so on through all the acids.

Sulphur is, however, susceptible of two degrees of oxygenation, the first of which produces sulphurous, and the second, sulphuric acid; and, as the neutral salts produced by these two acids have different properties, and are in fact different salts, it becomes necessary to distinguish those by peculiar terminations; we have therefore distinguished the neutral salts formed by the acids in the first or lesser degree of oxygenation, by changing the termination *at* into *ite*, as *sulphites, phosphites*, &c. Thus, oxygenated or acidified sulphur, in its two degrees of oxygenation, is capable of forming 48 neutral salts, 24 of which are sulphites, and as many sulphats: This is likewise the case with all the acids capable of two degrees of oxygenation.

It were both tiresome and unnecessary to follow these denominations through all the varieties of their possible applications; it is enough to have given the method of naming the various salts, which, when once well understood, is easily applicable to every possible combination. The name of the combustible and acidifiable body being once known, the names of the acid it is capable of forming, and of all the neutral combinations the acid is susceptible of entering into, are most readily remembered. . . .

TABLE OF SIMPLE SUBSTANCES

SIMPLE SUBSTANCES BELONGING TO ALL THE KINGDOMS OF NATURE, WHICH MAY BE CONSIDERED AS THE CHEMICAL ELEMENTS OF BODIES

New Names		Correspondent Old Names
ENGLISH	LATIN	
Light		Light
Caloric	Caloricum	Heat Principle or element of heat Fire, Igneous fluid Matter of fire and of heat
Oxygen	Oxygenum	Dephlogisticated air Empyreal air Vital air, or Base of vital air
Azot	Azotum	Phlogisticated air or gas Mephitis, or its base
Hydrogen	Hydrogenum	Inflammable air or gas, or the base of inflammable air

OXYDABLE AND ACIDIFIABLE SIMPLE SUBSTANCES NOT METALLIC

New Names		Correspondent Old Names
Sulphur	Sulphurum	The same names
Phosphorus	Phosphorum	
Carbon	Carbonum	The simple element of charcoal
Muriatic radical	Murium	Still unknown
Fluoric radical	Fluorum	
Boracic radical	Boracum	

OXYDABLE AND ACIDIFIABLE SIMPLE METALLIC BODIES

New Names			*Correspondent Old Names*
Antimony	Antimonium		Antimony
Arsenic	Arsenicum		Arsenic
Bismuth	Bismuthum		Bismuth
Cobalt	Cobaltum		Cobalt
Copper	Cuprum		Copper
Gold	Aurum		Gold
Iron	Ferrum		Iron
Lead	Plumbum		Lead
Manganese	Manganum	Regulus of	Manganese
Mercury	Mercurium		Mercury
Molybdena	Molybdenum		Molybdena
Nickel	Nickolum		Nickel
Platina	Platinum		Platina
Silver	Argentum		Silver
Tin	Stannum		Tin
Tungstein	Tungstenum		Tungstein
Zinc	Zincum		Zinc

SALIFIABLE SIMPLE EARTHY SUBSTANCES

New Names		*Correspondent Old Names*
Lime	Calca	Chalk, calcareous earth / Quicklime
Magnesia	Magnesia	Magnesia, base of Epsom salt / Calcined or caustic magnesia
Barytes	Baryta	Barytes, or heavy earth
Argil	Argilla	Clay, earth or alum
Silex	Silica	Siliceous or vitrifiable earth
Strontites	Strontyta	Newly discovered

345

Section I

Observations upon the Table of Simple Substances

The principal object of chemical experiments is to decompose natural bodies, so as separately to examine the different substances which enter into their composition. By consulting chemical systems, it will be found that this science of chemical analysis has made rapid progress in our own times. Formerly oil and salt were considered as elements of bodies, whereas later observation and experiment have shewn, that all salts, instead of being simple, are composed of an acid united to a base. The bounds of analysis have been greatly enlarged by modern discoveries; the acids are shewn to be composed of oxygen, as an acidifying principle common to all, united in each to a particular base. I have proved what Mr. Hassenfratz had before advanced, that these radicals of the acids are not all simple elements, many of them being, like the oily principle, composed of hydrogen and carbon. Even the bases of neutral salts have been proved by Mr. Berthollet to be compounds, as he has shewn that ammoniac is composed of azot and hydrogen.

Thus, as chemistry advances towards perfection, by dividing and subdividing, it is impossible to say where it is to end; and these things we at present suppose simple may soon be found quite otherwise. All we dare venture to affirm of any substance is, that it must be considered as simple in the present state of our knowledge, and so far as chemical analysis has hitherto been able to show. We may even presume that the earths must soon cease to be considered as simple bodies; they are the only bodies of the salifiable class which have no tendency to unite with oxygen; and I am much inclined to believe that this proceeds from their being already saturated with that element. If so, they will fall to be considered as compounds consisting of simple substances, perhaps metallic, oxydated to a certain degree. This is only hazarded as a probable conjecture; and I trust the reader will take care not to confound what I have related as truths, fixed on the firm basis of observation and experiment, with mere hypothetical speculations.

The fixed alkalies, potash, and soda, are omitted in the foregoing Table, because they are evidently compound substances, though we are ignorant as yet what are the elements they are composed of.

15

JOHN PLAYFAIR

John Playfair was born in Scotland in 1748. The son of a clergyman, he received his preuniversity education at home and was then packed off to school to qualify for the church. All too soon that training justified itself: the elder Reverend Playfair died, leaving the younger to assume his responsibilities to both parish and family. But John Playfair was not destined to live out his life as a country clergyman. Proceeding with the mathematical studies in which he had already distinguished himself, he eventually obtained a tutorial position in Edinburgh. Accession to a professorship of mathematics in 1785 secured him full membership in the celebrated scientific circle of Adam Smith, Joseph Black, and James Hutton. During the next thirty years, Playfair published comprehensive expositions of physics and mathematics, as well as shorter works on a variety of technical and historical subjects. He died in 1819 while preparing a second edition of his most significant work: *Illustrations of the Huttonian Theory of the Earth*.

At the end of the 18th century, few people were willing to admit that geology was a science. A century of cosmogonical speculation appeared to have produced nothing but impiety, for those geological theories which had stayed within Biblical bounds had been either self-contradictory, trivially refutable, or so fanciful as to be insusceptible of empirical confirmation. To Playfair, however, the situation was by no means as desperate as it was commonly depicted, for he was acquainted first-hand with a theory whose majestic simplicity promised to place the discipline on a secure footing. "Having been instructed by Dr. Hutton himself in his theory of the earth," and having lived "almost in the daily habit of discussing the questions" pertaining to it, Playfair was convinced that the neglect of so persuasive a system could only be owing to the obscurity of the author's exposition of it—that a lucid presentation of the theory (or was it simply a methodology?) would remove the obstacles to its acceptance. Accordingly, when Hutton died in 1797, Playfair embarked on the five-year effort that culminated in the *Illustrations*.

Clearly, Playfair succeeded in "explaining Dr. Hutton's Theory of the Earth in a manner more popular and perspicuous than is done in his own writings." His prose is splendid, his argument logically impeccable, as he asks implicitly and insistently, why the uniformity which seems so reasonable, and even compelling, in respect to inconceivable astronomical distances, should appear so unwarranted, and even sacrilegious, in connection with inconceivable geological times. His argument against the theological constraints that were still omnipresent in geological contexts is that which Galileo had used against long-forgotten restrictions on astronomical thought. Instead of challenging their general legitimacy, he merely pleads for reinterpretation of passages that oppose his own specific interests. In graphic terms, he spells out the argument for accepting at face value the fact that nature displays "no vestige of a beginning, no prospect of an end."

15

Illustrations of the Huttonian Theory of the Earth

Section III
Of the Phenomena Common to Stratified and Unstratified Bodies

92. The series of changes which fossil bodies are destined to undergo, does not cease with their elevation above the level of the sea; it assumes, however, a new direction, and from the moment that they are raised up to the surface, is constantly exerted in reducing them again under the dominion of the ocean. The solidity is now destroyed which was acquired in the bowels of the earth; and as the bottom of the sea is the great laboratory, where loose materials are mineralized and formed into stone, the atmosphere is the region where stones are decomposed, and again resolved into earth.

This decomposition of all mineral substances exposed to the air, is continual, and is brought about by a multitude of agents, both chemical and mechanical, of which some are known to us, and many, no doubt, remain to be discovered. Among the various aëriform fluids which compose our atmosphere, one is already distinguished as the grand principle of mineral decomposition; the others are not inactive, and to them we must add moisture, heat, and perhaps light; substances which, from their affinities to the elements of mineral bodies, have a power of entering into combination with them, and of thus diminishing the forces by which they are united to one another. By the action of air and moisture, the metallic particles, particularly the iron, which enters in such abundance into the composition of almost all fossils, becomes oxydated in such a degree as to lose its tenacity; so that the texture of the surface is destroyed, and a part of the body resolved into earth.

93. Some earths, again, such as the calcareous, are immediately dissolved by water; and though the quantity so dissolved be extremely small, the operation, by being continually renewed, produces a slow but

Published in Edinburgh, 1802.

perpetual corrosion, by which the greatest rocks must in time be subdued. The action of water in destroying hard bodies into which it has obtained entrance, is much assisted by the vicissitudes of heat and cold, especially when the latter extends as far as the point of congelation; for the water, when frozen, occupies a greater space than before, and if the body is compact enough to refuse room for this expansion, its parts are torn asunder by a repulsive force acting in every direction.

94. Besides these causes of mineral decomposition, the action of which we can in some measure trace, there are others known to us only by their effects.

We see, for instance, the purest rock crystal affected by exposure to the weather, its lustre tarnished, and the polish of its surface impaired, but we know nothing of the power by which these operations are performed. Thus also, in the precautions which the mineralogist takes to preserve the fresh fracture of his specimens, we have a proof how indiscriminately all the productions of the fossil kingdom are exposed to the attacks of their unknown enemies, and we perceive how difficult it is to delay the beginnings of a process which no power whatever can finally counteract.

95. The mechanical forces employed in the disintegration of mineral substances, are more easily marked than the chemical. Here again water appears as the most active enemy of hard and solid bodies; and, in every state, from transparent vapour to solid ice, from the smallest rill to the greatest river, it attacks whatever has emerged above the level of the sea, and labours incessantly to restore it to the deep. The parts loosened and disengaged by the chemical agents, are carried down by the rains, and, in their descent, rub and grind the superficies of other bodies. Thus water, though incapable of acting on hard substances by direct attrition, is the cause of their being so acted on; and, when it descends in torrents, carrying with it sand, gravel, and fragments of rock, it may be truly said to turn the forces of the mineral kingdom against itself. Every separation which it makes is necessarily permanent, and the parts once detached can never be united, save at the bottom of the ocean.

96. But it would far exceed the limits of this sketch, to pursue the causes of mineral decomposition through all their forms. It is sufficient to remark, that the consequence of so many minute, but indefatigable agents, all working together, and having *gravity* in their favour, is a system of universal decay and degradation, which may be traced over the whole surface of the land, from the mountain top to the sea shore. That we may perceive the full evidence of this truth, one of the most important in the natural history of the globe, we will begin our survey from the latter of these stations, and retire gradually toward the former.

97. If the coast is bold and rocky, it speaks a language easy to be in-

terpreted. Its broken and abrupt contour, the deep gulfs and salient promontories by which it is indented, and the proportion which these irregularities bear to the force of the waves, combined with the inequality of hardness in the rocks, prove, that the present line of the shore has been determined by the action of the sea. The naked and precipitous cliffs which overhang the deep, the rocks hollowed, perforated, as they are farther advanced in the sea, and at last insulated, lead to the same conclusion, and mark very clearly so many different stages of decay. It is true, we do not see the successive steps of this progress exemplified in the states of the same individual rock, but we see them clearly in different individuals; and the conviction thus produced, when the phenomena are sufficiently multiplied and varied, is as irresistible, as if we saw the changes actually effected in the moment of observation.

On such shores, the fragments of rock once detached, become instruments of further destruction, and make a part of the powerful artillery with which the ocean assails the bulwarks of the land: they are impelled against the rocks, from which they break off other fragments, and the whole are thus ground against one another; whatever be their hardness, they are reduced to gravel, the smooth surface and round figure of which, are the most certain proofs of a *detritus* which nothing can resist.

98. Again, where the sea-coast is flat, we have abundant evidence of the degradation of the land in the beaches of sand and small gravel; the sand banks and shoals that are continually changing; the alluvial land at the mouths of the rivers; the bars that seem to oppose their discharge into the sea, and the shallowness of the sea itself. On such coasts, the land usually seems to gain upon the sea, whereas, on shores of a bolder aspect, it is the sea that generally appears to gain upon the land. What the land acquires in extent, however, it loses in elevation; and, whether its surface increase or diminish, the depredations made on it are in both cases evinced with equal certainty.

99. If we proceed in our survey from the shores, inland, we meet at every step with the fullest evidence of the same truths, and particularly in the nature and economy of rivers. Every river appears to consist of a main trunk, fed from a variety of branches, each running in a valley proportioned to its size, and all of them together forming a system of valleys, communicating with one another, and having such a nice adjustment of their declivities, that none of them join the principal valley, either on too high or too low a level; a circumstance which would be infinitely improbable, if each of these valleys were not the work of the stream that flows in it.

If indeed a river consisted of a single stream, without branches, running in a straight valley, it might be supposed that some great concussion, or some powerful torrent, had opened at once the channel by which its waters are conducted to the ocean; but, when the usual form of a river is considered, the trunk divided into many branches, which rise at a great distance from one another, and these again subdivided into an infinity of smaller ramifications, it becomes strongly impressed upon the mind, that all these channels have been cut by the waters themselves; that they have been slowly dug out by the washing and erosion of the land; and that it is by the repeated touches of the same instrument, that this curious assemblage of lines has been engraved so deeply on the surface of the globe.

100. The changes which have taken place in the courses of rivers, are also to be traced, in many instances, by successive platforms of flat alluvial land, rising one above another, and marking the different levels on which the river has run at different periods of time. Of these, the number to be distinguished, in some instances, is not less than four, or even five; and this necessarily carries us back, like all the operations we are now treating of, to an antiquity extremely remote: for, if it be considered, that each change which the river makes in its bed, obliterates at least a part of the monuments of former changes, we shall be convinced, that only a small part of the progression can leave any distinct memorial behind it, and that there is no reason to think, that, in the part which we see, the beginning is included.

101. In the same manner, when a river undermines its banks, it often discovers deposits of sand and gravel, that have been made when it ran on a higher level than it does at present. In other instances, the same strata are seen on both the banks, though the bed of the river is now sunk deep between them, and perhaps holds as winding a course through the solid rock, as if it flowed along the surface; a proof that it must have begun to sink its bed, when it ran through such loose materials as opposed but a very inconsiderable resistance to its stream. A river, of which the course is both serpentine and deeply excavated in the rock, is among the phenomena, by which the slow waste of the land, and also the cause of that waste, are most directly pointed out.

102. It is, however, where rivers issue through narrow defiles among mountains, that the identity of the strata on both sides is most easily recognized, and remarked at the same time with the greatest wonder. On observing the Potomac, where it penetrates the ridge of the Allegany mountains, or the Irtish, as it issues from the defiles of Altai, there is no man, however little addicted to geological speculations, who does not immediately acknowledge, that the mountain was once continued quite across the space in which the river now flows; and, if he ventures to reason concerning the cause of so wonderful a change, he ascribes it to some great convulsion of nature, which has torn the mountain asunder, and opened a passage for the waters. It is only the philosopher, who has

deeply meditated on the effects which action long continued is able to produce, and on the simplicity of the means which nature employs in all her operations, who sees in this nothing but the gradual working of a stream, that once flowed as high as the top of the ridge which it now so deeply intersects, and has cut its course through the rock, in the same way, and almost with the same instrument, by which the lapidary divides a block of marble or granite.

103. It is highly interesting to trace up, in this manner, the action of causes with which we are familiar, to the production of effects, which at first seem to require the introduction of unknown and extraordinary powers; and it is no less interesting to observe, how skillfully nature has balanced the action of all the minute causes of waste, and rendered them conducive to the general good. Of this we have a most remarkable instance, in the provision made for preserving the soil, or the coat of vegetable mould, spread out over the surface of the earth. This coat, as it consists of loose materials, is easily washed away by the rains, and is continually carried down by the rivers into the sea. This effect is visible to every one; the earth is removed not only in the form of sand and gravel, but its finer particles suspended in the waters, tinge those of some rivers continually, and those of all occasionally; that is, when they are flooded or swollen with rains. The quantity of earth thus carried down, varies according to circumstances; it has been computed, in some instances, that the water of a river in a flood, contains earthy matter suspended in it, amounting to more than the two hundred and fiftieth part of its own bulk. The soil, therefore, is continually diminished, its parts being transported from higher to lower levels, and finally delivered into the sea. But it is a fact, that the soil, notwithstanding, remains the same in quantity, or at least nearly the same, and must have done so, ever since the earth was the receptacle of animal or vegetable life. The soil, therefore, is augmented from other causes, just as much, at an average, as it is diminished by that now mentioned; and this augmentation evidently can proceed from nothing but the constant and slow disintegration of the rocks. In the permanence, therefore, of a coat of vegetable mould on the surface of the earth, we have a demonstrative proof of the continual destruction of the rocks; and cannot but admire the skill, with which the powers of the many chemical and mechanical agents employed in this complicated work, are so adjusted, as to make the supply and the waste of the soil exactly equal to one another.

* * * *

108. These lessons, which the geologist is taught in flat and open countries, become more striking, by the study of those Alpine tracts,

where the surface of the earth attains its greatest elevation. If we suppose him placed for the first time in the midst of such a scene, as soon as he has recovered from the impression made by the novelty and magnificence of the spectacle before him, he begins to discover the footsteps of time, and to perceive, that the works of nature, usually deemed the most permanent, are those on which the characters of vicissitude are most deeply imprinted. He sees himself in the midst of a vast ruin, where the precipices which rise on all sides with such boldness and asperity, the sharp peaks of the granite mountains, and the huge fragments that surround their bases, do but mark so many epochs in the progress of decay, and point out the energy of those destructive causes, which even the magnitude and solidity of such great bodies have been unable to resist.

109. The result of a more minute investigation, is in perfect unison with this general impression. Whence is it, that the elevation of mountains is so obviously connected with the hardness and indestructibility of the rocks which compose them? Why is it, that a lofty mountain of soft and secondary rock is nowhere to be found; and that such chains, as the Pyrenees or the Alps, never consist of any but the hardest stone, of granite for instance, or of those primary strata, which, if we are to credit the preceding theory, have been twice heated in the fires, and twice tempered in the waters, of the mineral regions? Is it not plain that this arises, not from any direct connection between the hardness of stones, and their height in the atmosphere, but from this, that the waste and *detritus* to which all things are subject, will not allow soft and weak substances to remain long in an exposed and elevated situation? Were it not for this, the secondary rocks, being in position superincumbent on the primary, ought to be the highest of the two, and should cover the primary (as they no doubt have at one time done), in the highest as well as the lowest situations, or among the mountains as well as in the plains.

110. Again, wherefore is it, that among all mountains, remarkable for their ruggedness and asperity, the rock, on examination, is always found of very unequal destructibility, some parts yielding to the weather, and to the other causes of disintegration, much more slowly than the rest, and having strength sufficient to support themselves, when left alone, in slender pyramids, bold projections, and overhanging cliffs? Where, on the other hand, the rock wastes uniformly, the mountains are similar to one another; their swells and slopes are gentle, and they are bounded by a waving and continuous surface. The intermediate degrees of resistance which the rocks oppose to the causes of destruction, produce intermediate forms. It is this which gives to the mountains, of every different species of rock, a different habit and expression, and which, in

particular, has imparted to those of granite that venerable and majestic character, by which they rarely fail to be distinguished.

111. The structure of the valleys among mountains, shews clearly to what cause their existence is to be ascribed. Here we have first a large valley, communicating directly with the plain, and winding between high ridges of mountains, while the river in the bottom of it descends over a surface, remarkable, in such a scene, for its uniform declivity. Into this, open a multitude of transverse or secondary valleys, intersecting the ridges on either side of the former, each bringing a contribution to the main stream, proportioned to its magnitude; and, except where a cataract now and then intervenes, all having that nice adjustment in their levels, which is the more wonderful, the greater the irregularity of the surface. These secondary valleys have others of a smaller size opening into them; and, among mountains of the first order, where all is laid out on the greatest scale, these ramifications are continued to a fourth, and even a fifth, each diminishing in size as it increases in elevation, and as its supply of water is less. Through them all, this law is in general observed, that where a higher valley joins a lower one, of the two angles which it makes with the latter, that which is obtuse is always on the descending side; a law that is the same with that which regulates the confluence of streams running on a surface nearly of uniform inclination. This alone is a proof that the valleys are the work of the streams; and indeed what else but the water itself, working its way through obstacles of unequal resistance, could have opened or kept up a communication between the inequalities of an irregular and alpine surface.

112. Many more arguments, all leading to the same conclusion, may be deduced from the general facts, known in the the natural history of mountains; and, if the Oreologist would trace back the progress of waste, till he come in sight of that original structure, of which the remains are still so vast, he perceives an immense mass of solid rock, naked and unshapely, as it first emerged from the deep, and incomparably greater than all that is now before him. The operation of rains and torrents, modified by the hardness and tenacity of the rock, has worked the whole into its present form; has hollowed out the valleys, and gradually detached the mountains from the general mass, cutting down their sides into steep precipices at one place, and smoothing them into gentle declivities at another. From this has resulted a transportation of materials, which, both for the quantity of the whole, and the magnitude of the individual fragments, must seem incredible to every one, who has not learned to calculate the effects of continued action, and to reflect, that length of time can convert accidental into steady causes. Hence fragments of rock, from the central chain, are found to have travelled into distant valleys,

even where many inferior ridges intervene: hence the granite of Mount Blanc is seen in the plains of Lombardy, or on the sides of Jura; and the ruins of the Carpathian mountains lie scattered over the shores of the Baltic.

113. Thus, with Dr. Hutton, we shall be disposed to consider those great chains of mountains, which traverse the surface of the globe, as cut out of masses vastly greater, and more lofty than any thing that now remains. The present appearances afford no data for calculating the original magnitude of these masses, or the height to which they may have been elevated. The nearest estimate we can form is, where a chain or group of mountains, like those of Rosa in the Alps, is horizontally stratified, and where, of consequence, the undisturbed position of the mineral beds enables us to refer the whole of the present inequalities of the surface to the operation of waste or decay. These mountains, as they now stand, may not inaptly be compared to the pillars of earth which workmen leave behind them, to afford a measure of the whole quantity of earth which they have removed. As the pillars (considering the mountains as such), are in this case of less height than they originally were, so the measure furnished by them is but a limit, which the quantity sought must necessarily exceed.

114. Such, according to Dr. Hutton's theory, are the changes which the daily operations of waste have produced on the surface of the globe. These operations, inconsiderable if taken separately, become great, by conspiring all to the same end, never counteracting one another, but proceeding, through a period of indefinite extent, continually in the same direction. Thus every thing descends, nothing returns upward; the hard and solid bodies every where dissolve, and the loose and soft no where consolidate. The powers which tend to preserve, and those which tend to change the condition of the earth's surface, are never *in equilibrio;* the latter are, in all cases, the most powerful, and, in respect of the former, are like *living* in comparison of *dead* forces. Hence the law of decay is one which suffers no exception: The elements of all bodies were once loose and unconnected, and to the same state nature has appointed that they should all return.

115. It affords no presumption against the reality of this progress, that, in respect of man, it is too slow to be immediately perceived: The utmost portion of it to which our experience can extend, is evanescent, in comparison with the whole, and must be regarded as the momentary increment of a vast progression, circumscribed by no other limits than the duration of the world. Time performs the office of *integrating* the infinitesimal parts of which this progression is made up; it collects them

into one sum, and produces from them an amount greater than any that can be assigned.

116. While on the surface of the earth so much is everywhere going to decay, no new production of mineral substances is found in any region accessible to man. The instances of what are called petrifactions, or the formation of stony substances by means of water, which we sometimes observe, whether they be serruginous concretions, or calcareous, or, as happens in some rare cases, filiceous stalactites, are too few in number, and too inconsiderable in extent, to be deemed material exceptions to this general rule. The bodies thus generated, also, are no sooner formed, than they become subject to waste and dissolution, like all the other hard substances in nature; so that they but retard for a while the progress by which they are all resolved into dust, and sooner or later committed to the bosom of the deep.

117. We are not, however, to imagine, that there is no where any means of repairing this waste; for, on comparing the conclusion at which we are now arrived, viz. that the present continents are all going to decay, and their materials descending into the ocean, with the proposition first laid down, that these same continents are composed of materials which must have been collected from the decay of former rocks, it is impossible not to recognize two corresponding steps of the same progress; of a progress, by which mineral substances are subjected to the same series of changes, and alternately wasted away and renovated. In the same manner, as the present mineral substances derive their origin from substances similar to themselves; so, from the land now going to decay, the sand and gravel forming on the sea-shore, or in the beds of rivers; from the shells and corals which in such enormous quantities are every day accumulated in the bosom of the sea; from the driftwood, and the multitude of vegetable and animal remains continually deposited in the ocean: from all these we cannot doubt, that strata are now forming in those regions, to which nature seems to have confined the powers of mineral reproduction; from which, after being consolidated, they are again destined to emerge, and to exhibit a series of changes similar to the past.

118. How often these vicissitudes of decay and renovation have been repeated, is not for us to determine: they constitute a series, of which, as the author of this theory has remarked, we neither see the beginning nor the end; a circumstance that accords well with what is known concerning other parts of the economy of the world. In the continuation of the different species of animals and vegetables that inhabit the earth, we discern neither a beginning nor an end; and, in the planetary motions,

where geometry has carried the eye so far both into the future and the past, we discover no mark, either of the commencement or the termination of the present order. It is unreasonable, indeed, to suppose, that such marks should anywhere exist. The Author of nature has not given laws to the universe, which, like the institutions of men, carry in themselves the elements of their own destruction. He has not permitted, in his works, any symptom of infancy or of old age, or any sign by which we may estimate either their future or their past duration. He may put an end, as he no doubt gave a beginning, to the present system, at some determinate period; but we may safely conclude, that this great *catastrophe* will not be brought about by any of the laws now existing, and that it is not indicated by anything which we perceive.

119. To assert, therefore, that, in the economy of the world, we see no mark, either of a beginning or an end, is very different from affirming, that the world had no beginning, and will have no end. The first is a conclusion justified by common sense, as well as sound philosophy; while the second is a presumptuous and unwarrantable assertion, for which no reason from experience or analogy can ever be assigned. Dr. Hutton might, therefore, justly complain of the uncandid criticism, which, by substituting the one of these assertions for the other, endeavoured to load his theory with the reproach of atheism and impiety. Mr. Kirwan, in bringing forward this harsh and ill-founded censure, was neither animated by the spirit, nor guided by the maxims of true philosophy. By the spirit of philosophy, he must have been induced to reflect, that such poisoned weapons as he was preparing to use, are hardly ever allowable in scientific contest, as having a less direct tendency to overthrow the system, than to hurt the person of an adversary, and to wound, perhaps incurably, his mind, his reputation, or his peace. By the maxims of philosophy, he must have been reminded, that, in no part of the history of nature, has any mark been discovered, either of the beginning or the end of the present *order;* and that the geologist sadly mistakes, both the object of his science and the limits of his understanding, who thinks it his business to explain the means employed by INFINITE WISDOM for establishing the laws, which now govern the world.

By attending to these obvious considerations, Mr. Kirwan would have avoided a very illiberal and ungenerous proceeding; and, however he might have differed from Dr. Hutton as to the *truth* of his opinions, he would not have censured their *tendency* with such rash and unjustifiable severity.

But, if this author may be blamed for wanting the temper, or neglecting the rules, of philosophic investigation, he is hardly less culpable, for having so slightly considered the scope and spirit of a work which he

condemned so freely. In that work, instead of finding the world represented as the result of necessity or chance, which might be looked for, if
the accusations of atheism or impiety were well founded, we see everywhere the utmost attention to discover, and the utmost disposition to
admire, the instances of wise and beneficent design manifested in the
structure, or economy of the world. The enlarged views of these, which
his geological system afforded, appeared to Dr. Hutton himself as its
most valuable result. They were the parts of it which he contemplated
with greatest delight; and he would have been less flattered, by being
told of the ingenuity and originality of his theory, than of the addition
which it had made to our knowledge of *final causes*. It was natural,
therefore, that he should be hurt by an attempt to accuse him of opinions, so different from those which he had always taught; and if he answered Mr. Kirwan's attack with warmth or asperity, we must ascribe it
to the indignation excited by unmerited reproach.

120. But to return to the natural history of the earth: Though there
be in it no *data,* from which the commencement of the present order can
be ascertained, there are many by which the existence of that order may
be traced back to an antiquity extremely remote. The beds of primitive
schistus, for instance, contain sand, gravel, and other materials, collected,
as already shown, from the dissolution of mineral bodies, which bodies,
therefore, must have existed long before the oldest part of the present
land was formed. Again, in this gravel we sometimes find pieces of sand-
stone, and of other compound rocks, by which we are of course carried
back a step farther, so as to reach a system of things, from which the
present is the third in succession; and this may be considered as the most
ancient epoch, of which any memorial exists in the records of the fossil
kingdom.

121. Next in the order of time to the consolidation of the primary
strata, we must place their elevation, when, from being horizontal, and
at the bottom of the sea, they were broken, set on edge, and raised to
the surface. It is even probable, as formerly observed, that to this succeeded a depression of the same strata, and a second elevation, so that
they have twice visited the superior, and twice the inferior regions. During the second immersion, were formed, first, the great bodies of pudding-
stone, that in so many instances lie immediately above them; and next
were deposited the strata that are strictly denominated secondary.

122. The third great event, was the raising up of this compound body
of old and new strata from the bottom of the sea, and forming it into
the dry land, or the continents, as they now exist. Contemporary with
this, we must suppose the injection of melted matter among the strata,
and the consequent formation of the crystallized and unstratified rocks,

namely, the granite, metallic veins, and veins of prophyry and whin-stone. This, however, is to be considered as embracing a period of great duration; and it must always be recollected, that veins are found of very different formation; so that when we speak generally, it is perhaps im-possible to state anything more precise concerning their antiquity, than that they are posterior to the strata, and that the veins of whinstone seem to be the most recent of all, as they traverse every other.

123. In the fourth place, with respect to time, we must class the facts that regard the detritus and waste of the land, and must carefully dis-tinguish them from the more ancient phenomena of the mineral king-dom. Here we are to reckon the shaping of all the present inequalities of the surface; the formation of hills of gravel, and of what have been called tertiary strata, consisting of loose and unconsolidated materials; also collections of shells not mineralized, like those in Turaine; such petrifactions as those contained in the rock of Gibraltar, on the coast of Dalmatia, and in the caves of Bayreuth. The bones of land animals found in the soil, such as those of Siberia, or North America, are prob-ably more recent than any of the former.

124. These phenomena, then, are all so many marks of the lapse of time, among which the principles of geology enable us to distinguish a certain order, so that we know some of them to be more, and others to be less distant, but without being able to ascertain, with any exactness, the proportion of the immense intervals which separate them. These in-tervals admit of no comparison with the astronomical measures of time; they cannot be expressed by the revolutions of the sun or of the moon; nor is there any synchronism between the most recent epochs of the mineral kingdom, and the most ancient of our ordinary chronology.

125. On what is now said is grounded another objection to Dr. Hut-ton's theory, namely, that the high antiquity ascribed by it to the earth, is inconsistent with the system of chronology which rests on the authority of the Sacred Writings. This objection would no doubt be of weight, if the high antiquity in question were not restricted merely to the globe of the earth, but were also extended to the human race. That the origin of mankind does not go back beyond six or seven thousand years, is a position so involved in the narrative of the Mosaic books, that anything inconsistent with it, would no doubt stand in opposition to the testi-mony of those ancient records. On this subject, however, geology is silent; and the history of arts and sciences, when traced as high as any authentic monuments extend, refers the beginnings of civilization to a date not very different from that which has just been mentioned, and infinitely within the limits of the most recent of the epochs, marked by the physi-cal revolutions of the globe.

On the other hand, the authority of the Sacred Books seems to be but little interested in what regards the mere antiquity of the earth itself; nor does it appear that their language is to be understood literally concerning the *age* of that body, any more than concerning its *figure* or its *motion*. The theory of Dr. Hutton stands here precisely on the same footing with the system of COPERNICUS; for there is no reason to suppose, that it was the purpose of revelation to furnish a standard of geological, any more than of astronomical science. It is admitted, on all hands, that the Scriptures are not intended to resolve physical questions, or to explain matters in no way related to the morality of human actions; and if, in consequence of this principle, a considerable latitude of interpretation were not allowed, we should continue at this moment to believe, that the earth is flat; that the sun moves round the earth; and that the circumference of a circle is no more than three times its diameter.

It is but reasonable, therefore, that we should extend to the geologist the same liberty of speculation, which the astronomer and mathematician are already in possession of; and this may be done, by supposing that the chronology of MOSES relates only to the human race. This liberty is not more necessary to Dr. Hutton than to other theorists. No ingenuity has been able to reconcile the natural history of the globe with the opinion of its recent origin; and accordingly the cosmologies of Kirwan and De Luc, though contrived with more mineralogical skill, are not less forced and unsatisfactory than those of Burnet and Whiston.

126. It is impossible to look back on the system which we have thus endeavoured to illustrate, without being struck with the novelty and beauty of the views which it sets before us. The very plan and scope of it distinguish it from all other theories of the earth, and point it out as a work of great and original invention. The sole object of such theories has hitherto been to explain the manner in which the present laws of the mineral kingdom were first established, or began to exist, without treating of the manner in which they now proceed, and by which their continuance is provided for. The authors of these theories have accordingly gone back to a state of things altogether unlike the present, and have confined their reasonings, or their fictions, to a crisis which never has existed but once, and which never can return. Dr. Hutton, on the other hand, has guided his investigation by the philosophical maxim, *Causam naturalem et assiduam quaerimus, non raram et fortuitam*. His theory, accordingly, presents us with a system of wise and provident economy, where the same instruments are continually employed, and where the decay and renovation of fossils being carried on at the same time in the different regions allotted to them, preserve in the earth the conditions essential for the support of animal and vegetable life. We

have been long accustomed to admire that beautiful contrivance in nature, by which the water of the ocean, drawn up in vapour by the atmosphere, imparts, in its descent, fertility to the earth, and becomes the great cause of vegetation and of life; but now we find, that this vapour not only fertilizes, but creates the soil; prepares it from the solid rock, and, after employing it in the great operations of the surface, carries it back into the regions where all its mineral characters are renewed. Thus, the circulation of moisture through the air, is a prime mover, not only in the annual succession of the seasons, but in the great geological cycle, by which the waste and reproduction of entire continents is circumscribed. Perhaps a more striking view than this, of the wisdom that presides over nature, was never presented by any philosophical system, nor a greater addition ever made to our knowledge of final causes. It is an addition which gives consistency to the rest, by proving, that equal foresight is exerted in providing for the whole and for the parts, and that no less care is taken to maintain the constitution of the earth, than to preserve the tribes of animals and vegetables which dwell on its surface. In a word, it is the peculiar excellence of this theory, that it ascribes to the phenomena of geology an order similar to that which exists in the provinces of nature with which we are best acquainted; that it produces seas and continents, not by accident, but by the operation of regular and uniform causes; that it makes the decay of one part subservient to the restoration of another, and gives stability to the whole, not by perpetuating individuals, but by reproducing them in succession.

*   *   *   *

131. From this comparison it appears, that Dr. Hutton's theory is sufficiently distinct, even from the theories which approach to it most nearly, to merit, in the strictest sense, the appellation of *new* and *original*. There are indeed few inventions or discoveries, recorded in the history of science, to which nearer approaches were not made before they were fully unfolded. It therefore very well deserves to be distinguished by a particular name; and, if it behooves us to follow the analogy observed in the names of the two great systems, which at present divide the opinions of geologists, we may join Mr. Kirwan in calling this the PLUTONIC SYSTEM. For my own part, I would rather have it characterized by a less splendid, but juster name, that of the HUTTONIAN THEORY.

132.   The circumstance, however, which gives to this theory its peculiar character, and exalts it infinitely above all others, is the introduction of the principle of pressure, to modify the effects of heat when applied at

the bottom of the sea. This is in fact the key to the grand enigma of the mineral kingdom, where, while one set of phenomena indicates the action of fire, another set, equally remarkable, seems to exclude the possibility of that action, by presenting us with mineral substances, in such a state as they could never have been brought into by the operation of the fires we see at the surface of the earth. These two classes of phenomena are reconciled together, by admitting the power of compression to confine the volatile parts of bodies when heat is applied to them, and to force them, in many instances, to undergo fusion, instead of being calcined or dissipated by burning or inflammation. In this hypothesis, which some affect to consider as a principle gratuitously assumed, there appears to me nothing but a very fair and legitimate generalization of the properties of heat. Combustion and inflammation are chemical processes, to which other conditions are required, besides the presence of a high temperature. The state of the mineral regions makes it reasonable to presume, that these conditions are wanting in the bowels of the earth, where, of consequence, we have a right to look for nothing but expansion and fusion, the only operations which seem essential to heat, and inseparable from the application of it, in certain degrees, to certain substances. Though this principle, therefore, had no countenance from analogy, the admirable simplicity, and the unity, which it introduces into the phenomena of geology, would sufficiently justify the application of it to the theory of the earth.

As another excellence of this theory, I may, perhaps, be allowed to remark, that it extends its consequences beyond those to which the author of it has himself adverted, and that it affords, which no geological theory has yet done, a satisfactory explanation of the spheroidal figure of the earth.

133. Yet, with all these circumstances of originality, grandeur, and simplicity in its favour, with the addition of evidence as demonstrative as the nature of the subject will admit, this theory has probably many obstacles to overcome, before it meet the general approbation. The greatness of the objects which it sets before us, alarms the imagination; the powers which it supposes to be lodged in the subterraneous regions; a heat which has subdued the most refractory rocks, and has melted beds of marble and quartz; an expansive force, which has folded up, or broken the strata, and raised whole continents from the bottom of the sea; these are things with which, however certainly they may be proved, the mind cannot soon be familiarized. The change and movement also, which this theory ascribes to all that the senses declare to be most unalterable, raise up against it the same prejudices which formerly opposed the belief in the true system of the world; and it affords a curious proof, how little

such prejudices are subject to vary, that as ARISTARCHUS, an ancient follower of that system, was charged with impiety for moving the ever-lasting VESTA from her place, so Dr. Hutton, nearly on the same ground, has been subjected to the very same accusation. Even the length of time which this theory regards as necessary to the revolutions of the globe, is looked on as belonging to the marvellous; and man, who finds himself constrained by the want of time, or of space in almost all his undertakings, forgets, that in these, if in any thing, the riches of nature reject all limitation. (See Note XXVI)

The evidence which must be opposed to all these causes of incredulity, cannot be fully understood without much study and attention. It requires not only a careful examination of particular instances, but comprehensive views of the whole phenomena of geology; the comparison of things very remote with one another; the interpretation of the *obscure* by the *luminous,* and of the *doubtful* by the *decisive* appearances. The geologist must not content himself with examining the insulated specimens of his cabinet, or with pursuing the nice subtleties of mineralogical arrangement; he must study the relations of fossils, as they actually exist; he must follow nature into her wildest and most inaccessible abodes; and must select, for the places of his observations, those points, from which the variety and gradation of her works can be most extensively and accurately explored. Without such an exact and comprehensive survey, his mind will hardly be prepared to relish the true theory of the earth. *"Naturae enim vis atque majestas omnibus momentis fide caret, si quis modo partes atque non totam complectatur animo."*

134. If indeed this theory of the earth is as well founded as we suppose it to be, the lapse of time must necessarily remove all objections to it, and the progress of science will only develop its evidence more fully. As it stands at present, though true, it must be still imperfect; and it cannot be doubted, that the great principles of it, though established on an immovable basis, must yet undergo many modifications, requiring to be limited, in one place, or to be extended, in another. A work of such variety and extent cannot be carried to perfection by the efforts of an individual. Ages may be required to fill up the bold outline which Dr. Hutton has traced with so masterly a hand; to detach the parts more completely from the general mass; to adjust the size and position of the subordinate members; and to give to the whole piece the exact proportion and true coloring of nature.

This, however, in length of time, may be expected from the advancement of science, and from the mutual assistance which parts of knowledge, seemingly the most remote, often afford to one another. Not only may the observations of the mineralogist, in tracts yet unexplored, complete the enumeration of geological facts; and the experiments of the chemist, on substances not yet subjected to his analysis, afford a more intimate acquaintance with the nature of fossils, and a measure of the power of those chemical agents to which this theory ascribes such vast effects: but also, from other sciences less directly connected with the natural history of the earth, much information may be received. The accurate geographical maps and surveys which are now making; the soundings; the observations of currents; the barometrical measurements, may all combine to ascertain the reality, and to fix the quantity of those changes which terrestrial bodies continually undergo. Every new improvement in science affords the means of delineating more accurately the face of nature as it *now* exists, and of transmitting, to future ages, an account, which may be compared with the face of nature as it shall *then* exist. If, therefore, the science of the present times is destined to survive the physical revolutions of the globe, the HUTTONIAN THEORY may be confirmed by historical record; and the author of it will be remembered among the illustrious few, whose systems have been verified by the observations of succeeding ages, supported by facts unknown to themselves, and established by the decisions of a tribunal, slow, but infallible, in distinguishing between truth and falsehood.

FINIS

*   *   *   *

Note XXVI

Prejudices Relating to the Theory of the Earth

445. Among the prejudices which a new theory of the earth has to overcome, is an opinion, held, or affected to be held, by many, that geological science is not yet ripe for such elevated and difficult speculations. They would, therefore, get rid of these speculations, *by moving the previous question,* and declaring that at present we ought to have no theory at all. We are not yet, they allege, sufficiently acquainted with the phenomena of geology; the subject is so various and extensive, that our knowledge of it must for a long time, perhaps forever, remain extremely imperfect. And hence it is, that the theories hitherto proposed have succeeded one another with so great rapidity, hardly any of them having been able to last longer than the discovery of a new fact, or a fact unknown when it was invented. It has proved insufficient to connect this fact with the phenomena already known, and has therefore been justly abandoned. In this manner, they say, have passed away the theories

of Woodward, Burnet, Whiston, and even of Buffon; and so will pass, in their turn, those of Hutton and Werner.

446. This unfavourable view of geology ought not, however, to be received without examination; in science, presumption is less hurtful than despair, and inactivity is more dangerous than error.

One reason of the rapid succession of geological theories, is the mistake that has been made as to their object, and the folly of attempting to explain by them the first origin of things. This mistake has led to fanciful speculations that had nothing but their novelty to recommend them, and which, when that charm had ceased, were rejected as mere suppositions, incapable of proof. But if it is once settled, that a theory of the earth ought to have no other aim but to discover the laws that regulate the changes on the surface, or in the interior of the globe, the subject is brought within the sphere either of observation or analogy; and there is no reason to suppose, that man, who has numbered the stars, and measured their forces, shall ultimately prove unequal to this investigation.

447. Again, theories that have a rational object, though they be false or imperfect in their principles, are for the most part approximations to the truth, suited to the information at the time when they were proposed. They are steps, therefore, in the advancement of knowledge, and are terms of a series that must end when the real laws of nature are discovered. It is, on this account, rash to conclude, that in the revolutions of science, what has happened must continue to happen, and because systems have changed rapidly in time past, that they must necessarily do so in time to come.

He who would have reasoned so, and who had seen the ancient physical systems, at first all rivals to one another, and then swallowed up by the Aristotelian; the Aristotelian physics giving way to those of Descartes; and the physics of Descartes to those of Newton; would have predicted that these last were also, in their turn, to give place to the philosophy of some later period. This is, however, a conclusion that hardly any one will now be bold enough to maintain, after a hundred years of the most scrupulous examination have done nothing but add to the evidence of the NEWTONIAN SYSTEM. It seems certain, therefore, that the rise and fall of theories in times past, does not argue, that the same will happen in the time that is to come.

448. The multifarious and extremely diversified object of geological researches, does, no doubt, render the first steps difficult, and may very well account for the instability hitherto observed in such theories; but the very same thing gives reason for expecting a very high degree of certainty to be ultimately attained in these inquiries.

Where the phenomena are few and simple, there may be several different theories that will explain them in a manner equally satisfactory; and in such cases, the true and the false hypotheses are not easily distinguished from one another. When, on the other hand, the phenomena are greatly varied, the probability is, that among them, some of those *instantiae crucis* will be found, that exclude every hypothesis but one, and reduce the explanation given to the highest degree of certainty. It was thus, when the phenomena of the heavens were but imperfectly known, and were confined to a few general and simple facts, that the Philolaic could claim no preference to the Ptolemaic system: The former seemed a possible hypothesis; but as it performed nothing that the other did not perform, and was inconsistent with some of our most natural prejudices, it had but few adherents. The invention of the telescope, and the use of more accurate instruments, by multiplying and diversifying the facts, established its credit; and when not only the general laws, but also the inequalities, and disturbances of the planetary motions were understood, all physical hypotheses vanished, like phantoms, before the philosophy of NEWTON. Hence the number, the variety, and even the complication of facts, contribute ultimately to separate truth from falsehood; and the same causes which, in any case, render the first attempts toward a theory difficult, make the final success of such attempts just so much the more probable.

This maxim, however, though a general encouragement to the prosecution of geological inquiries, does not amount to a proof that we are yet arrived at the period when those inquiries may safely assume the form of a theory. But that we are arrived at such a period, appears clear from other circumstances.

*   *   *   *

457. The truth, indeed, is, that in physical inquiries, the work of theory and observation must go hand in hand, and ought to be carried on at the same time, more especially if the matter is very complicated, for there the clue of theory is necessary to direct the observer. Though a man may begin to observe without any hypothesis, he cannot continue long without seeing some general conclusion arise; and to this nascent theory it is his business to attend, because, by seeking either to verify or to disprove it, he is led to new experiments, or new observations. He is led also to the very experiments and observations that are of the greatest importance, namely, to those *instantiae crucis*, which are the *criteria* that naturally present themselves for the trial of every hypothesis. He is conducted to the places where the transitions of nature are most

perceptible, and where the absence of former, or the presence of new circumstances, excludes the action of imaginary causes. By this correction of his first opinion, a new approximation is made to the truth; and by the repetition of the same process certainty is finally obtained. Thus theory and observation mutually assist one another; and the spirit of system, against which there are so many and such just complaints, appears, nevertheless, as the animating principle of inductive investigation. The business of sound philosophy is not to extinguish this spirit, but to restrain and direct its efforts.

458. It is therefore hurtful to the progress of physical science to represent observation and theory as standing opposed to one another. Bergman has said, *"Observationes veras quam ingeniosissimas fictiones sequi praestat; naturae mysteria potius indagare quam divinare."*

If it is meant by this merely to say, that it is better to have facts without theory, than theory without facts, and that it is wiser to inquire into the secrets of nature, than to guess at them, the truth of the maxim will hardly be controverted. But if we are to understand by it, as some may perhaps have done, that all theory is mere fiction, and that the only alternative a philosopher has, is to devote himself to the study of facts unconnected by theory, or of theory unsupported by facts, the maxim is as far from the truth, as I am convinced it is from the real sense of Bergman. Such an opposition between the business of the theorist and the observer, can only occur when the speculations of the former are vague and indistinct, and cannot be so *embodied* as to become visible to the latter. But the philosopher who has ascended to his theory by a regular generalization of facts, and who descends from it again by drawing such palpable conclusions as may be compared with experience, furnishes the infallible means of distinguishing between *perfect science* and *ingenious fiction.* Of a geological theory that has stood this double test of the analytic and synthetic methods, Dr. Hutton has furnished us with an excellent instance, in his explanation of granite. The appearances which he observed in that stone led him to conclude, that it had been melted, and injected while fluid, among the stratified rocks already formed. He then considered, that if this is true, veins of granite must often run from the larger masses of that stone, and penetrate the strata in various directions; and this must be visible at those places where these different kinds of rock come into contact with one another. This led him to search in Arran and Glen-tilt for the phenomena in question; the result, as we have seen, afforded to his theory the fullest confirmation and to himself the high satisfaction which must ever accompany the success of candid and judicious inquiry.

459. It cannot, however, be denied, that the impartiality of an ob-

server may often be affected by system; but this is a misfortune against which the want of theory is not always a complete security. The partialities in favour of opinions are not more dangerous than the prejudices against them; for such is the spirit of system, and so naturally do all men's notions tend to reduce themselves into some regular form, that the very belief that there can be no theory, becomes a theory itself, and may have no inconsiderable sway over the mind of an observer. Besides, one man may have as much delight in pulling down, as another has in building up, and may choose to display his dexterity in the one occupation as well as in the other. The want of theory, then, does not secure the candor of an observer, and it may very much diminish his skill. The discipline that seems best calculated to promote both is a thorough knowledge of the methods of inductive investigation; an acquaintance with the history of physical discovery; and the careful study of those sciences in which the rules of philosophizing have been more successfully applied.

16

THOMAS YOUNG

A child prodigy who was reading fluently less than three years after he was born in 1773, Thomas Young was one of the last representatives of the antique species, natural philosopher, which failed in the struggle for survival with the specialists born of the growing complexity of science. Trained as a doctor, Young settled in London in 1799 to practice medicine. He was incapable of restricting himself to medicine, however. He also occupied the chair of natural philosophy at the Royal Institution for a time, fulfilling a heavy schedule of lectures, and later he served as Croonian lecturer for the Royal College of Physicians. Work deriving from his dual interest in medicine and physics effectively established modern physiological optics. He examined the muscular structure of the eye and explained how the curvature of the crystalline lens changes to focus objects at different distances. He was the first to describe astigmatism and the first to approach an adequate explanation of color blindness. Described as a man of "universal erudition" by the chemist Davy, he proved how correct Davy was by deciphering the Rosetta stone, the first step toward a reading knowledge of Egyptian hieroglyphs. If Young was the first to express the basic conceptions of the wave theory of light, he was not the man who won its acceptance. Already the specialist was replacing the natural philosopher, and when Young died in 1829, Augustin Fresnel was the man recognized as the founder of the wave theory of light.

In the 17th century, two competing conceptions of light had been formulated. On the one hand, light was held to be a pulse of motion transmitted through a medium. Christiaan Huygens' *Treatise of Light* (1690) gave the pulse conception of light its most compelling statement. On the other hand, the corpuscular conception argued that light consists of tiny particles of matter moving with immense velocity. Isaac Newton was its leading exponent. During the 18th century, the Newtonian position prevailed, partly because of Newton's commanding reputation no doubt, but largely because it explained more phenomena more success-

371

fully than its rival. Above all, Huygens' treatise did not contain any explanation of colors, whereas Newton's discoveries concerning white light and colors were easily accommodated to the corpuscular conception by assigning different sizes to the corpuscles that revealed different colors.

It was thus an old theory that Young revived, but to it he added improvements which gave it advantages that it had never held before. What had been a theory of irregular pulses became now a theory of waves. Young concentrated his attention on phenomena that Huygens had ignored, especially the periodic phenomena of diffraction and colors in thin films. To their explication he brought an insight derived from the study of sound—what he referred to as the "coalescence of musical sounds." The consequent ability adequately to explain a range of phenomena outside the competence of the corpuscular theory ultimately secured the acceptance of the wave conception of light.

16

On the Theory of Light and Colors

Although the invention of plausible hypotheses, independent of any connection with experimental observations, can be of very little use in the promotion of natural knowledge, yet the discovery of simple and uniform principles, by which a great number of apparently heterogeneous phenomena are reduced to coherent and universal laws, must ever be allowed to be of considerable importance towards the improvement of the human intellect.

The object of the present dissertation is not so much to propose any opinions which are absolutely new, as to refer some theories, which have been already advanced, to their original inventors, to support them by additional evidence, and to apply them to a great number of diversified facts; which have hitherto been buried in obscurity. Nor is it absolutely necessary in this instance to produce a single new experiment; for of experiments there is already an ample store, which are so much the more unexceptionable as they must have been conducted without the least partiality for the system by which they will be explained; yet some facts, hitherto unobserved, will be brought forward, in order to show the perfect agreement of that system with the multifarious phenomena of nature.

The optical observations of Newton are yet unrivalled; and, excepting some casual inaccuracies, they only rise in our estimation as we compare them with later attempts to improve on them. A further consideration of the colors of thin plates, as they are described in the second book of Newton's *Optics*, has converted that prepossession which I before entertained for the undulatory system of light into a very strong conviction of its truth and sufficiency, a conviction which has been since most strikingly confirmed by an analysis of the colors of striated substances. The phenomena of thin plates are indeed so singular that their general complexion is not without great difficulty reconcilable to any theory, however complicated, that has hitherto been applied to them; and some

---

Published in *The Philosophical Transactions of the Royal Society*, London, 1802.

of the principal circumstances have never been explained by the most gratuitous assumptions; but it will appear that the minutest particulars of these phenomena are not only perfectly consistent with the theory which will now be detailed, but that they are all the necessary consequences of that theory, without any auxiliary suppositions; and this by inferences so simple that they become particular corollaries, which scarcely require a distinct enumeration.

A more extensive examination of Newton's various writings has shown me that he was in reality the first that suggested such a theory as I shall endeavor to maintain; that his own opinions varied less from this theory than is now almost universally supposed; and that a variety of arguments have been advanced, as if to confute him, which may be found nearly in a similar form in his own works; and this by no less a mathematician than Leonard Euler, whose system of light, as far as it is worthy of notice, either was, or might have been, wholly borrowed from Newton, Hooke, Huygens, and Malebranche.

Those who are attached, as they may be with the greatest justice, to every doctrine which is stamped with the Newtonian approbation, will probably be disposed to bestow on these considerations so much the more of their attention, as they appear to coincide more nearly with Newton's own opinions. For this reason, after having briefly stated each particular position of my theory, I shall collect, from Newton's various writings, such passages as seem to be the most favorable to its admission; and although I shall quote some papers which may be thought to have been partly retracted at the publication of the *Optics*, yet I shall borrow nothing from them that can be supposed to militate against his maturer judgment.

HYPOTHESIS I

A luminiferous ether pervades the universe, rare and elastic in a high degree.

PASSAGES FROM NEWTON (omitted)

HYPOTHESIS II

Undulations are excited in this ether whenever a body becomes luminous.

Scholium. I use the word undulation in preference to vibration because vibration is generally understood as implying a motion which is continued alternately backward and forward by a combination of the momentum of the body with an accelerating force, and which is naturally more or less permanent; but an undulation is supposed to consist in vibratory motion transmitted successively through different parts of a medium without any tendency in each particle to continue its motion, except in consequence of the transmission of succeeding undulations from a distinct vibrating body; as in the air the vibrations of a chord produce the undulations constituting sound.

PASSAGES FROM NEWTON (omitted)

HYPOTHESIS III

The sensation of different colors depends on the different frequency of vibrations excited by light in the retina.

PASSAGES FROM NEWTON (omitted)

HYPOTHESIS IV

All material bodies have an attraction for the ethereal medium, by means of which it is accumulated within their substance, and for a small distance around them, in a state of greater density but not of greater elasticity.

It has been shown that the three former hypotheses, which, may be called essential, are literally parts of the more complicated Newtonian system. This fourth hypothesis differs perhaps, in some degree from any that have been proposed by former authors, and is diametrically opposite to that of Newton; but both being in themselves equally probable, the opposition is merely accidental, and it is only to be inquired which is the best capable of explaining the phenomena. Other suppositions might perhaps be substituted for this, and therefore I do not consider it as fundamental, yet it appears to be the simplest and best of any that have occurred to me.

PROPOSITION I

All impulses are propagated in a homogeneous elastic medium with an equable velocity.

Every experiment relative to sound coincides with the observation already quoted from Newton, that all undulations are propagated through the air with equal velocity; and this is further confirmed by calculations. If the impulse be so great as materially to disturb the density of the medium, it will be no longer homogeneous; but, as far as concerns our senses, the quantity of motion may be considered as infinitely small. It is surprising that Euler, although aware of the matter of fact, should still have maintained that the more frequent undulations are more rapidly propagated. It is possible that the actual velocity of the particles of the luminiferous ether may bear a much less proportion to the velocity of the undulations than in sound, for light may be excited by the motion of a body moving at the rate of only one mile in the time that light moves a hundred millions.

Scholium 1. It has been demonstrated that in different mediums the velocity varies in the subduplicate ratio of the force directly and of the density inversely.

Scholium 2. It is obvious, from the phenomena of elastic bodies and of sounds, that the undulations may cross each other without interruption; but there is no necessity that the various colors of white light should intermix their undulations, for, supposing the vibrations of the retina to continue but a five-hundredth of a second after their excitement, a million undulations of each of a million colors may arrive in distinct succession within this interval of time, and produce the same sensible effect as if all the colors arrived precisely at the same instant.

PROPOSITION II

An undulation conceived to originate from the vibration of a single particle must expand through a homogeneous medium in a spherical form, but with different quantities of motion in different parts.

For, since every impulse, considered as positive or negative, is propagated with a constant velocity, each part of the undulation must in equal times have passed through equal distances from the vibrating-point. And, supposing the vibrating particle, in the course of its motion, to proceed forward to a small distance in a given direction, the principal strength of the undulation will naturally be straight before it; behind it the motion will be equal in a contrary direction; and at right angles to the line of vibration the undulation will be evanescent.

Now, in order that such an undulation may continue its progress to any considerable distance, there must be in each part of it a tendency to preserve its own motion in a right line from the centre; for if the excess of force at any part were communicated to the neighboring particles, there can be no reason why it should not very soon be equalized throughout, or, in other words, become wholly extinct, since the motions in contrary directions would naturally destroy each other. The origin of sound from the vibration of a chord is evidently of this nature; on the contrary, in a circular wave of water every part is at the same instant either elevated or depressed. It may be difficult to show mathematically the mode in which this inequality of force is preserved, but the inference from the matter of fact appears to be unavoidable; and while the science of hydrodynamics is so imperfect that we cannot even solve the simple problem of the time required to empty a vessel by a given aperture, it cannot be expected that we should be able to account perfectly for so complicated a series of phenomena as those of elastic fluids. The theory of Huygens, indeed, explains the circumstances in a manner tolerably satisfactory. He supposes every particle of the medium to propagate a distinct undulation in all directions, and that the general effect is only perceptible where a portion of each undulation conspires in direction at the same instant; and it is easy to show that such a general undulation would in all cases proceed rectilinearly, with proportionate force; but, upon this supposition, it seems to follow that a greater quantity of force must be lost by the divergence of the partial undulations than appears to be consistent with the propagation of the effect to any considerable distance; yet it is obvious that some such limitation of the motion must naturally be expected to take place, for if the intensity of the motion of any particular part, instead of continuing to be propagated straight forward, were supposed to affect the intensity of a neighboring part of the undulation, an impulse must then have travelled from an internal to an external circle in an oblique direction, in the same time as in the direction of the radius, and consequently with a greater velocity, against the first proposition. In the case of water the velocity is by no means so rigidly limited as in that of an elastic medium. Yet it is not necessary to suppose, nor is it indeed probable, that there is absolutely not the least lateral communication of the force of the undulation, but that, in highly elastic mediums, this communication is almost insensible. In the air, if a chord be perfectly insulated so as to propagate exactly such vibrations as have been described, they will, in fact, be much less forcible than if the chord be placed in the neighborhood of a sounding-board, and probably in some measure because of this lateral communication of motions of an opposite tendency. And the different intensity of different parts of the same circular undulation may be observed by holding a common tuning-fork at arm's-length, while sounding, and turning it, from a plane directed to the ear, into a position perpendicular to that plane.

PROPOSITION III

A portion of a spherical undulation, admitted through an aperture into a quiescent medium, will proceed to be further propagated rectilinearly in concentric superficies, terminated laterally by weak and irregular portions of newly diverging undulations.

At the instant of admission the circumference of each of the undulations may be supposed to generate a partial undulation, filling up the nascent angle between the radii and the surface terminating the medium; but no sensible addition will be made to its strength by a divergence of motion from any other parts of the undulation, for want of a coincidence in time, as has already been explained with respect to the various force of a spherical undulation. If, indeed, the aperture bear but a small proportion to the breadth of an undulation, the newly generated undulation may nearly absorb the whole force of the portion admitted; and this is the case considered by Newton in the *Principia*. But no experiment can be made under these circumstances with light, on account of the minuteness of its undulations and the interference of inflection; and yet some faint radiations do actually diverge beyond any probable limits of inflection, rendering the margin of the aperture distinctly visible in all directions. These are attributed by Newton to some unknown cause, distinct from inflection and they fully answer the description of this proposition.

Let the concentric lines in Figure 1 represent the contemporaneous situation of similar parts of a number of successive undulations diverging from the point A; they will also represent the successive situations of each individual undulation: let the force of each undulation be represented by the breadth of the line, and let the cone of light ABC be

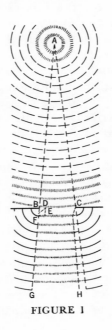

FIGURE 1

admitted through the aperture BC; then the principal undulations will proceed in a rectilinear direction towards GH, and the faint radiations on each side will diverge from B and C as centres, without receiving any additional force from any intermediate point D of the undulation, on account of the inequality of the lines DE and DF. But if we allow some little lateral divergence from the extremities of the undulations, it must diminish their force, without adding materially to that of the dissipated light; and their termination, instead of the right line BG, will assume the form CH, since the loss of force must be more considerable near to C than at greater distances. This line corresponds with the boundary of the shadow in Newton's first observation; and it is much more probable that such a dissipation of light was the cause of the increase of the shadow in that observation than that it was owing to the action of the inflecting atmosphere, which must have extended a thirtieth of an inch each way in order to produce it; especially when it is considered that the shadow was not diminished by surrounding the hair with a denser medium than air, which must in all probability have weakened and contracted its inflecting atmosphere. In other circumstances the lateral divergence might appear to increase, instead of diminishing, the breadth of the beam.

As the subject of this proposition has always been esteemed the most difficult part of the undulatory system, it will be proper to examine here the objections which Newton has grounded upon it.

"To me the fundamental supposition itself seems impossible—namely, that the waves or vibrations of any fluid can, like the rays of light, be propagated in straight lines, without a continual and very extravagant spreading and bending every way into the quiescent medium, where they are terminated by it. I mistake if there be not both experiment and demonstration to the contrary." *Phil. Trans.*, Nov. 1672.

"All motion propagated through a fluid diverges from a rectilinear progress into the unmoved spaces."

"Because the medium is denser there (in the middle of an undulation admitted) than in the spaces on either side, it will dilate itself as well towards those spaces on each hand, as towards the rare intervals between the pulses; therefore the pulses will dilate themselves on all sides into the unmoved parts with almost the same celerity with which they are propagated directly from the center; and will therefore fill up the whole space. This we find by experience in sounds." *Princip.*, lib. ii., prop. 42.

"Are not all hypotheses erroneous in which light is supposed to consist in pression or motion propagated through a fluid medium? If it consisted in pression or motion, propagated either in an instant, or in time, it would bend into the shadow. For pression or motion cannot be propagated in a fluid in right lines beyond an obstacle which stops part of the motion, but will bend and spread every way into the quiescent medium which lies beyond the obstacle. The waves on the surface of stagnating water passing by the sides of a broad obstacle which stops part of them, bend afterwards, and dilate themselves gradually into the quiet water behind the obstacle. The waves, pulses, or vibrations of the air, wherein sounds consist, bend manifestly, though not so much as the waves of water. For a bell or a cannon may be heard beyond a hill which intercepts the sight of the sounding body; and sounds are propagated as readily through crooked pipes as straight ones. But light is never known to follow crooked passages nor to bend into the shadow. For the fixed stars, by the interposition of any of the planets, cease to be seen. And so do the parts of the sun by the interposition of the moon, Mercury, or Venus. The rays which pass very near to the edges of any body are bent a little by the action of the body; but this bending is not towards but from the shadow, and is performed only in the passage of the ray by the body, and at a very small distance from it. So soon as the ray is past the body it goes right on." *Optics,* Qu. 28.

Now the proposition quoted from the *Principia* does not directly contradict this proposition; for it does not assert that such a motion must diverge equally in all directions; neither can it with truth be maintained that the parts of an elastic medium communicating any motion must propagate that motion equally in all directions. All that can be inferred by reasoning is that the marginal parts of the undulation must be somewhat weakened and that there must be a faint divergence in every direction; but whether either of these effects might be of sufficient magnitude to be sensible could not have been inferred from argument, if the affirmative had not been rendered probable by experiment.

As to the analogy with other fluids, the most natural inference from it is this: "The waves of the air, wherein sounds consist, bend manifestly, though not so much as the waves of water"; water being an inelastic and air a moderately elastic medium; but ether being most highly elastic, its waves bend very far less than those of the air, and therefore almost imperceptibly. Sounds are propagated through crooked passages, because their sides are capable of reflecting sound, just as light would be propagated through a bent tube, if perfectly polished within.

The light of a star is by far too weak to produce, by its faint divergence, any visible illumination of the margin of a planet eclipsing it; and the interception of the sun's light by the moon is as foreign to the question as the statement of inflection is inaccurate.

To the argument adduced by Huygens in favor of the rectilinear propagation of undulations Newton has made no reply; perhaps because of his own misconception of the nature of the motions of elastic mediums, as dependent on a peculiar law of vibration, which has been corrected by later mathematicians. On the whole, it is presumed that this proposition may be safely admitted as perfectly consistent with analogy and with experiment.

PROPOSITION IV

When an undulation arrives at a surface which is the limit of mediums of different densities, a partial reflection takes place proportionate in force to the difference of the densities.

This may be illustrated, if not demonstrated, by the analogy of elastic bodies of different sizes. "If a smaller elastic body strikes against a larger one, it is well known that the smaller is reflected more or less powerfully, according to the difference of their magnitudes: thus, there is always a reflection when the rays of light pass from a rarer to a denser stratum of ether; and frequently an echo when a sound strikes against a cloud. A greater body striking a smaller one propels it, without losing all its motion: thus, the particles of a denser stratum of ether do not impart the whole of their motion to a rarer, but, in their effort to proceed, they are recalled by the attraction of the refracting substance with equal force; and thus a reflection is always secondarily produced when the rays of light pass from a denser to a rarer stratum." But it is not absolutely necessary to suppose an attraction in the latter case, since the effort to proceed would be propagated backward without it, and the undulation would be reversed, a rarefaction returning in place of a condensation; and this will perhaps be found most consistent with the phenomena. . . .

PROPOSITION VIII

When two undulations, from different origins, coincide either perfectly or very nearly in direction, their joint effect is a combination of the motions belonging to each.

Since every particle of the medium is affected by each undulation, wherever the directions coincide, the undulations can proceed no otherwise than by uniting their motions, so that the joint motion may be the sum or difference of the separate motions, accordingly as similar or dissimilar parts of the undulations are coincident.

I have, on a former occasion, insisted at large on the application of this principle to harmonics; and it will appear to be of still more extensive utility in explaining the phenomena of colors. The undulations which are now to be compared are those of equal frequency. When the two series coincide exactly in point of time, it is obvious that the united velocity of the particular motions must be greatest, and, in effect at least, double the separate velocities; and also that it must be smallest, and, if the undulations are of equal strength, totally destroyed when the time of the greatest direct motion belonging to one undulation coincides with that of the greatest retrograde motion of the other. In intermediate states the joint undulation will be of intermediate strength; but by what laws this intermediate strength must vary cannot be determined without further data. It is well known that a similar cause produces in sound that effect which is called a beat; two series of undulations of nearly equal magnitude co-operating and destroying each other alternately, as they coincide more or less perfectly in the times of performing their respective motions.

*   *   *   *

Experiments and Calculations
Relative to Physical Optics

I. EXPERIMENTAL DEMONSTRATION OF THE GENERAL LAW OF
THE INTERFERENCE OF LIGHT

In making some experiments on the fringes of colors accompanying shadows, I have found so simple and so demonstrative a proof of the general law of the interference of two portions of light, which I have already endeavored to establish, that I think it right to lay before the Royal Society a short statement of the facts which appear to me so decisive. The proposition on which I mean to insist at present is simply this—that fringes of colors are produced by the interference of two portions of light; and I think it will not be denied by the most prejudiced that the assertion is proved by the experiments I am about to relate, which may be repeated with great ease whenever the sun shines, and without any other apparatus than is at hand to every one.

Experiment 1.   I made a small hole in a window-shutter, and covered it with a piece of thick paper, which I perforated with a fine needle. For greater convenience of observation I placed a small looking-glass without the window-shutter, in such a position as to reflect the sun's light in a direction nearly horizontal upon the opposite wall, and to cause the cone of diverging light to pass over a table on which were several little screens of card-paper. I brought into the sunbeam a slip of card about one-thirtieth of an inch in breadth, and observed its shadow, either on the wall or on other cards held at different distances. Besides the fringes of color on each side of the shadow, the shadow itself was divided by similar parallel fringes of smaller dimensions, differing in number according to the distance at which the shadow was observed, but leaving the middle of the shadow always white. Now these fringes were the joint effects of the portions of light passing on each side of the slip of card, and inflected, or rather diffracted, into the shadow; for a little screen being placed a few inches from the card so as to receive either edge of the shadow on its margin, all the fringes which had before been observed in the shadow on the wall immediately disappeared, although the light

---

Published in *The Philosophical Transactions of the Royal Society*, London, 1804.

inflected on the other side was allowed to retain its course, and although this light must have undergone any modification that the proximity of the other edge of the slip of card might have been capable of occasioning. When the interposed screen was more remote from the narrow card, it was necessary to plunge it more deeply into the shadow, in order to extinguish the parallel lines; for here the light diffracted from the edge of the object had entered farther into the shadow in its way towards the fringes. Nor was it for want of a sufficient intensity of light that one of the two portions was incapable of producing the fringes alone; for when they were both uninterrupted, the lines appeared, even if the intensity was reduced to one-tenth or one-twentieth.

Experiment 2. The crested fringes described by the ingenious and accurate Grimaldi afford an elegant variation of the preceding experiment and an interesting example of a calculation grounded on it. When a shadow is formed by an object which has a rectangular termination besides the usual external fringes there are two or three alterations of colors, beginning from the line which bisects the angle, disposed on each side of it in curves, which are convex towards the bisecting line, and which converge in some degree towards it as they become more remote from the angular point. These fringes are also the joint effect of the light which is inflected directly towards the shadow from each of the two outlines of the object; for if a screen be placed within a few inches of the object, so as to receive only one of the edges of the shadow, the whole of the fringes disappear; if, on the contrary, the rectangular point of the screen be opposed to the point of the shadow so as barely to receive the angle of the shadow on its extremity, the fringes will remain undisturbed.

II. COMPARISON OF MEASURES DEDUCED FROM VARIOUS EXPERIMENTS

If we now proceed to examine the dimensions of the fringes under different circumstances, we may calculate the differences of the lengths of the paths described by the portions of light which have thus been proved to be concerned in producing those fringes; and we shall find that where the lengths are equal the light always remains white; but that where either the brightest light or the light of any given color disappears and reappears a first, a second, or a third time, the differences of the lengths of the paths of the two portions are in arithmetical progression, as nearly as we can expect experiments of this kind to agree with each other. I shall compare, in this point of view, the measures deduced from several experiments of Newton and from some of my own.

In the eighth and ninth observations of the third book of Newton's *Optics* some experiments are related which, together with the third observation, will furnish us with the data necessary for the calculation. Two knives were placed, with their edges meeting at a very acute angle, in a beam of the sun's light, admitted through a small aperture, and the point of concourse of the two first lines bordering the shadows of the respective knives was observed at various distances. The results of six observations are expressed in the first three lines of Table I. On the supposition that the dark line is produced by the first interference of the light reflected from the edges of the knives, with the light passing in a straight line between them, we may assign, by calculating the difference of the two paths, the interval for the first disappearance of the brightest light, as it is expressed in the fourth line. Table II contains the results of a similar calculation from Newton's observations on the shadow of a hair; and Table III, from some experiments of my own of the same nature; the second bright line being supposed to correspond to a double interval, the second dark line to a triple interval, and the succeeding lines to depend on a continuation of the progression. The unit of all the tables is an inch.

TABLE I *Observation 9.* N

Distance of the knives from the aperture					101
Distance of the paper from the knives	$1\frac{1}{2}$	$3\frac{1}{3}$	$8\frac{3}{8}$	32	96	131
Distance between the edges of the knives opposite to the point of concourse	.012	.020	.034	.057	.081	.087
Interval of disappearance	.0000122	.0000155	.0000182	.0000167	.0000166	.0000166

TABLE II *Observation 3.* N

Breadth of the hair		1/280
Distance of the hair from the aperture		144
Distances of the scale from the aperture	150	252
(Breadths of the shadow	1/54	1/9)
Breadth between the second pair of bright lines	2/47	4/17
Interval of disappearance, or half the difference of the paths	.0000151	.0000173
Breadth between the third pair of bright lines	4/73	3/10
Interval of disappearance, one-fourth of the difference	.0000130	.0000143

TABLE III *Experiment 3*

Breadth of the object	.434
Distance of the object from the aperture	125
Distance of the wall from the aperture	250
Distance of the second pair of dark lines from each other	1.167
Interval of disappearance, one-third of the difference	.0000149

Experiment 4

Breadth of the wire	.083
Distance of the wire from the aperture	32
Distance of the wall from the aperture	250
(Breadth of the shadow, by three measurements	.815, .826, or .827; mean, .823)
Distance of the first pair of dark lines	1.165, 1.170, or 1.160; mean, 1.165
Interval of disappearance	.0000194
Distance of the second pair of dark lines	1.402, 1.395, or 1.400; mean, 1.399
Interval of disappearance	.0000137
Distance of the third pair of dark lines	1.594, 1.580, or 1.585; mean, 1.586
Interval of disappearance	.0000128

It appears, from five of the six observations of the first table, in which the distance of the shadow was varied from about 3 inches to 11 feet, and the breadth of the fringes was increased in the ratio of 7 to 1, that the difference of the routes constituting the interval of disappearance varied but one-eleventh at most; and that in three out of the five it agreed with the mean, either exactly or within 1/160 part. Hence we are warranted in inferring that the interval appropriate to the extinction of the brightest light is either accurately or very nearly constant.

But it may be inferred from a comparison of all the other observations that when the obliquity of the reflection is very great some circumstance takes place which causes the interval thus calculated to be somewhat greater; thus, in the eleventh line of the third table it comes out one-sixth greater than the mean of the five already mentioned. On the other hand, the mean of two of Newton's experiments and one of mine is a result about one-fourth less than the former. With respect to the nature of this circumstance I cannot at present form a decided opinion; but I conjecture that it is a deviation of some of the light concerned, from the rectilinear direction assigned to it, arising either from its natural diffraction, by which the magnitude of the shadow is also enlarged, or from some other unknown cause. If we imagined the shadow of the wire and the fringes nearest it to be so contracted that the motion of the light bounding the shadow might be rectilinear, we should thus make a sufficient compensation for this deviation; but it is difficult to point out what precise track of the light would cause it to require this correction.

The mean of the three experiments which appear to have been least affected by this unknown deviation gives .0000127 for the interval appropriate to the disappearance of the brightest light; and it may be inferred that if they had been wholly exempted from its effects the measure would have been somewhat smaller. Now the analogous interval, deduced from the experiments of Newton on this plate, is .0000112, which is about one-eighth less than the former result; and this appears to be a coincidence fully sufficient to authorize us to attribute these two classes of phenomena to the same cause. It is very easily shown, with respect to the colors of thin plates, that each kind of light disappears and reappears where the differences of the routes of two of its portions are in arithmetical progression; and we have seen that the same law may be in general inferred from the phenomena of diffracted light, even independently of the analogy.

The distribution of the colors is also so similar in both cases as to point immediately to a similarity in the causes. In the thirteenth observation of the second part of the first book Newton relates that the interval of the glasses where the rings appeared in red light was to the interval where they appeared in violet light as 14 to 9; and, in the eleventh observation of the third book, that the distances between the fringes, under the same circumstances, were the twenty-second and the twenty-seventh of an inch. Hence, deducting the breadth of the hair and taking the squares, in order to find the relation of the difference of the routes, we have the proportion of 14 to $9\frac{1}{4}$, which scarcely differs from the proportion observed in the colors of the thin plate.

We may readily determine from this general principle the form of the crested fringes of Grimaldi, already described; for it will appear that, under the circumstances of the experiment related, the points in which the differences of the lengths of the paths described by the two portions of light are equal to a constant quantity, and in which, therefore, the same kinds of light ought to appear or disappear, are always found in equilateral hyperbolas, of which the axes coincide with the outlines of the shadow, and the asymptotes nearly with the diagonal line. Such, therefore, must be the direction of the fringes; and this conclusion agrees perfectly with the observation. But it must be remarked that the parts near the outlines of the shadow are so much shaded off as to render the character of the curve somewhat less decidedly marked where it approaches to its axis. These fringes have a slight resemblance to the hyperbolic fringes observed by Newton; but the analogy is only distant.

*   *   *   *

IV. ARGUMENTATIVE INFERENCE RESPECTING THE NATURE OF LIGHT

The experiment of Grimaldi on the crested fringes within the shadow, together with several others of his observations equally important, has been left unnoticed by Newton. Those who are attached to the Newtonian theory of light, or to the hypothesis of modern opticians founded on views still less enlarged, would do well to endeavor to imagine anything like an explanation of these experiments derived from their own doctrines; and if they fail in the attempt, to refrain at least from idle declamation against a system which is founded on the accuracy of its application to all these facts, and to a thousand others of a similar nature.

From the experiments and calculation which have been premised, we may be allowed to infer that homogeneous light at certain equal distances in the direction of its motion is possessed of opposite qualities capable of neutralizing or destroying each other, and of extinguishing the light where they happen to be united; that these qualities succeed each other alternately in successive concentric superficies, at distances which are constant for the same light passing through the same medium. From the agreement of the measures, and from the similarity of the phenomena, we may conclude that these intervals are the same as are concerned in the production of the colors of thin plates; but these are shown, by the experiments of Newton, to be the smaller the denser the medium; and since it may be presumed that their number must necessarily remain unaltered in a given quantity of light, it follows, of course, that light moves more slowly in a denser than in a rarer medium; and this being granted, it must be allowed that refraction is not the effect of an attractive force directed to a denser medium. The advocates for the projectile hypothesis of light must consider which link in this chain of reasoning they may judge to be the most feeble, for hitherto I have advanced in this paper no general hypothesis whatever. But since we know that sound diverges in concentric superficies, and that musical sounds consist of opposite qualities, capable of neutralizing each other, and succeeding at certain equal intervals, which are different according to the difference of the note, we are fully authorized to conclude that there must be some strong resemblance between the nature of sound and that of light.

I have not, in the course of these investigations, found any reason to suppose the presence of such an inflecting medium in the neighborhood of dense substances as I was formerly inclined to attribute to them; and, upon considering the phenomena of the aberration of the stars, I am disposed to believe that the luminiferous ether pervades the substance of all material bodies, with little or no resistance, as freely, perhaps, as the wind passes through a grove of trees.

The observations on the effects of diffraction and interference may, perhaps, sometimes be applied to a practical purpose in making us cautious in our conclusions respecting the appearances of minute bodies viewed in a microscope. The shadow of a fibre, however opaque, placed in a pencil of light admitted through a small aperture, is always somewhat less dark in the middle of its breadth than in the parts on each side. A similar effect may also take place, in some degree, with respect to the image on the retina, and impress the sense with an idea of a transparency which has no real existence; and if a small portion of light be really transmitted through the substance, this may again be destroyed by its interference with the diffracted light, and produce an appearance of partial opacity, instead of uniform semi-transparency. Thus a central dark spot and a light spot, surrounded by a darker circle, may respectively be produced in the images of a semi-transparent and an opaque corpuscle, and impress us with an idea of a complication of structure which does not exist. In order to detect the fallacy, we make two or three fibres cross each other, and view a number of globules contiguous to each other; or we may obtain a still more effectual remedy by changing the magnifying power; and then, if the appearance remain constant in kind and in degree, we may be assured that it truly represents the nature of the substance to be examined. It is natural to inquire whether or not the figures of the globules of blood delineated by Mr. Hewson in the *Phil. Trans.,* vol. lxiii., for 1773, might not in some measure have been influenced by a deception of this kind; but, as far as I have hitherto been able to examine the globules with a lens of one-fiftieth of an inch focus, I have found them nearly such as Mr. Hewson has described them. . . .

*　　*　　*　　*

VI. EXPERIMENT ON THE DARK RAYS OF RITTER

Experiment 6.　The existence of solar rays accompanying light, more refrangible than the violet rays and cognizable by their chemical effects, was first ascertained by Mr. Ritter; but Dr. Wollaston made the same experiments a very short time afterwards without having been informed of what had been done on the Continent. These rays appear to extend beyond the violet rays of the prismatic spectrum, through a space nearly equal to that which is occupied by the violet. In order to complete the comparison of their properties with those of visible light, I was desirous of examining the effect of their reflection from a thin plate of air, capable of producing the well-known rings of colors. For this purpose I formed an image of the rings, by means of the solar microscope, with the apparatus which I have described in the Journals of the Royal Institution, and I threw this image on paper dipped in a solution of nitrate of silver, placed at the distance of about nine inches from the microscope. In the course of an hour portions of three dark rings were very distinctly visible, much smaller than the brightest rings of the colored image, and coinciding very nearly in their dimensions with the rings of violet light that appeared upon the interposition of violet glass. I thought the dark rings were a little smaller than the violet rings, but the difference was not sufficiently great to be accurately ascertained; it might be as much as 1/30 or 1/40 of the diameters, but not greater. It is the less surprising that the difference should be so small, as the dimensions of the colored rings do not by any means vary at the violet end of the spectrum so rapidly as at the red end. For performing this experiment with very great accuracy a heliostat would be necessary, since the motion of the sun causes a slight change in the place of the image; and leather impregnated with the muriate of silver would indicate the effect with greater delicacy. The experiment, however, in its present state, is sufficient to complete the analogy of the invisible with the visible rays, and to show that they are equally liable to the general law which is the principal subject of this paper. If we had thermometers sufficiently delicate, it is probable that we might acquire, by similar means, information still more interesting with respect to the rays of invisible heat discovered by Dr. Herschel; but at present there is great reason to doubt of the practicability of such an experiment.

17

SADI CARNOT

Scion of a family with strong scientific traditions, Sadi Carnot was a scientist almost by virtue of his birth in 1796. His father, Lazare Carnot, had been a prominent physicist and engineer, as Sadi himself and, later, his nephew were to be. The family was equally committed to a tradition of republican politics. The father, Lazare, sat on the notorious Committee of Public Safety and on the Directory during the period of the French Revolution. Sadi's brother participated prominently in the foundation both of the Second and of the Third French Republics, and his nephew was to be a President of the Third Republic. Sadi himself did not play a role in politics. Graduating from the *École Polytechnique* as a military engineer in 1814, he found not only a political career forestalled, but even a technical one effectively hamstrung by the Bourbon restoration of 1815. He devoted his brief career to the study of mathematics, chemistry, natural history, technology, and even economics, before an epidemic of cholera brought it to an end in 1832. His one published work, *Reflections on the Motive Power of Heat* (1824), is the source of the following selection.

In Carnot's age, a group of unexpected phenomena were forcing themselves upon the scientific community. The study of electricity, hitherto concerned exclusively with static phenomena, had been transformed by the discovery that chemical action can yield a current of electricity. A current, in turn, was found to produce chemical action. The recognized analogy of electricity and magnetism suddenly yielded the observation that a magnetic field surrounds an electric current. Faraday soon learned that a magnetic field in motion can generate an electric current as well. Not only could motion be transformed into electricity, but electricity could be transformed into motion by means of the motor. From the contemplation of the meaning of such processes of conversion and transformation, there ultimately emerged the highest generalization of 19th century physics, the law of the conservation of energy.

During the same period, the innumerable changes in life effected by the steam engine daily brought the scientist and the engineer face to face with the most striking conversion of all, the conversion of heat to motion or work. Its practical importance led engineers to seek higher levels of efficiency; the engineering problem raised theoretical issues for the scientist. Under what conditions does the pressure of the steam produce the maximum output from the engine? Is steam the ideal medium to use in an engine, or could the substitution of another increase efficiency? To such questions Carnot addressed his essay on the motive power of heat, an essay recognized as an important step toward the principle of the conservation of energy. But only a step toward it—Carnot himself did not state the principle. He expressed his conclusions in terms of traditional views of the nature of heat, and the principle of the conservation of energy could not be established before a different conception of heat replaced it.

17

Reflections on the Motive Power of Heat and on Engines Suitable for Developing this Power

It is well known that heat may be used as a cause of motion, and that the motive power which may be obtained from it is very great. The steam-engine, now in such general use, is a manifest proof of this fact.

To the agency of heat may be ascribed those vast disturbances which we see occurring everywhere on the earth; the movements of the atmosphere, the rising of mists, the fall of rain and meteors, the streams of water which channel the surface of the earth, of which man has succeeded in utilizing only a small part. To heat are due also volcanic eruptions and earthquakes. From this great source we draw the moving force necessary for our use. Nature, by supplying combustible material everywhere, has afforded us the means of generating heat and the motive power which is given by it, at all times and in all places, and the steam-engine has made it possible to develop and use this power.

The study of the steam-engine is of the highest interest, owing to its importance, its constantly increasing use, and the great changes it is destined to make in the civilized world. It has already developed mines, propelled ships, and dredged rivers and harbors. It forges iron, saws wood, grinds grain, spins and weaves stuffs, and transports the heaviest loads. In the future it will most probably be the universal motor, and will furnish the power now obtained from animals, from waterfalls, and from air-currents. Over the first of these motors it has the advantage of economy, and over the other two the incalculable advantage that it can be used everywhere and always, and that its work need never be interrupted. If in the future the steam-engine is so perfected as to render it less costly to construct it and to supply it with fuel, it will unite all desirable qualities and will promote the development of the industrial arts to an extent which it is difficult to foresee. It is, indeed, not only a powerful and convenient motor, which can be set up or transported anywhere,

Translated from the French by W. F. Magie, in *The Second Law of Thermodynamics*, New York: Harper & Company, 1899.

and substituted for other motors already in use, but it leads to the rapid extension of those arts in which it is used, and it can even create arts hitherto unknown.

The most signal service which has been rendered to England by the steam-engine is that of having revived the working of her coal-mines, which had languished and was threatened with extinction on account of the increasing difficulty of excavation and extraction of the coal. We may place in the second rank the services rendered in the manufacture of iron, as much by furnishing an abundant supply of coal, which took the place of wood as the wood began to be exhausted, as by the powerful machines of all kinds the use of which it either facilitated or made possible.

Iron and fire, as every one knows, are the mainstays of the mechanical arts. Perhaps there is not in all England a single industry whose existence is not dependent on these agents, and which does not use them extensively. If England were to-day to lose its steam-engines it would lose also its coal and iron, and this loss would dry up all its sources of wealth and destroy its prosperity; it would annihilate this colossal power. The destruction of its navy, which it considers its strongest support, would be, perhaps, less fatal.

The safe and rapid navigation by means of steamships is an entirely new art due to the steam-engine. This art has already made possible the establishment of prompt and regular communication on the arms of the sea, and on the great rivers of the old and new continents. By means of the steam-engine regions still savage have been traversed which but a short time ago could hardly have been penetrated. The products of civilization have been taken to all parts of the earth, which they would otherwise not have reached for many years. The navigation due to the steam-engine has in a measure drawn together the most distant nations. It tends to unite the peoples of the earth as if they all lived in the same country. In fact, to diminish the duration, the fatigue, the uncertainty and danger of voyages is to lessen their length.

The discovery of the steam-engine, like most human inventions, owes its birth to crude attempts which have been attributed to various persons and of which the real author is not known. The principal discovery consists indeed less in these first trials than in the successive improvements which have brought it to its present perfection. There is almost as great a difference between the first structures where expansive force was developed and the actual steam-engine as there is between the first raft ever constructed and a man-of-war.

If the honor of a discovery belongs to the nation where it acquired all its development and improvement, this honor cannot in this case be withheld from England: Savery, Newcomen, Smeaton, the celebrated Watt, Woolf, Trevithick, and other English engineers, are the real inventors of the steam-engine. At their hands it received each successive improvement. It is natural that an invention should be made, improved, and perfected where the need of it is most strongly felt.

In spite of labor of all sorts expended on the steam-engine, and in spite of the perfection to which it has been brought, its theory is very little advanced, and the attempts to better this state of affairs have thus far been directed almost at random.

The question has often been raised whether the motive power of heat is limited or not; whether there is a limit to the possible improvements of the steam-engine which, in the nature of the case, cannot be passed by any means; or if, on the other hand, these improvements are capable of indefinite extension. Inventors have tried for a long time, and are still trying, to find whether there is not a more efficient agent than water by which to develop the motive power of heat; whether, for example, atmospheric air does not offer great advantages in this respect. We propose to submit these questions to a critical examination.

The phenomenon of the production of motion by heat has not been considered in a sufficiently general way. It has been treated only in connection with machines whose nature and mode of action do not admit of a full investigation of it. In such machines the phenomenon is, in a measure, imperfect and incomplete; it thus becomes difficult to recognize its principles and study its laws. To examine the principle of the production of motion by heat in all its generality, it must be conceived independently of any mechanism or of any particular agent; it is necessary to establish proofs applicable not only to steam-engines but to all other heat-engines, irrespective of the working substance and the manner in which it acts.

The machines which are not worked by heat—for instance, those worked by men or animals, by water-falls, or by air currents—can be studied to their last details by the principles of mechanics. All possible cases may be anticipated, all imaginable actions are subject to general principles already well established and applicable in all circumstances. The theory of such machines is complete. Such a theory is evidently lacking for heat-engines. We shall never possess it until the laws of physics are so extended and generalized as to make known in advance all the effects of heat acting in a definite way on any body whatsoever.

We shall take for granted in what follows a knowledge, at least a superficial one, of the various parts which compose an ordinary steam-engine. We think it unnecessary to describe the fire-box, the boiler, the steam-chest, the piston, the condenser, etc.

The production of motion in the steam-engine is always accompanied by a circumstance which we should particularly notice. This circumstance is the re-establishment of equilibrium in the caloric—that is, its passage from one body where the temperature is more or less elevated to another where it is lower. What happens, in fact, in a steam-engine at work? The caloric developed in the fire-box as an effect of combustion passes through the wall of the boiler and produces steam, incorporating itself with the steam in some way. This steam, carrying the caloric with it, transports it first into the cylinder, where it fulfils some function, and thence into the condenser, where the steam is precipitated by coming in contact with cold water. As a last result the cold water in the condenser receives the caloric developed by combustion. It is warmed by means of the steam, as if it had been placed directly on the fire-box. The steam is here only a means of transporting caloric; it thus fulfils the same office as in the heating of baths by steam, with the exception that in the case in hand its motion is rendered useful.

We can easily perceive, in the operation which we have just described, the re-establishment of equilibrium in the caloric and its passage from a hotter to a colder body. The first of these bodies is the heated air of the fire-box; the second, the water of condensation. The re-establishment of equilibrium of the caloric is accomplished between them—if not completely, at least in part; for, on the one hand, the heated air after having done its work escapes through the smoke-stack at a much lower temperature than that which it had acquired by the combustion; and, on the other hand, the water of the condenser, after having precipitated the steam, leaves the engine with a higher temperature than that which it had when it entered.

The production of motive power in the steam-engine is therefore not due to a real consumption of the caloric, *but to its transfer from a hotter to a colder body*—that is to say, to the re-establishment of its equilibrium, which is assumed to have been destroyed by a chemical action such as combustion, or by some other cause. We shall soon see that this principle is applicable to all engines operated by heat.

According to this principle, to obtain motive power it is not enough to produce heat; it is also necessary to provide cold, without which the heat would be useless. For if there existed only bodies as warm as our furnaces, how would the condensation of steam be possible, and where could it be sent if it were once produced? It cannot be replied that it could be ejected into the atmosphere, as is done with certain engines, since the atmosphere would not receive it. In the actual state of things the atmosphere acts as a vast condenser for the steam, because it is at a lower temperature; otherwise it would soon be saturated, or, rather, would be saturated in advance.

Everywhere where there is a difference of temperature, and where the re-establishment of equilibrium of the caloric can be effected, the production of motive power is possible. Water vapor is one agent for obtaining this power, but it is not the only one; all natural bodies can be applied to this purpose, for they are all susceptible to changes of volume, to successive contractions and dilatations effected by alternations of heat and cold; they are all capable, by this change of volume, of overcoming resistances and thus of developing motive power. A solid body, such as a metallic bar, when alternately heated and cooled, increases and diminishes in length and can move bodies fixed at its extremities. A liquid, alternately heated and cooled, increases and diminishes in volume and can overcome obstacles more or less great opposed to its expansion. An aeriform fluid undergoes considerable changes of volume with changes of temperature; if it is enclosed in an envelope capable of enlargement, such as a cylinder furnished with a piston, it will produce movements of great extent. The vapors of all bodies which are capable of evaporation, such as alcohol, mercury, sulphur, etc., can perform the same function as water vapor. This, when alternately heated and cooled, will produce motive power in the same way as permanent gases, without returning to the liquid state. Most of these means have been proposed, several have been even tried, though, thus far, without much success.

We have explained that the motive power in the steam-engine is due to a re-establishment of equilibrium in the caloric; this statement holds not only for steam-engines but also for all heat-engines—that is to say, for all engines in which caloric is the motor. Heat evidently can be a cause of motion only through the changes of volume or of form to which it subjects the body; those changes cannot occur at a constant temperature, but are due to alternations of heat and cold; thus to heat any substance it is necessary to have a body warmer than it, and to cool it, one cooler than it. We must take caloric from the first of these bodies and transfer it to the second by means of the intermediate body, which transfer re-establishes, or, at least, tends to re-establish, equilibrium of the caloric.

At this point we naturally raise an interesting and important question: Is the motive power of heat invariable in quantity, or does it vary with the agent which one uses to obtain it—that is, with the intermediate body chosen on the subject of the action of heat?

It is clear that the question thus raised supposes given a certain quantity of caloric and a certain difference of temperature. For example, we suppose that we have at our disposal a body, *A*, maintained at the temperature 100 degrees, and another body, *B*, at 0 degrees, and inquire what quantity of motive power will be produced by the transfer of a given quantity of caloric—for example, of so much as is necessary to melt a kilogram of ice—from the first of these bodies to the second; we inquire if this quantity of motive power is necessarily limited; if it varies with the substance used to obtain it; if water vapor offers in this respect more or less advantage than vapor of alcohol or of mercury, than a permanent gas or than any other substance. We shall try to answer these questions in the light of the considerations already advanced.

We have previously called attention to the fact, which is self-evident, or at least becomes so if we take into consideration the changes of volume occasioned by heat, that *wherever there is a difference of temperature the production of motive power is possible.* Conversely, wherever this power can be employed, it is possible to produce a difference of temperature or to destroy the equilibrium of the caloric. Percussion and friction of bodies are means of raising their temperature spontaneously to a higher degree than that of surrounding bodies, and consequently of destroying that equilibrium in the caloric which had previously existed. It is an experimental fact that the temperature of gaseous fluids is raised by compression and lowered by expansion. This is a sure method of changing the temperature of bodies, and thus of destroying the equilibrium of the caloric in the same substance, as often as we please. Steam, when used in a reverse way from that in which it is used in the steam-engine, can thus be considered as a means of destroying the equilibrium of the caloric. To be convinced of this, it is only necessary to notice attentively the way in which motive power is developed by the action of heat on water vapor. Let us consider two bodies, *A* and *B*, each maintained at a constant temperature, that of *A* being higher than that of *B*; these two bodies, which can either give up or receive heat without a change of temperature, perform the functions of two indefinitely great reservoirs of caloric. We will call the first body the source and the second the refrigerator.

If we desire to produce motive power by the transfer of a certain quantity of heat from the body *A* to the body *B* we may proceed in the following way:

1. We take from the body *A* a quantity of caloric to make steam—that is, we cause *A* to serve as the fire-pot, or rather as the metal of the boiler in an ordinary engine; we assume the steam produced to be at the same temperature as the body *A*.

2. The steam is received into an envelope capable of enlargement, such as a cylinder furnished with a piston. We then increase the volume of this envelope, and consequently also the volume of the steam. The

temperature of the steam falls when it is thus rarefied, as is the case with all elastic fluids; let us assume that the rarefaction is carried to the point where the temperature becomes precisely that of the body B.

3. We condense the steam by bringing it in contact with B and exerting on it at the same time a constant pressure until it becomes entirely condensed. The body B here performs the function of the injected water in an ordinary engine, with the difference that it condenses the steam without mixing with it and without changing its own temperature. The operations which we have just described could have been performed in a reverse sense and order. There is nothing to prevent the formation of vapor by means of the caloric of the body B, and its compression from the temperature of B, in such a way that it acquires the temperature of the body A, and then its condensation in contact with A, under a pressure which is maintained constant until it is completely liquefied.

In the first series of operations there is at the same time a production of motive power and a transfer of caloric from the body A to the body B; in the reverse series there is at the same time an expenditure of motive power and a return of the caloric from B to A. But if in each case the same quantity of vapor has been used, if there is no loss of motive power or of caloric, the quantity of motive power produced in the first case will equal the quantity expended in the second, and the quantity of caloric which in the first case passed from A to B will equal the quantity which in the second case returns from B to A, so that an indefinite number of such alternating operations can be effected without the production of motive power or the transfer of caloric from one body to the other. Now if there were any method of using heat preferable to that which we have employed, that is to say, if it were possible that the caloric should produce, by any process whatever, a larger quantity of motive power than that produced in our first series of operations, it would be possible, by diverting a portion of this power, to effect a return of caloric, by the method just indicated, from the body B to the body A—that is, from the refrigerator to the source—and thus to re-establish things in their original state, and to put them in position to recommence an operation exactly similar to the first one, and so on: there would thus result not only the perpetual motion, but an indefinite creation of motive power without consumption of caloric or of any other agent whatsoever. Such a creation is entirely contrary to the ideas now accepted, to the laws of mechanics and of sound physics; it is inadmissible. We may hence conclude that *the maximum motive power resulting from the use of steam is also the maximum motive power which can be obtained by any other means.* We shall soon give a second and more rigorous demonstration of this law. What has been given should only be regarded as a sketch. . . .

According to the views now established we may with propriety compare the motive power of heat with that of a waterfall; both have a maximum which cannot be surpassed, whatever may be, on the one hand, the machine used to receive the action of the water and whatever, on the other hand, the substance used to receive the action of the heat. The motive power of falling water depends on the quantity of water and on the height of its fall; the motive power of heat depends also on the quantity of caloric employed and on that which might be named, which we, in fact, will call, *its descent*—that is to say, on the difference of temperature of the bodies between which the exchange of caloric is effected. In the fall of water the motive power is strictly proportional to the difference of level between the higher and lower reservoirs. In the fall of caloric the motive power doubtless increases with the difference of temperature between the hotter and colder bodies, but we do not know whether it is proportional to this difference. We do not know, for example, whether the fall of the caloric from 100 to 50 degrees furnishes more or less motive power than the fall of the same caloric from 50 degrees to zero. This is a question which we propose to examine later.

We shall give here a second demonstration of the fundamental proposition stated above and present this proposition in a more general form than we have before.

When a gaseous fluid is rapidly compressed its temperature rises, and when it is rapidly expanded its temperature falls. This is one of the best established facts of experience; we shall take it as the basis of our demonstration. When the temperature of a gas is raised and we wish to bring it back to its original temperature without again changing its volume, it is necessary to remove caloric from it. This caloric may also be removed as the compression is effected, so that the temperature of the gas remains constant. In the same way, if the gas is rarefied, we can prevent its temperature from falling, by furnishing it with a certain quantity of caloric. We shall call the caloric used in such cases, when it occasions no change of temperature, *caloric due to a change of volume*. This name does not indicate that the caloric belongs to the volume; it does not belong to it any more than it does to the pressure, and it might equally well be called *caloric due to a change of pressure*. We are ignorant of what laws it obeys in respect to changes of volume: it is possible that its quantity changes with the nature of the gas, or with its density or with its temperature. Experiment has taught us nothing on this subject; it has taught us only that this caloric is developed in greater or less quantity by the compression of elastic fluids.

This preliminary idea having been stated, let us imagine an elastic fluid—atmospheric air, for example—enclosed in a cylindrical vessel *abcd* furnished with a movable diaphragm or piston *cd;* let us assume

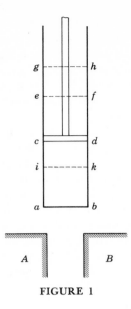

FIGURE 1

also the two bodies *A, B* both at constant temperatures, that of *A* being higher than that of *B,* and let us consider the series of operations which follow:

1. Contact of the body *A* with the air contained in the vessel *abcd* or with the wall of this vessel, which wall is supposed to be a good conductor of caloric. By means of this contact the air attains the same temperature as the body *A; cd* is the position of the piston.

2. The piston rises gradually until it takes the position *ef.* Contact is always maintained between the air and the body *A,* and the temperature thus remains constant during the rarefaction. The body *A* furnishes the caloric necessary to maintain a constant temperature.

3. The body *A* is removed and the air is no longer in contact with any body capable of supplying it with caloric; the piston, however, continues to move and passes from the position *ef* to the position *gh.* The air is rarefied without receiving caloric and its temperature falls. Let us suppose that it falls until it becomes equal to that of the body *B;* at this instant the piston ceases to move and occupies the position *gh.*

4. The air is brought in contact with the body *B;* it is compressed by the piston as it returns from the position *gh* to the position *cd.* The air, however, remains at a constant temperature on account of its contact with the body *B,* to which it gives up its caloric.

5. The body *B* is removed and the compression of the air continued. The temperature of the air, which is now isolated, rises. The compression

is continued until the air acquires the temperature of the body A. The piston during this time passes from the position cd to the position ik.

6. The air is again brought in contact with the body A; the piston returns from the position ik to the position ef, and the temperature remains constant.

7. The operation described in No. 3 is repeated, and then the operations 4, 5, 6, 3, 4, 5, 6, 3, 4, 5, and so on, successively.

In these various operations a pressure is exerted upon the piston by the air contained in the cylinder; the elastic force of this air varies with the changes of volume as well as with the changes of temperature; but we should notice that at equal volumes—that is, for similar positions of the piston—the temperature is higher during the expansions than during the compressions. During the former, therefore, the elastic force of the air is greater, and consequently the quantity of motive power produced by the expansions is greater than that which is consumed in effecting the compressions. Thus there remains an excess of motive power, which we can dispose of for any purpose whatsoever. The air has therefore served as a heat-engine; and it has been used in the most advantageous way possible, for there has been no useless re-establishment of equilibrium in the caloric.

All the operations described above can be carried out in a direct and in a reverse order. Let us suppose that after the sixth step, when the piston is at ef, it is brought back to the position ik, and that, at the same time, the air is kept in contact with the body A; the caloric furnished by this body during the sixth operation returns to its source—that is, to the body A—and the condition of things is the same as at the end of the fifth operation. If now we remove the body A and move the piston from ik to cd, the temperature of the air will fall as many degrees as it rose during the fifth operation and will equal that of the body B. A series of reverse operations to those above described could evidently be carried out; it is only necessary to bring the system into the same initial state and in each operation to carry out an expansion instead of a compression, and conversely.

The result of the first operation was the production of a certain quantity of motive power and the transfer of the caloric from the body A to the body B; the result of the reverse operation would be the consumption of the motive power produced and the return of the caloric from the body B to the body A; so that the two series of operations in a sense annul or neutralize each other.

The impossibility of making the caloric produce a larger quantity of motive power than that which we obtained in our first series of operations is now easy to prove. It may be demonstrated by an argument similar to that used previously. The argument will have even a greater degree of rigor: the air which serves to develop the motive power is brought back, at the end of each cycle of operations, to its original condition, which was, as we noticed, not quite the case with the steam.

We have chosen atmospheric air as the agency employed to develop the motive power of heat; but it is evident that the same reasoning would hold for any other gaseous substance, and even for all other bodies susceptible of changes of temperature by successive contractions and expansions—that is, for all bodies in Nature, at least, all those which are capable of developing the motive power of heat. Thus we are led to establish this general proposition:

The motive power of heat is independent of the agents employed to develop it; its quantity is determined solely by the temperatures of the bodies between which, in the final result, the transfer of the caloric occurs.

It is understood in this statement that the method used for developing motive power, whatever it may be, attains the highest perfection of which it is capable. This condition will be fulfilled, as we remarked above, if there is no change of temperature in the bodies which is not due to a change of volume or, which amounts to the same thing differently expressed, if the temperatures of the bodies which come in contact with each other are never perceptibly different.

Various methods of developing motive power may be adopted, either by the use of different substances or of the same substance in different states; for example, by the use of a gas at two different densities.

This remark leads us naturally to the interesting study of aeriform fluids, a study which will conduct us to new results concerning the motive power of heat, and will give us the means of verifying in some particular cases the fundamental proposition stated above.

It can easily be seen that our demonstration will be simplified if we suppose the temperatures of the bodies A and B to be very slightly different. Then the movements of the piston will be very small during operations 3 and 5, and these operations may be suppressed without perceptible influence on the development of motive power. That is, a very small change of volume ought to be sufficient to produce a very small change of temperature, and this change of volume is negligible compared with that of operations 4 and 6, which are unrestricted in extent.

If we suppress operations 3 and 5 in the series above described, it is reduced to the following:

1. Contact of the gas contained in *abcd* with the body *A*, and passage of the piston from *cd* to *ef*;

2. Removal of the body *A*, contact of the gas enclosed in *abef* with the body *B*, and return of the piston from *ef* to *cd*;

3. Removal of the body *B*, contact of the gas with the body *A*, and

passage of the piston from *cd* to *ef*—that is to say, a repetition of the first operation, and so on.

The motive power resulting from the operations 1, 2, 3, taken together, will evidently be the difference between that which is produced by the expansion of the gas while its temperature equals that of the body *A* and that which is consumed to compress the gas while its temperature equals that of the body *B*.

Let us suppose that the operations 1 and 2 are performed with two gases which are chemically different, but which are subjected to the same pressure—for example, that of the atmosphere; these gases behave in the same circumstances in exactly the same way—that is to say, their expansive forces, originally equal, remain so irrespective of changes of volume and temperature, provided that these changes are the same in both. This is an evident consequence of the laws of Mariotte and of MM. Gay-Lussac and Dalton, which laws are common to all elastic fluids, and in virtue of which the same relations exist in all these fluids between the volume, expansive force, and temperature. Since two different gases, taken at the same temperature and under the same pressure, should behave alike under the same circumstances, they should produce equal quantities of motive power when subjected to the operations above described. Now this implies, according to the fundamental proposition which we have established, that two equal quantities of caloric are employed in these operations—that is, that the quantity of caloric transferred from the body *A* to the body *B* is the same whichever of the two gases is used in the operations. The quantity of caloric transferred from the body *A* to the body *B* is evidently that which is absorbed by the gas in the increase of its volume, or that which it afterwards emits during compression. We are thus led to lay down the following proposition:

When a gas passes without change of temperature from one definite volume and pressure to another, the quantity of caloric absorbed or emitted is always the same, irrespective of the nature of the gas chosen as the subject of the experiment.

For example, consider 1 litre of air at the temperature of 100 degrees and under the pressure of 1 atmosphere; if the volume of this air is doubled, a certain quantity of heat must be supplied to it in order to maintain it at the temperature of 100 degrees. This quantity will be exactly the same if, instead of performing the operation with air, we use carbonic acid gas, nitrogen, hydrogen, vapor of water, or of alcohol—that is, if we double the volume of 1 litre of any one of these gases at the temperature of 100 degrees and under atmospheric pressure.

The same thing would be true, in the reverse sense, if the volume of the gas, instead of being doubled, were reduced one-half by compression.

The quantity of heat absorbed or set free by elastic fluids during their changes of volume has never been measured by direct experiment. Such an experiment would doubtless present great difficulties, but we have one result which for our purposes is nearly equivalent to it; this result has been furnished by the theory of sound, and may be received with confidence because of the rigor of the demonstration by which it has been established. It may be described as follows:

Atmospheric air will rise in temperature 1 degree centigrade when its volume is reduced by 1/116 by sudden compression.

The experiments on the velocity of sound were made in air under a pressure of 760 millimetres of mercury and at the temperature of 6 degrees; and it is only in these circumstances that Poisson's statement is applicable. We shall, however, for the sake of convenience, consider it to hold at a temperature of 0 degrees, which is only slightly different.

Air compressed by 1/116 and so raised in temperature 1 degree differs from air heated directly by the same amount only in its density. If we call the original volume V, the compression by 1/116 reduces it to $V - 1/116 \, V$. Direct heating under constant pressure, according to the law of M. Gay-Lussac, should increase the volume of the air by 1/267 of that which it would have at 0 degrees; thus the volume of the air is in one process reduced to $V - 1/116 \, V$, and in the other increased to $V + 1/267 \, V$. The difference between the quantities of heat present in the air in the two cases is evidently the quantity used to raise its temperature directly by 1 degree; thus the quantity of heat absorbed by the air in passing from the volume $V - 1/116 \, V$ to the volume $V + 1/267 \, V$ is equal to that which is necessary to raise its temperature 1 degree.

Let us now suppose that, instead of heating the air while subjected to a constant pressure and able to expand freely, we enclose it in an envelope not capable of expansion, and then raise its temperature 1 degree. The air thus heated 1 degree differs from air compressed by 1/116 by having its volume larger by 1/116. Thus, then, the quantity of heat which the air gives up by a reduction of its volume by 1/116 is equal to that which is required to raise its temperature 1 degree at constant volume. As the differences, $V - 1/116 \, V, V$, and $V + 1/267 \, V$, are small in comparison with the volumes themselves, we may consider the quantities of heat absorbed by the air in passing from the first of these volumes to the second, and from the first to the third, as sensibly proportional to the changes of volume. We thus obtain the following relation:

The quantity of heat required to raise the temperature of air under constant pressure 1 degree is to the quantity required to raise it 1 degree at constant volume in the ratio of the numbers

$$\frac{1}{116} + \frac{1}{267} \quad \text{to} \quad \frac{1}{116},$$

or, multiplying both terms by 116·267, in the ratio of the numbers 267 + 116 to 267.

This is the ratio between the capacity for heat of air under constant pressure and its capacity at constant volume. If the first of these two capacities is expressed by unity the other will be expressed by the number

$$\frac{267}{267 + 116}$$

or, approximately, 0.700. Their difference—1 — 0.700 or 0.300—will evidently express the quantity of heat which will occasion the increase of volume of the air when its temperature is raised 1 degree under constant pressure.

From the law of MM. Gay-Lussac and Dalton this increase of volume will be the same for all other gases; from the theorem demonstrated earlier, the heat absorbed by equal increments of volume is the same for all elastic fluids; we are thus led to establish the following proposition:

The difference between the specific heat under constant pressure and the specific heat at constant volume is the same for all gases.

It must be noticed here that all the gases are assumed to be taken at the same pressure—for example, the pressure of the atmosphere—and also that the specific heats are measured in terms of the volumes.

*   *   *   *

We have shown that the quantity of motive power developed by the transfer of caloric from one body to another depends essentially on the temperatures of the two bodies, but we have not discussed the relation between these temperatures and the quantities of motive power produced. It would seem at first natural enough to suppose that for equal differences of temperature the quantities of motive power produced are equal—that is, for example, that a given quantity of caloric passing from a body, A, kept at 100 degrees, to a body, B, kept at 50 degrees would develop a quantity of motive power equal to that which would be developed by the transfer of the same caloric from a body, B, kept at 50 degrees to a body, C, kept at zero. Such a law would indeed be a very remarkable one, but we do not see sufficient reason to admit it *a priori*. We shall examine this question by a rigorous method.

Let us suppose that the operations described earlier are performed successively on two quantities of atmospheric air equal in weight and volume but taken at different temperatures, and let us suppose also that the differences of temperature between the bodies A and B are the same in both cases; thus, for example, the temperatures of these bodies will be in one case 100° and 100° — h (h being infinitely small), and in the other, 1° and 1° — h. The quantity of motive power produced is in each case the difference between that which the gas furnishes by its expansion and that which must be used to restore it to its original volume. Now this difference is here the same in both cases, as we may satisfy ourselves by a simple argument, which we do not think it necessary to give in full; so that the motive power produced is the same. Let us now compare the quantities of heat used in the two cases. In the first case the quantity used is that which the body A imparts to the air in order to keep it at a temperature of 100 degrees during its expansion; in the second, it is that which the same body imparts to it to maintain its temperature at 1 degree during an exactly similar change of volume. If these two quantities were equal it is evident that the law which we have assumed would follow. But there is nothing to prove that it is so; we proceed to prove that these quantities of heat are unequal.

The air which we first supposed to occupy the space $abcd$ and to be at a temperature of 1 degree, may be made to occupy the space $abef$, and to acquire the temperature of 100 degrees by two different methods:

1. It may first be heated without change of volume, and then expanded while its temperature is kept constant.

2. It may be expanded while its temperature is kept constant, and then heated when it has acquired its new volume.

Let a and b be the quantities of heat used successively in the first of the two operations, and b' and a' the quantities used in the second; as the final result of these two operations is the same, the quantities of heat used in each should be equal; we then obtain

$$a + b = a' + b',$$

from which we have

$$a' - a = b - b'.$$

We represent by a' the quantity of heat necessary to raise the temperature of the gas from 1 to 100 degrees when it occupies the volume $abef$, and by a the quantity of heat necessary to raise the temperature of the gas from 1 to 100 degrees when it occupies the volume $abcd$.

The density of the air is less in the first case than in the second, and from the experiments of MM. Delaroche and Bérard, its capacity for heat should be a little greater.

As the quantity a' is greater than the quantity a, b should be greater than b', consequently, stating the proposition generally, we may say that:

The quantity of heat due to the change of volume of a gas becomes greater as the temperature is raised.

Thus, for example, more caloric is required to maintain at 100 degrees the temperature of a certain quantity of air whose volume is doubled than to maintain at 1 degree the temperature of the same quantity of air during a similar expansion.

These unequal quantities of heat will, however, as we have seen, produce equal quantities of motive power for equal descents of caloric occurring at different heights on the thermometric scale; from which we may draw the following conclusion:

The descent of caloric produces more motive power at lower degrees of temperature than at higher.

Thus a given quantity of heat will develop more motive power in passing from a body whose temperature is kept at 1 degree to another whose temperature is kept at zero than if the temperatures of these two bodies had been 101 and 100 respectively. It must be said that the difference should be very small; it would be zero if the capacity of air for heat remained constant in spite of changes of density. According to the experiments of MM. Delaroche and Bérard, this capacity varies very little, so little, indeed, that the differences noticed might strictly be attributed to errors of observation or to some circumstances which were not taken into account.

It would be out of the question for us, with the experimental data at our command, to determine rigorously the law by which the motive power of heat varies at different degrees of the thermometric scale. It is connected with the law of the variations of the specific heat of gases at different temperatures, which has not been determined with sufficient exactness. We shall now endeavor to determine definitively the motive power of heat, and in order to verify our fundamental proposition—that is, to show that the quantity of motive power produced is really independent of the agent used—we shall choose several such agents—atmospheric air, water vapor, and alcohol vapor.

Let us take first atmospheric air. The operation is effected according to the method indicated. We make the following hypotheses:

The air is taken under atmospheric pressure; the temperature of the body A is 1/1000 of a degree above zero and that of the body B is zero. We see that the difference is, as it should be, very small. The increase of the volume of the air in our operation will be 1/116 + 1/267 of the original volume; this is a very small increase considered absolutely, but large relatively to the difference of temperature between A and B.

The motive power developed by the two operations taken together will be very nearly proportional to the increase of volume and to the difference between the two pressures exerted by the air when its temperature is 0.001° and zero.

According to the law of M. Gay-Lussac, this difference is 1/267000 of the elastic force of the gas, or very nearly 1/267000 of the atmospheric pressure.

The pressure of the atmosphere is equal to that of a column of water 10 40/100 meters high; 1/267000 of this pressure is equal to that of a water column 1/267000 × 10.40 meters in height.

As for the increase of volume, it is, by hypothesis, 1/116 + 1/267 of the original volume—that is, of the volume occupied by 1 kilogram of air at zero, which is equal to 0.77 cubic meters, if we take into account the specific gravity of air; thus the product,

$$\left(\frac{1}{116} + \frac{1}{267}\right) 0.77 \frac{1}{267000} 10.40$$

expresses the motive power developed. This power is here estimated in cubic meters of water raised to the height of 1 meter.

If we carry out the multiplications indicated, we find for the product 0.000000372.

Let us now try to determine the quantity of heat used to obtain this result—that is, the quantity transferred from the body A to the body B. The body A furnishes:

1. The heat required to raise the temperature of 1 kilogram of air from zero to 0.001°.

2. The quantity required to maintain the temperature of the air at 0.001° when it undergoes an expansion of

$$\frac{1}{116} + \frac{1}{267}.$$

The first of these quantities of heat may be neglected, as it is very small in comparison with the second, which is equal to that required to raise the temperature of 1 kilogram of air under atmospheric pressure 1 degree.

The specific heat of air by weight is 0.267 that of water, from the experiments of MM. Delaroche and Bérard on the specific heat of gases. If, then, we take for the unit of heat the quantity required to raise 1 kilogram of water 1 degree, the quantity required to raise 1 kilogram of air 1 degree will be 0.267. Thus the quantity of heat furnished by the body A is

0.267 unit.

This quantity of heat is capable of producing 0.000000372 unit of motive power by its descent from 0.001 to zero.

For a descent one thousand times as great, or of one degree, the motive power will be very nearly one thousand times as great as this, or

0.000372.

Now if, instead of using 0.267 unit of heat, we use 1000 units, the motive power produced will be given by the proportion

$$\frac{0.267}{0.000372} = \frac{1000}{x}, \text{ from which } x = \frac{372}{267} = 1.395 \text{ units.}$$

Thus if 1000 units of heat pass from a body whose temperature is kept at 1 degree to another at zero, they will produce by their action on air

1.395 units of motive power.

We shall compare this result with that which is obtained from the action of heat on water vapor.

Let us suppose that 1 kilogram of water is contained in the cylinder *abcd* between the base *ab* and the piston *cd*, and let us assume also the existence of two bodies, *A, B,* each maintained at a constant temperature, that of *A* being higher than that of *B* by a very small quantity. We shall now imagine the following operations:

1. Contact of the water with the body *A*, change of the position of the piston from *cd* to *ef*, formation of vapor at the temperature of the body *A* to fill the vacuum made by the increase of the volume. We shall assume the volume *abef* to be large enough to contain all the water in a state of vapor;

2. Removal of the body *A*, contact of the vapor with the body *B*, precipitation of a part of this vapor, decrease of its elastic force, return of the piston from *ef* to *ab*, and liquefaction of the rest of the vapor by the effect of the pressure combined with the contact of the body *B*;

3. Removal of the body *B*, new contact of the water with the body *A*, return of the water to the temperature of this body, a repetition of the first operation, and so on.

The quantity of motive power developed in a complete cycle of operations is measured by the product of the volume of the vapor multiplied by the difference between its tensions at the temperatures of the body *A* and of the body *B* respectively.

The heat used—that is, that transferred from the body *A* to the body *B*—is evidently the quantity which is required to transform the water into vapor, always neglecting the small quantity necessary to restore the water from the temperature of the body *B* to that of the body *A*.

Let us suppose that the temperature of the body *A* is 100 degrees and that of the body *B* 99 degrees. From M. Dalton's table the difference of these tensions will be 26 millimetres of mercury or 0.36 meter of water. The volume occupied by the vapor is 1700 that of the water, so that, if we use 1 kilogram, it will be 1700 litres or 1.700 cubic meters. Thus the motive power developed is

$$1.700 \times 0.36 = 0.611 \text{ unit}$$

of the sort which we used before.

The quantity of heat used is the quantity required to transform the water into vapor, the water being already at a temperature of 100 degrees. This quantity has been determined by experiment; it has been found equal to 550 degrees, or, speaking with greater precision, to 550 of our units of heat.

Thus 0.611 unit of motive power result from the use of 550 units of heat.

The quantity of motive power produced by 1000 units of heat will be given by the proportion

$$550/0.611 = 1000/x,$$

from which

$$x = 611/550 = 1.112.$$

Thus 1000 units of heat transferred from a body maintained at 100 degrees to one maintained at 99 degrees will produce 1.112 units of motive power when acting on the water vapor. The number 1.112 differs by nearly $\frac{1}{4}$ from 1.395, which was the number previously found for the motive power developed by 1000 units of heat acting on air; but we must remember that in that case the temperature of the bodies A and B were 1 degree and zero, while in this case they are 100 and 99 degrees respectively. The difference is indeed the same, but the temperatures on the thermometric scale are not the same. In order to obtain an exact comparison it would be necessary to calculate the motive power developed by the vapor formed at 1 degree and condensed at zero, and also to determine the quantity of heat contained in the vapor formed at 1 degree. The law of MM. Clément and Desormes gives us this information. The heat used in turning water into vapor is always the same at whatever temperature the vaporization occurs. Therefore, since 550 degrees of heat are required to vaporize the water at the temperature of 100 degrees, we must have $550 + 100$, or 650 degrees, to vaporize the same weight of water at zero.

By using the data thus obtained, and reasoning in other respects quite in the same way as we did when the water was at 100 degrees, we readily see that 1.290 is the motive power developed by 1000 units of heat acting on water vapor between the temperatures of 1 degree and zero.

This number approaches 1.395 more nearly than the other.

It only differs by 1/13, which is not outside the limits of probable error, considering the large number of data of different sorts which we have found it necessary to use in making this comparison. Thus our fundamental law is verified in a particular case.

We shall now examine the case of heat acting on alcohol vapor.

The method used in this case is exactly the same as in the case of water vapor, but the data are different. Pure alcohol boils under ordinary pressure at 78.7° centigrade. According to MM. Delaroche and Bérard, 1 kilogram of this substance absorbs 207 units of heat when transformed into vapor at this same temperature, 78.7°.

The tension of alcohol vapor at 1 degree below its boiling-point is diminished by 1/25 and is 1/25 less than atmospheric pressure.

We find, by use of these data, that the motive power developed, in acting on 1 kilogram of alcohol at the temperatures 77.7° and 78.7°, would be 0.251 unit.

This results from the use of 207 units of heat. For 1000 units we must set the proportion

$$207/0.254 = 1000/x,$$

from which

$$x = 1.230.$$

This number is a little greater than 1.112, resulting from the use of water vapor at 100 and 99 degrees; but if we assume the water vapor to be employed at 78 and 77 degrees, we find, by the law of MM. Clément and Desormes, 1.212 for the motive power produced by 1000 units of heat. As we see, this number approaches 1.230 very nearly; it only differs from it by 1/50.

We should have liked to have made other comparisons of this kind—for example, to have calculated the motive power developed by the action of heat on solids and liquids, by the freezing of water, etc.; but in the present state of Physics we are not able to obtain the necessary data. The fundamental law which we wish to confirm seems, however, to need additional verifications to be put beyond doubt; it is based upon the theory of heat as it is at present established, and, it must be confessed, this does not appear to us to be a very firm foundation. New experiments alone can decide this question; in the mean time we shall occupy ourselves with the application of the theoretical ideas above stated, and shall consider them as correct in the examination of the various means proposed at the present time to realize the motive power of heat.

It has been proposed to develop power by the action of heat on solid bodies. The mode of procedure which most naturally presents itself to our minds is to firmly fix a solid body—a metallic bar, for example—by one of its extremities, and to attach the other extremity to a movable part of the machine; then by successive heating and cooling to cause the length of the bar to vary, and thus produce some movement. Let us endeavor to decide if this mode of developing motive power can be advantageous. We have shown that the way to get the best results in the production of motion by the use of heat is to so arrange the operations that all the changes of temperature which occur in the bodies are due to changes of volume. The more nearly this condition is fulfilled the better the heat will be utilized. Now, by proceeding in the manner just described, we are far from fulfilling this condition; no change of temperature is here due to a change of volume; but the changes are all due to the contact of bodies differently heated, to the contact of the metallic bar either with the body which furnishes the heat or with the body which absorbs it.

The only means of fulfilling the prescribed condition would be to act on the solid body exactly as we did on the air in the operations described earlier, but for this we must be able to produce considerable changes of temperature solely by the change of volume of the solid body, if, at least, we desire to use considerable descents of caloric. Now this seems to be impracticable, for several considerations lead us to think that the changes in the temperature of solids or liquids by compression and expansion are quite small.

1. We often observe in engines (in heat-engines particularly) solid parts which are subjected to very considerable forces, sometimes in one sense and sometimes in another, and although those forces are sometimes as great as the nature of the substances employed will permit, the changes in temperature are scarcely perceptible.

2. In the process of striking medals, of rolling plates, or of drawing wires, metals undergo the greatest compressions to which we can subject them by the use of the hardest and most resisting materials. Notwithstanding this the rise in temperature is not great, for if it were, the steel tools which we use in these operations would soon lose their temper.

3. We know that it is necessary to exert a very great force on solids and liquids to produce in them a reduction of volume comparable to that which they undergo by cooling (for example, by a cooling from 100 degrees to zero). Now, cooling requires a greater suppression of caloric than would be required by a simple reduction of volume. If this reduction were produced by mechanical means the heat emitted could not change the temperature of the body as many degrees as the cooling. It would, however, require the use of a force which would certainly be very considerable. Since solid bodies are susceptible to but small changes of temperature by changes of volume, and since, moreover, the condition for the best use of heat in the development of motive power is that any change of temperature should be due to a change of volume, solid bodies do not seem to be well adapted to realize this power.

This is equally true in the case of liquids; the same reasons could be given for rejecting them.

We shall not speak here of the practical difficulties, which are innumerable. The movements produced by the expansion and compression of solids or liquids can only be very small. To extend these movements we should be forced to use complicated mechanisms and also materials of the greatest strength to transmit enormous pressures; and, finally, the successive operations could only proceed very slowly compared with those of the ordinary heat-engine, so that even large and expensive machines would produce only insignificant results.

Elastic fluids, gases, or vapors are the instruments peculiarly fitted for the development of the motive power of heat; they unite all the conditions necessary for this service; they may be easily compressed, and possess the property of almost indefinite expansion; changes of volume occasion in them great changes of temperature, and finally they are very mobile, can be easily and quickly heated and cooled, and readily transported from one place to another, so that they are able to produce rapidly the effects expected of them.

We can easily conceive of many machines fitted for the developments of the motive power of heat by the use of elastic fluids, but however they are constructed in other respects, the following conditions must not be lost sight of:

1. The temperature of the fluid should first be raised to the highest degree possible, in order to obtain a great descent of caloric and consequently a great production of motive power.

2. For the same reason the temperature of the refrigerator should be as low as possible.

3. The operations must be so conducted that the transfer of the elastic fluid from the highest to the lowest temperature should be due to an increase of volume—that is, that the cooling of the gas should occur spontaneously by the effect of expansion.

The limits to which the temperature of the fluid can be raised in the first operation are determined only by the temperature of combustion; they are very much higher than ordinary temperatures. The limits of cooling are reached in the temperature of the coldest bodies which we can conveniently use in large quantities; the body most used for this purpose is the water available at the place where the operation is carried on.

As to the third condition, it introduces difficulties in the realization of the motive power of heat, when the object is to profit by great differences of temperature, that is to utilize great descents of caloric. For in that case the gas must change from a very high temperature to a very low one, by expansion, which requires a great change of volume and density. To effect this the gas must at first be subjected to a very high pressure, or it must acquire by expansion an enormous volume, either of which conditions is difficult to realize. The first necessitates the use of very strong vessels to contain the gas when it is at a high pressure and temperature; the second requires the use of vessels of a very large size.

In fact, these are the principal obstacles in the way of profitably using in steam-engines a large portion of the motive power of heat. We are of necessity limited to the use of a small descent of caloric, although the combustion of coal furnishes us with the means of obtaining a very great one. In the use of steam-engines the elastic fluid is rarely developed at a pressure higher than 6 atmospheres, which pressure corresponds to nearly 160 degrees centigrade, and condensation is rarely effected at a temperature much below 40 degrees; the descent of caloric from 160 to 40 degrees is 120 degrees, while we can obtain by combustion a descent of from 1000 to 2000 degrees.

To conceive of this better, we shall recall what we have previously called the descent of caloric: It is the transfer of heat from a body, *A*, at a high temperature to a body, *B*, whose temperature is lower. We say that the descent of caloric is 100 degrees or 1000 degrees when the difference of temperature between the bodies *A* and *B* is 100 or 1000 degrees. In a steam-engine working under a pressure of 6 atmospheres the temperature of the boiler is 160 degrees. This is the temperature of the body *A;* it is maintained by contact with the furnace at a constant temperature of 160 degrees, and affords a continual supply of the heat necessary to the formation of steam.

The condenser is the body *B;* it is maintained by means of a current of cold water at an almost constant temperature of 40 degrees, and continually absorbs the caloric which is carried to it by the steam from the body *A*. The difference of temperature between these two bodies is 160 — 40, or 120 degrees; it is for this reason that we say that the descent of caloric is in this case 120 degrees.

Coal is capable of producing by combustion a higher temperature than 1000 degrees, and the temperature of the cold water which we ordinarily use is about 10 degrees, so that we can easily obtain a descent of caloric of 1000 degrees, of which only 120 degrees are utilized by steam-engines, and even these 120 degrees are not all used to advantage; there are always considerable losses due to useless re-establishments of equilibrium in the caloric.

It is now easy to perceive the advantage of those engines which are called high-pressure engines over those in which the pressure is lower: *this advantage depends essentially upon the power of utilizing a larger descent of caloric*. The steam being produced under greater pressure is also at a higher temperature, and as the temperature of condensation is always nearly the same the descent of caloric is evidently greater.

But to obtain the most favorable results from high-pressure engines the descent of caloric must be used to the greatest advantage. It is not enough that the steam should be produced at a high temperature, but it is also necessary that it should attain a sufficiently low temperature by its expansion alone. It should thus be the characteristic of a good steam-engine not only that it uses the steam under high pressure, *but that it uses it under successive pressures which are very variable, very different from each other, and progressively decreasing.*

*   *   *   *

We shall conclude by showing how far we are from the realization, by means already known, of all the motive power of the combustibles.

A kilogram of coal burned in the calorimeter furnishes a quantity of heat capable of raising the temperature of about 7000 kilograms of water 1 degree—that is, from the definition given it furnishes 7000 units of heat. The largest descent of caloric which can be realized is measured by the difference of the temperature produced by combustion and that of the refrigerating body. It is difficult to see any limit to the temperature of combustion other than that at which the combination of the combustible with oxygen is effected. Let us assume, however, that this limit is 1000 degrees, which is certainly within the bounds of truth. We shall assume the temperature of the refrigerator to be 0 degrees.

We have calculated approximately the quantity of motive power developed by 1000 units of heat in passing from the temperature 100 to the temperature 99, and have found it to be 1.112 units, each equal to 1 cubic meter of water raised 1 meter.

If the motive power were proportional to the descent of caloric, if it were the same for each thermometric degree, nothing would be easier than to estimate it from 1000 to 0 degrees. Its value would be

$$1.112 \times 1000 = 1112.$$

But as this law is only approximate, and perhaps at high temperatures departs a good deal from the truth, we can only make a very rough estimate. Let us suppose the number 1112 to be reduced one-half—that is, to 560.

Since one kilogram of coal produces 7000 units of heat, and since the number 560 is referred to 1000 units, we must multiply it by 7, which gives us

$$7 \times 560 = 3920,$$

which is the motive power of one kilogram of coal.

In order to compare this theoretical result with the results of experiment, we shall inquire how much motive power is actually developed by one kilogram of coal in the best heat-engines known.

The engines which have thus far offered the most advantageous results are the large engines with two cylinders used in the pumping out of the tin and copper mines of Cornwall. The best results which they have furnished are as follows: Sixty-five million pounds of water have been raised one English foot by the burning of one bushel of coal (the weight of a bushel is 88 lbs.) This result is equivalent to raising 195 cubic meters of water one meter by the use of one kilogram of coal, which consequently produces 195 units of motive power.

195 units are only one-twentieth of 3920, the theoretical maximum; consequently only 1/20 of the motive power of the combustible has been utilized.

We have, moreover, chosen our example from among the best steam-engines known. Most of the others have been very inferior. For example, Chaillot's engine raises 20 cubic meters of water 33 meters in consuming 30 kilograms of coal, which is equivalent to 22 units of motive power to 1 kilogram, a result nine times less than that cited above, and one hundred and eighty times less than the theoretical maximum.

We should not expect ever to employ in practice all the motive power of the combustibles used. The efforts which one would make to attain this result would be even more harmful than useful if they led to the neglect of other important considerations. The economy of fuel is only one of the conditions which should be fulfilled by steam-engines; in many cases it is only a secondary consideration. It must often yield the precedence to safety, to the solidity and durability of the engine, to the space which it must occupy, to the cost of its construction, etc. To be able to appreciate justly in each case the considerations of convenience and economy which present themselves, to be able to recognize the most important of those which are only subordinate, to adjust them all suitably, and finally to reach the best result by the easiest method—such should be the power of the man who is called on to direct and co-ordinate the labors of his fellow-men, and to make them concur in attaining a useful purpose.

18

THEODOR SCHWANN

Theodor Schwann was born in Prussia in 1810, when the renaissance of German culture was leading German science toward the position of leadership it held until the advent of Nazi primitivism. Keeping step with the progress of German science was its migration to the university, now for the first time becoming a center of scientific research. Schwann's career was typical in its academic focus. After studying in three universities, he took his degree in medicine in 1834. The influence of Johannes Müller, an experimental physiologist of major importance, led Schwann to abandon medicine for science. Four years spent with Müller in Berlin witnessed at once the gestation of modern cytology and the climax of Schwann's life as a creative scientist. These years culminated in his *Microscopical Researches into the Accordance in the Structure and Growth of Animals and Plants* (1838), from which the following selection is taken. In 1839, Schwann accepted the chair in anatomy at the Catholic university of Louvain; later he moved to Liège, where he continued to lecture until shortly before his death in 1882.

Schwann's career fell during a crucial period in the development of biology. Since the appearance of the mechanical philosophy in the 17th century, most biological phenomena had resisted efforts to explain them in physico-chemical terms. In general, naturalists subscribed to the view that organic life is an ultimate which that cannot be reduced to merely physical terms. In Germany especially, during the early years of the 19th century when the romantic movement was at its height, vitalism enjoyed a wide vogue and, in the intellectual movement known as *Naturphilosophie,* it provided the core of a nonmechanical philosophy of nature. The same years of the early 19th century, however, also witnessed the growth of an experimental biology from the arsenal of which came the weapons for a new mechanistic assault on vitalism.

Fundamental to experimental biology was a reconsideration of the ultimate unit of life. Indeed, the first step in that direction was taken by the well-known vitalist, Bichat, who proposed that the seat of animal life is to be found, not in the soul as Western men had maintained since the Greek period, but in the various tissues of the body. In the study of plants, a more subtle unit, the cell, was exposed to investigators armed with the superior microscopes first available in the decade of the 1830's. Originally the word "cell" had been applied to a space enclosed by walls, such as the structure of cork reveals, but the discovery of the nucleus contributed to a completely different notion of the cell, not as a structure, but as a unit of growth and metabolism. Schwann's contemporary and friend, Matthias Schleiden, first generalized the role of the nucleated cell in plant life. In Schlieden's ideas, Schwann saw a means by which to comprehend the nature and formation of animal tissues on which he was working. Thus was born a major new generalization uniting all forms of life and placing the understanding of them on a new level.

18

Microscopical Researches, into the Accordance in the Structure and Growth of Animals and Plants

INTRODUCTION

Although plants present so great a variety of external form, yet they are no less remarkable for the simplicity of their internal structure. This extraordinary diversity in figure is produced solely by different modes of junction of simple elementary structures, which, though they present various modifications, are yet throughout essentially the same, namely, *cells*. The entire class of the Cellular plants consists only of cells; many of them are formed solely of homogeneous cells strung together, some of even a single cell. In like manner, the Vascular plants, in their earliest condition, consist merely of simple cells; and the pollen-granule, which, according to Schleiden's discovery, is the basis of the new plant, is in its essential parts only a cell. In perfectly-developed vascular plants the structure is more complex, so that not long since, their elementary tissues were distinguished as cellular and fibrous tissue, and vessels or spiral-tubes. Researches on the structure, and particularly on the development of these tissues, have, however, shown that these fibres and spiral-tubes are but elongated cells, and the spiral-fibres only spiral-shaped depositions upon the internal surface of the cells. Thus the vascular plants consist likewise of cells, some of which only have advanced to a higher degree of development. The lactiferous vessels are the only structure not as yet reduced to cells; but further observations are required with respect to their development. According to Unger they in like manner consist of cells, the partition-walls of which ·become obliterated.

Animals, which present a much greater variety of external form than is found in the vegetable kingdom, exhibit also, and especially the higher classes in the perfectly-developed condition, a much more complex structure in their individual tissues. How broad is the distinction

Translated from the German by Henry Smith, London, 1847.

421

between a muscle and a nerve, between the latter and cellular tissue, (which agrees only in name with that of plants,) or elastic or horny tissue, and so on. When, however, we turn to the history of the development of these tissues, it appears, that all their manifold forms originate likewise only from cells, indeed from cells which are entirely analogous to those of vegetables, and which exhibit the most remarkable accordance with them in some of the vital phenomena which they manifest. *The design of the present treatise is to prove this by a series of observations.*

It is, however, necessary to give some account of the vital phenomena of vegetable cells. Each cell is, within certain limits, an Individual, an independent Whole. The vital phenomena of one are repeated, entirely or in part, in all the rest. These Individuals, however, are not ranged side by side as a mere Aggregate, but so operate together, in a manner unknown to us, as to produce an harmonious Whole. The processes which go forward in the vegetable cells, may be reduced to the following heads: 1, the production of new cells; 2, the expansion of existing cells; 3, the transformation of the cell-contents, and the thickening of the cell-wall; 4, the secretion and absorption carried on by cells.

The excellent researches of Schleiden, which throw so much light upon this subject, form the principal basis for my more minute observations on these separate vital phenomena.

First, of the production of new cells. According to Schleiden, in Phænogamous plants, this process always (except as regards the cells of the Cambium) takes place within the already mature cells, and in a most remarkable manner from out of the well-known cell-nucleus. On account of the importance of the latter in reference to animal organization, I here introduce an abridgement of Schleiden's description of it. This structure—named by R. Brown, Areola or cell-nucleus, by Schleiden, Cytoblast—varies in its outline between oval and circular, according as the solid which it forms passes from the lenticular into the perfectly spheroidal figure. Its colour is mostly yellowish, sometimes, however, passing into an almost silvery white; and in consequence of its transparency, often scarcely distinguishable. It is coloured by iodine, according to its various modifications, from a pale yellow to the darkest brown. Its size varies considerably, according to its age, and according to the plants, and the different parts of a plant in which it is found, from 0.0001 to 0.0022 Paris inch. Its internal structure is granular, without, however, the granules, of which it consists, being very clearly distinct from each other. Its consistence is very variable, from such a degree of softness as that it almost dissolves in water, to a firmness which bears a considerable pressure of the compressorium without alteration of form.

In addition to these peculiarities of the cytoblast, already made known by Brown and Meyer, Schleiden has discovered in its interior a small corpuscle which, in the fully-developed cytoblast, looks like a thick ring, or a thick-walled hollow globule. It appears, however, to present a different appearance in different cytoblasts. Sometimes only the external sharply-defined circle of this ring can be distinguished, with a dark point in the centre—occasionally, and indeed most frequently, only a sharply circumscribed spot. In other instances this spot is very small, and sometimes cannot be recognized at all. As it will frequently be necessary to speak of this body in the following treatise, I will for brevity's sake name it the *"nucleolus."* According to Schleiden, sometimes two, more rarely three, or, as he has personally informed me, even four such nucleoli occur in the cytoblast. Their size is very various, ranging from the semidiameter of the cytoblast to the most minute point.

The following is Schleiden's description of the origin of the cells from the cytoblast. So soon as the cytoblasts have attained their full size, a delicate transparent vesicle, the young cell, rises upon their surface, and is placed upon the flat cytoblast like a watch-glass upon a watch. It is at this time so delicate that it dissolves in distilled water in a few minutes. It gradually expands, becomes more consistent, and at length so large, that the cytoblast appears only as a small body inclosed in one of the side walls. The portion of the cell-wall which covers the cytoblast on the inner side, is, however, extremely delicate and gelatinous, and only in rare instances to be observed; it soon undergoes absorption together with the cytoblast, which likewise becomes absorbed in the fully-developed cell. The cytoblasts are formed free within a cell, in a mass of mucus-granules, and the young cells lie also free in the parent cell, and assume, as they become flattened against each other, the polyhedral form. Subsequently the parent cell becomes absorbed. It cannot at present be stated with certainty that the formation of new cells *always* takes place from a cystoblast, and *always* within the existing cells, for the Cryptogamia have not as yet been examined in this respect, nor has Schleiden yet expressed his views in reference to the Cambium. Moreover, according to Mirbel, a formation of new cells on the outside of the previous ones takes place in the intercellular canals and on the surface of the plant in the Phanerogamia. A mode of formation of new cells, different from the above described, is exhibited in the multiplication of cells by division of the existing ones; in this case partition-walls grow across the old cell, if, as Schleiden supposes, this be not an illusion, inasmuch as the young cells might escape observation in consequence of their transparency, and at a later stage, their line of contact would be regarded as the partition wall of the parent cell.

The expansion of the cell when formed, is, either regular on all sides, in which case it remains globular, or it becomes polyhedral from flattening against the neighbouring cells, or it is irregular from the cell growing more vigorously in one or in several directions. What was formerly called the fibrous tissue, which contains remarkably elongated cells, is formed in this manner. These fibres also become branched, when different points of the cell-wall expand in different directions. This expansion of the cell-wall cannot be explained as a merely mechanical effect, which would continually tend to render the cell-membrane thinner. It is often even combined with a thickening of the cell-wall, and is probably effected by that process of nutrition called intus-susception. The flattening of the cells may also be ascribed to the same cause.

With regard to the changes which the cell-contents and cell-wall undergo during vegetation, I only take into consideration the thickening of the latter, as I have but a few isolated observations upon the transformations of the contents of animal cells, which however indicate analogous changes to those of plants. The thickening of the cell-walls takes place, either by the deposition from the original wall, of substances differing from, or more rarely, homogeneous with it, upon the internal surface of the cell, or by an actual thickening of the substance of the cell-wall. The first-mentioned form of deposition occurs in strata, at least this may be distinctly seen in many situations. Very frequently—according to Valentin, universally—these depositions take place in spiral lines; this is very distinct, for example, in the spiral canals and spiral cells. The thickening of the cell-membrane itself, although more rare, appears still in some instances indubitable, for instance, in the pollen-tubes, (e. g. Phormium tenax). Probably that extremely remarkable phenomenon of the motion of the fluid, which has now been observed in a great many cells of plants, is connected with the transformation of the cell-contents. In the Charæ, in which it is most distinct, a spiral motion may also be recognized in it. But, for the most part, the currents intersect each other in the most complex manner.

Absorption and Secretion may be classed as external operations of the vegetable cells. The disappearance of the parent cells in which young ones have formed, or of the cell-nucleus and of other structures, affords sufficient examples of absorption. Secretion is exhibited in the exudation of resin in the intercellular canals, and of a fluid containing sugar by the nectar-glands, &c. &c.

In all these processes each cell remains distinct, and maintains an independent existence. Examples, however, also occur in plants, where the cells coalesce, and this not merely with regard to their walls, but the cavities also. Schleiden has found that in the Cacti, the thickened walls of several cells unite to form a homogeneous substance, in which only the remains of the cell-cavities can be distinguished. . . .

After these preliminary remarks we pass on to animals. The similarity between some individual animal and vegetable tissues has already been frequently pointed out. Justly enough, however, nothing has been inferred from such individual points of resemblance. Every cell is not an analogous structure to a vegetable cell; and as to the polyhedral form, seeing that it necessarily belongs to all cells when closely compacted, it obviously is no mark of similarity further than in the circumstance of densely crowded arrangement. An analogy between the cells of animal tissues and the same elementary structure in vegetables can only be drawn with certainty in one of the following ways: either, 1st, by showing that a great portion of the animal tissues originates from, or consists of cells, each of which must have its particular wall, in which case it becomes probable that these cells correspond to the cellular elementary structure universally present in plants; or, 2dly, by proving, with regard to any one animal tissue consisting of cells, that, in addition to its cellular structure, similar forces to those of vegetable cells are in operation in its component cells; or, since this is impossible directly, that the phenomena by which the activity of these powers or forces manifests itself, namely, nutrition and growth, proceed in the same or a similar manner in them as in the cells of plants. I reflected upon the matter in this point of view in the previous summer, when, in the course of my researches upon the terminations of the nerves in the tail of the Larvæ of frogs, I not only saw the beautiful cellular structure of the Chorda Dorsalis in these larvæ, but also discovered the nuclei in the cells. J. Müller had already proved that the chorda dorsalis in fishes consists of separate cells, provided with distinct walls, and closely packed together like the pigment of the Choroid. The nuclei, which in their form are so similar to the usual flat nuclei of the vegetable cells that they might be mistaken for them, thus furnished an additional point of resemblance. As however the importance of these nuclei was not known, and since most of the cells of mature plants exhibit no nuclei, the fact led to no farther result. J. Müller had proved, with regard to the cartilage-corpuscles discovered by Purkinje and Deutsch in several kinds of cartilage, from their gradual transition into larger cells, that they were hollow, thus in a more extended sense of the word, cells; and Miescher also distinguishes an especial class of spongy cartilages of a cellular structure. Nuclei were likewise known in the cartilage-corpuscles. Müller, and subsequently Meckauer, having observed the projection of the cartilage-corpuscles at the edge of a preparation, it became very probable that at least some of them must be considered as cells in the restricted sense of the word, or as cavities inclosed by a membrane. Gurlt also, when describing one form of permanent cartilage, calls them vesicles. I next succeeded in actually observing the proper wall of the cartilage-corpuscles, first in the branchial cartilages of the frog's larvæ, and subsequently also in the fish, and also the accordance of all cartilage-corpuscles, and by this means in proving a cellular structure, in the restricted sense of the word, in all cartilages. During the growth of some of the cartilage-cells, a thickening of the cell-walls might also be perceived. Thus was the similarity in the process of vegetation of animal and vegetable cells still further developed. Dr. Schleiden opportunely communicated to me at this time his excellent researches upon the origin of new cells in plants, from the nuclei within the parent-cell. The previously enigmatical contents of the cells in the branchial cartilages of the frog's larvæ thus became clear to me; I now recognized in them young cells, provided with a nucleus. Meckauer and Arnold had already found fat-vesicles in the cartilage-corpuscles. As I soon afterwards succeeded in rendering the origin of young cells from nuclei within the parent-cells in the branchial cartilages very probable, the matter was decided. Cells presented themselves in the animal body having a nucleus, which in its position with regard to the cell, its form and modifications, accorded with the cytoblast of vegetable cells, a thickening of the cell-wall took place, and the formation of young cells within the parent-cell from a similar cytoblast, and the growth of these without vascular connexion was proved. This accordance was still farther shown by many details; and thus, so far as concerned these individual tissues, the desired evidence, that these cells correspond to the elementary cells of vegetables was furnished. I soon conjectured that the cellular formation might be a widely extended, perhaps a universal principle for the formation of organic substances. Many cells, some having nuclei, were already known; for example, in the ovum, epithelium, blood-corpuscles, pigment, &c. &c. It was an easy step in the argument to comprise these recognized cells under one point of view; to compare the blood-corpuscles, for example, with the cells of epithelium, and to consider these, as likewise the cells of cartilages and vegetables, as corresponding with each other, and as realizations of that common principle. This was the more probable, as many points of agreement in the progress of development of these cells were already known. C. H. Schultz had already proved the pre-existence of the nuclei of the blood-corpuscles, the formation of the vesicle around the same, and the gradual expansion of this vesicle. Henle had observed the gradual increase in size of the epidermal cells from the under layers of the epidermis, towards the upper ones. The growth of the germinal vesicle, observed by Purkinje, served also at first as an example of the growth of one cell within another, although it afterwards became more probable that it had not the signification of a cell, but of a cell-nucleus, and thus furnished proof that everything having the cellular form does not necessarily correspond to the cells of plants. A precise term for these cells, which correspond to those of plants, should be adopted; either *elementary* cells, or *vegetative* cells (vegetations-zellen). By still further examination, I constantly found this principle of cellular formation more fully realized. The germinal membrane was soon discovered to be composed entirely of cells, and shortly afterwards cell-nuclei, and subsequently also cells were found in all tissues of the animal body at their origin; so that all tissues consist of cells, or are formed by various modes, from cells. The other proof of the analogy between animal and vegetable cells was thus afforded.

* * * *

SECTION II

On Cells as the Basis of all Tissues of the Animal Body

The young cells contained within the cartilage-cells may be regarded as the elementary form of the tissues, and may be described as round cells having a characteristic nucleus, firmly attached to the internal surface of the wall. As the above were proved to correspond with the vegetable cells, it follows, that it is only necessary to trace back the elementary structure of the rest of the tissues to the same formation, in order to show their analogy also with the cells of plants. In some tissues this proof is easy, and immediately afforded; in others, however, it is obtained with much difficulty, and it would frequently be altogether impossible to demonstrate the cellular nature of some, if the connexion between the different steps in this investigation were lost sight of. The difficulty arises from the following circumstances: 1st. The minuteness of the cells; in consequence of which it is not only necessary to use a power magnifying from 400 to 500 diameters, but it is also frequently, indeed generally found impossible to press out their contents. 2dly. The delicate nature of the cell-membrane. When this has a certain density, its external as well as internal outline may be recognized, and the distinction between it and the cell-contents may thus be placed beyond a doubt. But if the cell-membrane be very delicate, the two outlines meet together in one line, and this may readily be regarded as the boundary line of a globule, not enclosed by a special enveloping membrane. 3dly. The similar power of refraction possessed by the cell-wall and cell-contents, in consequence of which the internal outline of the former cannot be observed. 4thly. The granulous nature of the cell-membrane, which when the contents are also granulous, cannot be distinguished from them. Lastly, the variety of form presented by the cells, for they may be flattened even to the total disappearance of the cavity, or elongated into cylinders and fibres. From these circumstances, many of the cells which now come before us for consideration, have been described as mere globules, or granules, terms which do not express their true signification, and even when they were spoken of as cells, or cells furnished with a nucleus, the description rested only upon a slight analogy, since but very few of them (for example, the pigment-cells), were proved to be actually hollow cells. But —as the precise signification of the nucleus is unknown, and as the cell-membrane is not proved to be anything essential to those cells (and this follows from their accordance with vegetable cells), upon the analogy with which the proof of the cellular nature of the rest of the globules provided with a nucleus will be based—there is no contradiction involved in the supposition that a nucleus may be contained in a solid globule as well as in a cell.

From the difficulties of this investigation above detailed, it will be seen that a given object may really be a cell, when even the common characteristics of that structure, namely, the perceptibility of the cell-membrane, and the flowing out of the cell-contents, cannot be brought under observation. The possibility that an object may be a cell, does not, however, advance us much; the presence of positive characteristics is necessary in order to enable us to regard it as such. In many instances these difficulties do not present themselves, and the cellular nature of the object is immediately recognized; in others, the impediments are not so great but that the distinction between cell-membrane and cell-contents is at least indicated, and in such cases other circumstances may advance that supposition to a certainty. The most important and abundant proof as to the existence of a cell is the presence or absence of the nucleus. Its sharp outline and dark colour render it in most instances easily perceptible; its characteristic figure, especially when it encloses nucleoli, and remarkable position in the globule under examination (being within it, but eccentrical, and separated from the surface only by the thickness of the assumed cell-wall,) all combine to prove it the cell-nucleus, and render its analogy with the nucleus of the young cells contained in cartilage, and with those of vegetables, as also the analogy between the globules under examination, in which it lies, and those cells, consequently the existence of a spherical cell-membrane in the globules, extremely probable. More than nine tenths of the globules in question present such a nucleus; in many the special cell-membrane is indubitable, in most it is more or less distinct. Under such circumstances, we may be permitted to conclude that all those globules which present a nucleus of the characteristic form and position, have also a cell-membrane, although, from the causes before specified, it may not be perceptible. The different tissues will also afford us many instances of other circumstances which tend to prove the existence of an actual cell-membrane. An example of what is referred to would be afforded by an instance, in which a certain corpuscle (furnished with a nucleus), about the cellular nature of which a doubt existed, could be proved to be only a stage of development, or modification in form, of an indubitable cell. The cell-nuclei and their distance from each other when scattered in a tissue, also serve as indications, when the outlines of the cells have to be sought for. They likewise serve to guide conjecture as to the earlier existence of separate cells, in instances where they have coalesced in the progress of development. When a globule does not exhibit a nucleus during any one of the stages of its development, it is either not a cell, or may at least be preliminarily rejected, if there be no other circumstances to prove it such. Fortunately, these cells devoid of nuclei are rare.

In addition, however, to the cellular nature of the elementary structures of animal tissues, there are yet other points of accordance between them and the cells of plants, which may generally be shown in the progress of their development, and which give increased weight to the evidence tending to prove that these elementary structures are cells. The exceedingly frequent, if not absolutely universal presence of the nucleus, even in the latest formed cells, proves its great importance for their existence. We cannot, it is true, at present assert that, with regard to all cells furnished with a nucleus, the latter is universally the primary and the cell the secondary formation, that is to say, that in every instance the cell is formed around the previously existing nucleus. It is probable, however, that such is the case generally, for we not only meet with separate nuclei in most of the tissues, distinct from those which have cells around them, but we also find that the younger the cells are, the smaller they are in proportion to the nucleus. The ultimate destiny also of the nucleus is similar to that of the vegetable cells. As in the last named, so in most animal cells it is subsequently absorbed, and remains as a permanent structure in some few only. In plants, according to Schleiden, the young cells are always developed within parent cells, and we have also seen such a development of new cells within those already formed in the chorda dorsalis and cartilage. If, however, any doubt existed as to whether the primary cells of these tissues were formed within previously existing parent cells, none such can arise in reference to many of the tissues next to be considered. We shall indeed frequently meet with a formation of young cells within older ones, but it is not the rule, and does not occur at all with regard to many of them.

The following admits of universal application to the formation of cells; there is, in the first instance, a *structureless* substance present, which is sometimes quite fluid, at others more or less gelatinous. This substance possesses within itself, in a greater or lesser measure according to its chemical qualities and the degree of its vitality, a capacity to occasion the production of cells. When this takes place the nucleus usually appears to be formed first, and then the cell around it. The formation of cells bears the same relation to organic nature that crystallization does to inorganic. The cell, when once formed, continues to grow by its own individual powers, but is at the same time directed by the influence of the entire organism in such manner, as the design of the whole requires. This is the fundamental phenomenon of all animal and vegetable vegetation. It is alike equally consistent with those instances in which young cells are formed within parent cells, as with those in which the formation goes on outside of them. The generation of the cells takes place in a fluid, or in a structureless substance in both cases. We will name this substance in which the cells are formed, cell-germinating material, or cytoblastema. It may be figuratively, but only figuratively, compared to the mother-lye from which crystals are deposited.

We shall refer to this point at greater length hereafter, and only anticipate our subject with this result of the investigation, in order to facilitate the comprehension of what follows.

In the previous section of this work we have discussed in detail the course of development of some of the animal cells, having taken the chorda dorsalis and cartilage for our examples. We are now required to prove, as far as is possible, that all the tissues either originate from, or consist of cells. We separate this investigation into two divisions. The first treats of the Ovum and Germinal membrane, in so far as they form the common basis of all the subsequent tissues. The second division embraces the permanent tissues of the animal body, with the omission of the two already described.

*   *   *   *

SECTION III

Review of the Previous Researches—The Formative Process of Cells—The Cell Theory

The two foregoing sections of this work have been devoted to a detailed investigation of the formation of the different tissues from cells, to the mode in which these cells are developed, and to a comparison of the different cells with one another. We must now lay aside detail, take a more extended view of these researches, and grasp the subject in its more intimate relations. The principal object of our investigation was to prove the accordance of the elementary parts of animals with the cells of plants. But the expression "plant-like life" is so ambiguous that it is received as almost synonymous with growth without vessels; and it was, therefore, explained that in order to prove this accordance, the elementary particles of animals and plants must be shown to be products of the same formative powers, because the phenomena attending their development are similar; that all elementary particles of animals and plants are formed upon a common principle. Having traced the formation of the separate tissues, we can more readily comprehend the object to be attained by this comparison of the different elementary particles with one another, a subject on which we must dwell a little, not only because it is the fundamental idea of these researches, but because all physiological deductions depend upon a correct apprehension of this principle.

When organic nature, animals and plants, is regarded as a Whole, in contradistinction to the inorganic kingdom, we do not find that all organisms and all their separate organs are compact masses, but that they are composed of innumerable small particles of a definite form. These elementary particles, however, are subject to the most extraordinary diversity of figure, especially in animals; in plants they are, for the most part or exclusively, cells. This variety in the elementary parts seemed to hold some relation to their more diversified physiological function in animals, so that it might be established as a principle, that every diversity in the physiological signification of an organ requires a difference in its elementary particles; and, on the contrary, the similarity of two elementary particles seemed to justify the conclusion that they were physiologically similar. It was natural that among the very different forms presented by the elementary particles, there should be some more or less alike, and that they might be divided, according to their similarity of figure, into fibres, which compose the great mass of the bodies of animals, into cells, tubes, globules, &c. The division was, of course, only one of natural history, not expressive of any physiological idea, and just as a primitive muscular fibre, for example, might seem to differ from one of areolar tissue, or all fibres from cells, so would there be in like manner a difference, however gradually marked between the different kinds of cells. It seemed as if the organism arranged the molecules in the definite forms exhibited by its different elementary particles, in the way required by its physiological function. It might be expected that there would be a definite mode of development for each separate kind of elementary structure, and that it would be similar in those structures which were physiologically identical, and such a mode of development was, indeed, already more or less perfectly known with regard to muscular fibres, blood-corpuscles, the ovum, and epithelium-cells. The only process common to all of them, however, seemed to be the expansion of their elementary particles after they had once assumed their proper form. The manner in which their different elementary particles were first formed appeared to vary very much. In muscular fibres they were globules, which were placed together in rows, and coalesced to form a fibre, whose growth proceeded in the direction of its length. In the blood-corpuscles it was a globule, around which a vesicle was formed, and continued to grow; in the case of the ovum, it was a globule, around which a vesicle was developed and continued to grow, and around this again a second vesicle was formed.

The formative process of the cells of plants was clearly explained by the researches of Schleiden, and appeared to be the same in all vegetable cells. So that when plants were regarded as something special, as quite distinct from the animal kingdom, one universal principle of development was observed in all the elementary particles of the vegetable organism, and physiological deductions might be drawn from it with regard to the independent vitality of the individual cells of plants, &c. But when the elementary particles of animals and plants were considered from a common point, the vegetable cells seemed to be merely a separate species, co-ordinate with the different species of animal cells, just as the entire class of cells was co-ordinate with the fibres, &c., and the uniform principle of development in vegetable cells might be explained by the slight physiological difference of their elementary particles.

The object, then, of the present investigation was to show, that the mode in which the molecules composing the elementary particles of organisms are combined does not vary according to the physiological signification of those particles, but that they are everywhere arranged according to the same laws; so that whether a muscular fibre, a nerve-tube, an ovum, or a blood-corpuscle is to be formed, a corpuscle of a certain form, subject only to some modifications, a cell-nucleus, is universally generated in the first instance; around this corpuscle a cell is developed, and it is the changes which one or more of these cells undergo that determine the subsequent forms of the elementary particles; in short, that there is one common principle of development for all the elementary particles of organisms.

In order to establish this point it was necessary to trace the progress of development in two given elementary parts, physiologically dissimilar, and to compare them with one another. If these not only completely agreed in growth, but in their mode of generation also, the principle was established that elementary parts, quite distinct in a physiological sense, may be developed according to the same laws. This was the theme of the first section of this work. The course of development of the cells of cartilage and of the cells of the chorda dorsalis was compared with that of vegetable cells. Were the cells of plants developed merely as infinitely minute vesicles which progressively expand, were the circumstances of their development less characteristic than those pointed out by Schleiden, a comparison, in the sense here required, would scarcely have been possible. We endeavoured to prove in the first section that the complicated process of development in the cells of plants recurs in those of cartilage and of the chorda dorsalis. We remarked the similarity in the formation of the cell-nucleus, and of its nucleolus in all its modifications, with the nucleus of vegetable cells, the pre-existence of the cell-nucleus and the development of the cell around it, the similar situation of the nucleus in relation to the cell, the growth of the cells, and the thickening of their wall during growth, the formation of cells within cells, and the transformation of the cell-contents just as in the cells of plants. Here, then, was a complete accordance in every known stage in the progress of development of two elementary parts which are quite distinct, in a physiological sense, and it was established that the principle of development in two such parts may be the same, and so far as could be ascertained in the cases here compared, it is really the same.

But regarding the subject from this point of view we are compelled to prove the universality of this principle of development, and such was the object of the second section. For so long as we admit that there are elementary parts which originate according to entirely different laws, and between which and the cells which have just been compared as to the principle of their development there is no connexion, we must presume that there may still be some unknown difference in the laws of the formation of the parts just compared, even though they agree in many points. But, on the contrary, the greater the number of physiologically different elementary parts, which, so far as can be known, originate in a similar manner, and the greater the difference of these parts in form and physiological signification, while they agree in the perceptible phenomena of their mode of formation, the more safely may we assume that all elementary parts have one and the same fundamental principle of development. It was, in fact, shown that the elementary parts of most tissues, when traced backwards from their state of complete development to their primary condition are only developments of cells, which so far as our observations, still incomplete, extend, seemed to be formed in a similar manner to the cells compared in the first section. As might be expected, according to this principle the cells, in their earliest stage, were almost always furnished with the characteristic nuclei, in some the pre existence of this nucleus, and the formation of the cell around it wa proved, and it was then that the cells began to undergo the various modifications, from which the diverse forms of the elementary parts of animals resulted. Thus the apparent difference in the mode of develop-ment of muscular fibres and blood-corpuscles, the former originating by the arrangement of globules in rows, the latter by the formation of a vesicle around a globule, was reconciled in the fact that muscular fibres are not elementary parts co-ordinate with blood-corpuscles, but that the globules composing muscular fibres at first correspond to the blood-corpuscles, and are like them, vesicles or cells, containing the charac-teristic cell-nucleus, which, like the nucleus of the blood-corpuscles, is probably formed before the cell. The elementary parts of all tissues are formed of cells in an analogous, though very diversified manner, so that it may be asserted, *that there is one universal principle of development for the elementary parts of organisms, however different, and that this principle is the formation of cells.* This is the chief result of the fore-going observations.

The same process of development and transformation of cells within a structureless substance is repeated in the formation of all the organs of an organism, as well as in the formation of new organisms; and the funda-mental phenomenon attending the exertion of productive power in organic nature is accordingly as follows: *a structureless substance is present in the first instance, which lies either around or in the interior of cells already existing; and cells are formed in it in accordance with certain laws, which cells become developed in various ways into the elementary parts of organisms.*

The development of the proposition, that there exists one general principle for the formation of all organic productions, and that this principle is the formation of cells, as well as the conclusions which may be drawn from this proposition, may be comprised under the term *cell-theory,* using it in its more extended signification, whilst in a more limited sense, by theory of the cells we understand whatever may be inferred from this proposition with respect to the powers from which these phenomena result.

But though this principle, regarded as the direct result of these more or less complete observations, may be stated to be generally correct, it must not be concealed that there are some exceptions, or at least differ-ences, which as yet remain unexplained. Such, for instance, is the splitting into fibres of the walls of the cells in the interior of the chorda dorsalis of osseous fishes. Several observers have also drawn attention to the fibrous structure of the firm substance of some cartilages. In the costal cartilages of old persons for example, these fibres are very distinct. They do not, however, seem to be uniformly diffused throughout the cartilage, but to be scattered merely here and there. I have not observed them at all in new-born children. It appears as if the previously structureless cytoblastema in this instance became split into fibres; I have not, however, investigated the point accurately. Our observations also fail to supply us with any explanation of the formation of the medullary canaliculi in bones, and an analogy between their mode of origin and that of capillary vessels, was merely suggested hypothetically. The formation of bony lamellæ around these canaliculi, is also an instance of the cytoblastema assuming a distinct form. But we will return presently to an explanation of this phenomenon that is not altogether improbable. In many glands, as for instance, the kidneys of a young mammalian fœtus, the stratum of cells surrounding the cavity of the duct, is enclosed by an exceedingly delicate membrane, which appears to be an elementary structure, and not to be composed of areolar tissue. The origin of this membrane is not at all clear, although we may imagine various ways of reconciling it with the formative process of cells.

These and similar phenomena may remain for a time unexplained. Although they merit the greatest attention and require further investigations, we may be allowed to leave them for a moment, for history shows that in the laying down of every general principle, there are almost always anomalies at first, which are subsequently cleared up.

The elementary particles of organisms, then, no longer lie side by side unconnectedly, like productions which are merely capable of classification in natural history, according to similarity of form; they are united by a common bond, the similarity of their formative principle, and they may be compared together and physiologically arranged in accordance with the various modifications under which that principle is exhibited. . . . The existence of a common principle of development for all the elementary parts of organic bodies lays the foundation of a new section of general anatomy, to which the term *philosophical* might be applied, having for its object— firstly, to prove the general laws by which the elementary parts of organisms are developed; and, secondly, to point out the different elementary parts in accordance with the general principle of development, and to compare them with one another.

*   *   *   *

THEORY OF THE CELLS

The whole of the foregoing investigation has been conducted with the object of exhibiting from observation alone the mode in which the elementary parts of organized bodies are formed. Theoretical views have been either entirely excluded, or where they were required, for the purpose of rendering facts more clear, or preventing subsequent repetitions, they have been so presented that it can be easily seen how much is observation and how much argument. But a question inevitably arises as to the basis of all these phenomena; and an attempt to solve it will be more readily permitted us, since by making a marked separation between theory and observation the hypothetical may be clearly distinguished from that which is positive. An hypothesis is never prejudicial so long as we are conscious of the degree of reliance which may be placed upon it, and of the grounds on which it rests. Indeed it is advantageous, if not necessary for science, that when a certain series of phenomena is proved by observation, some provisional explanation should be conceived that will suit them as nearly as possible, even though it be in danger of being overthrown by subsequent observations; for it is only in this manner that we are rationally led to new discoveries, which either establish or refute the explanation. It is from this point of view I would beg that the following theory of organization may be regarded; for the inquiry into the source of development of the elementary parts of organisms is, in fact, identical with the theory of organized bodies.

The various opinions entertained with respect to the fundamental powers of an organized body may be reduced to two, which are essentially different from one another. The first is, that every organism originates with an inherent power, which models it into conformity with a predominant idea, arranging the molecules in the relation necessary for accomplishing certain purposes held forth by this idea. Here, therefore, that which arranges and combines the molecules is a power acting with a definite purpose. A power of this kind would be essentially different from all the powers of inorganic nature, because action goes on in the latter quite blindly. A certain impression is followed of necessity by a certain change of quality and quantity, without regard to any purpose. In this view, however, the fundamental power of the organism would, inasmuch as it works with a definite individual purpose, be much more nearly allied to the immaterial principle, endued with consciousness which we must admit operates in man.

The other view is, that the fundamental powers of organized bodies agree essentially with those of inorganic nature, that they work altogether blindly according to laws of necessity and irrespective of any purpose, that they are powers which are as much established with the existence of matter as the physical powers are. It might be assumed that the powers which form organized bodies do not appear at all in inorganic nature, because this or that particular combination of molecules, by which the powers are elicited, does not occur in inorganic nature, and yet they might not be essentially distinct from physical and chemical powers. It cannot, indeed, be denied that adaptation to a particular purpose, in some individuals even in a high degree, is characteristic of every organism; but, according to this view, the source of this adaptation does not depend upon each organism being developed by the operation of its own power in obedience to that purpose, but it originates as in inorganic nature, in the creation of the matter with its blind powers by a rational Being. We know, for instance, the powers which operate in our planetary system. They operate, like all physical powers, in accordance with blind laws of necessity, and yet is the planetary system remarkable for its adaptation to a purpose. The ground of this adaptation does not lie in the powers, but in Him, who has so constituted matter with its powers, that in blindly obeying its laws it produces a whole suited to fulfil an intended purpose. We may even assume that the planetary system has an individual adaptation to a purpose. Some external influence, such as a comet, may occasion disturbances of motion, without thereby bringing the whole into collision; derangements may occur on single planets, such as a high tide, &c., which are yet balanced entirely by physical laws. As respects their adaptation to a purpose, organized bodies differ from these in degree only; and by this second view we are just as little compelled to conclude that the fundamental powers of organization operate according to laws of adaptation to a purpose, as we are in inorganic nature.

The first view of the fundamental powers of organized bodies may be called the *teleological*, the second the *physical* view. An example will show at once, how important for physiology is the solution of the question as to which is to be followed. If, for instance, we define inflammation and suppuration to be the effort of the organism to remove a foreign body that has been introduced into it; or fever to be the effort of the organism to eliminate diseased matter, and both as the result of the "autocracy of the organism," then these explanations accord with the teleological view. For, since by these processes the obnoxious matter is actually removed, the process which effects them is one adapted to an end; and as the fundamental power of the organism operates in accordance with definite purposes, it may either set these processes in action primarily, or may also summon further powers of matter to its aid, always, however, remaining itself the "primum movens." On the other hand, according to the physical view, this is just as little an explanation as it would be to say, that the motion of the earth around the sun is an effort of the fundamental power of the planetary system to produce a change of seasons on the planets, or to say, that ebb and flood are the reaction of the organism of the earth upon the moon.

In physics, all those explanations which were suggested by a teleological view of nature, as "horror vacui," and the like, have long been discarded. But in animated nature, adaptation—individual adaptation—to a purpose is so prominently marked, that it is difficult to reject all teleological explanations. Meanwhile it must be remembered that those explanations, which explain at once all and nothing, can be but the last resources, when no other view can possibly be adopted; and there is no such necessity for admitting the teleological view in the case of organized bodies. The adaptation to a purpose which is characteristic of organized bodies differs only in degree from what is apparent also in the inorganic part of nature; and the explanation that organized bodies are developed, like all the phenomena of inorganic nature, by the operation of blind laws framed with the matter, cannot be rejected as impossible. Reason certainly requires some ground for such adaptation, but for now it is sufficient to assume that matter with the powers inherent in it owes its existence to a rational Being. Once established and preserved in their integrity, these powers may, in accordance with their immutable laws of blind necessity, very well produce combinations, which manifest, even in a high degree, individual adaptation to a purpose. If, however, rational power interpose after creation merely to sustain, and not as an immediately active agent, it may, so far as natural science is concerned, be entirely excluded from the consideration of the creation.

But the teleological view leads to further difficulties in the explanation, and especially with respect to generation. If we assume each organism to be formed by a power which acts according to a certain predominant idea, a portion of this power may certainly reside in the ovum during generation; but then we must ascribe to this subdivision of the original power, at the separation of the ovum from the body of the mother, the capability of producing an organism similar to that which the power, of which it is but a portion, produced: that is, we must assume that this power is infinitely divisible, and yet that each part may perform the same actions as the whole power. If, on the other hand, the power of organized bodies reside, like the physical powers, in matter as such, and be set free only by a certain combination of the molecules, as, for instance, electricity is set free by the combination of a zinc and copper plate, then also by the conjunction of molecules to form an ovum the power may be set free, by which the ovum is capable of appropriating to itself fresh molecules, and these newly-conjoined molecules again by this very mode of combination acquire the same power to assimilate fresh molecules. The first development of the many forms of organized bodies—the progressive formation of organic nature indicated by geology —is also much more difficult to understand according to the teleological than the physical view.

Another objection to the teleological view may be drawn from the foregoing investigation. The molecules, as we have seen, are not immediately combined in various ways, as the purpose of the organism requires, but the formation of the elementary parts of organic bodies is regulated by laws which are essentially the same for all elementary parts. One can see no reason why this should be the case, if each organism be endued with a special power to frame the parts according to the purpose which they have to fulfil: it might much rather be expected that the formative principle, although identical for organs physiologically the same, would yet in different tissues be correspondingly varied. This resemblance of the elementary parts has, in the instance of plants, already led to the conjecture that the cells are really the organisms, and that the whole plant is an aggregate of these organisms arranged according to certain laws. But since the elementary parts of animals bear exactly similar relations, the individuality of an entire animal would thus be lost; and yet precisely upon the individuality of the whole animal does the assumption rest, that it possesses a single fundamental power operating in accordance with a definite idea.

Meanwhile we cannot altogether lay aside teleological views if all phenomena are not clearly explicable by the physical view. It is, however, unnecessary to do so, because an explanation, according to the teleological view, is only admissible when the physical can be shown to be impossible. In any case it conduces much more to the object of science to strive, at least, to adopt the physical explanation. And I would repeat that, when speaking of a physical explanation of organic phenomena, it is not necessary to understand an explanation by known physical powers, such, for instance, as that universal refuge electricity, and the like; but an explanation by means of powers which operate like the physical powers, in accordance with strict laws of blind necessity, whether they be also to be found in inorganic nature or not.

We set out, therefore, with the supposition that an organized body is not produced by a fundamental power which is guided in its operation by a definite idea, but is developed, according to blind laws of necessity, by powers which, like those of inorganic nature, are established by the very existence of matter. As the elementary materials of organic nature are not different from those of the inorganic kingdom, the source of the organic phenomena can only reside in another combination of these materials, whether it be in a peculiar mode of union of the elementary atoms to form atoms of the second order, or in the arrangement of these conglomerate molecules when forming either the separate morphological elementary parts of organisms, or an entire organism. We have here to do with the latter question solely, whether the cause of organic phenomena lies in the whole organism, or in its separate elementary parts. If this question can be answered, a further inquiry still remains as to whether the organism or its elementary parts possess this power through the peculiar mode of combination of the conglomerate molecules, or through the mode in which the elementary atoms are united into conglomerate molecules.

We may, then, form the two following ideas of the cause of organic phenomena, such as growth, &c. First, that the cause resides in the totality of the organism. By the combination of the molecules into a systematic whole, such as the organism is in every stage of its development, a power is engendered, which enables such an organism to take up fresh material from without, and appropriate it either to the formation of new elementary parts, or to the growth of those already present. Here, therefore, the cause of the growth of the elementary parts resides in the totality of the organism. The other mode of explanation is, that growth does not ensue from a power resident in the entire organism, but that each separate elementary part is possessed of an independent power, an independent life, so to speak; in other words, the molecules in each separate elementary part are so combined as to set free a power by which it is capable of attracting new molecules, and so increasing, and the whole organism subsists only by means of the reciprocal action of the single elementary parts. So that here the single elementary parts only exert an active influence on nutrition, and totality of the organism may indeed be a condition, but is not in this view a cause.

In order to determine which of these two views is the correct one, we must summon to our aid the results of the previous investigation. We have seen that all organized bodies are composed of essentially similar parts, namely, of cells; that these cells are formed and grow in accordance with essentially similar laws; and, therefore, that these processes must, in every instance, be produced by the same powers. Now, if we find that some of these elementary parts, not differing from the others, are capable of separating themselves from the organism, and pursuing an independent growth, we may thence conclude that each of the other elementary parts, each cell, is already possessed of power to take up fresh molecules and grow; and that, therefore, every elementary part possesses a power of its own, an independent life, by means of which it would be enabled to develop itself independently, if the relations which it bore to external parts were but similar to those in which it stands in the organism. The ova of animals afford us examples of such independent cells, growing apart from the organism. It may, indeed, be said of the ova of higher animals, that after impregnation the ovum is essentially different from the other cells of the organism; that by impregnation there is a something conveyed to the ovum, which is more to it than an external condition for vitality, more than nutrient matter; and that it might thereby have first received its peculiar vitality, and therefore that nothing can be inferred from it with respect to the other cells. But this fails in application to those classes which consist only of female individuals, as well as with the spores of the lower plants; and, besides, in the inferior plants any given cell may be separated from the plant, and then grow alone. So that here are whole plants consisting of cells, which can be positively proved to have independent vitality. Now, as all cells grow according to the same laws, and consequently the cause of growth cannot in one case lie in the cell, and in another in the whole organism; and since it may be further proved that some cells, which do not differ from the rest in their mode of growth, are developed independently, we must ascribe to all cells an independent vitality, that is, such combinations of molecules as occur in any single cell, are capable of setting free the power by which it is enabled to take up fresh molecules. The cause of nutrition and growth resides not in the organism as a whole, but in the separate elementary parts—the cells. The failure of growth in the case of any particular cell, when separated from an organized body, is as slight an objection to this theory, as it is an objection against the independent vitality of a bee, that it cannot continue long in existence after being separated from its swarm. The manifestation of the power which resides in the cell depends upon conditions to which it is subject only when in connexion with the whole (organism).

The question, then, as to the fundamental power of organized bodies resolves itself into that of the fundamental powers of the individual cells. We must now consider the general phenomena attending the formation of cells, in order to discover what powers may be presumed to exist in the cells to explain them. These phenomena may be arranged in two natural groups: first, those which relate to the combination of the molecules to form a cell, and which may be denominated the *plastic* phenomena of the cells; secondly, those which result from chemical changes either in the component particles of the cell itself, or in the surrounding cytoblastema, and which may be called *metabolic* phenomena (τὸ μεταβολικὸν, implying that which is liable to occasion or to suffer change).

$$* \qquad * \qquad * \qquad *$$

We see then how all the plastic phenomena in the cells may be compared with phenomena which, in accordance with the ordinary laws of crystallization, would probably appear if bodies capable of imbibition could be brought to crystallize. So long as the object of such a comparison were merely to render the representation of the process by which cells are formed more clear, there could not be much urged against it; it involves nothing hypothetical, since it contains no explanation; no assertion is made that the fundamental power of the cells really has something in common with the power by which crystals are formed. We have, indeed, compared the growth of organisms with crystallization, in so far as in both cases solid substances are deposited from a fluid, but we have not therefore asserted the identity of the fundamental powers. So far we have not advanced beyond the data, beyond a certain simple mode of representing the facts.

The question is, however, whether the exact accordance of the phenomena would not authorize us to go further. If the formation and growth of the elementary particles of organisms have nothing more in common with crystallization than merely the deposition of solid substances from out of a fluid, there is certainly no reason for assuming any more intimate connexion of the two processes. But we have seen, first, that the laws which regulate the deposition of the molecules forming the elementary particles of organisms are the same for all elementary parts; that there is a common principle in the development of all elementary parts, namely, that of the formation of cells; it was then shown that the power which induced the attachment of the new molecules did not reside in the entire organism, but in the separate elementary particles (this we called the plastic power of the cells) ; lastly, it was shown that the laws, according to which the new molecules combine to form cells, are (so far as our incomplete knowledge of the laws of crystallization admits of our anticipating their probability) the same as those by which substances capable of imbibition would crystallize. Now the cells do, in fact, consist only of material capable of imbibition; should we not then be justified in putting forth the proposition, that the formation of the elementary parts of organisms is nothing but a crystallization of substance capable of imbibition, and the organism nothing but an aggregate of such crystals capable of imbibition?

To advance so important a point as absolutely true, would certainly need the clearest proof; but it cannot be said that even the premises which have been set forth have in all points the requisite force. For too little is still known of the cause of crystallization to predict with safety (as was attempted above) what would follow if a substance capable of imbibition were to crystallize. And if these premises were allowed, there are two other points which must be proved in order to establish the proposition in question: 1. That the metabolic phenomena of the cells, which have not been referred to in the foregoing argument, are as much the necessary consequence of the faculty of imbibition, or of some other peculiarity of the substance of cells, as the plastic phenomena are. 2. That if a number of crystals capable of imbibition are formed, they must combine according to certain laws so as to form a systematic whole, similar to an organism. Both these points must be clearly proved, in order to establish the truth of the foregoing view. But it is otherwise if this view be adduced merely as an hypothesis, which may serve as a guide for new investigations. In such case the inferences are sufficiently probable to justify such an hypothesis, if only the two points just mentioned can be shown to accord with it.

With reference to the first of these points, it would certainly be impossible, in our ignorance as to the cause of chemical phenomena in general, to prove that a crystal capable of imbibition must produce chemical changes in substances surrounding it; but then we could not infer, from the manner in which spongy platinum is formed, that it would act so peculiarly upon oxygen and hydrogen. But in order to render this view tenable as a possible hypothesis, it is only necessary to see that it *may* be a consequence. It cannot be denied that it may: there are several reasons for it, though they certainly are but weak. For instance, since all cells possess this metabolic power, it is more likely to depend on a certain position of the molecules, which in all probability is essentially the same in all cells, than on the chemical combination of the molecules, which is very different in different cells. The presence, too, of different substances on the inner and the outer surface of the cell-membrane in some measure implies that a certain direction of the axes of the atoms may be essential to the metabolic phenomena of the cells. I think, therefore, that the cause of the metabolic phenomena resides in that definite mode of arrangement of the molecules which occurs in crystals, combined with the capacity which the solution has to penetrate between these regularly deposited molecules (by means of which, presuming the molecules to possess polarity, a sort of galvanic pile will be formed), and that the same phenomena would be observed in an ordinary crystal, if it could be rendered capable of imbibition. And then perhaps the differences of quality in the metabolic phenomena depend upon their chemical composition.

In order to render tenable the hypothesis contained in the second point, it is merely necessary to show that crystals capable of imbibition can unite with one another according to certain laws. If at their first formation all crystals were isolated, if they held no relation whatever to each other, the view would leave entirely unexplained how the elementary parts of organisms, that is, the crystals in question, become united to form a whole. It is therefore necessary to show that crystals do unite with each other according to certain laws, in order to perceive, at least, the possibility of their uniting also to form an organism, without the need of any further combining power. But there are many crystals in which a union of this kind, according to certain laws, is indisputable; indeed they often form a whole, so like an organism in its entire form, that groups of crystals are known in common life by the names of flowers, trees, &c. I need only refer to the ice-flowers on the windows, or to the lead-tree, &c. In such instances a number of crystals arrange themselves in groups around others, which form an axis. If we consider the contact of each crystal with the surrounding fluid to be an indispensable condition to the growth of crystals which are not capable of imbibition, but that those which are capable of imbibition, in which the solution can penetrate whole layers of crystals, do not require this condition, we perceive that the similarity between organisms and these aggregations of crystals is as great as could be expected with such difference of substance. As most cells require for the production of their metabolic phenomena, not only their peculiar nutrient fluid, but also the access of oxygen and the power of exhaling carbonic acid, or *vice versâ*; so, on the other hand, organisms in which there is no circulation of respiratory fluid, or in which at least it is not sufficient, must be developed in such a way as to present as extensive a surface as possible to the atmospheric air. This is the condition of plants, which require for their growth that the individual cells should come into contact with the surrounding medium in a similar manner, if not in the same degree, as occurs in a crystal tree, and in them indeed the cells unite into a whole organism in a form much resembling a crystal tree. But in animals the circulation renders the contact of the individual cells with the surrounding medium superfluous, and they may have more compact forms, even though the laws by which the cells arrange themselves are essentially the same.

The view then that organisms are nothing but the form under which substances capable of imbibition crystallize, appears to be compatible with the most important phenomena of organic life, and may be so far admitted, that it is a possible hypothesis, or attempt towards an explanation of these phenomena. It involves very much that is uncertain and paradoxical, but I have developed it in detail, because it may serve as a guide for new investigations. For even if no relation between crystallization and the growth of organisms be admitted in principle, this view has the advantage of affording a distinct representation of the organic processes; an indispensable requisite for the institution of new inquiries in a systematic manner, or for testing by the discovery of new facts a mode of explanation which harmonizes with phenomena already known.

19

CHARLES DARWIN

Charles Darwin, who was born in 1809, descended from a distinguished line from whom he inherited characteristics not otherwise acquired. On his mother's side, he was the grandson of Josiah Wedgwood; on his father's side, grandson of an eminent naturalist, Erasmus Darwin. Propelled toward his father's profession, medicine, he enrolled in Edinburgh University in 1825, to discover not only that anatomy disgusted him, but that surgery appalled him. The alternative was obvious, and in 1827 he settled into Christ's College, Cambridge, to read for the ministry. He appears to have studied the natural more than the literal revelation, and soon after he took his degree, he joined the expedition of the Beagle, which was setting sail primarily to survey South America for His Majesty's government. Upon his return, he married his cousin and settled on a country estate where the quiet life demanded by his uncertain health allowed him to devote his last forty years to natural history. Stories of his leisurely schedule of work abound, all belied by the quantity of his scientific output. Easily the best known of his works is the epochal *Origin of Species by Natural Selection* (1859) from which the following selection is taken. Like many valetudinarians, he outlived his healthy contemporaries, dying in 1882 at the ripe age of seventy-three.

The concept of organic evolution was one of the final steps in the demythologizing of nature, which has been an aspect of the rise of modern science. Modern physics and chemistry had excluded divine intervention from the ordinary operation of nature. The doctrine of original creation raised an issue distinct from the ordinary operation of nature, however, and if the doctrine of creation was sometimes challenged before the 19th century, it was not demonstrably toppled. The science of geology effectively challenged an aspect of the doctrine by proving to the satisfaction of those who would learn that the surface of the earth has been shaped by the uniform operation of impersonal forces over aeons of time. Significantly, Darwin was an accomplished geologist and a close friend of Charles Lyell, the greatest geologist of the day. The concept of evolution promised to do for the organic creation what uniformitarianism in geology had done for the inorganic. Part of Darwin's problem in the *Origin of Species* was to present a body of evidence that would establish evolution as a valid conclusion.

The concept of organic evolution was hardly new with Darwin. It had been in the air for well over half a century, and Darwin's own grandfather, Erasmus, had been the author of one of the early works expounding it. What no one had yet provided, however, was a plausible mechanism to account for evolution. The early evolutionary theories spoke in terms of an inherent vital force thrusting life up the evolutionary ladder, a concept in harmony with vitalistic *naturphilosophie*, but obviously in conflict with the mechanistic outlook that was coming to dominate biological science. The immediate triumph of Darwin's work derived from the plausible cause of evolution that it proposed.

19

On the Origin of Species by
Means of Natural Selection

Chapter I

Variation Under Domestication

CAUSES OF VARIABILITY

When we compare the individuals of the same variety or sub-variety of our older cultivated plants and animals, one of the first points which strikes us is, that they generally differ more from each other than do the individuals of any one species or variety in a state of nature. And if we reflect on the vast diversity of the plants and animals which have been cultivated, and which have varied during all ages under the most different climates and treatment, we are driven to conclude that this great variability is due to our domestic productions having been raised under conditions of life not so uniform as, and somewhat different from, those to which the parent species had been exposed under nature. There is, also, some probability in the view propounded by Andrew Knight, that this variability may be partly connected with excess of food. It seems clear that organic beings must be exposed during several generations to new conditions to cause any great amount of variation; and that, when the organisation has once begun to vary, it generally continues varying for many generations. No case is on record of a variable organism ceasing to vary under cultivation. Our oldest cultivated plants, such as wheat, still yield new varieties: our oldest domesticated animals are still capable of rapid improvement or modification. . . .

Indefinite variability is a much more common result of changed conditions than definite variability, and has probably played a more important part in the formation of our domestic races. We see indefinite variability

Taken from the sixth edition, London, 1872.

in the endless slight peculiarities which distinguish the individuals of the same species, and which cannot be accounted for by inheritance from either parent or from some more remote ancestor. Even strongly-marked differences occasionally appear in the young of the same litter, and in seedlings from the same seed-capsule. At long intervals of time, out of millions of individuals reared in the same country and fed on nearly the same food, deviations of structure so strongly pronounced as to deserve to be called monstrosities arise; but monstrosities cannot be separated by any distinct line from slighter variations. All such changes of structure, whether extremely slight or strongly marked, which appear amongst many individuals living together, may be considered as the indefinite effects of the conditions of life on each individual organism, in nearly the same manner as the chill affects different men in an indefinite manner, according to their state of body or constitution, causing coughs or colds, rheumatism, or inflammation of various organs. . . .

The results of the various, unknown, or but dimly understood laws of variation are infinitely complex and diversified. It is well worth while carefully to study the several treatises on some of our old cultivated plants, as on the hyacinth, potato, even the dahlia, &c.; and it is really surprising to note the endless points of structure and constitution in which the varieties and sub-varieties differ slightly from each other. The whole organisation seems to have become plastic, and departs in a slight degree from that of the parental type.

Any variation which is not inherited is unimportant for us. But the number and diversity of inheritable deviations of structure, both those of slight and those of considerable physiological importance, are endless. Dr. Prosper Lucas's treatise, in two large volumes, is the fullest and the best on this subject. No breeder doubts how strong is the tendency to inheritance; that like produces like is his fundamental belief: doubts have been thrown on this principle only by theoretical writers. When any deviation of structure often appears, and we see it in the father and child, we cannot tell whether it may not be due to the same cause having acted on both; but when amongst individuals, apparently exposed to the same conditions, any very rare deviation, due to some extraordinary combination of circumstances, appears in the parent—say, once amongst several million individuals—and it reappears in the child, the mere doctrine of chances almost compels us to attribute its reappearance to inheritance. Every one must have heard of cases of albinism, prickly skin, hairy bodies, &c., appearing in several members of the same family. If strange and rare deviations of structure are really inherited, less strange and commoner deviations may be freely admitted to be inheritable.

Perhaps the correct way of viewing the whole subject would be, to look at the inheritance of every character whatever as the rule, and non-inheritance as the anomaly.

*   *   *   *

PRINCIPLES OF SELECTION ANCIENTLY FOLLOWED, AND THEIR EFFECTS

Let us now briefly consider the steps by which domestic races have been produced, either from one or from several allied species. Some effect may be attributed to the direct and definite action of the external conditions of life, and some to habit; but he would be a bold man who would account by such agencies for the differences between a dray- and race-horse, a greyhound and bloodhound, a carrier and tumbler pigeon. One of the most remarkable features in our domesticated races is that we see in them adaptation, not indeed to the animal's or plant's own good, but to man's use or fancy. Some variations useful to him have probably arisen suddenly, or by one step; many botanists, for instance, believe that the fuller's teasel, with its hooks, which cannot be rivalled by any mechanical contrivance, is only a variety of the wild Dipsacus; and this amount of change may have suddenly arisen in a seedling. So it has probably been with the turnspit dog; and this is known to have been the case with the ancon sheep. But when we compare the dray-horse and race-horse, the dromedary and camel, the various breeds of sheep fitted either for cultivated land or mountain pasture, with the wool of one breed good for one purpose, and that of another breed for another purpose; when we compare the many breeds of dogs, each good for man in different ways; when we compare the game-cock, so pertinacious in battle, with other breeds so little quarrelsome, with "everlasting layers" which never desire to sit, and with the bantam so small and elegant; when we compare the host of agricultural, culinary, orchard, and flower-garden races of plants, most useful to man at different seasons and for different purposes, or so beautiful in his eyes, we must, I think, look further than to mere variability. We cannot suppose that all the breeds were suddenly produced as perfect and as useful as we now see them; indeed, in many cases, we know that this has not been their history. The key is man's power of accumulative selection: nature gives successive variations; man adds them up in certain directions useful to him. In this sense he may be said to have made for himself useful breeds.

The great power of this principle of selection is not hypothetical. It is certain that several of our eminent breeders have, even within a single lifetime, modified to a large extent their breeds of cattle and sheep. In order fully to realise what they have done, it is almost necessary to read several of the many treatises devoted to this subject, and to inspect the animals. Breeders habitually speak of an animal's organisation as something plastic, which they can model almost as they please. If I had space I could quote numerous passages to this effect from highly competent authorities. Youatt, who was probably better acquainted with the works of agriculturists than almost any other individual, and who was himself a very good judge of animals, speaks of the principle of selection as "that which enables the agriculturist, not only to modify the character of his flock, but to change it altogether. It is the magician's wand, by means of which he may summon into life whatever form and mould he pleases." Lord Somerville, speaking of what breeders have done for sheep, says: "It would seem as if they had chalked out upon a wall a form perfect in itself, and then had given it existence." In Saxony the importance of the principle of selection in regard to merino sheep is so fully recognised, that men follow it as a trade: the sheep are placed on a table and are studied, like a picture by a connoisseur; this is done three times at intervals of months, and the sheep are each time marked and classed, so that the very best may ultimately be selected for breeding.

What English breeders have actually effected is proved by the enormous prices given for animals with a good pedigree; and these have been exported to almost every quarter of the world. The improvement is by no means generally due to crossing different breeds; all the best breeders are strongly opposed to this practice, except sometimes amongst closely allied sub-breeds. And when a cross has been made, the closest selection is far more indispensable even than in ordinary cases. If selection consisted merely in separating some very distinct variety, and breeding from it, the principle would be so obvious as hardly to be worth notice; but its importance consists in the great effect produced by the accumulation in one direction, during successive generations, of differences absolutely inappreciable by an uneducated eye—differences which I for one have vainly attempted to appreciate. Not one man in a thousand has accuracy of eye and judgment sufficient to become an eminent breeder. If gifted with these qualities, and he studies his subject for years, and devotes his lifetime to it with indomitable perseverance, he will succeed, and may make great improvements; if he wants any of these qualities, he will assuredly fail. Few would readily believe in the natural capacity and years of practice requisite to become even a skilful pigeon-fancier.

The same principles are followed by horticulturists; but the variations are here often more abrupt. No one supposes that our choicest productions have been produced by a single variation from the aboriginal stock. We have proofs that this has not been so in several cases in which exact records have been kept; thus, to give a very trifling instance, the steadily-increasing size of the common gooseberry may be quoted. We see an astonishing improvement in many florists' flowers, when the flowers of the present day are compared with drawings made only twenty or thirty years ago. When a race of plants is once pretty well established, the seed-raisers do not pick out the best plants, but merely go over their seed-beds, and pull up the "rogues," as they call the plants that deviate from the proper standard. With animals this kind of selection is, in fact, likewise followed; for hardly any one is so careless as to breed from his worst animals.

In regard to plants there is another means of observing the accumulated effects of selection—namely, by comparing the diversity of flowers in the different varieties of the same species in the flower-garden; the diversity of leaves, pods, or tubers, or whatever part is valued, in the kitchen garden, in comparison with the flowers of the same varieties; and the diversity of fruit of the same species in the orchard, in comparison with the leaves and flowers of the same set of varieties. See how different the leaves of the cabbage are, and how extremely alike the flowers; how unlike the flowers of the heartsease are, and how alike the leaves; how much the fruit of the different kinds of gooseberries differ in size, colour, shape, and hairiness, and yet the flowers present very slight differences. It is not that the varieties which differ largely in some one point do not differ at all in other points; this is hardly ever—I speak after careful observation—perhaps never, the case. The law of correlated variation, the importance of which should never be overlooked, will ensure some differences; but, as a general rule, it can not be doubted that the continued selection of slight variations, either in the leaves, the flowers, or the fruit will produce races differing from each other chiefly in these characters.

It may be objected that the principle of selection has been reduced to methodical practice for scarcely more than three-quarters of a century; it has certainly been more attended to of late years, and many treatises have been published on the subject; and the result has been in a corresponding degree, rapid and important. But it is very far from true that the principle is a modern discovery. I could give several references to works of high antiquity, in which the full importance of the principle is acknowledged. In rude and barbarous periods of English history choice animals were often imported, and laws were passed to prevent their exportation: the destruction of horses under a certain size was ordered, and this may be compared to the "roguing" of plants by nurserymen. The principle of selection I find distinctly given in an ancient Chinese encyclopædia. Explicit rules are laid down by some of the Roman classical writers. From passages in Genesis, it is clear that the colour of domestic animals was at that early period attended to. Savages now sometimes cross their dogs with wild canine animals to improve the breed, and they formerly did so, as is attested by passages in Pliny. The savages in South Africa match their draught cattle by colour, as do some of the Esquimaux their teams of dogs. Livingstone states that good domestic breeds are highly valued by the negroes in the interior of Africa who have not associated with Europeans. Some of these facts do not show actual selection, but they show that the breeding of domestic animals was carefully attended to in ancient times, and is now attended to by the lowest savages. It would, indeed, have been a strange fact, had attention not been paid to breeding, for the inheritance of good and bad qualities is so obvious.

UNCONSCIOUS SELECTION

At the present time, eminent breeders try by methodical selection, with a distinct object in view, to make a new strain or sub-breed, superior to anything of the kind in the country. But, for our purpose, a form of Selection, which may be called Unconscious, and which results from every one trying to possess and breed from the best individual animals, is more important. Thus, a man who intends keeping pointers naturally tries to get as good dogs as he can, and afterwards breeds from his own best dogs, but he has no wish or expectation of permanently altering the breed. Nevertheless we may infer that this process, continued during centuries, would improve and modify any breed, in the same way as Bakewell, Collins, &c., by this very same process, only carried on more methodically, did greatly modify, even during their lifetime, the forms and qualities of their cattle. Slow and insensible changes of this kind can never be recognised unless actual measurements or careful drawings of the breeds in question have been made long ago, which may serve for comparison. In some cases, however, unchanged, or but little changed individuals of the same breed exist in less civilised districts, where the breed has been less improved. There is reason to believe that King Charles's spaniel has been unconsciously modified to a large extent since the time of that monarch. Some highly competent authorities are convinced that the setter is directly derived from the spaniel, and has probably been slowly altered from it. It is known that the English pointer has been greatly changed within the last century, and in this case the change has, it is believed, been chiefly effected by crosses with the fox-hound; but what concerns us is, that the change has been effected unconsciously and gradually, and yet so effectually, that, though the old Spanish pointer certainly came from Spain, Mr. Borrow has not seen, as I am informed by him, any native dog in Spain like our pointer.

By a similar process of selection, and by careful training, English race-horses have come to surpass in fleetness and size the parent Arabs, so that the latter, by the regulations for the Goodwood Races, are favoured in the weights which they carry. Lord Spencer and others have shown how the cattle of England have increased in weight and in early maturity, compared with the stock formerly kept in this country. By comparing the accounts given in various old treatises of the former and present state of carrier and tumbler pigeons in Britain, India, and Persia, we can trace the stages through which they have insensibly passed, and come to differ so greatly from the rock-pigeon.

*   *   *   *

Chapter II

Variation Under Nature

Before applying the principles arrived at in the last chapter to organic beings in a state of nature, we must briefly discuss whether these latter are subject to any variation. To treat this subject properly, a long cata-logue of dry facts ought to be given; but these I shall reserve for a future work. Nor shall I here discuss the various definitions which have been given of the term species. No one definition has satisfied all naturalists; yet every naturalist knows vaguely what he means when he speaks of a species. . . .

INDIVIDUAL DIFFERENCES

The many slight differences which appear in the offspring from the same parents, or which it may be presumed have thus arisen, from being observed in the individuals of the same species inhabiting the same con-fined locality, may be called individual differences. No one supposes that all the individuals of the same species are cast in the same actual mould. These individual differences are of the highest importance for us, for they are often inherited, as must be familiar to every one; and they thus afford materials for natural selection to act on and accumulate, in the same manner as man accumulates in any given direction individual differences in his domesticated productions. These individual differences generally affect what naturalists consider unimportant parts; but I could show by a long catalogue of facts, that parts which must be called im-portant, whether viewed under a physiological or classificatory point of view, sometimes vary in the individuals of the same species. I am con-vinced that the most experienced naturalist would be surprised at the number of the cases of variability, even in important parts of structure, which he could collect on good authority, as I have collected, during a course of years. It should be remembered that systematists are far from being pleased at finding variability in important characters, and that there are not many men who will laboriously examine internal and important organs, and compare them in many specimens of the same species. It would never have been expected that the branching of the main nerves close to the great central ganglion of an insect would have been variable in the same species; it might have been thought that changes of this nature could have been effected only by slow degrees; yet Sir J. Lubbock has shown a degree of variability in these main nerves in Coccus, which may almost be compared to the irregular branching of the stem of a tree. This philosophical naturalist, I may add, has also shown that the muscles in the larvæ of certain insects are far from uniform. Authors sometimes argue in a circle when they state that important organs never vary; for these same authors practically rank those parts as important (as some few naturalists have honestly confessed) which do not vary; and, under this point of view, no instance will ever be found of an important part varying; but under any other point of view many instances assuredly can be given. . . .

Some few naturalists maintain that animals never present varieties; but then these same naturalists rank the slightest difference as of specific value; and when the same identical form is met with in two distant countries, or in two geological formations, they believe that two distinct species are hidden under the same dress. The term species thus comes to be a mere useless abstraction, implying and assuming a separate act of creation. It is certain that many forms, considered by highly-competent judges to be varieties, resemble species so completely in character, that they have been thus ranked by other highly-competent judges. But to discuss whether they ought to be called species or varieties, before any definition of these terms has been generally accepted, is vainly to beat the air.

Many of the cases of strongly-marked varieties or doubtful species well deserve consideration; for several interesting lines of argument, from geographical distribution, analogical variation, hybridism, &c., have been brought to bear in the attempt to determine their rank; but space does not here permit me to discuss them. Close investigation, in many cases, will no doubt bring naturalists to agree how to rank doubtful forms. Yet it must be confessed that it is in the best known countries that we find the greatest number of them. I have been struck with the fact, that if any animal or plant in a state of nature be highly useful to man, or from any cause closely attracts his attention, varieties of it will almost universally be found recorded. These varieties, moreover, will often be ranked by some authors as species. Look at the common oak, how closely it has been studied; yet a German author makes more than a dozen species out of forms, which are almost universally considered by other botanists to be varieties; and in this country the highest botanical authorities and practical men can be quoted to show that the sessile and pedunculated oaks are either good and distinct species or mere varieties. . . .

Certainly no clear line of demarcation has as yet been drawn between species and sub-species—that is, the forms which in the opinion of some naturalists come very near to, but do not quite arrive at, the rank of species: or, again, between sub-species and well-marked varieties, or between lesser varieties and individual differences. These differences blend into each other by an insensible series; and a series impresses the mind with the idea of an actual passage.

Hence I look at individual differences, though of small interest to the systematist, as of the highest importance for us, as being the first steps towards such slight varieties as are barely thought worth recording in works on natural history. And I look at varieties which are in any degree more distinct and permanent, as steps towards more strongly-marked and permanent varieties; and at the latter, as leading to sub-species, and then to species. The passage from one stage of difference to another may, in many cases, be the simple result of the nature of the organism and of the different physical conditions to which it has long been exposed; but with respect to the more important and adaptive characters, the passage from one stage of difference to another, may be safely attributed to the cumulative action of natural selection, hereafter to be explained, and to the effects of the increased use or disuse of parts. A well-marked variety may therefore be called an incipient species; but whether this belief is justifiable must be judged by the weight of the various facts and considerations to be given throughout this work.

*   *   *   *

Chapter III

Struggle for Existence

Before entering on the subject of this chapter, I must make a few preliminary remarks, to show how the struggle for existence bears on Natural Selection. It has been seen in the last chapter that amongst organic beings in a state of nature there is some individual variability:

indeed I am not aware that this has ever been disputed. It is immaterial for us whether a multitude of doubtful forms be called species or sub-species or varieties; what rank, for instance, the two or three hundred doubtful forms of British plants are entitled to hold, if the existence of any well-marked varieties be admitted. But the mere existence of individual variability and of some few well-marked varieties, though necessary as the foundation for the work, helps us but little in understanding how species arise in nature. How have all those exquisite adaptations of one part of the organisation to another part, and to the conditions of life, and of one organic being to another being, been perfected? We see these beautiful co-adaptations most plainly in the woodpecker and the mistle-toe; and only a little less plainly in the humblest parasite which clings to the hairs of a quadruped or feathers of a bird; in the structure of the beetle which dives through the water; in the plumed seed which is wafted by the gentlest breeze; in short, we see beautiful adaptations everywhere and in every part of the organic world.

Again, it may be asked, how is it that varieties, which I have called incipient species, become ultimately converted into good and distinct species which in most cases obviously differ from each other far more than do the varieties of the same species? How do those groups of species, which constitute what are called distinct genera, and which differ from each other more than do the species of the same genus, arise? All these results, as we shall more fully see in the next chapter, follow from the struggle for life. Owing to this struggle, variations, however slight and from whatever cause proceeding, if they be in any degree profitable to the individuals of a species, in their infinitely complex relations to other organic beings and to their physical conditions of life, will tend to the preservation of such individuals, and will generally be inherited by the offspring. The offspring, also, will thus have a better chance of surviving, for, of the many individuals of any species which are periodically born, but a small number can survive. I have called this principle, by which each slight variation, if useful, is preserved, by the term Natural Selection, in order to mark its relation to man's power of selection. But the expression often used by Mr. Herbert Spencer of the Survival of the Fittest is more accurate, and is sometimes equally convenient. We have seen that man by selection can certainly produce great results, and can adapt organic beings to his own uses, through the accumulation of slight but useful variations, given to him by the hand of Nature. But Natural Selection, as we shall hereafter see, is a power incessantly ready for action, and is as immeasurably superior to man's feeble efforts, as the works of Nature are to those of Art.

We will now discuss in a little more detail the struggle for existence. In my future work this subject will be treated, as it well deserves, at greater length. The elder De Candolle and Lyell have largely and philosophically shown that all organic beings are exposed to severe competition. In regard to plants, no one has treated this subject with more spirit and ability than W. Herbert, Dean of Manchester, evidently the result of his great horticultural knowledge. Nothing is easier than to admit in words the truth of the universal struggle for life, or more difficult—at least I have found it so—than constantly to bear this conclusion in mind. Yet unless it be thoroughly engrained in the mind, the whole economy of nature, with every fact on distribution, rarity, abundance, extinction, and variation, will be dimly seen or quite misunderstood. We behold the face of nature bright with gladness, we often see superabundance of food; we do not see or we forget, that the birds which are idly singing round us mostly live on insects or seeds, and are thus constantly destroying life; or we forget how largely these songsters, or their eggs, or their nestlings, are destroyed by birds and beasts of prey; we do not always bear in mind, that, though food may be now superabundant, it is not so at all seasons of each recurring year.

THE TERM, STRUGGLE FOR EXISTENCE, USED IN A LARGE SENSE

I should premise that I use this term in a large and metaphorical sense including dependence of one being on another, and including (which is more important) not only the life of the individual, but success in leaving progeny. Two canine animals, in a time of dearth, may be truly said to struggle with each other which shall get food and live. But a plant on the edge of a desert is said to struggle for life against the drought, though more properly it should be said to be dependent on the moisture. A plant which annually produces a thousand seeds, of which only one of an average comes to maturity, may be more truly said to struggle with the plants of the same and other kinds which already clothe the ground. The mistletoe is dependent on the apple and a few other trees, but can only in a far-fetched sense be said to struggle with these trees, for, if too many of these parasites grow on the same tree, it languishes and dies. But several seedling mistletoes, growing close together on the same branch, may more truly be said to struggle with each other. As the mistletoe is disseminated by birds, its existence depends on them; and it may metaphorically be said to struggle with other fruit-bearing plants, in tempting the birds to devour and thus disseminate its seeds. In these several senses, which pass into each other, I use for convenience' sake the general term of Struggle for Existence.

GEOMETRICAL RATIO OF INCREASE

A struggle for existence inevitably follows from the high rate at which all organic beings tend to increase. Every being, which during its natural lifetime produces several eggs or seeds, must suffer destruction during some period of its life, and during some season or occasional year, otherwise, on the principle of geometrical increase, its numbers would quickly become so inordinately great that no country could support the product. Hence, as more individuals are produced than can possibly survive, there must in every case be a struggle for existence, either one individual with another of the same species, or with the individuals of distinct species, or with the physical conditions of life. It is the doctrine of Malthus applied with manifold force to the whole animal and vegetable kingdoms; for in this case there can be no artificial increase of food, and no prudential restraint from marriage. Although some species may be now increasing, more or less rapidly, in numbers, all cannot do so, for the world would not hold them.

There is no exception to the rule that every organic being naturally increases at so high a rate, that, if not destroyed, the earth would soon be covered by the progeny of a single pair. Even slow-breeding man has doubled in twenty-five years, and at this rate, in less than a thousand years, there would literally not be standing-room for his progeny. Linnæus has calculated that if an annual plant produced only two seeds— and there is no plant so unproductive as this—and their seedlings next year produced two, and so on, then in twenty years there should be a million plants. The elephant is reckoned the slowest breeder of all known animals, and I have taken some pains to estimate its probable minimum rate of natural increase; it will be safest to assume that it begins breeding when thirty years old, and goes on breeding till ninety years old, bringing forth six young in the interval, and surviving till one hundred years old; if this be so, after a period of from 740 to 750 years there would be nearly nineteen million elephants alive, descended from the first pair. . . .

The only difference between organisms which annually produce eggs or seeds by the thousand, and those which produce extremely few, is, that the slow-breeders would require a few more years to people, under favourable conditions, a whole district, let it be ever so large. The condor lays a couple of eggs and the ostrich a score, and yet in the same country the condor may be the more numerous of the two; the Fulmar petrel lays but one egg, yet it is believed to be the most numerous bird in the world. One fly deposits hundreds of eggs, and another, like the hippobosca, a single one; but this difference does not determine how many individuals of the two species can be supported in a district. A large number of eggs is of some importance to those species which depend on a fluctuating amount of food, for it allows them rapidly to increase in number. But the real importance of a large number of eggs or seeds is to make up for much destruction at some period of life; and this period in the great majority of cases is an early one. If an animal can in any way protect its own eggs or young, a small number may be produced, and yet the average stock be fully kept up; but if many eggs or young are destroyed, many must be produced, or the species will become extinct. It would suffice to keep up the full number of a tree, which lived on an average for a thousand years, if a single seed were produced once in a thousand years, supposing that this seed were never destroyed, and could be ensured to germinate in a fitting place. So that, in all cases, the average number of any animal or plant depends only indirectly on the number of its eggs or seeds.

In looking at Nature, it is most necessary to keep the foregoing considerations always in mind—never to forget that every single organic being may be said to be striving to the utmost to increase in numbers; that each lives by a struggle at some period of its life; that heavy destruction inevitably falls either on the young or old, during each generation or at recurrent intervals. Lighten any check, mitigate the destruction ever so little, and the number of the species will almost instantaneously increase to any amount.

*   *   *   *

COMPLEX RELATIONS OF ALL ANIMALS AND PLANTS TO EACH OTHER IN THE STRUGGLE FOR EXISTENCE

Many cases are on record showing how complex and unexpected are the checks and relations between organic beings, which have to struggle together in the same country. I will give only a single instance, which, though a simple one, interested me. In Staffordshire, on the estate of a relation, where I had ample means of investigation, there was a large and extremely barren heath, which had never been touched by the hand of man; but several hundred acres of exactly the same nature had been enclosed twenty-five years previously and planted with Scotch fir. The change in the native vegetation of the planted part of the heath was most remarkable, more than is generally seen in passing from one quite different soil to another: not only the proportional numbers of the heath-plants were wholly changed, but twelve species of plants (not counting grasses and carices) flourished in the plantations, which could not be found on the heath. The effect on the insects must have been still greater, for six insectivorous birds were very common in the plantations, which were not to be seen on the heath; and the heath was frequented by two or three distinct insectivorous birds. Here we see how potent has been the effect of the introduction of a single tree, nothing whatever else having been done, with the exception of the land having been enclosed, so that cattle could not enter. But how important an element enclosure is, I plainly saw near Farnham, in Surrey. Here there are extensive heaths with a few clumps of old Scotch firs on the distant hilltops: within the last ten years large spaces have been enclosed, and self-sown firs are now springing up in multitudes, so close together that all cannot live. When I ascertained that these young trees had not been sown or planted, I was so much surprised at their numbers that I went to several points of view, whence I could examine hundreds of acres of the unenclosed heath, and literally I could not see a single Scotch fir except the old planted clumps. But on looking closely between the stems of the heath, I found a multitude of seedlings and little trees which had been perpetually browsed down by the cattle. In one square yard, at a point some hundred yards distant from one of the old clumps, I counted thirty-two little trees and one of them, with twenty-six rings of growth had, during many years tried to raise its head above the stems of the heath, and had failed. No wonder that, as soon as the land was enclosed, it became thickly clothed with vigorously growing young firs. Yet the heath was so extremely barren and so extensive that no one would ever have imagined that cattle would have so closely and effectually searched it for food.

Here we see that cattle absolutely determine the existence of the Scotch fir; but in several parts of the world insects determine the existence of cattle. Perhaps Paraguay offers the most curious instance of this; for here neither cattle nor horses nor dogs have ever run wild, though they swarm southward and northward in a feral state; and Azara and Rengger have shown that this is caused by the greater number in Paraguay of a certain fly, which lays its eggs in the navels of these animals when first born. The increase of these flies, numerous as they are, must be habitually checked by some means, probably by other parasitic insects. Hence, if certain insectivorous birds were to decrease in Paraguay, the parasitic insects would probably increase; and this would lessen the number of the navel-frequenting flies—then cattle and horses would become feral, and this would certainly greatly alter (as indeed I have observed in parts of South America) the vegetation: this again would largely affect the insects; and this, as we have just seen in Staffordshire, the insectivorous birds, and so onwards in ever-increasing circles of complexity. Not that under nature the relations will ever be as simple as this. Battle within battle must be continually recurring with varying success; and yet in the long-run the forces are so nicely balanced, that the face of nature remains for long periods of time uniform, though assuredly the merest trifle would give the victory to one organic being over another. Nevertheless, so profound is our ignorance, and so high our presumption, that we marvel when we hear of the extinction of an organic being; and as we do not see the cause, we invoke cataclysms to desolate the world, or invent laws on the duration of the forms of life!

I am tempted to give one more instance showing how plants and animals remote in the scale of nature, are bound together by a web of complex relations. I shall hereafter have occasion to show that the exotic Lobelia fulgens is never visited in my garden by insects, and consequently, from its peculiar structure, never sets a seed. Nearly all our orchidaceous plants absolutely require the visits of insects to remove their pollen-masses and thus to fertilise them. I find from experiments that humble-bees are almost indispensable to the fertilisation of the heartsease (Violo tricolor), for other bees do not visit this flower. I have also found that the visits of bees are necessary for the fertilisation of some kinds of clover; for instance, 20 heads of Dutch clover (Trifolium repens) yielded 2,290 seeds, but 20 other heads protected from bees produced not one. Again, 100 heads of red clover (T. pratense) produced 2,700 seeds, but the same number of protected heads produced not a single seed. Humble-bees alone visit red clover, as other bees cannot reach the nectar. It has been suggested that moths may fertilise the clovers; but I doubt whether they could do so in the case of the red clover, from their weight not being sufficient to depress the wing petals. Hence we may infer as highly probable that, if the whole genus of humble-bees became extinct or very rare in England, the heartsease and red clover would become very rare, or wholly disappear. The number of humble-bees in any district depends in a great measure upon the number of field-mice, which destroy their combs and nests; and Col. Newman, who has long attended to the habits of humble-bees, believes that "more than two-thirds of them are thus destroyed all over England." Now the number of mice is largely dependent, as every one knows, on the number of cats; and Col. Newman says, "Near villages and small towns I have found the nests of humble-bees more numerous than elsewhere, which I attribute to the number of cats that destroy the mice." Hence it is quite credible that the presence of a feline animal in large numbers in a district might determine, through the intervention first of mice and then of bees, the frequency of certain flowers in that district!

In the case of every species, many different checks, acting at different periods of life, and during different seasons or years, probably come into play; some one check or some few being generally the most potent; but all will concur in determining the average number or even the existence of the species. In some cases it can be shown that widely-different checks act on the same species in different districts. When we look at the plants and bushes clothing an entangled bank, we are tempted to attribute their proportional numbers and kinds to what we call chance. But how false a view is this! Every one has heard that when an American forest is cut down a very different vegetation springs up; but it has been observed that ancient Indian ruins in the Southern United States, which must formerly have been cleared of trees, now display the same beautiful diversity and proportion of kinds as in the surrounding virgin forest. What a struggle must have gone on during long centuries between the several kinds of trees each annually scattering its seeds by the thousand; what war between insect and insect—between insects, snails, and other animals with birds and beasts of prey—all striving to increase, all feeding on each other, or on the trees, their seeds and seedlings, or on the other plants which first clothed the ground and thus checked the growth of the trees! Throw up a handful of feathers, and all fall to the ground according to definite laws; but how simple is the problem where each shall fall compared to that of the action and reaction of the innumerable plants and animals which have determined, in the course of centuries, the proportional numbers and kinds of trees now growing on the old Indian ruins!

The dependency of one organic being on another, as of a parasite on its prey, lies generally between beings remote in the scale of nature. This is likewise sometimes the case with those which may be strictly said to struggle with each other for existence, as in the case of locusts and grass-feeding quadrupeds. But the struggle will almost invariably be most severe between the individuals of the same species, for they frequent the same districts, require the same food, and are exposed to the same dangers. In the case of varieties of the same species, the struggle will generally be almost equally severe, and we sometimes see the contest soon decided: for instance, if several varieties of wheat be sown together, and the mixed seed be resown, some of the varieties which best suit the soil or climate, or are naturally the most fertile, will beat the others and so yield more seed, and will consequently in a few years supplant the other varieties. To keep up a mixed stock of even such extremely close varieties as the variously-coloured sweet peas, they must be each year harvested separately, and the seed then mixed in due proportion, otherwise the weaker kinds will steadily decrease in number and disappear. So again with the varieties of sheep; it has been asserted that certain mountain-varieties will starve out other mountain-varieties, so that they cannot be kept together. The same result has followed from keeping together different varieties of the medicinal leech. It may even be doubted whether the varieties of any of our domestic plants or animals have so exactly the same strength, habits, and constitution, that the original proportions of a mixed stock (crossing being prevented) could be kept up for half-a-dozen generations, if they were allowed to struggle together, in the same manner as beings in a state of nature, and if the seed or young were not annually preserved in due proportion.

STRUGGLE FOR LIFE MOST SEVERE BETWEEN INDIVIDUALS AND VARIETIES OF THE SAME SPECIES

As the species of the same genus usually have, though by no means invariably, much similarity in habits and constitution, and always in structure, the struggle will generally be more severe between them, if they come into competition with each other, than between the species of distinct genera. We see this in the recent extension over parts of the United States of one species of swallow having caused the decrease of another species. The recent increase of the missel-thrush in parts of Scotland has caused the decrease of the song-thrush. How frequently we hear of one species of rat taking the place of another species under the most different climates! In Russia the small Asiatic cockroach has everywhere driven before it its great congener. In Australia the imported hive-bee is rapidly exterminating the small, stingless native bee. One species of charlock has been known to supplant another species; and so in other cases. We can dimly see why the competition should be most severe between allied forms, which fill nearly the same place in the economy of nature; but probably in no one case could we precisely say why one species has been victorious over another in the great battle of life.

A corollary of the highest importance may be deduced from the foregoing remarks, namely, that the structure of every organic being is related, in the most essential yet often hidden manner, to that of all the other organic beings, with which it comes into competition for food or residence, or from which it has to escape, or on which it preys. This is obvious in the structure of the teeth and talons of the tiger; and in that of the legs and claws of the parasite which clings to the hair on the tiger's body. But in the beautifully plumed seed of the dandelion, and in the flattened and fringed legs of the water-beetle, the relation seems at first confined to the elements of air and water. Yet the advantage of plumed seeds no doubt stands in the closest relation to the land being already thickly clothed with other plants; so that the seeds may be widely distributed and fall on unoccupied ground. In the water-beetle, the structure of its legs, so well adapted for diving, allows it to compete with other aquatic insects, to hunt for its own prey, and to escape serving as prey to other animals.

The store of nutriment laid up within the seeds of many plants seems at first sight to have no sort of relation to other plants. But from the strong growth of young plants produced from such seeds, as peas and beans, when sown in the midst of long grass, it may be suspected that the chief use of the nutriment in the seed is to favour the growth of the seedlings, whilst struggling with other plants growing vigorously all around.

Look at a plant in the midst of its range, why does it not double or quadruple its numbers? We know that it can perfectly well withstand a little more heat or cold, dampness or dryness, for elsewhere it ranges into slightly hotter or colder, damper or drier districts. In this case we can clearly see that if we wish in imagination to give the plant the power of increasing in number, we should have to give it some advantage over its competitors, or over the animals which prey on it. On the confines of its geographical range, a change of constitution with respect to climate would clearly be an advantage to our plant; but we have reason to believe that only a few plants or animals range so far, that they are destroyed exclusively by the rigour of the climate. Not until we reach the extreme confines of life, in the Arctic regions or on the borders of an utter desert, will competition cease. The land may be extremely cold or dry, yet there will be competition between some few species, or between the individuals of the same species, for the warmest or dampest spots.

Hence we can see that when a plant or animal is placed in a new country amongst new competitors, the conditions of its life will generally be changed in an essential manner, although the climate may be exactly the same as in its former home. If its average numbers are to increase in its new home, we should have to modify it in a different way to what we should have had to do in its native country; for we should have to give it some advantage over a different set of competitors or enemies.

It is good thus to try in imagination to give to any one species an advantage over another. Probably in no single instance should we know what to do. This ought to convince us of our ignorance on the mutual relations of all organic beings; a conviction as necessary, as it is difficult to acquire. All that we can do, is to keep steadily in mind that each organic being is striving to increase in a geometrical ratio; that each at some period of its life, during some season of the year, during each generation or at intervals, has to struggle for life and to suffer great destruction. When we reflect on this struggle, we may console ourselves with the full belief, that the war of nature is not incessant, that no fear is felt, that death is generally prompt, and that the vigorous, the healthy, and the happy survive and multiply.

Chapter IV

Natural Selection; Or the Survival of the Fittest

How will the struggle for existence, briefly discussed in the last chapter, act in regard to variation? Can the principle of selection, which we have seen is so potent in the hands of man, apply under nature? I think we shall see that it can act most efficiently. Let the endless number of slight variations and individual differences occurring in our domestic productions, and, in a lesser degree, in those under nature, be borne in mind; as well as the strength of the hereditary tendency. Under domestication, it may be truly said that the whole organisation becomes in some degree plastic. But the variability, which we almost universally meet with in our domestic productions, is not directly produced, as Hooker and Asa Gray have well remarked, by man; he can neither originate varieties, nor prevent their occurrence; he can preserve and accumulate such as do occur. Unintentionally he exposes organic beings to new and changing conditions of life, and variability ensues; but similar changes of conditions might and do occur under nature. Let it also be borne in mind how infinitely complex and close-fitting are the mutual relations of all organic beings to each other and to their physical conditions of life; and consequently what infinitely varied diversities of structure might be of use to each being under changing conditions of life. Can it, then, be thought improbable, seeing that variations useful to man have undoubtedly occurred, that other variations useful in some way to each being in the great and complex battle of life, should occur in the course of many successive generations? If such do occur, can we doubt (remembering that many more individuals are born than can possibly survive) that individuals having any advantage, however slight, over others, would have the best chance of surviving and of procreating their kind? On the other hand, we may feel sure that any variation in the least degree injurious would be rigidly destroyed. This preservation of favourable individual differences and variations, and the destruction of those which are injurious, I have called Natural Selection, or the Survival of the Fittest. Variations neither useful nor injurious would not be affected by natural selection, and would be left either a fluctuating element, as perhaps we see in certain polymorphic species, or would ultimately become fixed, owing to the nature of the organism and the nature of the conditions.

Several writers have misapprehended or objected to the term Natural Selection. Some have even imagined that natural selection induces variability, whereas it implies only the preservation of such variations as arise and are beneficial to the being under its conditions of life. No one objects to agriculturists speaking of the potent effects of man's selection; and in this case the individual differences given by nature, which man for some object selects, must of necessity first occur. Others have objected that the term selection implies conscious choice in the animals which become modified; and it has even been urged that, as plants have no volition, natural selection is not applicable to them! In the literal sense of the word, no doubt, natural selection is a false term; but who ever objected to chemists speaking of the elective affinities of the various elements?—and yet an acid cannot strictly be said to elect the base with which it in preference combines. It has been said that I speak of natural selection as an active power or Deity; but who objects to an author speaking of the attraction of gravity as ruling the movements of the planets? Every one knows what is meant and is implied by such metaphorical expressions; and they are almost necessary for brevity. So again it is difficult to avoid personifying the word Nature; but I mean by Nature, only the aggregate action and product of many natural laws, and by laws the sequence of events as ascertained by us. With a little familiarity such superficial objections will be forgotten.

We shall best understand the probable course of natural selection by taking the case of a country undergoing some slight physical change, for instance, of climate. The proportional numbers of its inhabitants will almost immediately undergo a change, and some species will probably become extinct. We may conclude, from what we have seen of the intimate and complex manner in which the inhabitants of each country are bound together, that any change in the numerical proportions of the inhabitants, independently of the change of climate itself, would seriously affect the others. If the country were open on its borders, new forms would certainly immigrate, and this would likewise seriously disturb the relations of some of the former inhabitants. Let it be remembered how powerful the influence of a single introduced tree or mammal has been shown to be. But in the case of an island, or of a country partly surrounded by barriers, into which new and better adapted forms could not freely enter, we should then have places in the economy of nature which would assuredly be better filled up, if some of the original inhabitants were in some manner modified; for, had the area been open to immigration, these same places would have been seized on by intruders. In such cases, slight modifications, which in any way favoured the individuals of any species, by better adapting them to their altered conditions, would tend to be preserved; and natural selection would have free scope for the work of improvement.

We have good reason to believe, as shown in the first chapter, that changes in the conditions of life give a tendency to increased variability; and in the foregoing cases the conditions have changed, and this would manifestly be favourable to natural selection, by affording a better chance of the occurrence of profitable variations. Unless such occur, natural selection can do nothing. Under the term of "variations," it must never be forgotten that mere individual differences are included. As man can produce a great result with his domestic animals and plants by adding up in any given direction individual differences, so could natural selection, but far more easily from having incomparably longer time for action. Nor do I believe that any great physical change, as of climate, or any unusual degree of isolation to check immigration, is necessary in order that new and unoccupied places should be left, for natural selection to fill up by improving some of the varying inhabitants. For as all the inhabitants of each country are struggling together with nicely balanced forces, extremely slight modifications in the structure or habits of one species would often give it an advantage over others; and still further modifications of the same kind would often still further increase the advantage, as long as the species continued under the same conditions of life and profited by similar means of subsistence and defence. No country can be named in which all the native inhabitants are now so perfectly adapted to each other and to the physical conditions under which they live, that none of them could be still better adapted or improved; for in all countries, the natives have been so far conquered by naturalised productions, that they have allowed some foreigners to take firm possession of the land. And as foreigners have thus in every country beaten some of the natives, we may safely conclude that the natives might have been modified with advantage, so as to have better resisted the intruders.

As man can produce, and certainly has produced, a great result by his methodical and unconscious means of selection, what may not natural selection effect? Man can act only on external and visible characters: Nature, if I may be allowed to personify the natural preservation or survival of the fittest, cares nothing for appearances, except in so far as they are useful to any being. She can act on every internal organ, on every shade of constitutional difference, on the whole machinery of life. Man selects only for his own good: Nature only for that of the being which she tends. Every selected character is fully exercised by her, as is implied by the fact of their selection. Man keeps the natives of many climates in the same country; he seldom exercises each selected character in some peculiar and fitting manner; he feeds a long and a short beaked pigeon on the same food; he does not exercise a long-backed or long-legged quadruped in any peculiar manner; he exposes sheep with long and short wool to the same climate. He does not allow the most vigorous males to struggle for the females. He does not rigidly destroy all inferior animals, but protects during each varying season, as far as lies in his power, all his productions. He often begins his selection by some half-monstrous form; or at least by some modification prominent enough to catch the eye or to be plainly useful to him. Under nature, the slightest differences of structure or constitution may well turn the nicely-balanced scale in the struggle for life, and so be preserved. How fleeting are the wishes and efforts of man! how short his time! and consequently how poor will be his results, compared with those accumulated by Nature during whole geological periods! Can we wonder, then, that Nature's productions should be far "truer" in character than man's productions; that they should be infinitely better adapted to the most complex conditions of life, and should plainly bear the stamp of far higher workmanship?

It may metaphorically be said that natural selection is daily and hourly scrutinising, throughout the world, the slightest variations; rejecting those that are bad, preserving and adding up all that are good; silently and insensibly working, *whenever and wherever opportunity offers,* at the improvement of each organic being in relation to its organic and inorganic conditions of life. We see nothing of these slow changes in progress, until the hand of time has marked the lapse of ages, and then so imperfect is our view into long-past geological ages, that we see only that the forms of life are now different from what they formerly were.

In order that any great amount of modification should be effected in a species, a variety when once formed must again, perhaps after a long interval of time, vary or present individual differences of the same favourable nature as before; and these must be again preserved, and so onwards step by step. Seeing that individual differences of the same kind perpetually recur, this can hardly be considered as an unwarrantable assumption. But whether it is true, we can judge only by seeing how far the hypothesis accords with and explains the general phenomena of nature. On the other hand, the ordinary belief that the amount of possible variation is a strictly limited quantity is likewise a simple assumption.

Although natural selection can act only through and for the good of each being, yet characters and structures, which we are apt to consider as of very trifling importance, may thus be acted on. When we see leaf-eating insects green, and bark-feeders mottled-grey; the alpine ptarmigan white in winter, the red-grouse the colour of heather, we must believe that these tints are of service to these birds and insects in preserving them from danger. Grouse, if not destroyed at some period of their lives would increase in countless numbers; they are known to suffer largely from birds of prey; and hawks are guided by eyesight to their prey—so much so, that on parts of the Continent persons are warned not to keep white pigeons, as being the most liable to destruction. Hence natural selection might be effective in giving the proper colour to each kind of grouse, and in keeping that colour, when once acquired, true and constant. Nor ought we to think that the occasional destruction of an animal of any particular colour would produce little effect: we should remember how essential it is in a flock of white sheep to destroy a lamb with the faintest trace of black. We have seen how the colour of the hogs, which feed on the "paint-root" in Virginia, determines whether they shall live or die. In plants, the down on the fruit and the colour of the flesh are considered by botantists as characters of the most trifling importance: yet we hear from an excellent horticulturist, Downing, that in the United States, smooth-skinned fruits suffer far more from a beetle, a Curculio, than those with down; that purple plums suffer far more from a certain disease than yellow plums; whereas another disease attacks yellow-fleshed peaches far more than those with other coloured flesh. If, with all the aids of art, these slight differences make a great difference in cultivating the several varieties, assuredly, in a state of nature, where the trees would have to struggle with other trees, and with a host of enemies, such differences would effectually settle which variety, whether a smooth or downy, a yellow or purple fleshed fruit, should succeed.

In looking at many small points of difference between species, which, as far as our ignorance permits us to judge, seem quite unimportant, we must not forget that climate, food, &c., have no doubt produced some direct effect. It is also necessary to bear in mind that, owing to the law of correlation, when one part varies, and the variations are accumulated through natural selection, other modifications, often of the most unexpected nature, will ensue.

As we see that those variations which, under domestication, appear at any particular period of life, tend to reappear in the offspring at the same period—for instance, in the shape, size, and flavour of the seeds of the many varieties of our culinary and agricultural plants; in the caterpillar and cocoon stages of the varieties of the silk-worm; in the eggs of poultry, and in the colour of the down of their chickens; in the horns of our sheep and cattle when nearly adult—so in a state of nature natural selection will be enabled to act on and modify organic beings at any age, by the accumulation of variations profitable at that age, and by their inheritance at a corresponding age. If it profit a plant to have its seeds more and more widely disseminated by the wind, I can see no greater difficulty in this being effected through natural selection, than in the cotton-planter increasing and improving by selection the down in the pods on his cotton-trees. Natural selection may modify and adapt the larva of an insect to a score of contingencies, wholly different from those which concern the mature insect; and these modifications may affect, through correlation, the structure of the adult. So, conversely, modifications in the adult may affect the structure of the larva; but in all cases natural selection will ensure that they shall not be injurious: for if they were so, the species would become extinct.

Natural selection will modify the structure of the young in relation to the parent, and of the parent in relation to the young. In social animals it will adapt the structure of each individual for the benefit of the whole community; if the community profits by the selected change. What natural selection cannot do, is to modify the structure of one species, without giving it any advantage, for the good of another species; and though statements to this effect may be found in works of natural history, I cannot find one case which will bear investigation. A structure used only once in an animal's life, if of high importance to it, might be modified to any extent by natural selection; for instance, the great jaws possessed by certain insects, used exclusively for opening the cocoon—or the hard tip to the beak of unhatched birds, used for breaking the egg. It has been asserted, that of the best short-beaked tumbler-pigeons a greater number perish in the egg than are able to get out of it; so that fanciers assist in the act of hatching. Now if nature had to make the beak of a full-grown pigeon very short for the bird's own advantage, the process of modification would be very slow, and there would be simultaneously the most rigorous selection of all the young birds within the egg, which had the most powerful and hardest beaks, for all with weak beaks would inevitably perish; or, more delicate and more easily broken shells might be selected, the thickness of the shell being known to vary like every other structure.

It may be well here to remark that with all beings there must be much fortuitous destruction, which can have little or no influence on the course of natural selection. For instance a vast number of eggs or seeds are annually devoured, and these could be modified through natural selection only if they varied in some manner which protected them from their enemies. Yet many of these eggs or seeds would perhaps, if not destroyed, have yielded individuals better adapted to their conditions of life than any of those which happened to survive. So again a vast number of mature animals and plants, whether or not they be the best adapted to their conditions, must be annually destroyed by accidental causes, which would not be in the least degree mitigated by certain changes of structure or constitution which would in other ways be beneficial to the species. But let the destruction of the adults be ever so heavy, if the number which can exist in any district be not wholly kept down by such causes,—or again let the destruction of eggs or seeds be so great that only a hundredth or a thousandth part are developed,— yet of those which do survive, the best adapted individuals, supposing that there is any variability in a favourable direction, will tend to propagate their kind in larger numbers than the less well adapted. If the numbers be wholly kept down by the causes just indicated, as will often have been the case, natural selection will be powerless in certain beneficial directions; but this is no valid objection to its efficiency at other times and in other ways; for we are far from having any reason to suppose that many species ever undergo modification and improvement at the same time in the same area.

SEXUAL SELECTION

Inasmuch as peculiarities often appear under domestication in one sex and become hereditarily attached to that sex, so no doubt it will be under nature. Thus it is rendered possible for the two sexes to be modified through natural selection in relation to different habits of life, as is sometimes the case; or for one sex to be modified in relation to the other sex, as commonly occurs. This leads me to say a few words on what I have called Sexual Selection. This form of selection depends, not on a struggle for existence in relation to other organic beings or to external conditions, but on a struggle between the individuals of one sex, generally the males, for the possession of the other sex. The result is not death to the unsuccessful competitor, but few or no offspring. Sexual selection is, therefore, less rigorous than natural selection. Generally, the most vigorous males, those which are best fitted for their places in nature, will leave most progeny. But in many cases, victory depends not so much on general vigor, as on having special weapons, confined to the male sex. A hornless stag or spurless cock would have a poor chance of leaving numerous offspring. Sexual selection, by always allowing the victor to breed, might surely give indomitable courage, length to the spur, and strength to the wing to strike in the spurred leg, in nearly the same manner as does the brutal cockfighter by the careful selection of his best cocks. How low in the scale of nature the law of battle descends, I know not; male alligators have been described as fighting, bellowing, and whirling round, like Indians in a war-dance, for the possession of the females; male salmons have been observed fighting all day long; male stag-beetles sometimes bear wounds from the huge mandibles of other males; the males of certain hymenopterous insects have been frequently seen by that inimitable observer M. Fabre, fighting for a particular female who sits by, an apparently unconcerned beholder of the struggle, and then retires with the conqueror. The war is, perhaps, severest between the males of polygamous animals, and these seem oftenest provided with special weapons. The males of carnivorous animals are already well armed; though to them and to others, special means of defence may be given through means of sexual selection, as the mane of the lion, and the hooked jaw to the male salmon; for the shield may be as important for victory, as the sword or spear.

Amongst birds, the contest is often of a more peaceful character. All those who have attended to the subject, believe that there is the severest rivalry between the males of many species to attract, by singing, the females. The rock-thrush of Guiana, birds of paradise, and some others, congregate; and successive males display with the most elaborate care, and show off in the best manner, their gorgeous plumage; they likewise perform strange antics before the females, which, standing by as spectators, at last choose the most attractive partner. Those who have closely attended to birds in confinement well know that they often take individual preferences and dislikes: thus Sir R. Heron has described how a pied peacock was eminently attractive to all his hen birds. I cannot here enter on the necessary details; but if man can in a short time give beauty and an elegant carriage to his bantams, according to his standard of beauty, I can see no good reason to doubt that female birds, by selecting, during thousands of generations, the most melodious or beautiful males, according to their standard of beauty, might produce a marked effect. Some well-known laws, with respect to the plumage of male and female birds, in comparison with the plumage of the young, can partly be explained through the action of sexual selection on variations occurring at different ages, and transmitted to the males alone or to both sexes at corresponding ages; but I have not space here to enter on this subject.

Thus it is, as I believe, that when the males and females of any animal have the same general habits of life, but differ in structure, colour, or ornament, such differences have been mainly caused by sexual selection: that is, by individual males having had, in successive generations, some slight advantage over other males, in their weapons, means of defence, or charms, which they have transmitted to their male offspring alone. Yet, I would not wish to attribute all sexual differences to this agency: for we see in our domestic animals peculiarities arising and becoming attached to the male sex, which apparently have not been augmented through selection by man. The tuft of hair on the breast of the wild turkey-cock cannot be of any use, and it is doubtful whether it can be ornamental in the eyes of the female bird; indeed, had the tuft appeared under domestication, it would have been called a monstrosity.

ILLUSTRATIONS OF THE ACTION OF NATURAL SELECTION, OR THE SURVIVAL OF THE FITTEST

In order to make it clear how, as I believe, natural selection acts, I must beg permission to give one or two imaginary illustrations. Let us take the case of a wolf, which preys on various animals, securing some by craft, some by strength, and some by fleetness; and let us suppose that the fleetest prey, a deer for instance, had from any change in the country increased in numbers, or that other prey had decreased in numbers, during that season of the year when the wolf was hardest pressed for food. Under such circumstances the swiftest and slimmest wolves would have the best chance of surviving and so be preserved or selected,—provided always that they retained strength to master their prey at this or some other period of the year, when they were compelled to prey on other animals. I can see no more reason to doubt that this would be the result, than that man should be able to improve the fleetness of his greyhounds by careful and methodical selection, or by that kind of unconscious selection which follows from each man trying to keep the best dogs without any thought of modifying the breed. I may add, that, according to Mr. Pierce, there are two varieties of the wolf inhabiting the Catskill Mountains, in the United States, one with a light greyhound-like form, which pursues deer, and the other more bulky, with shorter legs, which more frequently attacks the shepherd's flocks.

*   *   *   *

Chapter XV

Recapitulation and Conclusion

. . . If we admit that the geological record is imperfect to an extreme degree, then the facts, which the record does give, strongly support the theory of descent with modification. New species have come on the stage slowly and at successive intervals; and the amount of change, after equal intervals of time, is widely different in different groups. The extinction of species and of whole groups of species which has played so conspicuous a part in the history of the organic world, almost inevitably follows from the principle of natural selection; for old forms are supplanted by new and improved forms. Neither single species nor groups of species reappear when the chain of ordinary generation is once broken. The gradual diffusion of dominant forms, with the slow modification of their descendants, causes the forms of life, after long intervals of time, to appear as if they had changed simultaneously throughout the world. The fact of the fossil remains of each formation being in some degree intermediate in character between the fossils in the formations above and below, is simply explained by their intermediate position in the chain of descent. The grand fact that all extinct beings can be classed with all recent beings, naturally follows from the living and the extinct being the offspring of common parents. As species have generally diverged in character during their long course of descent and modification, we can understand why it is that the more ancient forms, or early progenitors of each group, so often occupy a position in some degree intermediate between existing groups. Recent forms are generally looked upon as being, on the whole, higher in the scale of organisation than ancient forms; and they must be higher, in so far as the later and more improved forms have conquered the older and less improved forms in the struggle for life; they have also generally had their organs more specialised for different functions. This fact is perfectly compatible with numerous beings still retaining simple and but little improved structures, fitted for simple conditions of life; it is likewise compatible with some forms having retrograded in organisation, by having become at each stage of descent better fitted for new and degraded habits of life. Lastly, the wonderful law of the long endurance of allied forms on the same continent—of marsupials in Australia, of dentata in America, and other such cases—is intelligible, for within the same country the existing and the extinct will be closely allied by descent.

Looking to geographical distribution, if we admit that there has been during the long course of ages much migration from one part of the world to another, owing to former climatal and geographical changes and to the many occasional and unknown means of dispersal, then we can understand, on the theory of descent with modification, most of the great leading facts in Distribution. We can see why there should be so striking a parallelism in the distribution of organic beings throughout space, and in their geological succession throughout time; for in both cases the beings have been connected by the bond of ordinary generation, and the means of modification have been the same. We see the full meaning of the wonderful fact, which has struck every traveller namely, that on the same continent, under the most diverse conditions, under heat and cold, on mountain and lowland, on deserts and marshes, most of the inhabitants within each great class are plainly related; for they are the descendants of the same progenitors and early colonists. On this same principle of former migration, combined in most cases with modification, we can understand, by the aid of the Glacial period, the identity of some few plants, and the close alliance of many others, on the most distant mountains, and in the northern and southern temperate zones; and likewise the close alliance of some of the inhabitants of the sea in the northern and southern temperate latitudes, though separated by the whole intertropical ocean. Although two countries may present physical conditions as closely similar as the same species ever require, we need feel no surprise at their inhabitants being widely different, if they have been for a long period completely sundered from each other; for as the relation of organism to organism is the most important of all relations, and as the two countries will have received colonists at various periods and in different proportions, from some other country or from each other, the course of modification in the two areas will inevitably have been different.

On this view of migration, with subsequent modification, we see why oceanic islands are inhabited by only few species, but of these, why many are peculiar or endemic forms. We clearly see why species belonging to those groups of animals which cannot cross wide spaces of the ocean, as frogs and terrestrial mammals, do not inhabit oceanic islands; and why, on the other hand, new and peculiar species of bats, animals which can traverse the ocean, are often found on islands far distant from any continent. Such cases as the presence of peculiar species of bats on oceanic islands and the absence of all other terrestrial mammals, are facts utterly inexplicable on the theory of independent acts of creation.

The existence of closely allied or representative species in any two areas, implies, on the theory of descent with modification, that the same parent-forms formerly inhabited both areas; and we almost invariably find that wherever many closely allied species inhabit two areas, some identical species are still common to both. Wherever many closely allied yet distinct species occur, doubtful forms and varieties belonging to the same groups likewise occur. It is a rule of high generality that the inhabitants of each area are related to the inhabitants of the nearest source whence immigrants might have been derived. We see this in the striking relation of nearly all the plants and animals of the Galapagos archipelago, of Juan Fernandez, and of the other American islands, to the plants and animals of the neighbouring American mainland; and of those of the Cape de Verde archipelago, and of the other African islands to the African mainland. It must be admitted that these facts receive no explanation on the theory of creation.

The fact, as we have seen, that all past and present organic beings can be arranged within a few great classes, in groups subordinate to groups, and with the extinct groups often falling in between the recent groups, is intelligible on the theory of natural selection with its contingencies of extinction and divergence of character. On these same principles we see how it is, that the mutual affinities of the forms within each class are so complex and circuitous. We see why certain characters are far more serviceable than others for classification; why adaptive characters, though of paramount importance to the beings, are of hardly any importance in classification; why characters derived from rudimentary parts, though of no service to the beings, are often of high classificatory value; and why embryological characters are often the most valuable of all. The real affinities of all organic beings, in contradistinction to their adaptive resemblances, are due to inheritance or community of descent. The Natural System is a genealogical arrangement, with the acquired grades of difference, marked by the terms, varieties, species, genera, families, &c.; and we have to discover the lines of descent by the most permanent characters whatever they may be and of however slight vital importance.

The similar framework of bones in the hand of a man, wing of a bat, fin of the porpoise, and leg of the horse—the same number of vertebræ forming the neck of the giraffe and of the elephant—and innumerable other such facts, at once explain themselves on the theory of descent with slow and slight successive modifications. The similarity of pattern in the wing and in the leg of a bat, though used for such different purpose—in the jaws and legs of a crab—in the petals, stamens, and pistils of a flower, is likewise, to a large extent, intelligible on the view of the gradual modification of parts or organs, which were aboriginally alike in an early progenitor in each of these classes. On the principle of successive variations not always supervening at an early age, and being inherited at a corresponding not early period of life, we clearly see why the embryos of mammals, birds, reptiles, and fishes should be so closely similar, and so unlike the adult forms. We may cease marvelling at the embryo of an air-breathing mammal or bird having branchial slits and arteries running in loops, like those of a fish which has to breathe the air dissolved in water by the aid of well-developed branchiæ.

Disuse, aided sometimes by natural selection, will often have reduced organs when rendered useless under changed habits or conditions of life; and we can understand on this view the meaning of rudimentary organs. But disuse and selection will generally act on each creature, when it has come to maturity and has to play its full part in the struggle for existence, and will thus have little power on an organ during early life; hence the organ will not be reduced or rendered rudimentary at this early age. The calf, for instance, has inherited teeth, which never cut through the gums of the upper jaw, from an early progenitor having well-developed teeth; and we may believe, that the teeth in the mature animal were formerly reduced by disuse, owing to the tongue and palate, or lips, having become excellently fitted through natural selection to browse without their aid; whereas in the calf, the teeth have been left unaffected, and on the principle of inheritance at corresponding ages have been inherited from a remote period to the present day. On the view of each organism with all its separate parts having been specially created, how utterly inexplicable is it that organs bearing the plain stamp of inutility, such as the teeth in the embryonic calf or the shrivelled wings under the soldered wing-covers of many beetles, should so frequently occur. Nature may be said to have taken pains to reveal her scheme of modification, by means of rudimentary organs, of embryological and homologous structures, but we are too blind to understand her meaning.

20

J. J. THOMSON

Joseph John Thomson was born in the north of England in 1856. He began his higher education in Manchester, but soon secured a scholarship to Cambridge, where he completed his education and ultimately spent the rest of his life. Studying in the hallowed tradition of Newton's college, Thomson so distinguished himself that, at the age of 28, he was appointed to follow Rayleigh (and Maxwell) in the chair of experimental physics at Cambridge. Rarely has scientific talent been accurately recognized and properly rewarded so early. Thomson justified his nomination many times over, both as a researcher and as a teacher. In addition to conducting the fundamental investigations which earned him a Nobel Prize in 1906, "J.J." provided such a stimulating scientific atmosphere among his students that no less than seven eventual Nobel Laureates (including his own son) left the Cavendish Laboratory during his 34 years of leadership. When he himself left the Laboratory in 1918, it was to move up to master of Trinity College. In his later life, he received not only the academic honors appropriate to his achievements, but civil recognition as well: he was knighted in 1908, and on his death in 1940 was given the burial of a national hero in Westminster Abbey beside Newton and Darwin.

From the beginning of the 18th century, the luminous glow in a charged, evacuated globe was regarded as an important clue to the nature of electricity. For the early electricians, the supposed clue led to a dead end, and the phenomenon was essentially ignored after the novel work of Franklin. A century later, however, it came up for reconsideration in the remarkably different context of "conduction through rarified gases," and eventually fulfilled its initial promise. The basic phenomenon, a luminous streak between the electrodes, was soon found to be highly dependent on the extent of rarification—the higher the degree of exhaustion, the greater the size of certain dark spaces that interrupted the streaks. By the 1860's, the pumps and tubes were developed to the point at which the streak could be made to disappear altogether, giving way to a colored fluorescence on the wall of the glass tube. Objects placed in the path of the former streak cast shadows in such a way as to indicate that radiation of some kind proceeded in straight lines from the negative electrode. By 1880, it was notorious that "cathode rays" not only threw shadows, but could move light objects as well, and were themselves deflected by a magnet.

Particles or waves? That was the question. On the one hand, Faraday's laws of electrolysis had long been interpreted as implying the existence of a minimum quantity or atom of electricity; the name electron had, in fact, already been suggested for it. On the other hand, recent theoretical and experimental work by Maxwell and Hertz, respectively, had established some serious analogies between electricity and light, and the nature of light was well known. Another *experimentum crucis* was required.

20

Cathode Rays

The experiments discussed in this paper were undertaken in the hope of gaining some information as to the nature of the Cathode Rays. The most diverse opinions are held as to these rays; according to the almost unanimous opinion of German physicists they are due to some process in the æther to which—inasmuch as in a uniform magnetic field their course is circular and not rectilinear—no phenomenon hitherto observed is analogous: another view of these rays is that, so far from being wholly ætherial, they are in fact wholly material, and that they mark the paths of particles of matter charged with negative electricity. It would seem at first sight that it ought not to be difficult to discriminate between views so different, yet experience shows that this is not the case, as amongst the physicists who have most deeply studied the subject can be found supporters of either theory.

The electrified-particle theory has for purposes of research a great advantage over the ætherial theory, since it is definite and its consequences can be predicted; with the ætherial theory it is impossible to predict what will happen under any given circumstances, as on this theory we are dealing with hitherto unobserved phenomena in the æther, of whose laws we are ignorant.

The following experiments were made to test some of the consequences of the electrified-particle theory.

Charge Carried by the Cathode Rays

If these rays are negatively electrified particles, then when they enter an enclosure they ought to carry into it a charge of negative electricity. This has been proved to be the case by Perrin, who placed in front of a plane cathode two coaxial metallic cylinders which were insulated from each other: the outer of these cylinders was connected with the earth, the inner with a gold-leaf electroscope. These cylinders were closed except for two small holes, one in each cylinder, placed so that the

Published in *The Philosophical Magazine*, London, 1897.

481

cathode rays could pass through them into the inside of the inner cylinder. Perrin found that when the rays passed into the inner cylinder the electroscope received a charge of negative electricity, while no charge went to the electroscope when the rays were deflected by a magnet so as no longer to pass through the hole.

This experiment proves that something charged with negative electricity is shot off from the cathode, travelling at right angles to it, and that this something is deflected by a magnet; it is open, however, to the objection that it does not prove that the cause of the electrification in the electroscope has anything to do with the cathode rays. Now the supporters of the ætherial theory do not deny that electrified particles are shot off from the cathode; they deny, however, that these charged particles have any more to do with the cathode rays than a rifle-ball has with the flash when a rifle is fired. I have therefore repeated Perrin's experiment in a form which is not open to this objection. The arrangement used was as follows. Two coaxial cylinders (Figure 1) with slits in them are placed in a bulb connected with the discharge-tube; the cathode rays from the cathode A pass into the bulb through a slit in a metal plug fitted into the neck of the tube; this plug is connected with the anode and is put to earth. The cathode rays thus do not fall upon the cylinders unless they are deflected by a magnet. The outer cylinder is connected with the earth, the inner with the electrometer. When the cathode rays (whose path was traced by the phosphorescence on the glass) did not fall on the slit, the electrical charge sent to the electrometer when the induction-coil producing the rays was set in action

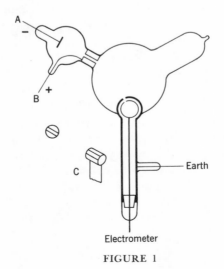

Electrometer

FIGURE 1

was small and irregular; when, however, the rays were bent by a magnet so as to fall on the slit there was a large charge of negative electricity sent to the electrometer. I was surprised at the magnitude of the charge; on some occasions enough negative electricity went through the narrow slit into the inner cylinder in one second to alter the potential of a capacity of 1.5 microfarads by 20 volts. If the rays were so much bent by the magnet that they overshot the slits in the cylinder, the charge passing into the cylinder fell again to a very small fraction of its value when the aim was true. Thus this experiment shows that however we twist and deflect the cathode rays by magnetic forces, the negative electrification follows the same path as the rays, and that this negative electrification is indissolubly connected with the cathode rays.

When the rays are turned by the magnet so as to pass through the slit into the inner cylinder, the deflexion of the electrometer connected with this cylinder increases up to a certain value, and then remains stationary although the rays continue to pour into the cylinder. This is due to the fact that the gas in the bulb becomes a conductor of electricity when the cathode rays pass through it, and thus, though the inner cylinder is perfectly insulated when the rays are not passing, yet as soon as the rays pass through the bulb the air between the inner cylinder and the outer one becomes a conductor, and the electricity escapes from the inner cylinder to the earth. Thus the charge within the inner cylinder does not go on continually increasing; the cylinder settles down into a state of equilibrium in which the rate at which it gains negative electricity from the rays is equal to the rate at which it loses it by conduction through the air. If the inner cylinder has initially a positive charge it rapidly loses that charge and acquires a negative one; while if the initial charge is a negative one, the cylinder will leak if the initial negative potential is numerically greater than the equilibrium value.

Deflexion of the Cathode Rays by an Electrostatic Field

An objection very generally urged against the view that the cathode rays are negatively electrified particles, is that hitherto no deflexion of the rays has been observed under a small electrostatic force, and though the rays are deflected when they pass near electrodes connected with sources of large differences of potential, such as induction-coils or electrical machines, the deflexion in this case is regarded by the supporters of the ætherial theory as due to the discharge passing between the electrodes, and not primarily to the electrostatic field. Hertz made the rays travel between two parallel plates of metal placed inside the discharge-tube, but found that they were not deflected when the plates were connected with a battery of storage-cells; on repeating this experiment I at

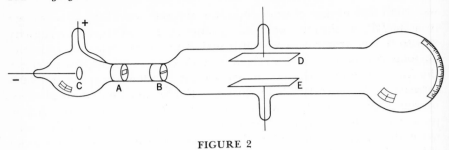

FIGURE 2

first got the same result, but subsequent experiments showed that the absence of deflexion is due to the conductivity conferred on the rarefied gas by the cathode rays. On measuring this conductivity it was found that it diminished very rapidly as the exhaustion increased; it seemed then that on trying Hertz's experiment at very high exhaustions there might be a chance of detecting the deflexion of the cathode rays by an electrostatic force.

The apparatus used is represented in Figure 2.

The rays from the cathode C pass through a slit in the anode A, which is a metal plug fitting tightly into the tube and connected with the earth; after passing through a second slit in another earth-connected metal plug B, they travel between two parallel aluminium plates about 5 cm. long by 2 broad and at a distance of 1·5 cm. apart; they then fall on the end of the tube and produce a narrow well-defined phosphorescent patch. A scale pasted on the outside of the tube serves to measure the deflexion of this patch. At high exhaustions the rays were deflected when the two aluminium plates were connected with the terminals of a battery of small storage-cells; the rays were depressed when the upper plate was connected with the negative pole of the battery, the lower with the positive, and raised when the upper plate was connected with the positive, the lower with the negative pole. The deflexion was proportional to the difference of potential between the plates, and I could detect the deflexion when the potential-difference was as small as two volts. It was only when the vacuum was a good one that the deflexion took place, but that the absence of deflexion is due to the conductivity of the medium is shown by what takes place when the vacuum has just arrived at the stage at which the deflexion begins. At this stage there is a deflexion of the rays when the plates are first connected with the terminals of the battery, but if this connexion is maintained the patch of phosphorescence gradually creeps back to its undeflected position. This is just what would happen if the space between the plates were a conductor, though a very bad one, for then the positive and negative ions between the plates would slowly diffuse, until the positive plate became coated with negative ions, the negative plate with positive ones; thus the electric intensity between the plates would vanish and the cathode rays be free from electrostatic force. Another illustration of this is afforded by what happens when the pressure is low enough to show the deflexion and a large difference of potential, say 200 volts, is established between the plates; under these circumstances there is a large deflexion of the cathode rays, but the medium under the large electromotive force breaks down every now and then and a bright discharge passes between the plates; when this occurs the phosphorescent patch produced by the cathode rays jumps back to its undeflected position. When the cathode rays are deflected by the electrostatic field, the phosphorescent band breaks up into several bright bands separated by comparatively dark spaces; the phenomena are exactly analogous to those observed by Birkeland when the cathode rays are deflected by a magnet, and called by him the magnetic spectrum.

A series of measurements of the deflexion of the rays by the electrostatic force under various circumstances will be found later on in the part of the paper which deals with the velocity of the rays and the ratio of the mass of the electrified particles to the charge carried by them. It may, however, be mentioned here that the deflexion gets smaller as the pressure diminishes, and when in consequence the potential-difference in the tube in the neighbourhood of the cathode increases. . . .

Magnetic Deflexion of the Cathode Rays in Different Gases

The deflexion of the cathode rays by the magnetic field was studied with the aid of the apparatus shown in Figure 3. The cathode was placed in a side-tube fastened on to a bell-jar; the opening between this tube and the bell-jar was closed by a metallic plug with a slit in it; this plug was connected with the earth and was used as the anode. The cathode rays passed through the slit in this plug into the bell-jar, passing in

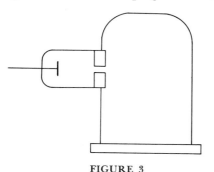

FIGURE 3

front of a vertical plate of glass ruled into small squares. The bell-jar was placed between two large parallel coils arranged as a Helmholtz galvanometer. The course of the rays was determined by taking photographs of the bell-jar when the cathode rays were passing through it; the divisions on the plate enabled the path of the rays to be determined. Under the action of the magnetic field the narrow beam of cathode rays spreads out into a broad fan-shaped luminosity in the gas. The luminosity in this fan is not uniformly distributed, but is condensed along certain lines. The phosphorescence on the glass is also not uniformly distributed; it is much spread out, showing that the beam consists of rays which are not all deflected to the same extent by the magnet. The luminosity on the glass is crossed by bands along which the luminosity is very much greater than in the adjacent parts. These bright and dark bands are called by Birkeland, who first observed them, the magnetic spectrum. The brightest spots on the glass are by no means always the terminations of the brightest streaks of luminosity in the gas; in fact, in some cases a very bright spot on the glass is not connected with the cathode by any appreciable luminosity, though there may be plenty of luminosity in other parts of the gas. . . .

As the cathode rays carry a charge of negative electricity, they are deflected by an electrostatic force as if they were negatively electrified, and are acted on by a magnetic force in just the way in which this force would act on a negatively electrified body moving along the path of these rays, I can see no escape from the conclusion that they are charges of negative electricity carried by particles of matter. The question next arises, What are these particles? are they atoms, or molecules, or matter in a still finer state of subdivision? To throw some light on this point, I have made a series of measurements of the ratio of the mass of these particles to the charge carried by it. To determine this quantity, I have used two independent methods. The first of these is as follows. Suppose we consider a bundle of homogeneous cathode rays. Let m be the mass of each of the particles, e the charge carried by it. Let N be the number of particles passing across any section of the beam in a given time; then Q the quantity of electricity carried by these particles is given by the equation

$$N e = Q.$$

We can measure Q if we receive the cathode rays in the inside of a vessel connected with an electrometer. When these rays strike against a solid body, the temperature of the body is raised; the kinetic energy of the moving particles being converted into heat; if we suppose that all this energy is converted into heat, then if we measure the increase in the temperature of a body of known thermal capacity caused by the impact of these rays, we can determine W, the kinetic energy of the particles, and if v is the velocity of the particles,

$$\tfrac{1}{2}Nmv^2 = W.$$

If ρ is the radius of curvature of the path of these rays in a uniform magnetic field H, then

$$\frac{mv}{e} = H\rho = I,$$

where I is written for $H\rho$ for the sake of brevity. From these equations we get

$$\frac{1}{2}\frac{m}{e}\,v^2 = \frac{W}{Q}.$$

$$v = \frac{2W}{QI},$$

$$\frac{m}{e} = \frac{I^2Q}{2W}.$$

Thus, if we know the values of Q, W, and I, we can deduce the values of v and m/e.

To measure these quantities, I have used tubes of three different types. The first I tried is like that represented in Figure 2, except that the plates E and D are absent, and two coaxial cylinders are fastened to the end of the tube. The rays from the cathode C fall on the metal plug B, which is connected with the earth, and serves for the anode; a horizontal slit is cut in this plug. The cathode rays pass through this slit, and then strike against the two coaxial cylinders at the end of the tube; slits are cut in these cylinders, so that the cathode rays pass into the inside of the inner cylinder. The outer cylinder is connected with the earth, the inner cylinder, which is insulated from the outer one, is connected with an electrometer, the deflexion of which measures Q, the quantity of electricity brought into the inner cylinder by the rays. A thermo-electric couple is placed beyond the slit in the inner cylinder; this couple is made of very thin strips of iron and copper fastened to very fine iron and copper wires. These wires passed through the cylinders, being insulated from them, and through the glass to the outside of the tube, where they were connected with a low-resistance galvanometer, the deflexion of which gave data for calculating the rise of temperature of the junction produced by the impact against it of the cathode rays. The strips of iron and copper were large enough to ensure that every cathode ray which entered the inner cylinder struck against the junction. In some of the tubes the strips of iron and copper were placed end to end, so that some of the rays struck against the iron, and others against the copper; in others, the strip of one metal was placed in front of the other; no difference, however, could be detected between the results got with these two arrangements. The strips of iron and copper were weighed, and the thermal capacity of the junction calculated. In one set of junctions this capacity was 5×10^{-3}, in another 3×10^{-3}. If we assume that the cathode rays which strike against the junction give their energy up to it, the deflexion of the galvanometer gives us W or $\frac{1}{2}Nmv^2$.

The value of I, *i.e.*, Hρ, where ρ is the curvature of the path of the rays in a magnetic field of strength H was found as follows. The tube was fixed between two large circular coils placed parallel to each other, and separated by a distance equal to the radius of either; these coils produce a uniform magnetic field, the strength of which is got by measuring with an ammeter the strength of the current passing through them. The cathode rays are thus in a uniform field, so that their path is circular. Suppose that the rays, when deflected by a magnet, strike against the glass of the tube at E (Figure 4), then, if ρ is the radius of the circular path of the rays,

$$2\rho = \frac{CE^2}{AC} + AC;$$

thus, if we measure CE and AC we have the means of determining the radius of curvature of the path of the rays.

The determination of ρ is rendered to some extent uncertain, in consequence of the pencil of rays spreading out under the action of the magnetic field, so that the phosphorescent patch at E is several millimetres long; thus values of ρ differing appreciably from each other will be got by taking E at different points of this phosphorescent patch. Part of this patch was, however, generally considerably brighter than the rest; when this was the case, E was taken as the brightest point; when such a point of maximum brightness did not exist, the middle of the patch was taken for E. The uncertainty in the value of ρ thus introduced amounted sometimes to about 20 per cent; by this I mean that if we took E first at one extremity of the patch and then at the other, we should get values of ρ differing by this amount.

The measurement of Q, the quantity of electricity which enters the

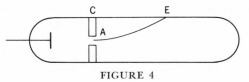

FIGURE 4

inner cylinder, is complicated by the cathode rays making the gas through which they pass a conductor, so that though the insulation of the inner cylinder was perfect when the rays were off, it was not so when they were passing through the space between the cylinders; this caused some of the charge communicated to the inner cylinder to leak away so that the actual charge given to the cylinder by the cathode rays was larger than that indicated by the electrometer. To make the error from this cause as small as possible, the inner cylinder was connected to the largest capacity available, 1.5 microfarad, and the rays were only kept on for a short time, about 1 or 2 seconds, so that the alteration in potential of the inner cylinder was not large, ranging in the various experiments from about .5 to 5 volts. Another reason why it is necessary to limit the duration of the rays to as short a time as possible, is to avoid the correction for the loss of heat from the thermo-electric junction by conduction along the wires; the rise in temperature of the junction was of the order 2°C.; a series of experiments showed that with the same tube and the same gaseous pressure Q and W were proportional to each other when the rays were not kept on too long.

Tubes of this kind gave satisfactory results, the chief drawback being that sometimes in consequence of the charging up of the glass of the tube, a secondary discharge started from the cylinder to the walls of the tube, and the cylinders were surrounded by glow; when this glow appeared, the readings were very irregular; the glow could, however, be got rid of by jumping and letting the tube rest for some time. The results got with this tube are given in Table I under the heading Tube 1.

The second type of tube was like that used for photographing the path of the rays (Figure 3); double cylinders with a thermo-electric junction like those used in the previous tube were placed in the line of fire of the rays, the inside of the bell-jar was lined with copper gauze connected with the earth. This tube gave very satisfactory results; we were never troubled with any glow round the cylinders, and the readings were most concordant; the only drawback was that as some of the connexions had to be made with sealing-wax, it was not possible to get the highest exhaustions with this tube, so that the range of pressure for this tube is less than that for Tube 1. The results got with this tube are given in Table I under the heading Tube 2.

The third type of tube was similar to the first, except that the openings in the two cylinders were made very much smaller; in this tube the slits in the cylinders were replaced by small holes, about 1.5 millim. in diameter. In consequence of the smallness of the openings, the magnitude of the effects was very much reduced; in order to get measurable results it was necessary to reduce the capacity of the condenser in connexion with the inner cylinder to .15 microfarad, and to make the galvanometer exceedingly sensitive, as the rise in temperature of the thermo-electric junction was in these experiments only about .5°C. on the average. The results obtained in this tube are given in Table I under the heading Tube 3.

The results of a series of measurements with these tubes are given in Table I.

TABLE I

Gas	Value of W/Q	I	m/e	v
Tube 1				
Air	4.6×10^{11}	230	$.57 \times 10^{-7}$	4×10^9
Air	1.8×10^{12}	350	$.34 \times 10^{-7}$	1×10^{10}
Air	6.1×10^{11}	230	$.43 \times 10^{-7}$	5.4×10^9
Air	2.5×10^{12}	400	$.32 \times 10^{-7}$	1.2×10^{10}
Air	5.5×10^{11}	230	$.48 \times 10^{-7}$	4.8×10^9
Air	1×10^{12}	285	$.4 \times 10^{-7}$	7×10^9
Air	1×10^{12}	285	$.4 \times 10^{-7}$	7×10^9
Hydrogen	6×10^{12}	205	$.35 \times 10^{-7}$	6×10^9
Hydrogen	2.1×10^{12}	460	$.5 \times 10^{-7}$	9.2×10^9
Carbonic acid	8.4×10^{11}	260	$.4 \times 10^{-7}$	7.5×10^9
Carbonic acid	1.47×10^{12}	340	$.4 \times 10^{-7}$	8.5×10^9
Carbonic acid	3.0×10^{12}	480	$.39 \times 10^{-7}$	1.3×10^{10}
Tube 2				
Air	2.8×10^{11}	175	$.53 \times 10^{-7}$	3.3×10^9
Air	4.4×10^{11}	195	$.47 \times 10^{-7}$	4.1×10^9
Air	3.5×10^{11}	181	$.47 \times 10^{-7}$	3.8×10^9
Hydrogen	2.8×10^{11}	175	$.53 \times 10^{-7}$	3.3×10^9
Air	2.5×10^{11}	160	$.51 \times 10^{-7}$	3.1×10^9
Carbonic acid	2×10^{11}	148	$.54 \times 10^{-7}$	2.5×10^9
Air	1.8×10^{11}	151	$.63 \times 10^{-7}$	2.3×10^9
Hydrogen	2.8×10^{11}	175	$.53 \times 10^{-7}$	3.3×10^9
Hydrogen	4.4×10^{11}	201	$.46 \times 10^{-7}$	4.4×10^9
Air	2.5×10^{11}	176	$.61 \times 10^{-7}$	2.8×10^9
Air	4.2×10^{11}	200	$.48 \times 10^{-7}$	4.1×10^9
Tube 3				
Air	2.5×10^{11}	220	$.9 \times 10^{-7}$	2.4×10^9
Air	3.5×10^{11}	225	$.7 \times 10^{-7}$	3.2×10^9
Hydrogen	3×10^{11}	250	1.0×10^{-7}	2.5×10^9

It will be noticed that the value of m/e is considerably greater for Tube 3, where the opening is a small hole, than for Tubes 1 and 2, where the opening is a slit of much greater area. I am of opinion that the values of m/e got from Tubes 1 and 2 are too small, in consequence of the leakage from the inner cylinder to the outer by the gas being rendered a conductor by the passage of the cathode rays. . . .

From these determinations we see that the value of m/e is independent of the nature of the gas, and that its value 10^{-7} is very small compared with the value 10^{-4}, which is the smallest value of this quantity previously known, and which is the value for the hydrogen ion in electrolysis.

Thus for the carriers of the electricity in the cathode rays m/e is very small compared with its value in electrolysis. The smallness of m/e may be due to the smallness of m or the largeness of e, or to a combination of these two. That the carriers of the charges in the cathode rays are small compared with ordinary molecules is shown, I think, by Lenard's results as to the rate at which the brightness of the phosphorescence produced by these rays diminishes with the length of path travelled by the ray. If we regard this phosphorescence as due to the impact of the charged particles, the distance through which the rays must travel before the phosphoresence fades to a given fraction (say $1/e$) of its original intensity, will be some moderate multiple of the mean free path. Now Lenard found that this distance depends solely upon the density of the medium, and not upon its chemical nature or physical state. In air at atmospheric pressure the distance was about half a centimetre, and this must be comparable with the mean free path of the carriers through air at atmospheric pressure. But the mean free path of the molecules of air is a quantity of quite a different order. The carrier, then, must be small compared with ordinary molecules.

The two fundamental points about these carriers seem to me to be (1) that these carriers are the same whatever the gas through which the discharge passes, (2) that the mean free paths depend upon nothing but the density of the medium traversed by these rays.

It might be supposed that the independence of the mass of the carriers of the gas through which the discharge passes was due to the mass concerned being the quasi mass which a charged body possesses in virtue of the electric field set up in its neighbourhood; moving the body involves the production of a varying electric field, and, therefore, of a certain amount of energy which is proportional to the square of the velocity. This causes the charged body to behave as if its mass were increased by a quantity, which for a charged sphere is $\tfrac{2}{3} e^2/\mu a$, where e is the charge and a the radius of the sphere. If we assume that it is this mass which we are concerned with in the cathode rays, since m/e would vary as e/a, it affords no clue to the explanation of either of the properties (1 and 2) of these rays. This is not by any means the only objection to this hypothesis, which I only mention to show that it has not been overlooked.

The explanation which seems to me to account in the most simple and straightforward manner for the facts is founded on a view of the constitution of the chemical elements which has been favourably entertained by many chemists: this view is that the atoms of the different chemical elements are different aggregations of atoms of the same kind. In the form in which this hypothesis was enunciated by Prout, the atoms of the different elements were hydrogen atoms; in this precise form the hypothesis is not tenable, but if we substitute for hydrogen some unknown primordial substance X, there is nothing known which is inconsistent with this hypothesis, which is one that has been recently supported by Sir Norman Lockyer for reasons derived from the study of the stellar spectra.

If, in the very intense electric field in the neighbourhood of the cathode, the molecules of the gas are dissociated and are split up, not into the ordinary chemical atoms, but into these primordial atoms, which we shall for brevity call corpuscles; and if these corpuscles are charged with electricity and projected from the cathode by the electric field, they would behave exactly like the cathode rays. They would evidently give a value of m/e which is independent of the nature of the gas and its pressure, for the carriers are the same whatever the gas may be; again, the mean free paths of these corpuscles would depend solely upon the density of the medium through which they pass. For the molecules of the medium are composed of a number of such corpuscles separated by considerable spaces; now the collision between a single corpuscle and the molecule will not be between the corpuscles and the molecule as a whole, but between this corpuscle and the individual corpuscles which form the molecule; thus the number of collisions the particle makes as it moves through a crowd of these molecules will be proportional, not to the number of the molecules in the crowd, but to the number of the individual corpuscles. The mean free path is inversely proportional to the number of collisions in unit time, and so is inversely proportional to the number of corpuscles in unit volume; now as these corpuscles are all of the same mass, the number of corpuscles in unit volume will be proportional to the mass of unit volume, that is the mean free path will be inversely proportional to the density of the gas. We see, too, that so long as the distance between neighbouring corpuscles is large compared with the linear dimensions of a corpuscle the mean free path will be independent of the way they are arranged, provided the number in unit volume remains constant, that is the mean free path will depend only on the density of the medium traversed by the corpuscles, and will be independent of its chemical nature and physical state: this from Lenard's very remarkable measurements of the absorption of the cathode rays by various media, must be a property possessed by the carriers of the charges in the cathode rays.

Thus on this view we have in the cathode rays matter in a new state, a state in which the subdivision of matter is carried very much further than in the ordinary gaseous state: a state in which all matter—that is, matter derived from different sources such as hydrogen, oxygen, &c.—is of one and the same kind; this matter being the substance from which all the chemical elements are built up.

With appliances of ordinary magnitude, the quantity of matter produced by means of the dissociation at the cathode is so small as almost to preclude the possibility of any direct chemical investigation of its properties. Thus the coil I used would, I calculate, if kept going uninterruptedly night and day for a year, produce only about one three-millionth part of a gramme of this substance.

The smallness of the value of m/e is, I think, due to the largeness of e as well as the smallness of m. There seems to me to be some evidence that the charges carried by the corpuscles in the atom are large compared with those carried by the ions of an electrolyte. In the molecule of HCl, for example, I picture the components of the hydrogen atoms as held together by a great number of tubes of electrostatic force; the components of the chlorine atom are similarly held together, while only one stray tube binds the hydrogen atom to the chlorine atom. The reason for attributing this high charge to the constituents of the atom is derived from the values of the specific inductive capacity of gases: we may imagine that the specific inductive capacity of a gas is due to the setting in the electric field of the electric doublet formed by the two oppositely electrified atoms which form the molecule of the gas. The measurements of the specific inductive capacity show, however, that this is very approximately an additive quantity: that is, that we can assign a certain value to each element, and find the specific inductive capacity of HCl by adding the value for hydrogen to the value for chlorine; the value of H_2O by adding twice the value for hydrogen to the value for oxygen, and so on. Now the electrical moment of the doublet formed by a positive charge on one atom of the molecule and a negative charge on the other atom would not be an additive property; if, however, each atom had a definite electrical moment, and this were large compared with the electrical moment of the two atoms in the molecule, then the electrical moment of any compound, and hence its specific inductive capacity, would be an additive property. For the electrical moment of the atom, however, to be large compared with that of the molecule, the charge on the corpuscles would have to be very large compared with those on the ion.

If we regard the chemical atom as an aggregation of a number of primordial atoms, the problem of finding the configurations of stable equilibrium for a number of equal particles acting on each other according to some law of force—whether that of Boscovich, where the force between them is a repulsion when they are separated by less than a certain critical distance, and an attraction when they are separated by a distance, or even the simpler case of a number of mutually repellent particles held together by a central force—is of great interest in connexion with the relation between the properties of an element and its atomic weight. Unfortunately the equations which determine the stability of such a collection of particles increase so rapidly in complexity with the number of particles that a general mathematical investigation is scarcely possible. We can, however, obtain a good deal of insight into the general laws which govern such configurations by the use of models, the simplest of which is the floating magnets of Professor Mayer. In this model the magnets arrange themselves in equilibrium under their mutual repulsions and a central attraction caused by the pole of a large magnet placed above the floating magnets.

A study of the forms taken by these magnets seems to me to be suggestive in relation to the periodic law. Mayer showed that when the number of floating magnets did not exceed 5 they arranged themselves at the corners of a regular polygon—5 at the corners of a pentagon, 4 at the corners of a square, and so on. When the number exceeds 5, however, this law no longer holds: thus 6 magnets do not arrange themselves at the corners of a hexagon, but divide into two systems, consisting of 1 in the middle surrounded by 5 at the corners of a pentagon. For 8 we have two in the inside and 6 outside; this arrangement in two systems, an inner and an outer, lasts up to 18 magnets. After this we have three systems: an inner, a middle, and an outer; for a still larger number of magnets we have four systems, and so on.

Mayer found the arrangement of magnets shown on page 495, where, for example, 1.6.10.12 means an arrangement with one magnet in the middle, then a ring of six, then a ring of ten, and a ring of twelve outside.

Now suppose that a certain property is associated with two magnets forming a group by themselves; we should have this property with 2 magnets, again with 8 and 9, again with 19 and 20, and again with 34, 35, and so on. If we regard the system of magnets as a model of an atom, the number of magnets being proportional to the atomic weight, we

1.	2.	3.	4.	5.
$\left\{\begin{array}{l}1.5\\1.6\\1.7\end{array}\right.$	$\left\{\begin{array}{l}2.6\\2.7\end{array}\right.$	$\left\{\begin{array}{l}3.7\\3.8\end{array}\right.$	$\left\{\begin{array}{l}4.8\\4.9\end{array}\right.$	5.9
$\left\{\begin{array}{l}1.5.9\\1.6.9\\1.6.10\\1.6.11\end{array}\right.$	$\left\{\begin{array}{l}2.7.10\\2.8.10\\2.7.11\end{array}\right.$	$\left\{\begin{array}{l}3.7.10\\3.7.11\\3.8.10\\3.8.11\\3.8.12\\3.8.13\end{array}\right.$	$\left\{\begin{array}{l}4.8.12\\4.8.13\\4.9.12\\4.9.13\end{array}\right.$	$\left\{\begin{array}{l}5.9.12\\5.9.13\end{array}\right.$
$\left\{\begin{array}{l}1.5.\ 9.12\\1.5.\ 9.13\\1.6.\ 9.12\\1.6.10.12\\1.6.10.13\\1.6.11.12\\1.6.11.13\\1.6.11.14\\1.6.11.15\\1.7.12.14\end{array}\right.$	$\left\{\begin{array}{l}2.7.10.15\\2.7.12.14\end{array}\right.$	$\left\{\begin{array}{l}3.7.12.13\\3.7.12.14\\3.7.13.14\\3.7.13.15\end{array}\right.$	$\left\{\begin{array}{l}4.9.13.14\\4.9.13.15\\4.9.14.15\end{array}\right.$	

should have this property occurring in elements of atomic weight 2, (8, 9), 19, 20, (34, 35). Again, any property conferred by three magnets forming a system by themselves would occur with atomic weights 3, 10, and 11; 20, 21, 22, 23, and 24; 35, 36, 37 and 39; in fact, we should have something quite analogous to the periodic law, the first series corresponding to the arrangement of the magnets in a single group, the second series to the arrangement in two groups, the third series in three groups, and so on.

21

THOMAS HUNT MORGAN

Thomas Hunt Morgan was born in Lexington, Kentucky, in 1866. Although his family's roots were in New England, its allegiance was to the South (his uncle had been the Civil War commander of "Morgan's Raiders"), and young Morgan began his academic career in his home town at the State College of Kentucky. Pursuing an interest in nature which he had known from his youth, he went on to graduate studies at Johns Hopkins, where he took the Ph.D. in 1890. His first teaching position was at Bryn Mawr. In 1904, he moved to Columbia as professor of experimental biology, and it was there that he and his numerous students conducted their epoch-making researches in genetics. His last move was in 1928, to the California Institute of Technology, where he accepted the challenge of establishing *ab initio* a division of biological sciences. He was awarded the Nobel Prize in Physiology and Medicine in 1933, and died in Pasadena in 1945.

   With the advent of evolution as a serious scientific theory, the subject of inheritance assumed a significance it had never previously held. As a result, it received considerable attention. Like virtually every other biological problem of the day, however, it was investigated not so much for its own sake, as for the light it might shed on the mechanics of evolution. Thus, concern with inheritance focused on elucidating the means by which characters are transmitted (since such knowledge was expected to indicate the extent to which acquired characteristics can be transmitted), rather than on determining the frequencies with which they are transmitted. When Mendel answered the latter question, he was ignored, because he was the only one asking it. About the time that Morgan began his professional career, the situation was beginning to change. In place of the multitudinous minor variations whereby one species had been supposed to be converted into another, sudden gross variations were increasingly invoked to account for the origins of species. By 1900, Mendel's rules describing the inheritance pattern of unit characters were rediscovered by three independent investigators, and the discipline, which was soon to be christened "genetics," was on its way.

Soon after the publication of De Vries' results in 1900, Morgan visited his botanical garden near Amsterdam. From that time on, he showed an increasing interest in the subject of heredity. The initial manifestation of that interest was his third book, *Evolution and Adaption,* from which most of the following selection is taken. Its title indicates clearly the significance in Morgan's mind of Mendel's laws of segregation and de Vries' theory of mutations. By 1908-1909, Morgan, originally trained as an embryologist, was actively experimenting with mice and rats in an attempt to produce mutations artificially. Shortly thereafter, he turned to the tiny Drosophila—commonly termed the fruit fly and (later) humorously referred to as a creation conceived especially for the benefit of geneticists. Within a year, he published the succinct report which comprises the final portion of this selection—the first in what was to be a long line of spectacular results.

21

Evolution and Adaptation

Discontinuous Variation

Galton, in his book on "Natural Inheritance," points out that "the theory of natural selection might dispense with a restriction for which it is difficult to see either the need or the justification, namely, that the course of evolution always proceeds by steps that are severally minute and that become effective only through accumulation." An apparent reason, it is suggested, for this common belief "is founded on the fact that whenever search is made for intermediate forms between widely divergent varieties, whether they are of plants or of animals, of weapons or utensils, of customs, religion, or language, or of any other product of evolution, a long and orderly series can usually be made out, each member of which differs in an almost imperceptible degree from the adjacent specimens. But it does not at all follow because these intermediate forms have been found to exist, that they were the very stages that were passed through in the course of evolution. Counter evidence exists in abundance, not only of the appearance of considerable sports, but of their remarkable stability in hereditary transmission." Comparing such an apparently continuous series with machines, Galton concludes, "If, however, all the variations of any machine that had ever been invented were selected and arranged in a museum, each would differ so little from its neighbors as to suggest the fallacious inference that the successive inventions of that machine had progressed by means of a very large number of hardly discernible steps."

Bateson, also, in his "Materials for the Study of Variation," speaks of the two possible ways in which variations may arise. He points out that it has been tacitly assumed that the transitions have been continuous, and that this assumption has introduced many gratuitous difficulties. Chief of these is the difficulty that in their initial and imperfect stages many variations would be useless. "Of the objections that have been brought against the Theory of Natural Selection, this is by far the most serious." He continues: "The same objection may be expressed in a form

Published in New York: The Macmillan Company, 1903.

which is more correct and comprehensive. We have seen that the differences between species on the whole are Specific, and are differences of kind forming a discontinuous Series, while the diversities of environment to which they are subject are, on the whole, differences of degree, and form a continuous Series; it is, therefore, hard to see how the environmental differences can thus be made in any sense the directing cause of Specific differences, which by the Theory of Natural Selection they should be. This objection of course includes that of the utility of minimal Variations."

"Now the strength of this objection lies wholly in the supposed continuity of the process of Variation. We see all organized nature arranged in a discontinuous series of groups differing from each other by differences which are Specific; on the other hand, we see the diverse environments to which these forms are subject passing insensibly into each other. We must admit, then, that if the steps by which the diverse forms of life have varied from each other have been insensible—if, in fact, the forms ever made up a continuous series—these forms cannot have been broken into a discontinuous series of groups by a continuous environment, whether acting directly as Lamarck would have, or as selective agent as Darwin would have. This supposition has been generally made and admitted, but in the absence of evidence as to Variation it is nevertheless a gratuitous assumption, and, as a matter of fact, when the evidence as to Variation is studied, it will be found to be in a great measure unfounded."

There is a fair number of cases on record in which discontinuous variations have been seen to take place. Darwin himself has given a number of excellent examples, and Bateson, in the volume referred to above, has brought together a large and valuable collection of facts of this kind.

Some of the most remarkable of these instances have been already referred to and need only be mentioned here. The black-shouldered peacock, the ancon ram, the turnspit dog, the merino sheep, tailless and hornless animals, are all cases in point. In several of these it has been discovered that the young inherit the peculiarities of their parents if the new variations are bred together; and what is more striking, if the new variation is crossed with the parent form, the young are like one or the other parent, and not intermediate in character. This latter point raises a question of fundamental importance in connection with the origin of species.

Darwin states that he knows of *no cases in which, when different species or even strongly marked varieties are crossed, the hybrids are like one form or the other*. They show, he believes, always a blending of the peculiarities of the two parents. He then makes the following significant statement: "All the characters above enumerated which are transmitted in a perfect state to some of the offspring and not to others—such as distinct colors, nakedness of skin, smoothness of leaves, absence of horns or tail, additional toes, pelorism, dwarfed structure, etc., have all been known to appear suddenly in individual animals or plants. From this fact, and from the several slight, aggregated differences which distinguish domestic races and species from each other, not being liable to this peculiar form of transmission, we may conclude that it is in some way connected with the sudden appearance of the characters in question."

Darwin has, incidentally, raised here a question of the most far-reaching import. If it should prove true, as he believes, that inheritance of this kind of discontinuous variation is also discontinuous, and that we do not get the same result when distinct species are intercrossed, or even when well-marked domestic races are interbred, then he has, indeed, placed a great obstacle in the path of those who have tried to show that new species have arisen through discontinuous variation of this sort.

If wild species, when crossed, give almost invariably intermediate forms, then it may appear that we are going against the only evidence that we can hope to obtain if we claim that discontinuous variation, of the kind that sports are made of, has supplied the material for evolution. If, furthermore, when distinct races of domesticated animals are crossed, we do not get discontinuous inheritance, it might, perhaps, with justness be claimed that this instance is paralleled by what takes place when wild species are crossed. And if domesticated forms have been largely the result of the selection of fluctuating variations, as Darwin believes, then a strong case is apparently made out in favor of Darwin's view that continuous variation has given the material for the process of evolution in nature. Whether selection or some other factor has directed the formation of the new species would not, of course, be shown, nor would it make any difference in the present connection.

Before we attempt to reach a conclusion on this point let us analyze the facts somewhat more closely.

In the first place, a number of these cases of discontinuous variation are of the nature of abnormalities. The appearance of extra fingers or toes in man and other mammals is an example of this sort. This abnormality is, if inherited at all, inherited completely; that is, if present the extra digit is perfect, and never appears in an intermediate condition, even when one of the parents was without it. The most obvious interpretation of this fact is that when the material out of which the fingers are to develop is divided up, or separated into its component parts, one more part than usual is laid down. Similarly, when a flower belonging to the triradiate type gives rise to a quadriradiate form—as sometimes occurs—the new variation seems to depend simply on the material being subdivided once more than usual; perhaps because a little more of it is present, or because it has a somewhat different shape. My reasons for making a surmise of this sort are based on certain experimental facts in connection with the regeneration of animals. It has been shown in several cases that it is possible to produce more than the normal number of parts by simply dividing the material so that each part becomes more or less a new whole, and the total number of parts into which the material becomes subdivided is increased. It seems not improbable that phenomena of this sort have occurred in the course of evolution, although it is, of course, possible that those characters that define species do not belong to this class of variation. To take an example. There are nine neck-vertebræ in some birds, but in the swan the number is twenty-five. We cannot suppose that the ancestor of the swan gradually added enough materially to make up one new vertebra and then another, but at least one new whole vertebra was added at a time; and we know several cases in which the number of vertebræ in the neck has suddenly been increased by the addition of one more than normal, and the new vertebra is perfectly formed from the first.

In cases of this sort we can easily understand that the inheritance must be either of one kind or the other, since intermediate conditions are impossible, when it comes to the question of one or not one; but if one individual had one and another six vertebræ, then it would be theoretically possible for the hybrid to have three.

This brings us to a question that should have been spoken of before in regard to the inheritance of discontinuous variation. It sometimes occurs that a variation, which appears in other respects to be discontinuous, is inherited in a blended form. Thus the two kinds of variation may not always be so sharply separated as one might be led to believe. There may be two different kinds of discontinuous variation in respect to inheritance, or there may be variations that are only to a greater or a less extent inherited discontinuously; and it seems not improbable that both kinds occur.

This diversion may not appear to have brought us any nearer to the solution of the difficulty that Darwin's statement has emphasized, except in so far as it may show that the lines are not so sharply drawn as may have seemed to be the case. The solution of the difficulty is, I believe, as follows.

The discontinuity referred to by Darwin relates to cases in which only a single step (or mutation) has been taken, and it is a question of inheritance of one or not one. If, however, six successive steps should be taken in the same direction, then when such a form is crossed with the original form, the hybrid may inherit only three of the steps and stand exactly midway between the parent forms; or it may inherit four, or five, or three, or two steps and stand correspondingly nearer to the one or to the other parent. Thus while it may not be possible to halve a single step (hence one-sided inheritance), yet when more than one step has been taken the inheritance may be divided. There is every evidence that most of the Linnæan (wild) species that Darwin refers to have diverged from the parent form, and from each other, by a number of successive steps; hence on crossing, the hybrid often stands somewhere between the two parent forms. On this basis not only can we meet Darwin's objection, but the point of view gives an interesting insight into the problem of inheritance and the formation of species.

The whole question of inheritance has assumed a new aspect; first on account of the work of De Vries in regard to the appearance of discontinuous variation in plants; and secondly, on account of the remarkable discoveries of Gregor Mendel as to the laws of inheritance of discontinuous variations. Mendel's work, although done in 1865, was long neglected, and its importance has only been appreciated in the last few years. We shall take up Mendel's work first, and then that of De Vries.

Mendel's Law

The importance of Mendel's results and their wide application is apparent from the results in recent years of De Vries, Correns, Tschermak, Bateson, Castle, and others. Mendel carried out his experiments on the pea, *Pisum sativum.* Twenty-two varieties were used, which had been proven by experiment to be pure breeds. When crossed they gave perfectly fertile offspring. Whether they all have the value of varieties of a single species, or are different subspecies, or even independent species, is of little consequence so far as Mendel's experiments are concerned. The flower of the pea is especially suitable for experiments of this kind. It cannot be accidentally fertilized by foreign pollen, because the reproductive organs are inclosed in the keel of the flower, and, as a rule, the anthers burst and cover the stigma of the same flower with its own pollen before the flower opens. In order to cross-fertilize the plants it is necessary to open the young buds before the anthers are mature and carefully remove all the anthers. Foreign pollen may be then, or later, introduced.

The principle involved in Mendel's law may be first stated in a theoretical case, from which a certain complication that appears in the actual results may be removed (Figure 1).

If *A* represent a variety having a certain character, and *B* another variety in which the same character is different, let us say ·in color, and

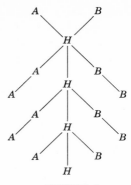

FIGURE 1

if these two individuals, one of each kind, are crossed, the hybrid may be represented by H. If a number of these hybrids are bred together, their descendants will be of three kinds; some will be like the grandparent, A, in regard to the special character that we are following, some will be like the other grandparent, B, and others will be like the hybrid parent, H. Moreover, there will be twice as many with the character H, as with A, or with B.

If now we proceed to let these A's breed together, it will be found that their descendants are all A, forever. If the B's are bred together they produce only B's. But when the H's are bred together they give rise to H's, A's, and B's, as shown in the accompanying diagram. In each generation, the A's will also breed true, the B's true, but the H's will give rise to the three kinds again, and always in the same proportion.

Thus it is seen that the hybrid individuals continue to give off the pure original forms, in regard to the special character under consideration. The numerical relation between the numbers is also a striking fact. Its explanation is, however, quite simple, and will be given later.

In the actual experiment the results appear somewhat more complicated because the hybrid cannot be distinguished from one of the original parents, but the results really conform exactly to the imaginary case given above. The accompanying diagram (Figure 2) will make clearer the account that follows.

The hybrid, A(B), produced by crossing A and B is like A so far as the special character that we will consider is concerned. In reality the character that A stands for is only dominant, that is, it has been inherited discontinuously, while the other character, represented by B, is latent, or recessive as Mendel calls it. Therefore, in the table, it is included in parentheses. If the hybrids, represented by this form A(B), are bred together, there are produced two kinds of individuals, A's and B's, of

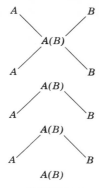

FIGURE 2

which there are three times as many A's as B's. It has been found, however, that some of these A's are pure forms, as indicated by the A on the
left in our table, while the others, as shown by their subsequent history,
are hybrids, $A(B)$. There are also twice as many of these $A(B)$'s as of the
pure A's (or of the B's). Thus the results are really the same as in our
imaginary case, only obscured by the fact that the A's and the $A(B)$'s are
exactly alike to us in respect to the character chosen. We see also why
there appear to be three times as many A's as B's. In reality the results
are 1 A, 2 $A(B)$, 1 B.

In subsequent generations the results are the same as in this one, the
A's giving rise only to A, the B's to B, and the $A(B)$'s continuing to split
up into the three forms, as shown in our diagram. Mendel found the
same law to hold for all the characters he examined, including such
different ones as the form of the seed, color of seed-albumen, coloring
of seed-coat, form of the ripe pods, position of flowers, and length of stem.

Mendel also carried out a series of experiments in which several differentiating characters are associated. In the first experiment the parental
plants (varieties) differed in the form of the seed and in the color of
the albumen. The two characters of the seed plant are designated by the
capital letters A and B; and of the pollen plant by small a and b. The
hybrids will be, of course, combinations of these, although only certain
characters may dominate. Thus in the experiments, the parents are AB
(seed plant) and ab (pollen plant), with the following seed characters:

Seed parent   { A form round   Pollen parent   { a form angular
    AB { B albumen yellow ab { b albumen green

When these two forms were crossed the seeds appeared round and
yellow like those of the parent, AB, *i.e.* these two characters dominated
in the hybrid.

The seeds were sown, and in turn yielded plants which when self-fertilized gave four kinds of seeds (which frequently all appeared in the same pod). Thus 556 seeds were produced by 15 plants, having the following characters:

> AB 315 round and yellow
> Ab 101 angular and yellow
> aB 108 round and green
> ab 32 angular and green

These figures stand almost in the relation of 9:3:3:1.
These seeds were sown again in the following year and gave:

From the round yellow seeds:

> AB 38 round and yellow seeds
> ABb 65 round yellow and green seeds
> AaB 60 round yellow and angular yellow seeds
> AaBb 138 round yellow and green, angular yellow
> and green seeds

From the angular yellow seeds:

> aB 28 angular yellow seeds
> aBb 68 angular yellow and green seeds

From the round green seeds:

> Ab 35 round green seeds
> Aab 67 round angular seeds

From the angular green seeds:
> ab 30 angular green seeds

Thus there were 9 different kinds of seeds produced. There had been separated out at this time 38 individuals like the parent seed plant, AB, and 30 like the parent pollen plant, ab. Since these had come from similar seeds of the preceding generation they may be looked upon as pure at this time. The forms Ab and aB are also constant forms which do not subsequently vary. The remainder are still mixed or hybrid in character. By successive self-fertilizations it is possible gradually to separate out from these the pure types of which they are compounded.

Without going into further detail it may be stated that the offspring of the parent hybrids, having two pairs of differentiating characters, are represented by the series:

> AB Ab aB ab 2 ABb 2 aBb 2 Aab 2 ABa 2 AaBb

This series is really a combination of the two series:

$$A + 2\,Aa + a$$
$$B + 2\,Bb + b$$

Mendel even went farther, and used two parent varieties having three differentiating characters, as follows:

	ABC seed parent		abc pollen plant
⎰	A form round	⎰	a form angular
⎨	B albumen yellow	⎨	b albumen green
⎱	C seed-coat grey brown	⎱	c seed-coat white

The results, as may be imagined, were quite complex, but can be expressed by combining these series:

$$A + 2\,Aa + a$$
$$B + 2\,Bb + b$$
$$C + 2\,Cc + c$$

In regard to the two latter experiments, in which two and three characters respectively were used, it is interesting to point out that the form of the hybrid more nearly approaches "to that one of the parental plants which possesses the greatest number of dominant characters." If, for instance, the seed plant has short stem, terminal white flowers, and simply inflated pods; the pollen plant, on the other hand, a long stem, violet-red flowers distributed along the stem, and constricted pods—then the hybrid resembles the seed parent only in the form of the pod; in its other characters it agrees with the pollen plant. From this we may conclude that, if two varieties differing in a large number of characters are crossed, the hybrid might get some of its dominant characters from one parent, and other dominant characters from the other parent, so that, unless the individual characters themselves were studied, it might appear that the hybrids are intermediate between the two parents, while in reality they are only combinations of the dominant characters of the two forms. But even this is not the whole question.

Mendel points out that, from knowing the characters of the two parent forms (or varieties), one could not prophesy what the hybrid would be like without making the actual trial. Which of the characters of the two parent forms will be the dominant ones, and which recessive, can only be determined by experiment. Moreover, the hybrid characters are something peculiar to the hybrid itself, and to itself alone, and not simply the combination of the characters of the two forms. Thus in one case a hybrid from a tall and a short variety of pea was even taller than the taller parent variety. Bateson lays much emphasis on this point, believing it to be an important consideration in all questions relating to hybridization and inheritance.

The theoretical interpretation that Mendel has put upon his results is so extremely simple that there can be little doubt that he has hit on the real explanation. The results can be accounted for if we suppose that the hybrid produces egg-cells and pollen-cells, each of which is the bearer of only one of the alternative characters, dominant or recessive as the case may be. If this is the case, and if on an average there are the same number of egg-cells and pollen-cells, having one or the other of these kinds of characters, then on a random assortment meeting of egg-cells and pollen-cells, Mendel's law would follow. For, 25 per cent of dominant pollen grains would meet with 25 per cent dominant egg-cells; 25 per cent recessive pollen grains would meet with 25 per cent recessive egg-cells; while the remaining 50 per cent of each kind would meet each other. Or, as Mendel showed by the following scheme (Figure 3) :

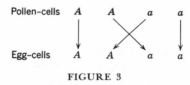

FIGURE 3

Or more simply by this scheme (Figure 4) :

FIGURE 4

Mendel's results have received confirmation by a number of more recent workers, and while in some cases the results appear to be complicated by other factors, yet there can remain little doubt that Mendel has discovered one of the fundamental laws of heredity.

It has been found that there are some cases in which the sort of inheritance postulated by Mendel's law does not seem to hold, and, in fact, Mendel himself spoke of such cases. He found that some kinds of hybrids do not break up in later generations into the parent forms. He also points out that in cases of discontinuity the variations in each character must be separately regarded. In most experiments in crossing, forms are chosen which differ from each other in a multitude of characters, some of which are continuous and others discontinuous, some capable of blending with their contraries while others are not. The observer in attempting to discover any regularity is confused by the complications thus introduced. Mendel's law could only appear in such cases by the use of an overwhelming number of examples which are beyond the possibilities of experiment.

Let us now examine the bearing of these discoveries on the questions of variation which were raised in the preceding pages. It should be pointed out, however, that it would be premature to do more than indicate, in the most general way, the application of these conclusions. The chief value of Mendel's results lies in their relation to the theory of inheritance rather than to that of evolution.

In the first place, Mendel's results indicate that we cannot make any such sharp distinction as Darwin does between the results of inheritance of discontinuous and of continuous variations. As Mendel's results show, it is the separate characters that must be considered in each case, and not simply the sum total of characters.

The more general objection that Darwin has made may appear to hold, nevertheless. He thinks that the evolution of animals and plants cannot rest primarily on the appearance of discontinuous variations, because they occur rarely and would be swamped by intercrossing. If Mendel's law applies to such cases, that is, if a cross were made between such a sport and the original form, the hybrid in this case, if self-fertilized, would begin to split up into the two original forms. But, on the other hand, it could very rarely happen that the hybrid did fertilize its own eggs, and, unless this occurred, the hybrid, by crossing with the parent forms in each generation, would soon lose all its characters inherited from its "sport" ancestor. Unless, therefore, other individuals gave rise to sports at the same time, there would be little chance of producing new species in this way. We see then that discontinuity in itself, unless it involved infertility with the parent species, of which there is no evidence, cannot be made the basis for a theory of evolution, any more than can individual differences, for the swamping effect of inter-crossing would in both cases soon obliterate the new form. If, however, a species begins to give rise to a large number of individuals of the same kind through a process of discontinuous variation, then it may happen that a new form may establish itself, either because it is adapted to live under conditions somewhat different from the parent form, so that the dangers of intercrossing are lessened, or because the new form may absorb the old one. It is also clear, from what has gone before, that the new form can only cease to be fertile with the parent form, or with its sister forms, after it has undergone such a number of changes that it is no longer able to combine the differences in a new individual. This result will depend both on the kinds of the new characters, as well as the amounts of their difference. This brings us to a consideration of the results of De Vries, who has studied the first steps in the formation of new species in the "mutations" of the evening primrose.

The Mutation Theory of De Vries

De Vries defines the mutation theory as the conception that "the characters of the organism are made up of elements ('Einheiten') that are sharply separated from each other. These elements can be combined in groups, and in related species the same combinations of elements recur. Transitional forms like those that are so common in the external features of animals and plants do not exist between the elements themselves, any more than they do between the elements of the chemist."

This principle leads, De Vries says, in the domain of the descent theory to the conception that species have arisen from each other, not continuously, but by steps. Each new step results from a new combination as compared with the old one, and the new forms are thereby completely and sharply separated from the species from which they have come. The new species is all at once there; it has arisen from the parent form without visible preparation and without transitional steps.

The mutation theory stands in sharp contrast to the selection theory. The latter uses as its starting-point the common form of variability known as individual or fluctuating variation; but according to the mutation theory there are two kinds of variation that are entirely different from each other. "The fluctuating variation can, as I hope to show, not overstep the bounds of the species, even after the most prolonged selection—much less can this kind of variation lead to the production of new, constant characters." Each peculiarity of the organism has arisen from a preceding one, not through the common form of variation, but through a sudden change that may be quite small but is perfectly definite. This kind of variability that produces new species, De Vries calls mutability; the change itself he calls a mutation. The best-known examples of mutations are those which Darwin called "single variations" or "sports."

De Vries recognizes the following kinds of variation.

First, the polymorphic forms of the systematists. The ordinary groups which, following Linnæus, we call species, are according to De Vries collective groups, which are the outcome of mutations. Many such Linnæan species include small series of related forms, and sometimes even large numbers of such forms. These are as distinctly and completely separated from each other as are the best species. Generally these small groups are called varieties, or subspecies—varieties when they are separated by a single striking character, subspecies when they differ in the totality of their characters, in the so-called habitus.

These groups have already been recognized by some investigators as elementary species, and have been given corresponding binary names. Thus there are recognized two hundred elementary species of the form formerly called *Draba verna*.

When brought under cultivation these elementary species are constant in character and transmit their peculiarities truly. They are not local races in the sense that they are the outcome in each generation of special external conditions. Many other Linnæan species are in this respect like *Draba verna*, and most varieties, De Vries thinks, are really elementary species.

Second, the polymorphism due to intercrossing is the outcome of different combinations of hereditary qualities. There are here, De Vries says, two important classes of facts to be kept strictly apart—scientific experiment, and the results of the gardener and of the cultivator. The experimenter chooses for crossing, species as little variable as possible; the gardener and cultivator on the other hand prefer to cross forms of which one at least is variable, because the variations may be transmitted to the hybrid, and in this way a new form be produced.

New elementary characters arise in experiments in crossing only through variability, not through crossing itself.

Third, variability in the ordinary sense, that is, individual variability, includes those differences between the individual organs that follow Quetelet's theory of chance. This kind of variability is characterized by its presence at all times, in all groups of individuals.

De Vries recalls Galton's apt comparison between variability and a polyhedron which can roll from one face to another. When it comes to rest on any particular face, it is in stable equilibrium. Small vibrations or disturbances may make it oscillate, but it returns always to the same face. These oscillations are like the fluctuating variations. A greater disturbance may cause the polyhedron to roll over on to a new face, where it comes to rest again, only showing the ever present fluctuations around its new centre. The new position corresponds to a mutation. It may appear from our familiarity with the great changes that we associate with the idea of discontinuous variability, that a mutation must also involve a considerable change. Such, however, De Vries says, is not the case. In fact, numerous mutations are smaller than the extremes of fluctuating variation. For example, the different elementary species of *Draba verna* are less different from each other than the forms of leaves on a tree. The essential differences between the two kinds of variation is that the mutation is constant, while the continuous variation fluctuates back and forth.

The following example is given by De Vries to illustrate the general point of view in regard to varieties and species. The species *Oxalis corniculata* is a "collective" species that lives in New Zealand. It has been described as having seven well-characterized varieties which do not live together or have intermediate forms. If we knew only this group, there would be no question that there are seven good species. But in other countries intermediate forms exist, which exactly bridge over the differences between the seven New Zealand forms. For this reason all the forms have been united in a single species.

Another example is that of the fern, *Lomaria procera*, from New Zealand, Australia, South Africa, and South America. If the forms from only one country be considered, they appear to be different species; but if all the forms from the different parts of the world be taken into account, they constitute a connected group, and are united into one large species.

It will be seen, therefore, that the limits of a collective species are determined solely by the deficiencies in the genealogical tree of the elementary species. If all the elementary species in one country were destroyed, then the forms living in other countries that had been previously held together because of those which have now been destroyed, would, after the destruction, become true species. In other words: "The Linnæan species are formed by the disappearance of other elementary species, which at first connected all forms. This mode of origin is a purely historical process, and can never become the subject of experimental investigation." Spencer's famous expression, the "survival of the fittest," is incomplete, and should read the "survival of the fittest species." It is, therefore, not the study of Linnæan species that has a physiological interest, but it is the study of the elementary species of which the Linnæan species are made up, that furnishes the all-important problem for experimental study.

De Vries gives a critical analysis of a number of cases in which new races have been formed under domestication. He shows very convincingly that, whenever the result has been the outcome of the selection of fluctuating variations, the product that is formed can only be kept to its highest point of development by the most rigid and ever watchful care. If selection ceases for only a few generations, the new form sinks back at once to its original level. Many of our cultivated plants have really arisen, not by selection of this sort, but by mutations; and there are a number of recorded cases where the first and sudden appearance of a new form has been observed. In such cases as these there is no need for selection, for if left to themselves there is no return to the original form. If, however, after a new mutation has appeared in this way, we subject its fluctuating variations to selection, we can keep the new form up to its most extreme limit, but can do nothing more.

Another means, frequently employed, by which new varieties have been formed is by bringing together different elementary species under cultivation. For instance, there are a large number of wild elementary species of apples, and De Vries believes that our different races of apples owe their origin in part to these different wild forms. Crossing, cultivation, and selection have done the rest.

De Vries points out some of the inconsistencies of those who have attempted to discriminate between varieties and species. The only rule that can be adhered to is that a variety differs from a species to which it belongs in only one or in a few characters. Most so-called varieties in nature are really elementary species, which differ from their nearest relatives, not in one character only, but in nearly all their characters. There is no ground, De Vries states, for believing them to be varieties. If it is found inconvenient to rank them under the names of the old Linnæan species, it will be better, perhaps, to treat them as subspecies, but De Vries prefers to call them elementary species.

In regard to the distribution of species in nature, it may be generally stated that the larger the geographical domain so much the larger is the number of elementary species. They are found to be heaped up in the centre of their area of distribution, but are more scattered at the periphery.

In any one locality each Linnæan species has as a rule only one or a few elementary species. The larger the area the more numerous the forms. From France alone Jordan had brought together in his garden 50 elementary species of *Draba verna*. From England, Italy, and Austria there could be added 150 more. This polymorphism is, De Vries thinks, a general phenomenon, although the number of forms is seldom so great as in this case.

Amongst animals this great variety of forms is not often met with, yet amongst the mammalia and birds of North America there are many cases of local forms or races, some of which at least are probably mutations. This can only be proven, however, by actually transferring the forms to new localities in order to find out if they retain their original characters, or become changed into another form. It seems not improbable that many of the forms are not the outcome of the external conditions under which the animal now lives, but would perpetuate themselves in a new environment.

From the evidence that his results have given, De Vries believes it is probable that mutation has occurred in all directions. In the same way that Darwin supposed that individual or fluctuating variations are scattering, so also De Vries believes that the new forms that arise through mutation are scattering. On this point it seems to me that De Vries may be too much prejudiced by his results with the evening primrose. If, as he supposes, many forms, generally ranked as varieties, are really elementary species, it seems more probable that the mutation of a form may often be limited to the production of one or of only a very few new forms. The single variations, or sports, point even more strongly in favor of this interpretation. Moreover, the general problem of evolution from a purely theoretical point of view is very much simplified, if we assume that the kinds of mutating forms may often be very limited, and that mutations may often continue to occur in a direct line. On this last point, De Vries argues that the evidence from paleontology cannot be trusted, for all that we can conclude from fossil remains is that certain mutations have dominated, and have been sufficiently abundant to leave a record. In other words, the conditions may have been such that only certain forms could find a foothold.

De Vries asks whether there are for each species periods of mutation when many and great changes take place, and periods when relatively little change occurs. The evidence upon which to form an opinion is scanty, but De Vries is inclined to think that such periods do occur. It is at least certain from our experience that there are long periods when we do not see new forms arising, while at other times, although we know very few of them, epidemics of change may take place. The mutative period which De Vries found in the evening primrose is the best-known example of such a period of active mutation. Equally important for the descent theory is the idea that the same mutation may appear time after time. There is good evidence to show that this really occurs, and in consequence the chances for the perpetuation of such a form are greatly increased. Delbœuf, who advocated this idea of the repeated reappearance of a new form, has also attempted to show that if this occurs the new form may become established without selection of any kind taking place—the time required depending upon the frequency with which the new form appears. This law of Delbœuf, De Vries believes, is correct from the point of view of the mutation theory. It explains, in a very simple way, the existence of numerous species-characters that are entirely useless, such, for instance, as exist between the different elementary species of *Draba verna*. "According to the selection theory only useful characters can survive; according to the mutation theory, useless characters also may survive, and even those that may be hurtful to a small degree."

*   *   *   *

Conclusions

From the evidence given in the preceding pages it appears that the line between fluctuating variations and mutations may be sharply drawn. If we assume that mutations have furnished the material for the process of evolution, the whole problem appears in a different light from that in which it was placed by Darwin when he assumed that the fluctuating variations are the kind which give the material for evolution.

From the point of view of the mutation theory, species are no longer looked upon as having been slowly built up through the selection of individual variations, but the elementary species, at least, appear at a single advance, and fully formed. This need not necessarily mean that great changes have suddenly taken place, and in this respect the mutation theory is in accord with Darwin's view that *extreme* forms that rarely appear, "sports," have not furnished the material for the process of evolution.

As De Vries has pointed out, each mutation may be different from the parent form in only a slight degree for each point, although all the points may be different. The most unique feature of these mutations is the constancy with which the new form is inherited. It is this fact, not previously fully appreciated, that De Vries' work has brought prominently into the foreground. There is another point of great interest in this connection. Many of the groups that Darwin recognized as varieties correspond to the elementary species of De Vries. These varieties, Darwin thought, are the first stages in the formations of species, and, in fact, cannot be separated from species in most cases. The main difference between the selection theory and the mutation theory is that the one supposes these varieties to arise through selection of individual variations, the other supposes that they have arisen spontaneously and at once from the original form. The development of these varieties into new species is again supposed, on the Darwinian theory, to be the result of further selection, on the mutation theory, the result of the appearance of new mutations.

In consequence of this difference in the two theories, it will not be difficult to show that the mutation theory escapes some of the gravest difficulties that the Darwinian theory has encountered. Some of the advantages of the mutation theory may be briefly mentioned here.

1. Since the mutations appear fully formed from the beginning, there is no difficulty in accounting for the incipient stages in the development of an organ, and since the organ may persist, even when it has no value to the race, it may become further developed by later mutations and may come to have finally an important relation to the life of the individual.

2. The new mutations may appear in large numbers, and of the different kinds those will persist that can get a foot-hold. On account of the large number of times that the same mutations appear, the danger of becoming swamped through crossing with the original form will be lessened in proportion to the number of new individuals that arise.

3. If the time of reaching maturity in the new form is different from

that in the parent forms, then the new species will be kept from crossing with the parent form, and since this new character will be present from the beginning, the new form will have much better chances of surviving than if a difference in time of reaching maturity had to be gradually acquired.

4. The new species that appear may be in some cases already adapted to live in a different environment from that occupied by the parent form; and if so, it will be isolated from the beginning, which will be an advantage in avoiding the bad effects of intercrossing.

5. It is well known that the differences between related species consists largely in differences of unimportant organs, and this is in harmony with the mutation theory, but one of the real difficulties of the selection theory.

6. Useless or even slightly injurious characters may appear as mutations, and if they do not seriously affect the perpetuation of the race, they may persist.

Sex Limited Inheritance in Drosophila

In a pedigree culture of *Drosophila* which had been running for nearly a year through a considerable number of generations, a male appeared with white eyes. The normal flies have brilliant red eyes.

The white-eyed male, bred to his red-eyed sisters, produced 1,237 red-eyed offspring, (F_1), and 3 white-eyed males. The occurrence of these three white-eyed males (F_1) (due evidently to further sporting) will, in the present communication, be ignored.

The F_1 hybrids, inbred, produced:

> 2,459 red-eyed females,
> 1,011 red-eyed males,
> 782 white-eyed males.

No white-eyed females appeared. The new character showed itself therefore to be sex limited in the sense that it was transmitted only to the grandsons. But that the character is not incompatible with femaleness is shown by the following experiment.

The white-eyed male (mutant) was later crossed with some of his daughters (F_1), and produced:

> 129 red-eyed females,
> 132 red-eyed males,
> 88 white-eyed females,
> 86 white-eyed males.

The results show that the new character, white eyes, can be carried over to the females by a suitable cross, and is in consequence in this sense not limited to one sex. It will be noted that the four classes of individuals occur in approximately equal numbers (25 per cent.).

An Hypothesis to Account for the Results. The results just described can be accounted for by the following hypothesis. Assume that all of the spermatozoa of the white-eyed male carry the "factor" for white eyes "W"; that half of the spermatozoa carry a sex factor "X," the other half lack it; *i.e.*, the male is heterozygous for sex. Thus the symbol for the male is "WWX," and for his two kinds of spermatozoa WX—W.

Published in *Science,* Volume 32, 1910. Morgan's term "sex limited" has since been changed to sex *linked.*

Assume that all of the eggs of the red-eyed female carry the red-eyed "factor" R; and that all of the eggs (after reduction) carry one X each; the symbol for the red-eyed female will be therefore RRXX and that for her eggs will be RX—RX.

When the white-eyed male (sport) is crossed with his red-eyed sisters, the following combinations result:

$$WX - W \text{ (male)}$$
$$RX - RX \text{ (female)}$$

RWXX (50%)	— RWX (50%)
Red female	Red male

When these F_1 individuals are mated, the following table shows the expected combinations that result:

$$RX - WX \ (F_1 \text{ female})$$
$$RX - W \ (F_1 \text{ male})$$

RRXX	RWXX	— RWX	WWX
(25%)	(25%)	(25%)	(25%)
Red female	Red female	Red male	White male

It will be seen from the last formulæ that the outcome is Mendelian in the sense that there are three reds to one white. But it is also apparent that all of the whites are confined to the male sex.

It will also be noted that there are two classes of red females—one pure RRXX and one hybrid RWXX—but only one class of red males (RWX). This point will be taken up later. In order to obtain these results it is necessary to assume, as in the last scheme, that, when the two classes of the spermatozoa are formed in the F_1 red male (RWX), R and X go together—otherwise the results will not follow (with the symbolism here used). This all-important point can not be fully discussed in this communication.

The hypothesis just utilized to explain these results first obtained can be tested in several ways.

Verification of Hypothesis

First Verification. If the symbol for the white male is WWX, and for the white female WWXX, the germ cells will be WX—W (male) and WX—WX (female), respectively. Mated, these individuals should give:

$$WX - W \text{ (male)}$$
$$WX - WX \text{ (female)}$$

WWXX (50%)	— WWX (50%)
White female	White male

All of the offspring should be white, and male and female in equal numbers; this in fact is the case.

Second Verification. As stated, there should be two classes of females in the F_2 generation, namely, RRXX and RWXX. This can be tested by pairing individual females with white males. In the one instance (RRXX) all the offspring should be red—

$$\begin{array}{c} RX - RX \text{ (female)} \\ \underline{WX - W \text{ (male)}} \\ RWXX - RWX \end{array}$$

and in the other instance (RWXX) there should be four classes of individuals in equal numbers, thus:

$$\begin{array}{c} RX - WX \text{ (female)} \\ \underline{WX - W \text{ (male)}} \\ RWXX—WWXX - RWX—WWX \end{array}$$

Tests of the F_2 red females show in fact that these two classes exist.

Third Verification. The red F_1 females should all be RWXX, and should give with any white male the four combinations last described. Such in fact is found to be the case.

Fourth Verification. The red F_1 males (RWX) should also be heterozygous. Crossed with white females (WWXX) all the female offspring should be red-eyed, and all the male offspring white-eyed, thus:

$$\begin{array}{c} RX - W \text{ (red male)} \\ \underline{WX - WX \text{ (white female)}} \\ RWXX - WWX \end{array}$$

Here again the anticipation was verified, for all of the females were red-eyed and all of the males were white-eyed.

Crossing the New Type With Wild
Males and Females

A most surprising fact appeared when a white-eyed female was paired to a wild, red-eyed male, *i.e.*, to an individual of an unrelated stock. The anticipation was that wild males and females alike carry the factor for red eyes, but the experiments showed that all wild males are heterozygous for red eyes, and that all the wild females are homozygous. Thus when the white-eyed female is crossed with a wild red-eyed male, all of the female offspring are red-eyed, and all of the male offspring white-eyed. The results can be accounted for on the assumption that the wild male is RWX. Thus:

$$\frac{\text{RX} - \text{W (red male)}}{\text{WX} - \text{WX (white female)}}$$
$$\text{RWXX (50\%)} - \text{WWX (50\%)}$$

The converse cross between a white-eyed male RWX and a wild, red-eyed female shows that the wild female is homozygous both for X and for red eyes. Thus:

$$\frac{\text{WX} - \text{W (white male)}}{\text{RX} - \text{RX (red female)}}$$
$$\text{RWXX (50\%)} - \text{RWX (50\%)}$$

The results give, in fact, only red males and females in equal numbers.

General Conclusions

The most important consideration from these results is that in every point they furnish the converse evidence from that given by Abraxas as worked out by Punnett and Raynor. The two cases supplement each other in every way, and it is significant to note in this connection that in nature only females of the sport *Abraxas lacticolor* occur, while in *Drosophila* I have obtained only the male sport. Significant, too, is the fact that analysis of the result shows that the wild female *Abraxas grossulariata* is heterozygous for color and sex, while in *Drosophila* it is the male that is heterozygous for these two characters.

Since the wild males (RWX) are heterozygous for red eyes, and the female (RXRX) homozygous, it seems probable that the sport arose from a change in a single egg of such a sort that instead of being RX (after reduction) the red factor dropped out, so that RX became WX or simply OX. If this view is correct it follows that the mutation took place in the egg of a female from which a male was produced by combination with the sperm carrying no X, no R (or W in our formulæ). In other words, if the formula for the eggs of the normal female is RX—RX, then the formula for the particular egg that sported will be WX; *i. e.*, one R dropped out of the egg leaving it WX (or no R and one X), which may be written OX. This egg we assume was fertilized by a male-producing sperm. The formula for the two classes of spermatozoa is RX—O. The latter, O, is the male-producing sperm, which combining with the egg OX (see above) gives OOX (or WWX), which is the formula for the white-eyed male mutant.

The transfer of the new character (white eyes) to the female (by crossing a white-eyed male, OOX to a heterozygous female (F_1)) can therefore be expressed as follows:

OX — O (white male)

RX — OX (F₁ female)

RXOX—RXO – OOXX—OOX

| Red | Red | White | White |
| female | male | female | male |

It now becomes evident why we found it necessary to assume a coupling of R and X in one of the spermatozoa of the red-eyed F₁ hybrid (RXO). The fact is that this R and X are combined, and have never existed apart.

It has been assumed that the white-eyed mutant arose by a male-producing sperm (O) fertilizing an egg (OX) that had mutated. It may be asked what would have been the result if a female-producing sperm (RX) had fertilized this egg (OX)? Evidently a heterozygous female RXOX would arise, which, fertilized later by any normal male (RX—O) would produce in the next generation pure red females RRXX, red heterozygous females RXOX, red males RXO, and white males OOX (25 per cent). As yet I have found no evidence that white-eyed sports occur in such numbers. Selective fertilization may be involved in the answer to this question.

22

IRVING LANGMUIR

Irving Langmuir was born in Brooklyn in 1881 to a family whose circumstances and outlook provided him with exceptional schooling opportunities for an American of that era. Beginning with preparatory studies in Paris and Philadelphia, he took a degree in metallurgy at Columbia, then proceeding to Göttingen for the Ph.D. in chemistry in 1906. After a brief stint at teaching, he accepted a position at the General Electric Company Research Laboratory (Schenectady, N.Y.), where he remained for the rest of his professional life. With a unique access to industry, Langmuir worked not only on the usual problems of purely theoretical interest, but also on those having immediate technological applications. The result was numerous contributions in the pure and applied realms of both physics and chemistry, among which those to atomic theory and the development of the modern light bulb (1912) are the most notable examples. His achievements were recognized by the award of the Nobel Prize for chemistry in 1932. He died in 1957.

With the discovery of the electron at the turn of the century, physicists embarked on the task of determining the structure of the atom. Most of their progress in the undertaking developed from study of contemporaneously discovered phenomena: X-rays and radioactivity. Radioactivity yielded to investigation first, revealing a so-called α-component which was a positively (and doubly) charged particle identifiable with the element helium, whose terrestrial existence had itself been recognized for less than a decade. Rutherford's experiments with the passage of these α-particles through metallic foils produced the surprising result that some of them "bounced." Analysis of the deflections indicated that the mass of the atom was concentrated in a very small nucleus containing positive unit charges in numbers corresponding to about half the atomic weight of the element. Naturally, negative unit charges (i.e., electrons) had to be assumed to exist in equal numbers at distances relatively remote from the nucleus. Considerations of stability dictated that they be in motion, and when the electrodynamic consequences of that motion were resolved by Bohr in 1913, the well-known planetary model of the atom was established. Confirmation of Rutherford's generalization regarding the charge on atomic nuclei appeared in the same year. The diffraction of X-rays on crystals exposed them as waves of extremely high frequencies which were peculiar to the elements from which they were generated. The frequencies displayed a remarkable regularity, ordering the chemical elements in almost perfect accord with the periodic table and providing a rationale for the order in terms of increasing magnitudes of atomic charge.

That the physicists had uncovered a tool of great practical importance to chemistry was obvious: the new physical basis of the periodical table removed anomalies in the order of certain recognized elements and provided a means of arbitrating claims to the discovery of new ones. But might the new development also have far-reaching *theoretical* implications? Could this fresh evidence for the century-old conviction that chemical forces were ultimately electrical be utilized to explain chemical behavior at a level never previously attained?

22

The Arrangement of Electrons
in Atoms and Molecules

The problem of the structure of atoms has been attacked mainly by physicists who have given little consideration to the chemical properties which must ultimately be explained by a theory of atomic structure. The vast store of knowledge of chemical properties and relationships, such as is summarized by the Periodic Table, should serve as a better foundation for a theory of atomic structure than the relatively meager experimental data along purely physical lines.

Kossel and Lewis have had marked success in attacking the problem in this way. The present paper aims to develop and somewhat modify these theories. Lewis, rejecting the physical data as being insufficient or inconclusive, reasons from chemical facts that the electrons in atoms are normally stationary in position. These electrons arrange themselves in a series of concentric shells, the first shell containing two electrons, while all other shells tend to hold eight. The outermost shell however may hold 2, 4, or 6, instead of 8. The 8 electrons in a shell are supposed to be placed symmetrically at the corners of a cube or in pairs at the corners of a regular tetrahedron. When atoms combine they usually hold some of their outer electrons in common, two electrons being thus held for each chemical bond. These electrons may form parts of both atomic shells of 8 electrons. By means of these postulates Lewis is able to give an extraordinarily satisfactory explanation of the periodic arrangement of the elements and to explain in detail most of their chemical properties. He confines his attention, however, exclusively to the inert gases, the alkali and the alkaline earth metals, the halogens, boron, aluminium, scandium, carbon, silicon, nitrogen, phosphorus, arsenic, antimony, bismuth, oxygen, sulfur, selenium, and tellurium, a total of 35 out of the 88 known elements. The theory in its present form does not apply at all satisfactorily to any of the other elements.

Reprinted from the *Journal of the American Chemical Society*, Volume 41, June 1919, pp. 868-892 and 931-932. Copyright 1919 by the American Chemical Society. Reprinted by permission of the copyright owner.

Kossel's theory has many points of similarity. He conceives of the electrons as located in a plane in concentric rings, rotating in orbits about the nucleus. Certain arrangements, corresponding to those of the inert gases, are supposed to be of unusual stability and all the other atoms, in forming compounds tend to give up or take up electrons so that their electrons may become arranged like those of the inert gases. Kossel considers only the elements up to cerium, a total of 57. His theory does not satisfactorily account for the properties of the elements from vanadium to zinc or from columbium to silver and is only partially satisfactory for any of the elements above vanadium. In other words, its main success is limited to the first 23 elements. The theory does not lend itself nearly as well as that of Lewis to the detailed explanation of the properties of elements and their compounds. A rather thorough review and discussion of these and other recent theories of atomic structure has been published by S. Dushman.

There is much chemical evidence, especially in the field of stereochemistry, that the primary valence forces between atoms act in directions nearly fixed with respect to each other. This can only be satisfactorily accounted for by electrons arranged in three dimensions.

Kossel attempts to explain the tetrahedral arrangement of the carbon valences by arguing that 4 spheres drawn in by strong forces towards a central atom must arrange themselves as a tetrahedron and that if the forces are great enough they will not be able to shift their positions. It is evident that even this structure would not have the requisite symmetry for the carbon atom, when the plane of the electron orbit is taken into account. But there is, moreover, conclusive evidence, even when carbon atoms are surrounded by less than 4 other atoms, that the forces act in definite directions. For example, if wood is carbonized under certain conditions a charcoal is obtained having about the same volume as the wood. This is notably true when such a substance as finely divided tungsten trioxide is reduced in very dry hydrogen. The volumes occupied are in some cases 20 or 25 times as great as that of the corresponding solid in crystalline form. The whole behavior of such bodies, especially in regard to their sintering at higher temperatures, indicates that the atoms are arranged in branching chains in which most atoms are surrounded by only two or three others. Since the bodies are definitely solid it must follow that the atoms are not able to shift their relative positions except when acted on by strong external forces. Such structures are inconceivable if atoms contain only electrons revolving in orbits about the nuclei.

Further evidence for the stationary electrons has been obtained by Hull who finds that the intensities of the lines in the X-ray spectra of crystals are best accounted for on the theory that the electrons occupy definite positions in the crystal lattice.

In attempting to determine the arrangement of electrons in atoms we must be guided by the numbers of electrons which make up the atoms of the inert gases; in other words by the atomic numbers of these elements, namely, helium 2, neon 10, argon 18, krypton 36, xenon 54, and niton 86.

Rydberg has pointed out that these numbers are obtained from the series

$$N = 2\,(1+2^2+2^2+3^2+3^2+4^2+)\,.$$

The factor two suggests a fundamental two-fold symmetry for all stable atoms. By a consideration of this equation and principles of symmetry and by constant checking against the Periodic Table and the specific properties of elements I have been led to the postulates given below. Some of these may seem in themselves to be very improbable and will undoubtedly need to be modified as more facts are acquired. But it is felt that all contain a fundamental basis of truth and that, although future modifications may make them take rather different forms, their application in predicting properties of elements will not be greatly altered.

The first postulate is concerned particularly with the structure of the stable atoms of the inert gases.

Postulate 1. The electrons in the atoms of the inert gases are arranged about the nucleus in pairs symmetrically placed with respect to a plane passing through the nucleus which we may call the equatorial plane. The atoms are symmetrical with respect to a polar axis perpendicular to the plane and passing through the nucleus. They have also 4 secondary planes of symmetry passing through the polar axis and making 45° angles with each other. The symmetry thus corresponds to that of a tetragonal crystal. Since the electrons must occur in pairs symmetrical to the equatorial plane there are no electrons in this plane.

Postulate 2. The electrons in the atoms are distributed through a series of concentric spherical shells. All the shells in a given atom are of equal thickness. If the mean of the inner and outer radii be considered to be the effective radius of the shell then the radii of the different shells stand in the ratio 1:2:3:4, and the effective surfaces of the shells are in the ratio $1:2^2:3^2:4^2$.

Postulate 3. Each spherical shell is divided into a number of cellular spaces. The thickness of these cells measured in a radial direction is equal to the thickness of the shell and is therefore the same (Postulate 2) for all the cells in the atom. In any given atom the cells occupy equal areas in their respective shells. All the cells in an atom have therefore equal volumes. The first postulate, regarding symmetry, applies also to the location of the cells. The first shell therefore contains two cells obtained by dividing the shell into two equal parts by the equatorial plane. The second shell having 4 times the surface (Postulate 2) contains 8 cells. The third shell thus contains 18 while the fourth contains 32 cells. Or if we consider only one hemisphere the numbers in the successive shells are 1, 4, 9 and 16.

Postulate 4. Each of the two innermost cells can contain only one electron but each of the other cells is capable of holding two. There can be no electrons in the outside shell until all the inner shells contain their maximum numbers of electrons. In the outside shell two electrons can occupy a single cell only when all other cells contain at least one electron. We may assume that two electrons occupying the same cell are at different distances from the nucleus. Each shell, containing its full quota of electrons, thus consists of two "layers". We will find it convenient to refer to these layers of electrons by the symbols I, IIa, IIb, IIIa, IIIb, and IVa where the Roman numerals denote the shell containing the layer. Helium, neon, argon, krypton, or xenon, contains, respectively, the first 1, 2, 3, 4, or 5 of these layers, while niton contains all six.

The two-fold symmetry assumed in Postulate 1 is derived from the factor 2 which occurs in Rydberg's equation. The 4-fold symmetry is derived from the remarkable numerical relation brought out in the following table:

				No. of cells	
Shell	Radius	n		in axis	in zones
I	 1	1		1	0
II	 2	4		0	4
III	 3	9		1	8
IV	 4	16		0	16

Here n represents the number of cells in one of the hemispheres of the shell. If this number is odd one of the cells must lie along the polar axis; all other cells must be distributed in zones about this axis.

We see from this table that the number of cells which must be arranged in zones is always a multiple of 4. We can therefore assume tetragonal symmetry for the atoms of the inert gases.

Postulates 2 and 3 offer perhaps the simplest possible explanation of the occurrence of the terms 1, 2^2, 3^2 and 4^2, in Rydberg's relation. There are some reasons for believing that the shells close to the nucleus would lie closer together. These reasons are based mainly on the assumption that Coulomb's inverse square law holds even at short distances, and for this assumption there is little experimental evidence, except in the case of forces between two positive nuclei (Rutherford's scattering experiments). It is probable that the law of force is quite different for electrons bound in an atom and for positive or negative particles passing through the atom.

The assumption of the existence of cells independent of the electrons in them, seems to be needed to account for the properties of elements above the rare earths. It is however closely related to Bohr's assumption of the existence of stationary states. The passage of an electron from one cell to another probably causes the emission of a spectrum line. It should be noted that the numbers 1, 2^2, 3^2, 4^2, etc., also occur in Bohr's theory in the determining of the location of the stationary orbits. It is probable that a common explanation will be found for both theories.

Postulate 4 seems necessary to take into account that the terms 2^2, 3^2, etc., in Rydberg's series occur twice. It seems to denote a remarkable tendency like that suggested by Postulate 1 for the electrons to form pairs.

From the steady progression in the properties of the different inert gases, however, we must conclude that the two electrons in a single cell do not exert very strong forces on each other.

The first 4 postulates give us a definite conception of the arrangement of the electrons in the atoms of the inert gases. Helium consists of two electrons symmetrically placed with respect to the nucleus. This same pair exists (as Shell I) in the atoms of all the other inert gases and determines the position of the polar axis. Neon contains a second shell (IIa) containing 8 electrons arranged at the corners of two squares placed symmetrically with respect to the equatorial plane and parallel to it. These positions probably correspond fairly closely to the corners of a cube, but the effect of the two electrons in the first shell should be to shorten the cube in the direction of the polar axis. Argon is just like neon, except that there is a second layer of 8 electrons (IIb) in the second shell. The two inner shells of krypton are like the two shells of argon, but in addition it has a third shell containing 18 electrons. Two of these electrons are located at the ends of the polar axis while the other 16 are placed symmetrically to the axis and to the equatorial plane and to the electrons in the inner shells. In all probability 4 of the 8 electrons in each hemisphere are located in the same plane as those in the second shell, while the other 4 are in planes making a 45° angle with these.

Xenon is like krypton except for the addition of another layer (IIIb) of electrons in the third shell.

Niton has in addition to the 3 shells of xenon a fourth shell containing 32 electrons, 16 for each hemisphere. We have no data by which to determine the exact arrangement of these, but it is obvious that the 16 can be arranged with a high degree of symmetry with respect to the underlying layer of 8 electrons (in each hemisphere).

The following postulates deal with the forces and tendencies which govern the arrangement of electrons in the outside layer of atoms other than those of the inert gases:

Postulate 5. It is assumed that electrons contained in the same cell are nearly without effect on each other. But the electrons in the outside layer tend to line themselves up (in a radial direction) with those of the underlying shell because of a magnetic field probably always to be associated with electrons bound in atoms. (Parson's magneton theory.) This attraction may be more or less counteracted by the electrostatic repulsion between the outside electrons and those in the underlying shell. The electrons in the outside layer also repel each other and thus tend to distribute themselves among the available cells so as to be as far apart as possible. The actual positions of equilibrium depend on a balance between these 3 sets of forces together with the attractive force exerted by the nucleus.

Postulate 6. When the number of electrons in the outside layer is small, the magnetic attraction exerted by the electrons of the inner shells tends to predominate over the electrostatic repulsion, but when the atomic number and the number of electrons in the outside layer increase, the electrostatic forces gradually become the controlling factor. As a result, when there are few electrons in the outer layer these arrange themselves in the cells over those of the underlying shell, but where the outside layer begins to approach its full quota of electrons the cells over the underlying electrons tend to remain empty.

Postulate 7. The properties of the atoms are determined by the number and arrangement of electrons in the outside layer and the ease with which they are able to revert to more stable forms by giving up or taking up electrons, or by sharing their outside electrons with atoms with which they combine. The tendencies to revert to the forms represented by the atoms of the inert gases are the strongest, but there are a few other forms of high symmetry such as those corresponding to certain possible forms of nickel, palladium, erbium and platinum atoms towards which atoms have a weaker tendency to revert (by giving up electrons only).

We may now apply these 7 postulates to derive the properties of the chemical elements. We will first go through the list of elements dealing only with broad features and will later consider the properties of certain elements in more detail. At present we will confine our attention to the properties of the elements in atomic condition—we shall discuss only their tendencies to take up or give up electrons. The properties of the elements in solid or liquid form or in their compounds involve forces acting between different atoms and therefore can be best considered after we have discussed the formation of molecules. The properties of the atoms up to argon fit in well with even the older arrangements of the periodic table. In fact, the present theory and Lewis' theory resemble each other very closely as far as their application to these first 18 elements is concerned.

Table I, to which it will be convenient to refer frequently during the following discussion, contains a list of all the elements, arranged in order of their atomic numbers. The table is designed to show the way in which the electrons are arranged in the different shells. The numbers forming the first horizontal line denote the number of electrons in the outside layer of the atom. The first vertical column gives the index number of this outside layer. Thus boron has 3 electrons in the IIa layer, chromium has 6 in the IIIa layer.

TABLE I *Classification of the Elements According to the Arrangement of Their Electrons*

Layer.	$E=0$	1	2	3	4	5	6	7	8	9	10
I		H	He								
IIa	2	He	Li	Be	B	C	N	O	F	Ne		
IIb	10	Ne	Na	Mg	Al	Si	P	S	Cl	A		
IIIa	18	A	K	Ca	Sc	Ti	V	Cr	Mn	Fe	Co	Ni
			11	12	13	14	15	16	17	18		
IIIa	28	Niβ	Cu	Zn	Ga	Ge	As	Se	Br	Kr		
IIIb	36	Kr	Rb	Sr	Y	Zr	Cb	Mo	43	Ru	Rh	Pd
			11	12	13	14	15	16	17	18		
IIIb	46	Pdβ	Ag	Cd	In	Sn	Sb	Te	I	Xe		
IVa	54	Xe	Cs	Ba	La	Ce	Pr	Nd	61	Sa	Eu	Gd
			11	12	13	14	15	16	17	18		
IVa			Tb	Ho	Dy	Er	Tm	Tm$_2$	Yb	Lu		
		14	15	16	17	18	19	20	21	22	23	24
IVa	68	Erβ	Tmβ	Tm$_2\beta$	Ybβ	Luβ	Ta	W	75	Os	Ir	Pt
			25	26	27	28	29	30	31	32		
IVa	78	Ptβ	Au	Hg	Tl	Pb	Bi	RaF	85	Nt		
IVb	86	Nt	87	Ra	Ac	Th	Ux$_2$	U				

Hydrogen $(N = 1)$ has a single electron. It is therefore (Postulates 1 and 7) unsaturated and tends to take up an electron in order to assume the symmetrical form characteristic of helium. The valence of hydrogen is therefore unity.

With helium $(N = 2)$ the first shell is completed. Beyond this point any additional electrons must go into the first layer of the second shell (IIa). There are 8 cells in this layer (Postulate 3) so that 8 electrons can be added before the atoms again acquire the stability of an inert gas. In lithium $(N = 3)$ the single electron in the second shell is easily detached so that the atom reverts to the stable form that corresponds to helium, thus forming a univalent cation. In Figure 1 the positive and negative valences of the elements are plotted against their atomic numbers. It is seen that up to $N = 17$ the maximum positive valency increases regularly up to the halogens (with the exception of oxygen and fluorine). This maximum valency is determined by the number of electrons which are given up when the atom reverts to that of the next lower inert gas.

In beryllium and boron the properties are determined largely by the ability of the atom to revert to the form corresponding to helium. The actual arrangement of the electrons in the atoms of these elements is thus of little significance. In carbon the 4 electrons in the second shell tend to arrange themselves (Postulate 5) at the corners of a tetrahedron, for in this way they can get as far apart as possible. With nitrogen no symmetrical arrangement of the 5 electrons is possible. We shall see that this leads nitrogen to form a series of very unusual compounds. Whereas the properties of the elements from lithium up to carbon vary in a rather regular progression, the properties of carbon and nitrogen form a very sharp discontinuity. The constant valence of carbon—the variable of nitrogen; the high melting point of carbon—the low melting point of nitrogen; the very great inertness and stability of most carbon compounds—the very great activity and often explosive properties of nitrogen compounds—all these illustrate this fundamental break in properties. We shall see that a somewhat similar break occurs in each case where the atom becomes equally unsymmetrical, namely in the fifth element of each succeeding shell, thus the breaks occur at nitrogen (IIa), phosphorus (IIb), vanadium (IIIa), columbium (IIIb), and praseodymium (IVa).

First Long Period

Beyond argon we soon come into a region where most periodic relations begin to fail. It will therefore be well to examine the present theory rather critically.

With potassium we begin to form a new shell—the third. There are

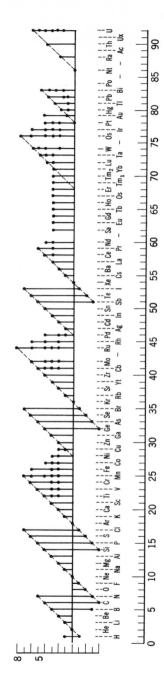

FIGURE 1

533

now cells enough to hold 9 electrons in each hemisphere. (Postulate 3.) The first few electrons arrange themselves in much the same way as in the first two periods. Thus potassium, calcium, scandium have properties closely related to those of sodium, magnesium and aluminium. In the first two periods the properties of the atoms just beyond carbon and silicon were electronegative in character because their atoms tended to assume the stable forms corresponding to neon and argon by taking up electrons. But in the third period the conditions are quite different. Thus in the atoms of the eighth element of this period, iron, only 4 out of the 9 outside cells in each hemisphere contain electrons. This atom therefore does not have the stability of those of the inert gases and there is thus little tendency for the elements of lower atomic number to take up electrons. The elements titanium, vanadium, chromium, manganese, have therefore predominantly electropositive character. In Table I the differences between the properties of these elements and those of the corresponding elements in the earlier periods is indicated by the heavy lines enclosing these elements. These, lines also express the mutual resemblance between the elements.

We can go much further in predicting the properties. The maximum valence of the elements is determined by the ability of their atoms to revert to argon, thus vanadium has a valency of 5, chromium 6, and manganese 7. It will be shown that in the formation of acid radicals with high valences the electrons, although they are given up to oxygen atoms, yet remain within the field of force of the original atom. In other words, the acid-forming atoms share their electrons with oxygen atoms but do not lose them completely. In compounds in which these high valences occur the properties are like those of the corresponding elements of the previous period. Thus vanadates resemble phosphates, chromates resemble sulfates and permanganates are like perchlorates. But when these elements have other valences their properties do not show such relationships.

The electropositive character of potassium, calcium and scandium is determined by the ease with which they revert to argon. Elements like vanadium, chromium and manganese, however, cannot form positive ions by reverting to argon for they would have to give up completely 5, 6 and 7 electrons, respectively. The large electrostatic forces involved prevent the formation of ions with such large charges. The electropositive character of these elements must manifest itself therefore by the formation of ions with fewer charges. The tendency to give up electrons is dependent on the presence of electronegative elements capable of taking up the electrons. In general, we may suppose that the atoms in a metal are held to each other by very strong forces as indicated for example by the high heats of evaporation. If the metal goes into solution a large amount of energy must be expended in separating these atoms and in removing some of their electrons. This energy is supplied by the energy of combination of the electronegative elements with the electrons separated from the atoms when they go into solution in the form of ions. Now if a metal forms divalent ions, more energy can be supplied than if it forms univalent ions. On the other hand it will be more difficult to separate two electrons than one electron from an atom. Thus we may suppose in a given case that univalent ions will not form because the energy supplied by the combination of a single electron with the electronegative atom is not sufficient to separate the metal from the others. On the other hand quadrivalent ions may not form because the energy necessary to separate 4 electrons from the atom may be greater than that which can be supplied by the combination of the 4 electrons with the electronegative element. It may happen however that both divalent and tervalent ions can form with about equal ease.

As a matter of fact, if we examine Figure 1, we see that the elements vanadium, chromium, manganese, iron, all form divalent and tervalent cations but form no univalent or quadrivalent ions in solution. The fact that they all form ions of the same valence with so nearly the same ease shows that the stability of these electrons in these atoms is very nearly the same. But this is just what our theory would lead us to expect.

For the elements under consideration only 5 to 8 out of the 18 cells in the third shell are filled with electrons. Furthermore, the tendency of the electrons to line up (Postulate 6) with the underlying electrons of the second shell is gradually being weakened by the mutual electrostatic repulsion. Therefore, the tendencies of these elements to give up electrons do not differ greatly. . . .

In the atoms of iron there are 8 electrons in the third shell, or 4 in each hemisphere. According to Postulate 6 the magnetic forces will make these electrons take positions as close as possible to those of the underlying shell. We may therefore picture the structure of the iron atom as follows: Close to the nucleus are two electrons. The 24 remaining electrons arrange themselves in 3 layers at the corners of 3 concentric cubes (slightly flattened) whose diagonals coincide. Although this atom possesses about as high a degree of symmetry as that of argon it differs radically from the latter in that the outer shell is not saturated, only 4 of the 9 cells in each hemisphere being occupied by electrons (Postulate 3). Furthermore, the number of electrons in the outside shell is beginning to be so great that the electrostatic repulsion (Postulate 6) tends to decrease the stability of this arrangement. These are the fundamental reasons that the elements of smaller atomic number like chromium and manganese do not exhibit the electronegative properties of sulfur and chlorine.

In cobalt and nickel whose atomic numbers are, respectively, one and two units larger than that of iron, the *extra* electrons can no longer be arranged over those in the underlying shell. Let us consider the way that the electrons in nickel arrange themselves. In the outside shell there are 5 electrons in each hemisphere and these tend to arrange themselves over the underlying 4 electrons (II*b*). The only position of reasonable symmetry which the extra electron can take is directly over the center of the square formed by the 4 electrons of the second shell. In other words, the electron goes into the polar axis of the atom. In cobalt there is an electron at one end of the polar axis but not at the other.

The present theory thus explains in a perfectly satisfactory way the anomalous position of iron, cobalt and nickel in the periodic table.

Second Long Period

Beyond krypton the second layer in the third shell begins to be filled. The first of the 18 electrons needed to complete this layer (Postulates 3 and 4) arrange themselves with respect to the 8 electrons in the second shell (Postulate 5), just as in the first long period, so that ruthenium has a structure analogous to iron. The 18 electrons in the first layer of the third shell, however, make the symmetry much less perfect than it was in the case of iron. The properties of these elements are more complicated than those of the first long period and there is a greater tendency to form insoluble salts and secondary valence compounds. The elements up to ruthenium are slightly diamagnetic or slightly paramagnetic, but from ruthenium to palladium there is a large increase in susceptibility. This reaches a sharp maximum with palladium and then drops suddenly to a negative value for silver. There is thus the same marked discontinuity as was observed between nickel and copper. But the susceptibility of palladium is only about equal to that of manganese and is thus of quite a different order of magnitude from that of iron, cobalt, or nickel.

According to our theory there can be no doubt but that the extra two electrons in palladium arrange themselves in the polar axis. In the elements beyond this point the electrons around the polar axis seek positions as far as possible from the electrons in the second shell, so that the atoms tend to revert to a β-form of the palladium atom. Thus silver forms colorless univalent ions, cadmium divalent, etc. These properties and their explanation are so nearly like those of the first long period that we need not consider them in more detail.

The "Rare Earth" Period

After xenon the fourth shell begins. There are 32 cells to be filled by electrons before the atom again reaches the stability of an inert gas (niton). The first 3 or 4 elements have predominantly electropositive character and form positive ions whose valency increases by steps of one due to the tendency to revert to xenon. As more electrons are added they will tend, according to Postulate 6, to arrange themselves over the 18 of the underlying third shell, just as in the first long period the electrons arranged themselves over the 8 underlying ones in the second shell. This process yields a series of similar elements having about the same valence, just as we found among the elements from titanium to nickel. By referring to Table I we see that this family of elements corresponds exactly with the rare earth elements. The eighteenth element from xenon is lutecium, and this marks definitely the last of the rare earths. . . .

The Uranium Period

With niton the first layer of electrons in the fourth shell is completed. As we add more electrons we should expect to go through the same cycle as that of the rare earth period. The properties of the first two or three elements are determined primarily by the ease with which they give up electrons. Thus radium very closely resembles barium, differing from it in chemical properties only by its slightly greater secondary valence which manifests itself here by slightly decreased solubility of its salts.

Thorium resembles cerium and zirconium, the elements of similar constitution.

Beyond thorium we might expect another series of elements analogous to the rare earths up to an atomic number of 104 if the nuclei of such elements were stable enough to exist under ordinary conditions. However, the properties of uranium do not bear out this supposition. Uranium is not closely related in its properties to neodymium, nor in fact does it closely resemble any other element. It would seem therefore that it is not safe from our present knowledge to make definite predictions as to the properties of other possible elements of this period.

The Mechanism of Chemical Action and the Structure and Properties of Compounds

The preceding theory of structure of the atoms in the two short periods is nearly the same as that postulated by Lewis. Lewis has discussed how a theory of valence may be derived from this structure. He considers the nature of the single, double and triple bonds, the structure of the ammonium ion, iodine and oxygen molecules, ions such as sulfate perchlorate, etc., the tetrahedral arrangement of the electrons around the nucleus in the carbon atoms, etc. In this way he has fully demonstrated the general value and applicability of the theory. Unfortunately Lewis' treatment of this subject was rather brief and perhaps for this reason it does not seem to have met with the general acceptance which it deserves.

It therefore seems desirable to consider in some detail how this theory may be applied to the predication of the properties of the first 18 elements and their compounds. In doing so we shall considerably extend Lewis' theory and because of the more definite conceptions of atomic structure which we have developed we will be able to apply a somewhat different viewpoint. In particular we shall attempt to explain the "physical" as well as the "chemical" properties of compounds. The predication of these properties depends mainly on Postulates 8, 9, 10 and 11 given below. Following Lewis' practice we will refer to the outside electrons forming an uncompleted shell or layer as "the shell" of the atom, while the whole inner portion, consisting of shells and layers each containing its full quota of electrons, will be called the kernel.

Postulate 8. The very stable arrangements of electrons corresponding to those of the inert gases are characterized by strong internal but unusually weak external fields of force. The magnetic and electrostatic forces are each very nearly internally balanced. The smaller the atomic number of the element the weaker are these external fields.

Postulate 9. The pair of electrons in the helium atom represents the most stable possible arrangement. A stable pair of this kind forms only under the direct influence of positive charges.

The positive charges producing the stable pair may be:

(*a*)   The nucleus of any element.
(*b*)   Two hydrogen nuclei.
(*c*)   A hydrogen nucleus together with the kernel of an atom.
(*d*)   Two atomic kernels.

These are listed in the order of their stability.

As we have seen from the previous discussion on atomic structure, the tendency to form a pair of electrons about the nucleus of any atom overpowers the tendency to form other arrangements so that the stable pair constitutes the first shell of all the elements except hydrogen. The tendency for the pair to form around two atomic kernels (Case *d*) is weak and thus only in exceptional cases, under some outside compelling influence does this combination occur.

Postulate 10. After the very stable pairs (Postulate 9) the next most stable arrangement of electrons is the group of 8 such as forms the outside layer in atoms of neon and argon. We shall call this stable group of

8 electrons the "octet." Any atom up to argon having more than two positive charges on its kernel tends to take up electrons to form an octet. The greater the charge on the kernel the stronger is this tendency. In exceptional cases, the octet can form about a complex kernel, that is, about a structure containing the kernels of two atoms bound together by a pair of electrons (Postulate 9d).

Postulate 11, *Electrons Held in Common.* Two octets may hold 1, 2, or sometimes even 3 pairs of electrons in common. A stable pair and an octet may hold a pair of electrons in common. An octet may share an even number of its electrons with 1, 2, 3, or 4 other octets. No electrons can form parts of more than two octets.

The fact that only an even number of electrons can be held in common probably signifies that the tendency to form stable pairs between the two kernels according to Postulate 9 is a vital factor in the sharing of electrons between octets.

When octets combine together by sharing their electrons fewer electrons are required than if the octets remain separate. Thus when two octets containing a total of 16 electrons combine so as to hold a pair in common, two electrons are set free. Two octets held together by one, two, or three pairs of electrons thus contain 14, 12, or 10 electrons, respectively. When we consider that the shells of all atoms except those of the inert gases are unsaturated, we see how necessary it is for the atoms to share their electrons with each other if the stable pairs and octet are to be formed.

Lewis discusses two possible arrangements of the electrons in the octet. They may be placed at the 8 corners of a cube or they may be located in pairs at the 4 corners of a regular tetrahedron. In view of Postulates 5 and 11 it would seem that the electrons in the octet are normally arranged in positions corresponding to the corners of a cube but that the electrons which are held in common between two octets and a stable pair, are drawn together by magnetic forces to form pairs. Thus we look upon electrons in the atoms as able to move from their normal positions under the influence of magnetic and electrostatic forces. This view does not conflict with that of Postulate 3 according to which the electrons are in cellular spaces. Thus we might assume when there are 8 outside cells that these are in the form of octants of a sphere. In the atom of neon, or the kernel of sodium, or in the chlorine ion the 8 electrons would be arranged nearly at the centers of the octants, but in compounds where pairs of electrons are shared by other atoms, the two electrons forming the pairs are displaced over near the boundaries of the octants and are thus able to come sufficiently close together for the magnetic forces to cause them to form stable pairs.

We are now in a position to apply the theory to explain the properties of the elements and their compounds.

Hydrogen $N = 1$; $E = 1$.* Hydrogen atoms are very active chemically because they tend to combine with any other atoms capable of supplying electrons by which the stable pairs can be formed. We should expect a hydrogen atom to constitute a doublet of high moment which would tend to attract all other bodies. Thus atomic hydrogen is very strongly adsorbed on surfaces. When two hydrogen atoms come in contact their two electrons form a stable pair (Postulate 9b) under the influence of the two nuclei so that a molecule, H_2, is produced. This molecule has an unusually weak external field (Postulate 8) and therefore hydrogen has a very low boiling point and is relatively inert chemically except in so far as it can be made to split up into atoms.

Helium $N = 2$; $E = O$. In the helium atom the stable pair already exists. Since this is the most stable arrangement of electrons and has the weakest stray field (Postulate 8), helium forms no chemical compounds and has the lowest boiling point and highest ionizing potential of any known substance. Hydrogen has a higher boiling point and lower ionizing potential than helium because the mutual repulsion of the two nuclei forces these apart and increases the strength of the external field.

First Short Period

Lithium $N = 3$; $E = 1$. Two of the electrons form a stable pair which completes the first shell. The extra electron, just as does that of the hydrogen atom, tends to make the atom very active chemically. Lithium atoms are electric doublets and therefore attract one another. There is however now little or no tendency to form stable pairs of electrons (Postulate 9) since the kernels of the lithium atoms are not simple nuclei as were those of hydrogen. Thus after one lithium atom has drawn another one to it there is still just as great a force tending to draw in a third. The electrostatic forces involved are just like those holding together a crystal of sodium chloride. The positively charged lithium kernels and the free electrons will therefore arrange themselves in space in a continuous lattice in a manner quite analogous to that of sodium and chlorine atoms in crystals of sodium chloride. Lithium atoms when allowed to come into contact with each other do not form molecules but form a crystalline solid containing free electrons as part of the lattice structure which is therefore a metallic conductor of electricity. When lithium is melted the structure is not essentially changed except in re-

---

* We will use E to denote the number of electrons in the shell of the atom as given in Table I.

gard to the regularity of the lattice. The free electrons still occur between the lithium kernels, and the metallic conduction persists. The strong force exerted by the positively and negatively charged particles on each other makes it difficult to separate the atoms. The great difference between the boiling points of lithium and those of hydrogen and helium is understandable.

When lithium is heated to a sufficiently high temperature, the thermal agitation is able to overcome in some degree even these strong forces so that the lithium evaporates. It is easy to see however that the vapor is monatomic. The energy necessary to separate two atoms of lithium from the surface is about twice that required to separate one, but the kinetic energy of a molecule of two atoms is the same as that of one, so that the momentum is only $\sqrt{2}$ times that of a single atom. Or to look at the problem another way, suppose that a diatomic molecule of lithium, Li_2, does evaporate from the surface, the kinetic energy of agitation of these atoms with respect to each other is the same as when the atoms formed part of the surface. But the forces holding the atoms together in space are in general much less than those which originally held the atoms to the surface. Thus if we assume that the space lattice is like that of sodium chloride each charged particle in the interior has 6 oppositely charged particles around it. A particle in the surface usually has two or three neighboring oppositely charged particles. For these reasons even if some diatomic lithium molecules should leave the surface they would dissociate into atoms at a rate, large compared to that at which they evaporate from the surface. In any case the resultant vapor is monatomic.

The attractive forces between the electrons and the lithium kernels prevent their separation and hence lithium vapor is normally a nonconductor of electricity.

If lithium atoms and hydrogen atoms are brought together the extra electron of the lithium atom and the electron of the hydrogen atom combine together to form a stable pair with the hydrogen nucleus at its center (Postulate 9a). The lithium kernels thus become lithium ions, Li^+, while the hydrogen nuclei surrounded by the pair of electrons are negatively charged hydrogen ions, H^-. These charged particles would be attracted to each other but since there is no tendency for negative *ions* to form pairs about positive kernels there would be no tendency to form molecules. The lithium and hydrogen ions form a crystalline solid having the composition LiH. Since there are no free electrons, the solid body is a non-conductor of electricity. If melted, however, the positively and negatively charged particles should be able to move under the influence of an electric field so that molten LiH should be an electrolyte (as Lewis has pointed out) in which hydrogen should appear at the anode. The comparative ease with which an electron can be taken from a lithium atom by an electronegative element makes univalent lithium ions stable in water solutions.

The theory thus not only accounts for the chemical activity and valence of hydrogen and lithium as compared to helium, but explains the ordinary properties, such as boiling point, electric conductivity, ionizing potential, etc.

Beryllium $N = 4$; $E = 2$. The first two electrons form the stable pair, leaving two electrons in the second shell. Since the atom can give up two electrons easily, it forms a divalent ion.

Boron $N = 5$; $E = 3$. The 3 electrons in the outer shell give this element its tervalent character. The small volume of the atom makes it incapable of forming a tervalent cation. Boron has therefore a more electronegative character than the previously considered elements.

Carbon $N = 6$; $E = 4$; *Nitrogen* $N = 7$; $E = 5$; *Oxygen* $N = 8$; $E = 6$. We shall consider these 3 elements together because the application of the theory is best illustrated by the compounds they form with each other and with hydrogen. The properties of the atoms up to this point have been determined by their ability to give up one or more electrons. With carbon and the elements which follow it there is less tendency to part with electrons, and more tendency to take up electrons to form a new octet. This opens up new possibilities in the formation of compounds and as a result we find a remarkable contrast between the properties of oxygen and nitrogen and those of lithium and beryllium. The ordinary theory of valence has nowhere been more strikingly useful than in the chemistry of carbon compounds. Among compounds of carbon with hydrogen and oxygen the valence almost without exception can be taken as four for carbon, two for oxygen and one for hydrogen. This simple theory makes it possible to predict with certainty the existence of great numbers of compounds and the non-existence of others.

When nitrogen is introduced into organic compounds there is often much more uncertainty in using this theory of valence. But among the compounds of nitrogen with oxygen the same theory is almost useless. Who, for example, would ever have been able to predict the existence of such compounds as are represented by the formulas N_2O, NO, NO_2, N_2O_4, N_2O_3 and N_2O_5 or HNO, HNO_2, HNO_3, etc., by applying the valence theory that has been so successful in organic chemistry? But because of its great success in its special field this theory has been nearly universally used even for inorganic compounds. To explain the existence of the above oxides of nitrogen it has thus been assumed that the valence of nitrogen may be one, two, 3, 4 or 5. It is obvious that such a theory must predict the existence of an unlimited number of compounds which do not exist at all. For example, we should have such compounds as are indicated by the formulas NH, NH$_2$, NH$_4$, or NCl, NCl$_2$, NCl$_4$ and NCl$_5$.

The degree to which any given theory of atomic structure is able to explain the success of the ordinary valence theory for carbon compounds and its failure for nitrogen compounds should serve as a measure of the value of the theory and should afford information as to whether the theory corresponds to the actual structure of the atoms.

*   *   *   *

General Conclusions

The theory of atomic structure advanced in the present paper not only explains in a satisfactory manner the general properties and relationships of all the elements, but also gives a theory of the formation and structure of compounds which agrees excellently with the facts. It leads directly to a valence theory for organic compounds which is the exact equivalent of the ordinary theory. When applied to the structure of complex inorganic compounds it leads to a theory practically identical with that of Werner. In cases like those of the oxides of nitrogen, etc., which have not previously been explained by any theory of valence the results are thoroughly satisfactory. The structure of the nitrogen, carbon monoxide and hydrocyanic acid molecules are accounted for and new relationships are obtained.

Under these conditions the postulates underlying the theory receive strong support. In fact, the results seem to establish the fundamental correctness of most of the postulates. The recent advances in the physics of the electron have been largely along the lines of Bohr's theory. It is generally assumed that the electrons are revolving all in one plane, in orbits about the nucleus. Such a view is wholly inconsistent with that of the present paper. Bohr's theory has had marked success in explaining and even in predicting new facts connected with the spectra of hydrogen, helium and lithium, and must therefore contain important elements of truth.

It will probably be possible to reconcile the two theories. As has already been pointed out, Bohr's stationary states have a close resemblance to the cells postulated in the present theory. The series of numbers 1, ¼, ⅑, 1/25 occur in much the same way in both theories.

The cellular structure postulated here also seems to be closely related to J. J. Thomson's theory of atomic structure in which he postulates tubes of force. It seems as though each cell in the present theory is analogous to the inner end of one of Thomson's cylindrical tubes of force.

This view suggests that in an atom the electrons are acted on by a repulsive force inversely proportional to the cube of the distance from the nucleus and an attractive force proportional to $1/\tau^2$ where τ is the index number of the shell in which the electron is located. Thus instead of the force varying continuously, as in Coulomb's law, it varies discontinuously in proportion to 1, $\frac{1}{4}$, $\frac{1}{9}$, $\frac{1}{25}$, etc., and only at large distances where τ is very large does the force vary approximately continuously. In some such way we may hope to be led to a modification of Bohr's theory in which the electrons do not rotate about the nucleus.